BOTTOM LINE YEAR BOOK 2012

BY THE EDITORS OF

Bottom Line
PERSONAL

www.BottomLinePublications.com

Contents

6 • PRIVATE AND PERSONAL

PART TWO: YOUR MONEY

7 • MONEY MOVES

8 • INSIDE INSURANCE

PART THREE: YOUR FINANCIAL FUTURE

12 • RICHER RETIREMENT

13 • LASTING LEGACY

PART FOUR: YOUR LEISURE

14 • TRAVEL TALK

Preface

We are happy to bring you our brand-new *Bottom Line Year Book 2012*. You will find numerous helpful and practical ideas for yourself and everyone in your family.

At Bottom Line Publications, it is our mission to provide all of our readers with the best information to help them gain better health, greater wealth, more wisdom, extra time and increased happiness.

The *Year Book 2012* represents the very best and the most useful *Bottom Line* articles from the past year. Whether you are looking for ways to get the most from your money or land a job in this tough economy…reduce your blood pressure naturally or assert your rights in the hospital…revive the romance in your marriage or get more organized, you'll find it all here…and so much more.

Over the past 30 years, we have built a network of thousands of expert sources.

When you consult the *2012 Year Book*, you are accessing a stellar group of authorities in fields that range from natural and conventional medicine…to shopping, investing, taxes and insurance…to cars, travel, security and self-improvement. Our advisers are affiliated with the premier universities, financial institutions, law firms and hospitals. These experts are truly among the most knowledgeable people in the country.

As a reader of a *Bottom Line* book, you can be assured that you are receiving reliable, well-researched and up-to-date information from a trusted source.

We are very confident that the *Bottom Line Year Book 2012* can help you and your family have a healthier, wealthier, wiser life. Enjoy!

The Editors, *Bottom Line/Personal*
Stamford, CT

1

Health Hotline

Aspirin Is Still the Miracle Pill! Strong Evidence That It Helps Prevent Cancer, Stroke, More

Even though a lot of people think of aspirin as simply "a good old drug" that relieves pain and helps to prevent heart attack and stroke, researchers now are finding strong evidence that it may fight other devastating medical conditions—including cancer and dementia.

Latest development: A study recently published in *The Lancet* showed that people who regularly take aspirin have a dramatically reduced risk of dying from cancer—up to 58% lower, in some instances. Other recent research suggests that aspirin also may help promote prostate health and perhaps even curb one's risk for Alzheimer's.

With all these positive findings, you might assume that everyone should now be taking an aspirin, a *nonsteroidal anti-inflammatory drug* (NSAID). But aspirin can trigger certain serious—and sometimes hidden—side effects. *Here's how to safely take aspirin to reduce your risk for...*

CANCER

Previous studies have shown that regularly taking aspirin may reduce one's risk of dying from colorectal cancer by 35% and one's risk of dying from the most common form of breast cancer (*estrogen-receptor positive*) by up to 28%.

Stefan Gluck, MD, PhD, Sylvester Professor, department of medicine at University of Miami Miller School of Medicine in Miami, Florida. He is associate division chief for clinical affairs in the division of hematology and oncology, and is former clinical director of the Braman Family Breast Cancer Institute, also in Miami. He has written numerous articles for professional journals, including the *American Journal of Clinical Oncology, Clinical Cancer Research,* the *American Journal of Therapeutics* as well as the *International Journal of Medical Sciences.*

But the recent *Lancet* study, which looked at data from more than 25,000 patients, concluded that taking low-dose aspirin every day was associated with even greater reductions in some cancer deaths.

For example, aspirin reduced the mortality from colorectal cancers by 40%...lung cancer by 30%...and esophageal cancer by 58%.

How aspirin helps fight cancer: It inhibits the effects of *cyclooxygenase-2* (COX-2) enzymes, which promote a type of cell damage that can lead to cancer.

My advice: I often recommend daily low-dose (81 milligrams [mg]) aspirin for patients who have one or more risk factors for any of the cancers mentioned earlier. For example, a patient who has multiple polyps in the colon would be a good candidate. So would patients with a personal/family history of breast, lung or pancreatic cancer.

If aspirin causes any side effects such as stomach bleeding: Ask your doctor about taking *celecoxib* (Celebrex), a COX-2 inhibitor in the NSAID class. This drug reduces inflammation but is less likely than aspirin to cause gastrointestinal (GI) bleeding.

Typical dose: 400 mg daily.

Note: Celecoxib may increase risk for heart disease and stroke. If you have heart disease, talk to your doctor about the risks versus benefits of taking celecoxib.

ENLARGED PROSTATE

A Mayo Clinic study, published in the *American Journal of Epidemiology*, found that men who took aspirin or some other NSAID, such as *ibuprofen* (Advil), daily were 25% less likely to develop the moderate-to-severe symptoms of prostate enlargement—also known as *benign prostatic hyperplasia* (BPH). Symptoms include frequent and/or urgent urination and a weak urine stream.

Researchers speculate that inflammation has a role in BPH, which would explain the benefit of aspirin and other NSAIDs.

My advice: If you suffer BPH symptoms, ask your doctor about taking aspirin daily.

ALZHEIMER'S DISEASE

A study of nearly 13,500 people, published in the journal *Neurology*, found that people who regularly used aspirin or another type of NSAID were 23% less likely to be diagnosed with Alzheimer's than those who didn't take one of these drugs. It's possible that the drugs decrease the accumulation of plaques in the brain, which have been linked to Alzheimer's.

My advice: Don't take aspirin as an Alzheimer's preventive. The research is not quite strong enough yet to make it worth risking aspirin's side effects. However, if you regularly take aspirin or another NSAID for some other condition, such as arthritis, you may also be reducing your Alzheimer's risk.

HEART ATTACK AND STROKE

Roughly one of every five American adults now takes a daily aspirin to help prevent the blood clots that can lead to a heart attack or stroke.

Even patients who go to emergency rooms with heart attack symptoms such as chest pain or discomfort are now routinely given aspirin. A large multicenter study found that people who took aspirin within 24 hours of a heart attack were 23% less likely to die than those who didn't get aspirin therapy.

For men of all ages and women age 65 and older, a daily aspirin has been shown to help prevent or reduce the risk for a first and second heart attack. For women of all ages, studies show that aspirin therapy reduces risk for a first stroke. For not known reasons, aspirin does not appear to prevent stroke in men.

My advice: Talk to your doctor about your risk factors for heart attack and stroke—the most common include high blood pressure, elevated cholesterol, diabetes, a sedentary lifestyle and/or a family or individual history of heart disease. Your physician may recommend that you take 81 mg of aspirin (one baby aspirin) daily if you have one or more of these risk factors.

If you think you're having a heart attack: Immediately chew, then swallow, one uncoated regular-strength (325 mg) aspirin or two to four baby aspirin. Taking aspirin this way can decrease clotting within 10 to 15 minutes. Do not take aspirin if you think you may be having a stroke—testing is required to determine whether the stroke is caused by a blood clot or bleeding in the brain (aspirin can worsen bleeding).

THE DOWNSIDE OF ASPIRIN

Roughly 50,000 Americans die every year from GI bleeding triggered in part by aspirin or other NSAIDs. High doses are more likely to cause problems, but even low-dose aspirin can cause bleeding in some patients.

To protect yourself: Be sure to talk to your doctor before taking aspirin—at any dose—on a daily basis. Let him/her know if you develop stomach pain, cramping or other symptoms after taking it.

If you experience symptoms when taking aspirin, ask your doctor about trying out the enteric-coated variety. It is less likely to cause stomach problems, and it appears to thin the blood and reduce cancer risks as effectively as regular aspirin. However, enteric-coated aspirin can still cause bleeding in some people.

What most people don't know: Aspirin-related damage to the stomach/GI tract may not cause symptoms.

To detect problems: Ask your doctor to perform a fecal occult blood test about three months after you start aspirin therapy and annually thereafter.

If it's more convenient, think about using an over-the-counter test (such as Hemoccult or ColoCARE) that can pick up small amounts of blood in the stool, which can indicate damage to the GI tract. Discuss this first with your physician.

Caution: Risk for bleeding is increased if aspirin is combined with certain prescription medications, including *warfarin* (Coumadin), corticosteroids and some antidepressants, as well as various supplements, including *ginkgo biloba, fish oil* and *willow bark.* Taking another NSAID, such as ibuprofen, with aspirin also increases bleeding risk.

Using high doses of aspirin has been shown to cause ringing in the ears (*tinnitus*) and/or loss of hearing in some people, so be sure to have your hearing checked if you notice any changes in your hearing while taking aspirin.

Best Time of Day to Take Aspirin

The best time to take an aspirin for heart health is at bedtime. Aspirin counters the clot-promoting effects of *cortisol,* a hormone whose levels are highest in the morning. It takes aspirin time to reach peak clot-fighting effectiveness, so taking an aspirin at a typical bedtime—10 pm—means that it will reach its peak effectiveness when production of cortisol peaks.

Also: Aspirin may be less likely to cause stomach irritation when taken at night, after dinner.

David Sherer, MD, an anesthesiologist near Washington, DC, and coauthor of *Dr. David Sherer's Hospital Survival Guide* (Claren).

The *Hidden* Risk Factors For Heart Attack

Robert M. Stark, MD, a preventive cardiologist in private practice in Greenwich, Connecticut. He is also a clinical assistant professor of medicine at the Yale University School of Medicine in New Haven, Connecticut, and medical director of the Cardiovascular Prevention Program at Greenwich Hospital (affiliated with the Yale New Haven Heart Institute). Dr. Stark is a Fellow of the American College of Cardiology.

We have all been told how important it is to control all of the major risk factors for heart attack and coronary artery disease. We know, for example, not to smoke...to maintain LDL (bad) cholesterol at safe levels...raise HDL (good) cholesterol as high as possible...keep blood pressure below 120/80...and monitor our blood levels of *C-reactive protein* and *homocysteine*—a protein and amino acid that, when elevated, indicate increased heart attack risk.

What you may not know: Cardiovascular risk factors are synergistic, so any one of the risk factors mentioned above increases the effect of other risk factors.

Example: Even slightly elevated cholesterol or blood pressure becomes more dangerous in the presence of smaller, lesser-known risk factors such as…

• **Steroid medications.** Most people now recognize that *nonsteroidal anti-inflammatory drugs,* which include the prescription medication *celecoxib* (Celebrex) and over-the-counter products such as *ibuprofen* (Advil) and *naproxen* (Aleve), can increase heart attack and stroke risk by making blood platelets sticky. However, steroid drugs are perhaps the most dangerous of the "stealth" risk factors for heart attack.

The steroids, which include *cortisone, prednisone* and *prednisolone* (Orapred), are prescribed for inflammatory conditions such as colitis, inflammatory bowel disease, psoriasis, asthma and rheumatoid arthritis.

Besides raising cholesterol levels and blood pressure slightly, steroids also tend to promote the entry of cholesterol into the artery wall to form atherosclerotic plaque deposits.

Important: Only oral and injectable forms of steroid medications carry these risks—the inhaled form used to treat asthma does not.

Taking steroid medications also raises risk for *atrial fibrillation*, an irregular heartbeat associated with increased risk for stroke.

Self-defense: Avoid using oral and injectable steroids if at all possible. If you must use them, make sure your levels of cholesterol and blood pressure are very well-managed…have the lowest possible dose…and, whenever possible, avoid using them for more than a week or two.

Important: Abrupt discontinuation of steroids, without gradually tapering off, may cause serious side effects. Always consult your physician before stopping a steroid medication.

• **Stress.** Both chronic and acute stress can be hard on the heart—but in slightly different ways.

Chronic stress, such as from ongoing financial pressures or a strained relationship, raises blood levels of the stress hormones *epinephrine* (adrenaline), *norepinephrine* and *cortisol*, accelerating buildup of dangerous plaque in the coronary arteries much as steroid drugs do.

Self-defense: Address the underlying cause of the chronic stress…engage in daily aerobic exercise, which burns off excess epinephrine in the bloodstream and reduces anxiety…and practice stress-reduction techniques, such as biofeedback and meditation, which have been shown to lower epinephrine and norepinephrine levels.

Acute stress, such as from the sudden death of your spouse, not only increases stress hormones but also causes the coronary arteries to constrict. In addition, acute stress increases the heart's need for, and consumption of, oxygen. If you already have a partially blocked coronary artery due to buildup of plaque, this constriction and increased oxygen consumption can contribute to a dangerous shortage of blood flow to the heart.

Self-defense: If you are confronted with either acute or chronic stress, ask your physician to consider prescribing a beta-blocker, such as *propranolol* (Inderal), *atenolol* (Tenormin) or *metoprolol* (Lopressor). These drugs are typically used to treat heart conditions and high blood pressure. However, beta-blockers also protect against the detrimental arterial effect that evolves with stress and can be taken as long as stress-related symptoms occur. These drugs are not recommended for anyone with low blood pressure, asthma or an abnormally low heart rate.

• **Sleep apnea.** People who suffer from this condition cease breathing during their sleep for a few seconds at a time many times each night. *Sleep apnea* not only disrupts sleep but also is associated with an increased risk for heart attack and heart disease.

Self-defense: Half of people with mild sleep apnea (those who cease breathing five to 15 times per hour) and 20% of those with moderate apnea (15 to 30 breathing stoppages every hour) have so-called positional sleep apnea—that is, the disturbed breathing happens only when the person is sleeping on his/her back.

Good solution: A relatively new strap-on foam device called Zzoma, which forces you to lie on your side, appears to help prevent positional sleep apnea (available for $99.95* from the manufacturer at 877-799-9662 or on-line at *www.zzomasleep.com*).

For more serious cases, *continuous positive airway pressure* (CPAP), a type of therapy in which the sleeper wears a mask that blows air into his nostrils, helps reduce apnea symptoms. For anyone who finds the CPAP mask uncomfortable, oral appliances, prescribed by dentists, also help reduce apnea symptoms.

●**Anemia.** With this condition, the blood's ability to carry oxygen is impaired. This can bring on chest pain (*angina*) or even a heart attack in people whose coronary arteries are partially blocked. Get medical attention if you have chest pain.

Self-defense: Anemia often can be treated with iron, vitamin B-12 or folic acid supplements or medications. After you have sought medical attention for chest pain, be sure that your physician tests you for anemia.

●**A chlamydia infection.** *Chlamydia pneumoniae* is a bacterium found in the respiratory tract of more than two million Americans. Different from the germ that causes the sexually transmitted disease chlamydia, C. pneumoniae is associated with increased risk for coronary artery disease, possibly because it contributes to arterial inflammation.

Self-defense: If you have signs of a respiratory infection, your doctor may advise you to get a blood test for C. pneumoniae. Antibiotics can effectively treat an infection caused from this bacterium.

●**Vitamin K deficiency.** Vitamin K (found mostly in meats, cheeses and leafy green vegetables) has been shown to reduce cardiovascular risk in people by more than 50% and also has prevented hardening of the arteries in animal studies. Vitamin K is also produced from the bacteria naturally residing in the intestine. Researchers have found, however, that most people do not get enough vitamin K in their diets.

Self-defense: To ensure that you get enough of this crucial vitamin, ask your doctor about taking a high-dose vitamin K supplement (100 mcg daily for adults). Because vitamin K can

*Price subject to change.

minimize the effects of blood-thinning medication, it is *never* recommended for anyone taking *warfarin* (Coumadin) or another blood thinner.

●**Horizontal earlobe creases.** Though no one knows why, some research has shown that people who have a horizontal crease in one or both of their earlobes may be at increased risk for coronary artery disease.

Self-defense: While there is nothing that can be done to change this risk factor, anyone with such creases should be especially careful about monitoring other cardiovascular risk factors.

When the Temperature Decreases, Heart Attack Risk Increases

Researchers analyzed 84,010 hospital admissions for heart attacks over four years.

Result: For every half-degree decrease in temperature, relative risk for heart attack increased by 2%. Adults ages 75 to 84 were especially vulnerable.

Theory: Cold temperatures could increase blood pressure, thickness in the blood and the heart's workload.

Self-defense: In winter, bundle up when going outdoors and closely monitor other heart attack risk factors, including stress and body weight.

Krishnan Bhaskaran, PhD, lecturer, statistical epidemiology, London School of Hygiene & Tropical Medicine, University of London, UK.

Height and Heart Health

Researchers analyzed 52 studies involving more than three million adults.

Results: Men who were shorter than five feet six inches and women who were shorter than five feet were found to be 1.5 times more likely, on average, to develop heart disease than taller people and had a 52% higher risk for heart attack.

Theory: Shorter people have smaller blood vessels that clog more easily.

If you are shorter in height: Attend to all modifiable risk factors for heart disease, including obesity, physical inactivity and smoking.

Tuula Paajanen, MD, researcher, department of forensic medicine, University of Tampere, Finland.

Simple Toe-Touch Test Reveals Heart Health

When 526 men and women (ages 20 to 83) were asked to reach for their toes while seated on the ground with their legs flat and their backs straight against a wall, poor trunk flexibility (reach that was farthest from toes) was linked to high blood pressure and predicted arterial stiffness (the precursor to heart disease).

Theory: Flexibility might delay age-related arterial stiffening.

Self-defense: Enhance flexibility through regular stretching, Pilates or yoga.

Kenta Yamamoto, PhD, research fellow, integrative physiology department at University of North Texas in Fort Worth.

The 15-Minute Test That Could Save Your Life

Rebecca Shannonhouse, editor, *Bottom Line/Health*, Boardroom Inc., Stamford, Connecticut.

The standard risk factors used to predict cardiovascular disease, such as age, sex, low HDL ("good") cholesterol, smoking and high blood pressure, don't tell the whole story.

You can appear to be relatively healthy and at a low risk for coronary artery disease but

actually have a higher risk than you realize—and an increased risk for such conditions as heart attack and stroke.

Underrecognized marker for coronary artery disease: The thickness of the *carotid* (neck) arteries, which carry blood up from the heart to the brain.

Important new finding: When ultrasound was used to measure the thickness of the carotid artery wall and to detect the presence of plaque in 13,145 participants, about 12% who would have been classified as having a low or intermediate risk of developing heart disease were found to actually belong in a higher-risk group—and may require medication.

"There should be no plaque in the carotid artery," says cardiologist Vijay Nambi, MD, lead author of the study, which recently appeared in the *Journal of the American College of Cardiology*. All patients with plaque have a significantly higher risk of getting cardiovascular disease, regardless of their other risk factors.

Used in combination with other tests (such as those for blood pressure and cholesterol), carotid imaging with ultrasound allows doctors to more accurately determine who is at higher risk for heart disease. This 15-minute test is noninvasive, painless and usually costs $150 to $200.* Patients should ask if the test is covered by their insurance.

*Prices subject to change.

TV Hazardous to Your Heart

Watching TV increases risk for heart disease. Every hour per day spent watching television increases the risk of dying from heart disease by 18%—and also raises the risk of dying from stroke or cancer.

Reason: Long-term daily sedentary behavior has a negative effect on blood sugar and fats.

David Dunstan, PhD, researcher at Baker IDI Heart and Diabetes Institute, Victoria, Australia, and leader of a study of 8,800 adults, published in *Circulation*.

Working Long Hours Raises Risk for Heart Problems 60%!

Long work hours are linked to problems in the heart.

Recent finding: Individuals who regularly worked three or more hours beyond the standard eight-hour day had a 60% higher risk for heart-related problems, including deadly heart attacks and angina, than workers who maintained regular hours.

A possible reason: People who frequently work long hours tend to be type A personalities—aggressive, competitive and tense. This can make them more susceptible to heart disease, although researchers are not yet certain why. It may be related to unhealthy lifestyles and high stress levels.

Marianna Virtanen, PhD, an epidemiologist, Finnish Institute of Occupational Health, Helsinki, and leader of a study of more than 10,000 office workers, ages 35 to 55, published in *European Heart Journal*.

Statins May Hurt Immunity

Cholesterol drugs may lower immunity to bacterial infections. In recent experiments, the statin *simvastatin* (Zocor) inhibited the activity of *macrophages* (immune cells that destroy bacteria) and increased production of *cytokines* (the substances that trigger and sustain inflammation).

Result: Bacterial infections might last longer, though there is no evidence that the drug makes people more susceptible to an infection. Other statins are likely to affect immunity in a similar way.

Cosima T. Baldari, PhD, professor of molecular biology, University of Siena, Siena, Italy, and senior author of a study published in *Journal of Leukocyte Biology*.

New Statin Side Effects

Statins are linked to cataracts and kidney failure, in addition to previously known effects on both the liver and muscles. Risks are highest during the initial year of use, according to a big recent study of the popular cholesterol-lowering medications, which included *atorvastatin* (Lipitor), *fluvastatin* (Lescol) and *simvastatin* (Zocor).

Better news: The research suggests that statins decrease risk for esophageal cancer.

Bottom line: Discuss benefits and risks of statins with your physician.

Julia Hippisley-Cox, MD, professor of clinical epidemiology and general practice, University of Nottingham, Nottingham, United Kingdom, and coauthor of a study of 2,004,692 patients, published in *British Medical Journal* (*BMJ*).

High Cholesterol Linked to Dementia

High cholesterol at midlife raises dementia risk. People with cholesterol levels above 240 mg/dL when they are in their 40s are 57% more likely to develop Alzheimer's later in life than people with levels less than 200 mg/dL. Those with borderline-high cholesterol—from 200 mg/dL to 239 mg/dL—have an increased risk for vascular dementia.

Four-decade study of 9,844 members of Kaiser Permanente Medical Care Program of Northern California, reported in *University of California, Berkeley, Wellness Letter*.

A Quick Check-In With Your Doc Can Fix High BP *Fast*

Try this simple strategy to see if it lowers your blood pressure…

Recent study: Researchers tracked 5,042 adults with diabetes and high blood pressure for four years. Those who saw their doctors at least once a month reduced their blood pressure to healthy levels in 1.8 months, on average, compared with 29.4 months, on average, for those with doctor visits twice a year.

If you have high blood pressure: Discuss with your physician the optimal frequency of doctor visits. Seeing a physician's assistant or e-mailing your doctor with the results of at-home blood pressure monitoring also may be options.

Alexander Turchin, MD, assistant professor of medicine, division of endocrinology, diabetes and hypertension, Brigham and Women's Hospital, Boston.

drank skim milk or had skim milk with cocoa powder twice daily for one month, the cocoa drinkers had significantly lower levels of inflammatory biomarkers related to hardening of the arteries (*atherosclerosis*).

A theory: Cocoa powder contains plant-derived compounds known as flavonoids, which have anti-inflammatory effects.

If you are at risk to get atherosclerosis (due to family history, high blood pressure or diabetes): Consider drinking about 1.5 tablespoons of cocoa powder (with little or no sugar) mixed with about 8.5 ounces of skim milk or water once or twice daily.

Ramon Estruch, MD, senior consultant, department of internal medicine, University of Barcelona, Spain.

When Blood Pressure Drugs Can *Raise* Blood Pressure

Researchers analyzed 945 adults who had elevated *systolic* (the top number) blood pressure.

Results: Among those who had low levels of the blood pressure–controlling enzyme *renin* and were treated with a *beta-blocker* or an *angiotensin-converting enzyme (ACE) inhibitor*, 16% had a significant increase in systolic pressure.

When prescribed a blood pressure drug: Ask your doctor to check your levels of renin— if high, a *diuretic* or *calcium channel blocker* may be a better medication option.

Michael Alderman, MD, a distinguished professor emeritus of medicine, Albert Einstein College of Medicine, Bronx, New York.

Tasty Inflammation Fighter

In recent research, when 47 adults (age 55 and older) with high risk for heart disease

Vitamin K Impacts Blood Thinners—Check Your Multivitamin

Multivitamins may change how blood thinners work. Vitamin K, which helps blood to clot and can be included in many multivitamins, can impact the effectiveness of blood thinners, such as *warfarin* (Coumadin).

Important: Speak with your doctor if you are taking a blood thinner and a multivitamin with vitamin K. It is important to keep your levels of vitamin K consistent.

Sarah L. Booth, PhD, director, Vitamin K Laboratory, Jean Mayer USDA Human Nutrition Research Center on Aging at Tufts University, Boston.

Calcium Concern

Calcium from supplements, including antacids such as Tums and Rolaids, elevates blood calcium quickly, which may contribute to artery disease. Calcium in food is absorbed slowly. If you are taking supplements on medical advice, do not stop without speaking with your physician.

One possibility: Spreading the total dose throughout the day instead of taking it all at once.

Ian Reid, MD, a professor on the faculty of medical and health sciences, University of Auckland, New Zealand, and leader of an analysis of clinical trials involving about 12,000 people, published in *BMJ Online First.*

Diet Soda Danger

People who drink diet soda have a higher risk for stroke and heart attack.

Recent finding: People who drank diet soda every day were nearly 50% more likely to have a vascular event, such as a stroke, even after accounting for such risk factors as age, gender, smoking and alcohol consumption.

Note: People who drink diet soda every day may have different eating habits than those who don't drink diet soda, which may contribute to cardiovascular problems.

Hannah E. Gardener, ScD, an epidemiologist in the Clinical Research Division, Miller School of Medicine, University of Miami, Florida, and leader of a study of the dietary habits of 2,564 people.

Shingles Increases Stroke Risk

Having shingles anywhere on the body increases the risk of having a stroke over the next 12 months by about 30%. Having eye-related (*ocular*) shingles increases the risk by more than 400%. People who have had shingles should take extra care to decrease stroke risk. Get exercise regularly…maintain a healthy, low-sodium, low-fat diet…do not smoke…and, if it's necessary, take medication to control blood pressure and cholesterol.

Daniel T. Lackland, DrPH, professor of epidemiology, department of neurosciences, Medical University of South Carolina, Charleston, and spokesperson for the American Stroke Association, *www.strokeassociation. org.*

A Single Alcoholic Drink *Doubles* Your Stroke Risk!

Stroke risk gets *doubled* in the hour after you have just one alcoholic beverage. The heightened risk for *ischemic* stroke goes away within three hours.

Theory: Alcohol may temporarily increase blood pressure or affect the blood's ability to clot.

Self-defense: Avoid consumption of many drinks in a short time because this may cause a sharp increase in stroke risk. One drink is defined as 12 ounces of beer…four ounces of wine…1.5 ounces of 80-proof spirits…or one ounce of 100-proof spirits.

Murray A. Mittleman, MD, DrPH, director of the Cardiovascular Epidemiology Research Unit at Beth Israel Deaconess Medical Center, Harvard Medical School in Boston, and leader of a study published in *Stroke.*

3-D TV Health Danger

A 3-D TV poses risks to health. The makers of 3-D televisions, such as Samsung, have warned that people with certain serious medical conditions, including epilepsy or a family history of stroke, as well as people who are tired or under the influence of alcohol, should not watch 3-D television or movies. 3-D could trigger an epileptic seizure or stroke and can lead to headaches, migraines and nausea.

Melvin Schrier, OD, retired optometrist and vision consultant, Rancho Palos Verdes, California.

If You Have a Stroke...

Rebecca Shannonhouse, editor, *Bottom Line/Health*, Boardroom Inc., 281 Tresser Blvd., Stamford, Connecticut 06901.

We've long known that you must go to the hospital *immediately* if you think you or a loved one might be having a stroke.

Now: The American Academy of Neurology has released a new guideline that states the standard use of a *computed tomography (CT) scan* to diagnose acute *ischemic stroke* (when an artery to the brain is blocked) should be replaced with a *magnetic resonance imaging (MRI) scan.*

The change resulted, in part, from a study that found MRIs accurately diagnosed stroke in 83% of cases, versus 26% for CT scans. The panel added that the decision on which imaging tool to use is influenced by the availability of MRI.

Many hospitals do not have MRI machines or they are located far from the emergency room, says Steven R. Messé, MD, a neurologist at the Hospital of the University of Pennsylvania in Philadelphia.

Even though MRIs are more sensitive than CT scans, the tests are equally effective at detecting bleeding in the brain—a condition that will worsen if *tPA*, the standard treatment for an ischemic stroke, is given.

The key is to get to the hospital. Once you're there, you can ask to be transferred, if necessary, to a different hospital with an accredited stroke center, where you will have rapid access to an MRI.

Use the FAST test to help recognize stroke symptoms: **F**ace (does just one side of the face droop?)...**A**rms (can both be lifted?)...**S**peech (can the patient speak without slurring words and understand what is being spoken?)...and **T**ime (if you see any of these signs, call 911 *immediately*).

FDA Approves Botox for Stroke Rehab

Recently the FDA approved the use of Botox* to treat elbow, wrist and finger spasticity that so many stroke patients experience. The injections temporarily block connections between certain nerves and muscles, stopping the spasms and improving patients' ability to grasp objects, dress themselves and perform other activities. Botox also may help relax leg and foot muscles in stroke patients.

Ralph L. Sacco, MD, president, American Heart Association (*www.heart.org*). He is also professor and chair of neurology, Miller School of Medicine at University of Miami and neurologist-in-chief, Jackson Memorial Hospital, both in Miami, Florida.

*The FDA requires Botox to carry a warning label saying that the material has the potential to spread from the injection site to other parts of the body, with risk of serious complications.

Stroke Rehab Made *Much* Easier

Yaffa Liebermann, PT, GCS, a physical therapist who is board certified by the American Physical Therapy Association and a geriatric clinical specialist. Founder and CEO of Prime Rehabilitation Services, Inc., in Yorktown Heights, New York, she has worked with stroke survivors for 44 years as a practicing physical therapist. Liebermann is the author of *Stroke Restoration* (Prime Rehabilitation Services, Inc.).

Until relatively recently, physicians and physical therapists believed that a person who underwent physical rehabilitation immediately following a stroke would reach maximum recovery within six months.

Now: Researchers have discovered that an intensive program of physical therapy can produce positive results for many stroke survivors far beyond this time frame.

Even though physical rehabilitation ideally begins as soon as possible following a stroke (to stimulate function of brain cells and help prevent joint stiffness and muscle weakness), the following techniques can be used by most people who are trying to regain function and mobility—no matter how long ago the stroke was experienced…*

SURVIVING A STROKE

There are approximately 5.5 million people in the US who have survived a stroke. About two-thirds of stroke survivors lose basic functional abilities, such as movement, speech and balance. Without enough blood, brain cells die and the abilities controlled by the parts of the brain affected by the stroke are lost.

The severity of the disability depends on the size of the stroke. Some people who have a stroke may experience weakness in an arm or leg, but more extreme cases can involve paralysis.

Problem: Stroke rehabilitation (typically administered by a physical therapist) is offered at hundreds of facilities across the US, but many stroke patients stop exercising when they complete their initial rehabilitation program.**

This is an important issue because research indicates that repetition is the best way to improve *neuroplasticity*—the brain's ability to "rewire" itself to promote recovery.

Solution: Stroke survivors can incorporate into their daily activities basic techniques that focus on three main areas that are crucial to continued rehabilitation. Because they are all so simple and easy to perform, these strategies do not even feel like formal exercise and can be used with or without the help of a physical therapist.

STRATEGY 1:
CHALLENGE THE WEAK SIDE

It's tempting, if you've had a stroke, to use the stronger side of your body. For example, you might prefer to put your weight on your stronger leg when you stand up or use your stronger arm to perform tasks. However, you must shift weight to your weak side to regain movement.

What to do: To begin, bear your body weight as evenly as possible on both legs when you stand to improve muscle tone and normalize your movements. Use your stronger hand to

*Before starting this regimen, discuss the strategies with your doctor and/or a physical therapist.

**To locate a stroke rehabilitation center near you, contact the Commission on Accreditation of Rehabilitation Facilities (888-281-6531, *www.carf.org*).

support yourself and/or ask someone to stand beside you. You can practice this while standing behind a stable chair, holding on to a table or gripping a counter. Whenever possible, try to stand with equal weight on both feet.

Also helpful: If you have leg weakness, tap your feet whenever possible while standing or sitting. If you have weakness in an arm, use both hands to drum your fingers on a tabletop for several minutes every day. While seated, lean on your weak arm (for one to two minutes—but stop if you feel pain) while keeping your elbow straight. Repeat on your other arm. Do this several times daily.

STRATEGY 2:
MASTER TRUNK CONTROL

The trunk—or core—of the body provides strength for virtually all movements. But if one side of the body is weakened, the corresponding side of the trunk is not as strong, which forces the other side to do more. Strengthening the trunk develops more stability, which improves posture and helps to facilitate easier movement of the arms and legs.

What to do: If you've had a relatively mild stroke, observe yourself in a standing position in front of a full-length mirror. If you lean to one side, that is generally your stronger side. Even though you may think that you would know whether you have weakness in certain parts of your body, you should look in a mirror because it is common to reposition your body to accommodate an injury without even realizing it.

To strengthen your trunk: Do rotation exercises (on your own, if possible, or with the help of a physical therapist or family member). To begin, lie on your back in bed, bend your knees, then slowly move your legs from side to side. Do this for about 10 minutes or until you feel fatigued first thing in the morning and at bedtime.

Also helpful: Once you can stand up from a seated position and distribute your weight evenly on both legs, stand near a waist-high surface, such as a desk or a counter. In each hand, roll an object, such as a can or bottle, on the surface. Do this for about 10 minutes or until you feel fatigued.

For the lower body: Hold on to the back of a stable chair and lift one leg backward as high as you comfortably can without leaning forward. Hold the position for a few seconds, then repeat on the other side. Do three sets of 10 repetitions on each leg three times weekly. When this becomes easy, ask your doctor or physical therapist about adding a light ankle weight to each leg.

STRATEGY 3:
USE THE POWER OF YOUR BREATH

Many people who suffer a stroke are greatly weakened by the experience and, as a result, may suffer from shortness of breath. But correct breathing techniques practiced in rehabilitation prepare patients to cope with stressful situations (such as stair climbing) and to overcome shortness of breath.

What to do: To improve breathing skills, exhale twice as long as you inhale.

Example: A few times a day, inhale for a count of three and exhale for a count of six.

Since deep inhalations may cause feelings of light-headedness in some stroke survivors, do not repeat the inhalation-exhalation series more than five times in a row. If someone is able to gently massage your shoulders at the same time, this often helps to release tension and promote good airflow.

Make a game: Whenever you bend your trunk, exhale for a count of six, and inhale for a count of three when you straighten up. Also, try exhaling when you reach for a cup or when you stoop down to retrieve an object. Then inhale as you sit back to drink or stand.

New Way to Prevent Diabetes-Related Blindness

In a recent studty, after a year of treatment, almost half of patients with *diabetic macular edema* (diabetes-connected swelling of the central part of the retina) treated with lasers and the injectable drug *ranibizumab* (Lucentis)

showed substantial visual improvement—versus 28% of patients who were treated with lasers alone.

Neil M. Bressler, MD, retina division chief and professor of ophthalmology at Wilmer Eye Institute, Johns Hopkins University School of Medicine, Baltimore, and coauthor of a study of 691 patients with diabetic macular edema, published in *Ophthalmology*.

Diabetes Drugs That Increase Fracture Risk

The diabetes medications Actos and Avandia may increase fracture risk in women over age 50. Higher doses are associated with greater risk. Postmenopausal women should be careful to consume adequate amounts of calcium and vitamin D to protect their bone health.

William H. Herman, MD, MPH, director of the Michigan Diabetes Research and Training Center, University of Michigan, Ann Arbor, and leader of a study published in *The Journal of Clinical Endocrinology & Metabolism*.

Beware of These Popular Packaged Foods and Drinks: Research Raises Questions About Potential Health Risks

Olga Naidenko, PhD, a senior scientist working for the Washington, DC–located Environmental Working Group, *www.ewg.org*, a nonprofit, research-based organization dedicated to protecting public health and the environment. She specializes in the effects of toxic chemicals on human health.

When you buy a food product, you probably don't give much thought to the lining of the food cans, for example, or other material used for packaging. But you should be aware that some materials used to package popular food and beverages are potentially dangerous. *For example…*

• **Candy bars, fast food, microwave popcorn, stick butter and take-out pizza.** These fatty foods are frequently packaged in materials made with a grease-resistant coating that contains *perfluorooctanoic acid* (PFOA), the chemical commonly used in stain- and water-resistant coatings.

Problem: Traces of PFOA invariably remain from the manufacturing process, according to an FDA study. PFOA is highly toxic, and once ingested, it remains in your body for years.

Animal studies have linked it to increased risk for liver, pancreatic and testicular cancers, birth defects and developmental problems, a weakened immune system as well as elevated cholesterol.

Self-defense: Avoid any foods wrapped in grease-resistant paper.

Ask personnel at restaurants to put food directly in a paper bag (or to wrap it in foil first, for some foods) without using the usual grease-resistant paper wrap or cardboard containers (especially when ordering egg breakfast sandwiches, French fries and chicken nuggets—all of which tested highest in PFOA levels in one study). Never heat up foods in grease-resistant paper—this increases PFOA exposure.

When heating food in the microwave, I prefer covering it with waxed paper instead of plastic wrap (if it's natural waxed paper and not chemically treated grease-resistant paper wrap). Use foil when not heating food in a microwave.

Also avoid microwave-ready popcorn—the bags contain PFOA in the lining. Instead, buy loose popcorn and pop it on the stovetop in a pot with a small amount of oil or use an electric hot-air popper. If you can't avoid grease-resistant packaging, as with store-bought butter, take it out of the wrapping immediately and store in a glass or ceramic container.

• **Beverages in bottles and canned foods and beverages.** *Bisphenol A* (BPA) is a component of hard, clear polycarbonate plastics that are used for bottled water and beverages and in the linings of many canned foods.

While BPA, unlike PFOA, is excreted from the body, 93% of Americans who have been tested have traces of BPA in their urine, according to a recent government analysis.

BPA's health risks stem from its estrogen-like effects while in the body. Animal studies have linked BPA exposure to reproductive problems, which include miscarriage, infertility and birth defects, as well as increased risk for breast and prostate cancers, liver damage, cardiovascular disease, diabetes and metabolic and nerve disorders.

BPA is included in many beverage bottles and five-gallon water-cooler bottles, as well as the epoxy lining of many food and beverage cans. Canned chicken soup and ravioli are the worst offenders.

Also dangerous: Canned tomatoes. That's because tomatoes' high acid makeup causes BPA to leach into the food more readily, as well as the cans of any kind of food that have been on the shelf for a long time. While no such period has been defined, scientists know that the leaching of BPA from can linings is an ongoing process while cans are in supermarkets or stored at home.

Self-defense: Try to limit your consumption of canned foods and beverages, substituting fresh produce or products in glass containers whenever possible. Eden Organic (at 888-424-3336 and *www.edenfoods.com*) is one company currently using BPA-free lining for most of its canned foods. Tomatoes are available in protective white enamel-lined cans that have minute levels of BPA.

Finally, avoid drinking from plastic beverage bottles or five-gallon plastic water-cooler bottles with the numeral "7" in the recycling triangle on the bottom of the bottle or the letters "PC" (for *polycarbonate*).

For those concerned about tap-water quality, the best option is to install a water filter. (Learn about filtration systems from *www.ewg. org/tap-water/getawaterfilter*).

• **Food and drinks packaged in Styrofoam.** *Polystyrene* (found in Styrofoam food and beverage containers) has been found to leach into liquids and food—particularly in the presence of heat, fats, acid and alcohol. Polystyrene invariably contains residual traces of the chemical styrene, which has been linked to nerve damage and cancer risk.

Self-defense: Do not drink beverages from Styrofoam cups—especially any heated liquids such as coffee, tea (particularly tea with lemon, which appears to increase leaching) or hot chocolate…fatty liquids, such as milk…or alcoholic drinks.

The same goes for fatty liquids, such as olive oil and oil-based sauces and dressings, which also should not be stored in Styrofoam.

Avoid meats and other foods packaged with a Styrofoam backing. When ordering take-out food, request non-Styrofoam containers. Never microwave food in Styrofoam.

Important: It may seem difficult to follow all of this advice all of the time, but you are likely to benefit from just being aware of the risks and limiting your exposure whenever possible.

Cancer Risk in Your Driveway?

Many asphalt driveways and parking lots in the US are sealed using coal-tar–based sealant.

A recent finding: The sealant will wear off and get tracked into homes. House dust from ground-floor apartments close to parking lots covered with coal-tar–based sealants showed concentrations of carcinogens that were, on average, 25 times higher than house dust from ground-floor apartments with other types of parking lot surfaces, such as unsealed asphalt pavement and concrete.

To determine if a sealant is coal-tar–based, look for the *Chemical Abstracts Service* (CAS) number "65996-93-2" on the product's material safety data sheet (MSDS). You can find resources for locating the MSDS at *www.ilpi.com/msds* or inquire when you buy the sealant.

Barbara Mahler, PhD, hydrologist, US Geological Survey, Austin, Texas, and leader of a study of coal-tar dust in apartments in Austin, Texas, published in *Environmental Science & Technology*.

Hidden Poisons in Your Clothes…and in Your Mattress, Mouthwash, More

Myron W. Wentz, PhD, a microbiologist located in Salt Lake City, who founded Gull Laboratories and developed the first commercially available diagnostic test for the Epstein-Barr virus. Later, he started up USANA Health Sciences, headquartered in Salt Lake City, and Sanoviv Medical Institute in National City, California. He is also coauthor of *The Healthy Home: Simple Truths to Protect Your Family from Hidden Household Dangers* (Vanguard). His Web site is *www.myhealthyhome.com*.

Dangerous chemicals are all around us, even in everyday items that we think of as safe. *Some of the most common dangers—and what to do…*

WRINKLE-FREE FABRICS

Perfluorochemicals (PFCs) are added to fabrics for durability, stain resistance and wrinkle resistance. Clothing labeled "no iron," "permanent press" and "wrinkle-free" usually contain PFCs. PFCs are extremely long-lasting in the body because they cannot be broken down and eliminated. They accumulate in the body's cells and have been linked with reproductive and developmental toxicity, as well as cancers of the liver and bladder.

The chemicals in clothing may be absorbed through the skin or inhaled when they outgas from the fabrics. Numerous cycles through the washer may release some, but not all, of the PFC coating from the fabrics.

In addition, synthetic fibers, including polyester and nylon, may contain substances such as *polyvinyl chloride*, a recognized carcinogen, and *phthalates*, a group of chemicals that disrupts hormones.

What to use instead: Clothes made from 100% all-natural fibers, such as cotton, linen, wool and cashmere and that are not labeled "wrinkle-free," "stain resistant," "static resistant," etc.

DRY CLEANING

A chemical cleaning solution, usually *perchloroethylene* (perc), is used to saturate clothing and remove dirt and stains. Unfortunately, plenty of the solution remains in clothing fibers after the cleaning is done.

Exposure to perc has been linked to kidney and liver damage. It causes cancer in laboratory animals. Even a short-term exposure can result in dizziness, headaches and/or a rapid heart rate. One study that looked at air samples found elevated levels of perc for up to 48 hours after dry-cleaned fabrics were brought into the home.

California and other states have mandated that dry cleaners stop using perc by the year 2023. *In the meantime, you can…*

• **Air it out.** Remove the plastic from dry-cleaned fabrics and hang them outdoors or in a garage or other well-ventilated area for one to two days. If they still have a chemical smell, air them out for another day or two.

• **Use a barrier layer.** Wear a T-shirt or tank top underneath a jacket or other clothing that has been dry-cleaned.

• **Locate a "green" dry cleaner.** Look for one that uses *liquid carbon dioxide*. To find a green cleaner, log on to *www.greencleaners council.com*.

MATTRESSES

Most innerspring and foam mattresses are made with *polyurethane*, a product so flammable that it is known as "solid gasoline." To counteract that, manufacturers are required to add chemicals with flame-retardant properties. Before 2005, these included highly toxic *polybrominated diphenyl ethers*. Since then, to help combat flammability, manufacturers have added the dangerous heavy metal antimony… and brominated fire retardants, which can disrupt hormone activity and may interfere with normal brain functions.

If you're sleeping on a mattress made prior to 2005, consider replacing it. A good choice is an organic mattress. These usually use natural latex (from rubber trees) and/or naturally flame-resistant wool.

If you do buy a synthetic mattress, remove it from the packaging and let it outgas in the garage or outdoors for several days before you sleep on it.

Also helpful: A natural latex mattress topper or an organic cotton or wool mattress protector can provide a barrier between you and the flame-retardant materials.

LIGHT AT NIGHT

Most people don't think of light as a "toxin," but when it comes at the wrong time, it could create toxic effects. Humans evolved to be exposed to light during the day, not at night, but since the invention of electric lights, we rarely experience a completely dark night.

The risk: Even a blink of light at night signals the body's *pineal gland* to curtail the production of *melatonin*, frequently known as the "hormone of darkness." Low levels of melatonin can reduce immunity…increase the oxidation that can lead to degenerative diseases such as heart disease…and impair our natural sleep-wake cycles.

• **Keep your bedroom dark.** Make sure that drapes and blinds fit snugly to block out all external light at night.

• **Opt for red light.** Use electronic devices, including night-lights, that are illuminated with red light. Melatonin appears to be more sensitive to blue lights, including those commonly used on alarm clocks, DVD players, etc.

MOUTHWASHES AND ANTIPERSPIRANTS

The antiperspirants contain aluminum compounds, which in high doses can increase the risk for cancer and neurological conditions like Parkinson's and Alzheimer's diseases.

Most mouthwashes contain the germ killers *phenol*, *cresol* and *ethanol* that are used in bathroom disinfectants, though in reduced concentrations. These ingredients and others such as *formaldehyde* can be harmful when absorbed by soft tissue and/or swallowed. *Instead try…*

• **Freshen your breath by using a tongue scraper** (available at drugstores) rather than a chemical-filled mouthwash, and brush your teeth with baking soda.

• **Avoid using antiperspirants,** especially during the cooler months and on weekends when it may not matter so much if you sweat a little. Deodorant (without an antiperspirant) is an option for people concerned about odor.

DRYER SHEETS, DETERGENTS AND FABRIC SOFTENERS

If a product smells "clean," it's probably bad for your health. The National Academy of Science reports that up to 95% of the substances used to create fragrances in detergents, dryer sheets or fabric softeners are petroleum-based synthetic chemicals that can cause asthma, impair the lungs and nervous system and cause cancer.

Luckily, your laundry is one everyday part of life in which you can easily eliminate unnecessary chemicals…

•**Opt for nontoxic all-natural detergents.** These are readily available in many supermarkets. Good brands include Seventh Generation, Method and Nellie's.

•**Ask yourself if you actually need dryer sheets and fabric softeners.** If you feel that you must use such products, you can find reusable cloth dryer sheets online. These dryer sheets are not coated with chemicals, unlike disposable dryer sheets, and they contain carbon fiber that helps eliminate static electricity in the dryer.

Or you can try one-half cup of white vinegar in place of fabric softener in the washer to reduce static cling and soften clothing.

Warning: Don't combine vinegar and bleach in the same load—toxic fumes could result.

Popular Drink Raises Pancreatic Cancer Risk

In a recent finding, people who drank two or more sugar-sweetened soft drinks a week had an 87% higher risk for pancreatic cancer than people who drank less soda.

Reason: Unclear. It could mean that people who drink a lot of soda have poor health habits in general, raising their risk for cancer.

Also: People who drank fruit juice—which includes many nutrients and typically has less sugar than soft drinks—didn't carry the same cancer risk.

Mark A. Pereira, PhD, MPH, an associate professor, School of Public Health, University of Minnesota, Minneapolis, and leader of a study of 60,524 people, published in *Cancer Epidemiology, Biomarkers Prevention.*

Even Small Skin Moles Can Be Cancerous

Current guidelines from the American Academy of Dermatology, Skin Cancer Foundation and American Cancer Society state that only moles larger than a pencil eraser (about six millimeters) may indicate melanoma.

But: One recent study shows that 22% of invasive melanomas are smaller than that.

Best: You and your doctor should check all moles, regardless of size. In particular, small dark-colored moles that have irregular borders should be checked. Give yourself a full body exam and/or check with your dermatologist.

Stuart M. Goldsmith, MD, dermatologist, Southwest Georgia Dermatology, Albany, Georgia.

Skin Cancer Danger In the Car

Harmful rays coming from the sun can go through *side* and *rear* car windows. Most windshields are made using laminated glass, which prevents the windshield from shattering in an accident. Laminated glass blocks the sun's damaging rays. Most cars' side and rear windows are *not* laminated glass, so rays can penetrate, possibly damaging skin and setting the stage for skin cancer.

Self-defense: Always wear sunscreen, even when traveling in a vehicle. Consider having sunlight-control film applied to rear and side windows.

Mayo Clinic Health Letter, 200 First St. SW, Rochester, Minnesota 55905, *www.healthletter.mayoclinic.com.*

New Med for Advanced Skin Cancer

Apromising new drug for advanced skin cancer is in trials.

Background: About half of melanoma patients have the *BRAF* gene mutation that promotes tumor growth.

Recent study: When 49 participants who had advanced BRAF-positive melanoma took PLX4032, an oral BRAF inhibitor, 81% of their tumors shrank by at least one-third within two months. In three patients, tumors disappeared. Relapse occurred after nine months, on average, compared to about two months with standard treatment.

If you have advanced melanoma: Visit *www.clinicaltrials.gov*. Search "PLX4032" to find trials that are recruiting patients.

Keith Flaherty, MD, director of the developmental therapeutics section of the cancer center at Massachusetts General Hospital, Boston.

New Concern About Secondhand Smoke

Secondhand smoke has now been shown to increase risk of mental illness. Nonsmokers exposed to secondhand smoke were one-and-a-half times more likely to develop psychological distress, such as depression and anxiety, than people not exposed—and the greater the exposure, the higher the chance of mental illness. Psychiatric hospitalizations were almost three times as likely for exposed nonsmokers.

Mark Hamer, MD, a senior research fellow, department of epidemiology and public health at University College London in England, and leader of an analysis of data from the Scottish Health Survey of 1998 and 2003, published in *Archives of General Psychiatry*.

FDA Bans Misleading Terms from Cigarette Labels

Cigarettes can no longer be labeled *light*, *low-tar* or *mild*. Cigarettes with these labels are no safer than regular cigarettes, so the FDA has banned this language.

USA Today, www.usatoday.com.

Another Harmful Substance Found in Cigarettes...

Cigarettes contain harmful bacteria as well as toxic chemicals. Among the bacteria are types linked to blood and lung infections and food poisoning.

Not known: Whether the bacteria survive the burning process and enter smokers' lungs. Researchers think it is likely.

Amy R. Sapkota, PhD, MPH, environmental health researcher and assistant professor, University of Maryland School of Public Health, College Park, and leader of a research study which was published in *Environmental Health Perspectives*.

Longer Stint with Nicotine Patch Boosts Quitting Success

Wearing the nicotine patch over 24 weeks may improve smokers' chances of quitting. Patches are designed to be used for no more than eight to 10 weeks. However, in a controlled test, 32% of smokers who used the patch for 24 weeks had not smoked during the final week of wearing the patch—compared with 20% of participants who had used the patch for eight weeks. The patch reduces cravings and withdrawal symptoms by releasing a slow, steady dose of nicotine through the skin. Patch-related side effects were about the same at 24 weeks as at eight to 10 weeks.

Robert Schnoll, PhD, associate professor, department of psychiatry, University of Pennsylvania, Philadelphia, and the leader of a study of 568 smokers, published in *Annals of Internal Medicine.*

Breakthrough Cancer Therapy Provides New Hope to Those with Inoperable Tumors

Christopher Taylor Barry, MD, PhD, an associate professor of surgery at the University of Rochester Medical Center in Rochester, New York. A leading pioneer in IRE procedures, Dr. Barry also is a member of the American Society of Transplant Surgeons and the Transplantation Society and has authored numerous professional articles in such journals as *Nature Biotechnology, Journal of Gastroenterology and Hepatology* and the *American Journal of Transplantation.* Dr. Barry reports that he has no financial interest in or special arrangements regarding the NanoKnife or AngioDynamics, its maker.

A "shocking" treatment some physicians believe offers hope to cancer patients with tumors that would have been inoperable in the past is now being used in 16 medical centers across the US.

Specially trained doctors can now use long, needlelike probes to administer high-voltage bursts of electricity to tumors that are difficult to remove surgically. The minimally invasive procedure, known as *irreversible electroporation* (or IRE), targets cancer cells that are then engulfed and removed by the body's immune system.

Intended benefits: Because IRE doesn't involve traditional "open" surgery, patients may experience minimal pain after the procedure. Some of them can go home from the hospital the same day. And because this treatment generates little heat and the probes are precisely positioned through tiny incisions in the skin, there's a very low risk for damage to nearby nerves, blood vessels or organs.

Anecdotal evidence based on procedures that have been performed using IRE shows that this approach has proved successful in treating cancers of the liver, kidneys, pancreas, prostate and lungs. Thus far, the device has been used to perform about 300 procedures worldwide. In the future, it may be used for treating many different varieties of cancer, including malignancies of the breast and brain.

Important caveat: The device that is used to administer IRE, known as a NanoKnife, has not yet undergone randomized studies comparing it with other treatments—an important step in scientific research. Some doctors are concerned about the lack of clinical data.

MORE PRECISION, LESS PAIN?

Traditional cancer treatments, such as surgical removal or the destruction of cells with extreme heat (*radiofrequency ablation*) or cold (*cryoablation*), are somewhat imprecise, even with skilled hands. These procedures not only can damage some of the healthy tissue that surrounds the tumor, but also can result in scar tissue that causes pain.

With IRE, it's now possible to attack tumors on an almost unthinkably small ("nano") scale. These electrical pulses punch very tiny holes in the walls of cancer cells and cause them to die. However, because of the lack of a head-to-head comparison with other techniques, it is unclear whether less pain is involved or precision is superior with IRE.

The NanoKnife has received FDA approval for *soft-tissue ablation* (removal) based on a regulatory provision that allows expedited approval without rigorous scientific testing. The approval was granted because the NanoKnife was considered sufficiently similar to another medical instrument currently in use—one that is used to destroy tissue during heart surgery.

Use of IRE is not intended to replace older cancer treatments. For now, it is mainly used for treating cancers that aren't readily removed with other procedures. It provides doctors an additional tool when treating tumors that are smaller than 5 cm (or approximately 2 inches), are located in hard-to-reach areas or that can't be removed without a high risk of damaging nearby structures.

WHO MAY BENEFIT

The expected precision of IRE, and the fact that it may be less likely to produce scar tissue or damage healthy tissue than other procedures, means that there may be a lower risk for complications.

Example: Men who undergo prostate surgery often suffer from impotence or urinary incontinence because of the damage to critical nerves. This damage has thus far been less likely with IRE.

In the future, IRE could become an important treatment for patients who can't withstand the trauma of major surgery. It is performed under general anesthesia but is much faster than traditional surgery and is less physically taxing.

However, the anesthesia must be "deep" to keep patients completely immobile during the procedure. Otherwise, the probes could shift and potentially damage healthy tissue or fail to destroy portions of the tumor. Potential complications include inadvertent perforation of an organ or tissue, hemorrhage or infection.

HOW IT WORKS

Once the individual is anesthetized, a *computed tomography (CT) scanner* or *ultrasound device* is used to guide the placement of the probes. The doctor then uses a foot pedal to generate electrical bursts (each one lasting less than 100-millionths of a second) that kill the cancer cells within a particular area.

IRE treatment can cover an area that measures roughly 3 cm by 4 cm in less than four minutes. It is less effective for tumors larger than 5 cm. The standard treatment consists of a series of 90 electrical pulses.

Because this technology is so new, it is not yet widely available in the US. It's being used, and studied, in Europe and Australia.

Not all insurers cover the cost of treatment with IRE. Some cite a current lack of scientific evidence when declining claims for coverage.

For a list of medical centers in the US where IRE is performed with the NanoKnife device, go to *www.bottomlinepublications.com/special.*

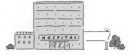

Sleep Apnea and GI Disorders Are Often Linked

In a recent finding, of 42 men and women with *obstructive sleep apnea* (temporary cessation of breathing during sleep) or a history of snoring, 83.3% had at least one *gastrointestinal tract* (GI) disorder, such as *hiatal hernia* (in which part of the stomach protrudes through an opening in the diaphragm) or *gastric reflux* (in which stomach contents back up into the esophagus).

If you have sleep apnea or snore regularly: Ask your doctor to refer you to a gastroenterologist for a comprehensive checkup.

Nora Siupsinskiene, MD, PhD, professor of otorhinolaryngology (the study of ear, nose and throat disease), Kaunas University of Medicine, Lithuania.

Surprising Risk for Knee Arthritis

Researchers measured leg lengths of 3,026 participants who had knee osteoarthritis or were at risk for it (due to factors such as family history or obesity).

Results: Adults having one leg that was at least 0.4 inches shorter than the other were 1.5 times more likely to develop knee arthritis within 2.5 years than those without the leg-length disparity.

Theory: The shorter leg travels farther to reach the ground and strikes with a greater force, setting the stage for arthritis.

If you're at risk for knee arthritis: Have your doctor measure your leg lengths. If they differ, ask about corrective measures, such as shoe inserts and physical therapy.

William F. Harvey, MD, assistant professor of medicine, Tufts Medical Center, Boston.

Think Twice Before Getting a Steroid Shot

Corticosteroid injections often cause worse outcomes over the long term. These shots often are given to treat tennis elbow and other forms of noninflammatory tendon pain, and may give pain relief for up to eight weeks.

Recent finding: When examined after six months and then again after one year, patients treated with corticosteroid injections had more pain than those treated with physical therapy or even by simply taking a wait-and-see approach to the injury.

Possible reasons: Steroids might weaken tendons' internal structure or the initial pain relief may lead patients to resume activities before they have healed properly.

Bill Vicenzino, PhD, professor, sports physiotherapy, University of Queensland, Brisbane, Australia. He led an analysis of 41 studies, published in *The Lancet*.

Best Shoe Choices for Arthritis

In an analysis of the gaits of 31 men and women who had osteoarthritis symptoms, including knee pain, stability shoes (a type of walking shoe with thick midsole cushioning) and clogs were found to put 15% greater force on knee joints than wearing flat and flexible walking shoes, flip-flops or no shoes.

Theory: Shoe stiffness prevents the natural foot flexion that may help lessen the force that walking places on joints.

If you have, or are at risk for, knee osteoarthritis: Wear flat, flexible sneakers that have arch support for everyday outdoor walking and no shoes while indoors.

Caution: Flip-flops could increase the risk of falling.

Najia Shakoor, MD, associate professor of internal medicine, Rush Medical College, Chicago.

If Steroid Shots Fail...

Hyaluronic acid injections may be a good idea if steroid injections have not relieved osteoarthritis pain in your knee. Steroid injections for rheumatoid arthritis or osteoarthritis are more affordable and can be injected into many joints, including elbows, hips, knees and shoulders. Benefits last up to six months.

Hyaluronic acid injections (such as Hyalgan or Synvisc) are designed to lubricate joints for increased mobility and decreased pain. However, these injections are FDA-approved only for knee joints in people with osteoarthritis.

Treatment with hyaluronic acid may require one injection or up to five given over several weeks. No up-to-date evidence compares hyaluronic injections with steroid injections. When benefits from hyaluronic injections occur, they can last up to six months (and possibly longer), but not all patients experience benefits.

Scott Zashin, MD, clinical associate professor of medicine, Rheumatic Disease Division, University of Texas, Southwestern Medical School, Dallas.

Pill That Relieves Fibromyalgia *and* CFS

Relief for *fibromyalgia* and *chronic fatigue syndrome* (CFS) symptoms could be had from a prescription sleeping pill. Taken at bedtime, Xyrem (chemical name *sodium oxybate*) can help decrease the pain, fatigue, stiffness, disturbed sleep patterns and other symptoms associated with fibromyalgia and CFS. But Xyrem is not approved for this use—the FDA has approved it only for the treatment of *narcolepsy* (severe daytime sleepiness)—so insurers may not cover the cost unless it is needed for the FDA-approved purpose.

A less expensive alternative: The dietary supplement *D-Ribose*, available online and in health-food stores. It is a simple sugar found naturally in the body and may be even more effective than Xyrem.

Jacob Teitelbaum, MD, medical director, Fibromyalgia & Fatigue Centers, Inc., in Addison, Texas, *www.end fatigue.com*.

Ointments vs. Oral Drugs for Pain

Painkilling ointments are just as effective as oral drugs for certain types of pain.

Recent finding: Topical NSAIDs relieved pain associated with osteoarthritis in the knee and hand and musculoskeletal injuries, such as tendinitis, just as effectively as oral NSAIDs. The topical NSAIDs are absorbed through the skin, so there is little risk for gastrointestinal bleeding. Currently, only three are available, all by prescription—Voltaren Gel, the Flector Patch and liquid Pennsaid.

Roger Chou, MD, an associate professor of medical informatics and clinical epidemiology, and medicine, School of Medicine, Oregon Health & Science University, Portland.

Bone Drug Causes Hip Fractures?

Taking osteoporosis drugs may cause brittle bones. *Bisphosphonates* such as Actonel, Boniva, Fosamax and Reclast can lead to deterioration in quality of bones and increased hip fractures. These drugs are extremely effective in the first years of use. But after four or five years, if bone density is no longer improving, talk to your doctor about taking a "drug holiday" from bisphosphonates.

Joseph Lane, MD, chief of the Metabolic Bone Disease Service, Hospital for Special Surgery, New York City, and leader of a study of women and long-term bisphosphonate use.

Save Your Sight— Symptoms to Watch For

Marjory Abrams, president of Boardroom Inc., 281 Tresser Blvd., Stamford, Connecticut 06901.

At my last vision checkup, my eye doctor warned me that I have a higher-than-average risk to get *acute-angle-closure glaucoma*. My increased risk stems from my eye structure. I possess a very narrow drainage angle—that is the location where the iris and the cornea meet and fluid from the inner eye flows through. Ophthalmologist Mildred M.G. Olivier, MD, the director of the Midwest Glaucoma Center in Chicago and a board member of Prevent Blindness America, explained that the angle narrows further with age, thereby increasing the risk for a blockage. Fluid build-up can cause a rapid increase in eye pressure. This can damage the optic nerve unless it is relieved, typically through laser surgery. The surgery, known as *laser iridotomy,* also can be used prophylactically to maintain drainage.

Vital first-aid: Anyone who develops sudden eye pain, severe headache, blurred vision and/or sees colored halos (there may also be nausea and/or vomiting) needs to go straight to an emergency room. An eye specialist can determine whether the problem is glaucoma and surgery is needed. Without proper treatment, you may lose vision in one eye within days—maybe even hours.

Eye anatomy also can place people at high risk for a detached retina—as my close friend learned recently after she had emergency surgery for retinal detachment and had to keep her face downward for more than one month so that her eye could heal. My friend is very nearsighted. The elongated shape of her eye makes the retina more susceptible to tearing. If the retina tears, *vitreous fluid* inside the eye might leak through, eventually causing the retina to detach. The longer the retina remains detached, the greater the risk for loss of vision. Symptoms of a detached retina include an increased number of flashes and floaters and a "curtain" that seems to come down over part of the eye's vision.

Vital first-aid: Anyone who experiences even one of the symptoms of detached retina should seek help right away. People who are extremely nearsighted should have their eyes checked every six months. Procedures using lasers or freezing can repair tears and keep the retina intact.

New Treatment for Macular Degeneration Gets FDA Approval

When researchers placed the *Implantable Miniature Telescope* into one eye of 219 adults who had severe blind spots induced by age-related macular degeneration, 75% reported improved reading, writing and face recognition. Unlike external aids for vision, including magnifying glasses, this telescope replaces the natural lens within the eye, allowing for natural movement as it magnifies and redirects images.

Henry Hudson, MD, retinist in private practice, Retina Centers, PC, Tucson, Arizona.

Cataract Danger

When scientists examined data on about 200,000 adults age 65 and older, those taking a *selective serotonin reuptake inhibitor* (*SSRI*) *antidepressant* were 15% more likely to develop cataracts than those not taking SSRIs. Those diagnosed with cataracts had been taking SSRIs for nearly two years, on average.

If you take an SSRI: Discuss cataract risk with your doctor.

Mahyar Etminan, PharmD, assistant professor of medicine, University of British Columbia, Vancouver.

Less Invasive Cataract Treatment Being Tested

A new cataract treatment uses an infrared laser to "bleach" the age-induced yellowing of the lens. The procedure, now being tested, takes about a half-hour and could eventually be done in mobile clinics. Cataracts now are treated with invasive lens-replacement surgery by a team of eye surgeons. Cataracts are the number-one cause of blindness in the world.

Line Kessel, MD, PhD, ophthalmologist at Glostrup Hospital, University of Copenhagen, Copenhagen, Denmark, and the leader of a study published in an online medical journal called *PLoS One*.

Six Common Myths About LASIK

Daniel S. Durrie, MD, a volunteer clinical professor in the department of ophthalmology and director of refractive surgery services at the University of Kansas School of Medicine in Kansas City. The spokesperson for the American Academy of Ophthalmology, he also is the founder and director of Durrie Vision, a refractive surgery practice in Overland Park, Kansas, *www. durrievision.com*. Dr. Durrie has published dozens of scientific articles and papers in professional medical publications.

Vision-correcting laser surgery has become so commonplace these days that virtually all of us either know someone who has had the procedure or even have had it ourselves.

Laser-assisted in situ keratomileusis (LASIK) is, in fact, the most commonly performed elective surgery worldwide.

Problem: Despite the popularity of LASIK, most people don't fully understand what it entails—or what it can and cannot do.

Common myths...

Myth 1: **It is not "real" surgery.** LASIK simply requires eyedrops for anesthesia, and most patients experience little or no pain. But LASIK, which involves reshaping the cornea to improve vision, is still surgery—and it's not a trivial procedure.

What happens: A laser cuts a hinged flap away from the front of the eye, which is folded back to access and reshape the cornea. This changes how light focuses on the retina, thus improving vision.

Like any surgical procedure, LASIK has risks.

Example: In unusual cases, patients suffer postsurgical side effects, such as eye dryness, oversensitivity to lights and/or seeing glare or halos at night. These problems typically clear up within a few weeks, but some patients continue to have discomfort for up to a year.

The more serious risk: Long-term vision impairment—that is, being able to read fewer lines on the eye chart. This affects fewer than one in 10,000 patients nationwide, and could be caused by a poorly made flap, infection or problems with healing. In rare cases, patients continue to have dryness or visual disturbances (such as glare) for the rest of their lives. This can potentially be treated with medicated eyedrops or further surgery.

Important note: Only medical doctors are allowed to perform LASIK surgery. He or she should be board certified from the American Board of Ophthalmology,* which ensures that the surgeon has completed the rigorous examination process required by this board.

Before consenting to do the procedure, the physician needs to perform a comprehensive exam. The exam should take at least 60 to 90 minutes and include reviewing your detailed medical history and measuring your cornea with special equipment to ensure that you're a good candidate for LASIK and that your risk for complications is low (check details below). When you see the doctor for your consultation, also be sure to ask about the age of his equipment. Lasers older than about five years won't have the latest improvements.

Myth 2: **Everyone with vision impairment can have LASIK.** Virtually everyone who wears contact lenses or eyeglasses will notice better vision after undergoing LASIK. This does not mean that it's always the right procedure.

Patients with eye problems that go beyond simply requiring glasses, such as *keratoconus* (when the normally round cornea becomes irregular), an unusually thin cornea, large pupil size or dry eye syndrome, should not undergo LASIK. The risk for complications—or bad results—is too high.

In addition, LASIK is not recommended for patients who have macular degeneration, cataracts or other eye diseases, or for those with diabetic retinopathy or disorders of the optic

*To find out if a doctor is board certified, contact the American Board of Medical Specialties, 866-275-2267, *www.abms.org.*

nerves. These patients may be candidates for other types of surgical procedures to address their conditions.

Myth 3: **LASIK is only for nearsightedness.** That's not true. In fact, LASIK is as effective for farsightedness (*hyperopia*) as it is for nearsightedness (*myopia*).

The process of reshaping the cornea will depend on your specific type of vision problem. If you're nearsighted, your cornea is too steep and the surface of the cornea will be slightly flattened to correct your vision. If you're farsighted, more tissue might be removed from the sides to make the cornea steeper.

Myth 4: **LASIK doesn't work for astigmatism.** LASIK is better than glasses or contact lenses for treating astigmatism, in which one's vision is out of focus due to a cornea that is not perfectly round. That is because the surgeon can change the shape of the cornea at a precise location with LASIK.

Myth 5: **LASIK does not eliminate the need for reading glasses.** Age-related vision loss, or *presbyopia,* happens to virtually everyone after about the age of 40. It has nothing to do with the shape of the cornea. Instead, the eye's lens loses its ability to focus on nearby objects. This is why people sometimes read by holding a book or a menu farther away from their eyes.

LASIK does not eliminate presbyopia, but it can be used to improve both distance and close-up vision, a technique known as blended vision.

Unlike monovision, in which one eye is fully corrected for distance vision while the other is fully corrected for close up, blended vision is a compromise. The dominant eye is corrected for distance vision, and the nondominant eye is adjusted slightly toward near vision.

This approach allows patients to see better from all distances. Many can read or do close work (such as using the computer) without using reading glasses. At the same time, they can see faces or signs at a distance. With blended vision, only some patients need reading glasses in low light or to read fine print.

The problem with traditional monovision is that the brain can't always adjust to the large disparity between the two eyes. But most patients adjust to blended vision within a few days after LASIK.

Myth 6: **LASIK doesn't ever need to be repeated.** LASIK permanently changes the shape of the cornea. However, the eyes can change with age whether or not you have had LASIK. This means that many patients eventually will need a subsequent procedure just as they need to change their prescription for glasses now and then. This typically happens many years after LASIK surgery as the eye ages.

In rare cases (fewer than 5% of all patients), LASIK can result in under- or overcorrection due to the laser removing too much or too little tissue from the eye. When this happens, you will need a follow-up surgery to see clearly.

Important: Ask your doctor about this risk before undergoing LASIK. Most specialists will charge a minimal amount, or nothing, for surgery to fix under- or overcorrection.

Concerned About Mercury in Your Mouth? Ask for This Instead...

Ask your dentist about getting porcelain if you need to have a tooth filled but are concerned about amalgam.

A recent development: An FDA advisory committee has recommended that the agency review its 2009 ruling stating that the mercury from amalgam fillings poses no health risk. The American Dental Association maintains that amalgam fillings are safe, but new data has raised additional concerns that mercury vapors from these fillings may harm the body—especially the brain and kidneys.

If you prefer not to receive an amalgam filling: Talk about options with your dentist. Porcelain is superior to resin because it does not degrade over time the way resin can.

Alan Winter, DDS, a periodontist in private practice, New York City.

Cell-Phone Danger

In a recent study, 200 adults with or without *tinnitus* (a ringing in the ears) completed questionnaires about cell-phone use.

Conclusion: People who use cell phones for at least 10 minutes each day for four years or longer are nearly twice as likely to develop tinnitus as non–cell-phone users.

Theory: Electromagnetic fields emitted by cell phones may damage the brain's auditory pathways. More research is needed.

Self-defense: Minimize cell-phone usage as much as possible. When on a cell phone, use the speakerphone mode or a headset.

Michael Kundi, PhD, professor and head, Institute of Environmental Health, Medical University of Vienna, Austria.

Racing Heart? Anxiety? It Could Be an Overactive Thyroid

Rebecca S. Bahn, MD, professor of medicine in the division of endocrinology, diabetes metabolism and nutrition at the Mayo Clinic in Rochester, Minnesota. Dr. Bahn is chair of the task force that developed the recent hyperthyroidism guidelines from the American Thyroid Association, *www.thyroid.org*, and American Association of Clinical Endocrinologists, *www.aace.com*. She also has authored more than 100 professional articles on thyroid disorders.

A rapid heart rate (100 or more beats per minute)…an increased appetite that's accompanied by an unexplained weight loss (of perhaps five to 15 pounds over several weeks' time)…sweating…anxiety…a mild hand or a finger tremor…difficulty sleeping…and fatigue can point to a number of different health problems.

So it's not surprising that many doctors fail to identify these symptoms as red alerts for *hyperthyroidism* (overactive thyroid). Because the symptoms also can be subtle—especially in older adults—hyperthyroidism is often difficult to diagnose.

Screening to detect hyperthyroidism, which affects about 2.5 million Americans, requires a blood test that measures *thyroid-stimulating hormone* (TSH). The thyroid hormones called *T3* (*triiodothyronine*) and *T4* (*thyroxine*) sometimes are also measured. The TSH test, which should be part of the annual physical for men and women beginning at age 40, is also used to screen for *hypothyroidism* (underactive thyroid). For more on hypothyroidism, go to the end of this article.

WHAT IS HYPERTHYROIDISM?

When the thyroid (a butterfly-shaped gland located at the base of the neck) manufactures too much thyroid hormone, the malfunction is known as hyperthyroidism. With hyperthyroidism, metabolism speeds up, causing such symptoms as rapid heartbeat and sudden, unexplained weight loss.

A recent development: Updated treatment recommendations for hyperthyroidism out of the American Thyroid Association and American Association of Clinical Endocrinologists, based on the latest scientific evidence. *Highlights of the new guidelines…*

GRAVES' DISEASE

Hyperthyroidism is most commonly caused by *Graves' disease*, an autoimmune disorder in which the antibodies that normally protect against bacteria and other invaders attack the thyroid gland, stimulating excess production of thyroid hormones. If left untreated, Graves' disease can lead to heart rhythm disorders, congestive heart failure and osteoporosis.

There are three main treatments that control symptoms of Graves' disease—*antithyroid medication* (which lowers amounts of thyroid hormones)…*radioactive iodine* (to shrink the thyroid gland)…and *surgery* (to remove the thyroid gland).

What is new: The new guidelines say that all three of these options should be considered by the patient and physician, which contrasts with doctors' previous belief that radioactive iodine was the best treatment for most people with hyperthyroidism because it is easy to administer (it's taken by mouth) and effective.

• **Antithyroid medication will reduce the thyroid's hormone production.** Treatment for 12 to 18 months produces lasting remission in 20% to 30% of the people with hyperthyroidism. Side effects may include rash, hives, occasional fever, joint or muscle pain and, rarely, a reduction in white blood cells that can lead to life-threatening infection.

With antithyroid medication, the thyroid remains functional. However, it takes more than one year to determine whether the medication will work. If it does not, radioactive iodine or surgery will likely be required.

Latest drug therapy approach: The two antithyroid medications, *methimazole* (Tapazole) and *propylthiouracil* (PTU), used to be considered interchangeable, but the updated guidelines say that PTU should be used only in special circumstances (for example, early in a pregnancy)—the drug can cause serious liver damage, sometimes resulting in death.

• **Radioactive iodine.** With this treatment, you swallow a small capsule containing a radioactive chemical, which is absorbed by the thyroid. Over several weeks or months, radioactivity will destroy the overactive thyroid hormone-producing cells and shrink the thyroid gland.

The risks are lowest with radioactive iodine, but it takes six weeks to two months for the treatment to reach its full effect.

Be sure to discuss with your physician any precautions you should take to protect those around you from the radiation.

• **Surgery (or *thyroidectomy*) removes the thyroid gland and is immediately effective.** Serious complications, such as damage to the nearby calcium-regulating (*parathyroid*) glands or vocal cords, can result but are rare when the procedure is performed by an experienced surgeon.

Almost everyone who has radioactive iodine therapy or surgery must take thyroid hormone supplements for life to maintain adequate thyroid hormone levels.

WHEN EYE DAMAGE OCCURS

In roughly one of every four people with Graves' disease, the condition also affects the eyes. Sometimes it is too mild to be noticed without an exam, but in about 20% of those with Graves' eye disease, the eyelids swell…

the eyes become dry, irritated and sensitive to light…and they may develop a bulging appearance. Some people feel pressure behind the eyes. The disorder usually lasts one to two years and often improves on its own. In 3% to 5% of cases, the condition is severe enough to threaten sight.

Only recently have doctors begun to understand why Graves' eye disease occurs. In part, it's because the same antibodies that cause hyperthyroidism attack cells in the back of the eye, turning them into fat cells. These fat cells secrete chemicals that attract water and lead to inflammation, resulting in swelling and tissue damage.

Treatment for Graves' eye disease attempts to minimize the damage—utilizing steroids to decrease inflammation…or surgery (for example, to remove excess tissue behind the eye to reduce a bulging appearance).

What's new: Since Graves' eye disease may worsen in some 15% of patients when hyperthyroidism is treated with radioactive iodine, the updated guidelines recommend that a patient who has a mild, active case of the eye disorder discuss with his/her doctor whether to include a *corticosteroid*, such as *prednisone* (Sterapred), to reduce the irritation and swelling behind the eyeball and to prevent bulging eyes from worsening. If you have moderate or severe eye disease that is active, you should probably avoid radioactive iodine until your eye symptoms improve.

A recent breakthrough: Researchers are hopeful that drugs such as *rituximab*, originally approved for the treatment of *lymphoma* and now being used experimentally for Graves' eye disease, will block the inflammatory reaction that causes eye damage.

THYROID NODULES

Another main cause of hyperthyroidism is the existence of one or more hyperfunctioning nodules (or growths) within the thyroid. Nodules, which are usually noncancerous, are more common past age 60.

What's new: According to the guidelines, surgery and radioactive iodine are the only treatment options for most people who have thyroid nodules—antithyroid medication only

temporarily reverses the hyperthyroidism. Surgery is best if cancer is suspected (based on a fine-needle aspiration biopsy of the nodule)… or if the thyroid is enlarged enough to interfere with breathing.

FOR UNDERACTIVE THYROIDS

An underactive thyroid (*hypothyroidism*) is much more common than hyperthyroidism. It affects about 9.5 million Americans and has its own constellation of symptoms, including sluggishness, sensitivity to cold, constipation, fatigue, muscle aches and depression.

Because it may also lead to weight gain, elevated cholesterol and high blood pressure, hypothyroidism raises the risk for heart disease. *Important new research…*

Recent finding I: Older people with subclinical hypothyroidism (so mild that it causes few or no symptoms) were found to be more cognitively impaired than others.

Recent finding II: Women with a history of hypothyroidism were found to be at significantly increased risk for liver cancer.

The treatment for hypothyroidism involves taking an appropriate dosage of thyroid hormone, which is safe and generally free of side effects and risks.

Alzheimer's Warning Signs

When researchers analyzed 511 men and women (average age 78) with memory problems, they found that those who had at least three symptoms of mental lapses (drowsiness, excessive daytime sleeping, periods of muddled thinking and/or staring into space) were nearly five times more likely to develop Alzheimer's disease than peers without mental lapses.

If a loved one exhibits these symptoms: Consider having a physician assess him/her for Alzheimer's disease.

James E. Galvin, MD, professor of neurology and psychiatry at New York University Langone School of Medicine, New York City.

Alzheimer's Disease: Myths and Truths

Alzheimer's Association, 225 N. Michigan Ave., Chicago 60601, *www.alz.org*.

Alzheimer's disease is a very frightening diagnosis—one that we all hope never to face. Unfortunately, there are many myths about what can cause Alzheimer's or increase your risk for the disease.

Here, we set the record straight…

Myth: The use of aluminum is linked to the disease.

Truth: No study has confirmed any link between Alzheimer's and aluminum.

Myth: The low-calorie sweetener aspartame causes memory loss.

Truth: There is no scientific evidence of this.

Myth: Flu vaccine raises Alzheimer's risk.

Truth: Several studies show the opposite—that flu shots reduce risk for Alzheimer's. Past exposure to specific types of vaccines may be related to a lower risk for Alzheimer's because aging and Alzheimer's may involve changes in immune responses.

Myth: Amalgam tooth fillings increase Alzheimer's risk.

Truth: There is no evidence that these fillings—which contain 50% mercury—are linked to Alzheimer's disease.

Dreams That Predict Disease

Physically acting out violent dreams while sleeping can predict brain disease. About two-thirds of people, age 50 years and older, with *REM sleep behavior disorder* (or RBD)—which causes increasingly violent dreams and physical enactment of these nightmares while sleeping, such as trying to fight off an attacker—eventually develop some *neurodegenerative* disease, such as Parkinson's or dementia. These conditions might not develop for more than 15 years after RBD episodes first occur. At present, there are not any treatments available to delay or prevent the future development of these diseases once RBD emerges. However, RBD can be controlled using medications, such as *clonazepam*.

Carlos H. Schenck, MD, faculty member, Minnesota Regional Sleep Disorders Center, Minneapolis, and co-author of a RBD editorial published in *Neurology*.

Common OTC Pill Reduces Parkinson's Risk 40%

Ibuprofen lowers risk for Parkinson's. People who took ibuprofen at least twice per week were 40% less likely to develop Parkinson's disease than individuals who did not. Regular use of other painkillers, such as aspirin and *acetaminophen*, was not associated with lowering Parkinson's risk. Talk to your doctor about the benefits and risks of regular *ibuprofen* use.

Xiang Gao, MD, PhD, research scientist and assistant professor in medicine at Harvard School of Public Health and Harvard Medical School, Boston, and leader of a study of 136,197 people, presented at a meeting of the American Academy of Neurology.

When Depression Won't Go Away…Breakthrough Treatments Offer Relief When Nothing Else Does

C. Edward Coffey, MD, the Kathleen and Earl Ward chair of psychiatry and professor of neurology and psychiatry at the Henry Ford Health System located in Detroit. He's the author of more than 130 scientific publications and book chapters and is the editor of several textbooks, including *Textbook of Geriatric Neuropsychiatry* (American Psychiatric Press) and the *Guide to Neuropsychiatric Therapeutics* (Lippincott Williams & Wilkins). Dr. Coffey also serves on the editorial boards of several journals.

For 10% to 20% of people treated for depression, nothing seems to help. They've tried all the standard treatments, including psychotherapy and powerful prescription antidepressants, but they're still depressed.

Recent development: Treatments that use electrical stimulation are being used by an increasing number of Americans to fight off depression.*

For example…

ECT: THE MODERN VERSION

Electroconvulsive therapy (or ECT) has been used for decades, but only relatively recently has it begun to lose some of its stigma.

Today, it remains the quickest, most effective treatment available for severe depression that does not respond to other treatments. In fact, one major study found that 86% of severely depressed people recovered from their depression and were able to go back to their normal lives.

Note: ECT induces a remission of the episode of depression, but it does not cure the illness. Benefits typically last for two to three weeks.

What's involved: A brief electrical current passes through the brain to cause a controlled brain seizure—a powerful wave of brain activity—that does not lead to the violent jerking that most people associate with a seizure. No one knows for sure why ECT helps ease severe depression.

Ten to 12 sessions (15 to 20 minutes each), over three weeks, are typical. The symptoms should decrease in severity or may even stop.

When it's used: ECT is prescribed for those who have not responded to antidepressants. But sometimes it is the first treatment tried, not the last—when new patients are suicidal or homicidal…when depression includes symptoms such as hallucinations or delusions…or when a person can't function at all.

Its safety and side effects: Unlike the ECT administered in years past, the current procedure is performed under general anesthesia with a muscle relaxant to prevent a physical convulsion. Supplemental oxygen protects the brain and heart from the increased workload created by the seizure.

The stimulation is typically applied in brief pulses and just to one side of the brain, which causes fewer side effects than traditional bilateral ECT.

Memory side effects are common but usually mild and temporary. Aside from the standard risks associated with general anesthesia, common short-term side effects include headache, upset stomach and muscle ache.

Other depression treatments that use electrical stimulation…

HEALING MAGNETISM

Repetitive transcranial magnetic stimulation (rTMS), which was FDA approved in 2008 for depression, uses a powerful magnetic field to generate electrical currents inside of brain cells. While ECT stimulates a broad swath on one side of the brain, rTMS targets the specific areas that regulate mood, virtually eliminating effects on memory.

When it's used: rTMS is for people who are mildly to moderately depressed and have not responded to one to three antidepressants and often have also tried psychotherapy. In practice, some psychiatrists offer rTMS sooner to patients with less severe depression who don't want to take medication.

Although rTMS is less powerful than ECT, it can still be helpful. One study found that 30% of patients who hadn't responded to antidepressants recovered from their depression after treatment with rTMS.

What is involved: Your doctor will hold a magnetic coil against your head while you are seated in a reclining chair. You will hear clicks and may feel a tapping sensation. You can resume normal activities immediately afterward. Five 30- to 45-minute sessions every week for four to six weeks are typical.

Safety and side effects: rTMS is noninvasive, and it requires no anesthesia. One 2008 study with 325 patients found that side effects (typically brief headaches or scalp discomfort) were relatively few and mild. You may not be able to receive rTMS, however, if you have a metal implant (including some tooth implants) anywhere near the head or if you have a cardiac pacemaker.

NERVE TO BRAIN

With *vagus nerve stimulation* (VNS), electrical pulses travel to the brain via a large nerve

---

*Electroconvulsive treatment is typically covered by insurance. Check with your insurance company about the other treatments mentioned in this article.

in the neck. The 30-second pulses are generated every few minutes from a small, battery-driven device that is surgically implanted just below the collarbone.

When it's used: The FDA approved VNS in 2005 for treatment of chronic (lasting longer than two years) or recurrent depression that hadn't responded to at least four antidepressants. VNS helped nearly 30% of treatment-resistant patients in several studies.

What is involved: Surgery to implant the generator and electrode can take one to two hours and is performed under local anesthesia. The device is programmed and activated externally one week later. It may take several months until the depression symptoms diminish or are eliminated. For this reason, VNS is not appropriate for severe depression.

Safety and side effects: Since minor surgery is involved, there is some risk of bleeding and infection and discomfort around the area where the device was implanted. Some people experience hoarseness, a tickling sensation or cough when the pulse is on, or difficulty breathing during exercise. A magnet can be used to turn off the device if the side effects are particularly bothersome, such as during exercise. Afterward, you can turn the device back on.

ON THE HORIZON

Other treatments for depression now being studied offer the potential for a more targeted stimulation, which would improve effectiveness and minimize side effects…

•**Deep brain stimulation (DBS)** involves implanting wires inside brain tissue to provide continuous stimulation that alters brain function. DBS is already used for Parkinson's disease.

•**Magnetic seizure therapy (MST).** During this therapy, a magnetic field generates electrical impulses that are strong enough to trigger a seizure (although ECT also induces a seizure, with MST, the stimulation is more targeted).

To learn more about clinical trials using either of these therapies, log on to *www.clinical trials.gov.*

High Altitude Linked to Increased Suicide Risk

People living 6,500 feet or more above sea level have two-thirds higher risk for suicide than people living at sea level. States with the highest suicide rates include Arizona, Colorado, Idaho, Montana, Nevada, New Mexico, Oregon, Utah and Wyoming, which all have some regions that are at least 6,500 feet above sea level.

Possible reason: The slightly lower oxygen intake at higher altitudes may affect people with mood disorders.

Self-defense: People with mood disorders who visit high-altitude areas should be aware that their conditions may worsen.

Perry F. Renshaw, MD, PhD, professor of psychiatry, University of Utah, Salt Lake City, and leader of a study of an analysis of altitude and suicide rates, published online in American Journal of Psychiatry.

Trans Fats Increase Depression Risk 48%

Trans fats have been shown to increase depression risk.

Recent finding: Individuals who consumed more than 1.5 grams (g) of trans fats per day increased their risk for clinical depression by 48%. The more trans fats, the higher the risk. (None of the study volunteers suffered from depression at the start of the study.)

Trans fats increase inflammation, which can interfere with brain transmitters and disrupt mood.

Almudena Sánchez-Villegas, BPharm, PhD, associate professor of preventive medicine, University of Las Palmas de Gran Canaria, Las Palmas, Spain, and lead author of a study of 12,059 people, published in PLoS One.

Do You Use Reusable Shopping Bags? What You Must Know...

Bacteria thrive in reusable shopping bags. Half of the reusable bags in a recent study showed bacterial growth, and 12% contained *E.coli* bacteria, which can cause severe intestinal illness.

Self-defense: Wash the bags with soap and water (by hand or in a washing machine). Do not carry raw foods, such as meats and produce, in reusable bags. Do not leave the empty bags in a warm car—bacterial counts rise significantly in just two hours.

Charles P. Gerba, PhD, professor, department of soil, water and environmental science, University of Arizona, Tucson, and leader of a study of bacteria in reusable shopping bags.

Alert: "Prewashed" Greens May *Still* Contain Bacteria

Packaged salad greens may be high in bacteria despite the labels saying *prewashed* and *triple-washed*. Lab tests found unacceptable levels of *coliform* bacteria in 39% of 208 containers of 16 brands of packaged greens. And 23% contained unacceptable amounts of *Enterococcus*. Both bacteria indicate poor sanitation and fecal contamination. The highest of bacteria amounts were found in bags containing spinach and those within five days of their use-by dates.

Self-defense: Select packaged salad greens that are not close to their use-by dates, and rinse well before eating.

Laboratory study commissioned by and reported in *Consumer Reports,* 101 Truman Ave., Yonkers, New York 10703, *www.consumerreports.org.*

Healthier Spinach

Store-bought spinach offers higher nutrient levels than spinach kept in the dark.

Reason: Lighting in the store mimics sunlight closely enough to cause *photosynthesis*, which increases spinach's levels of vitamins C, E, K and folate.

Gene Lester, PhD, adjunct professor and research plant physiologist, US Department of Agriculture in Beltsville, Maryland, and lead author of a study on spinach.

Better Sushi Choice

When researchers compared the mercury content of tuna sushi sold in 54 restaurants and 15 supermarkets across three states, restaurant tuna sometimes contained up to 50% more mercury than supermarket tuna.

Theory: Supermarket tuna sushi is usually made with yellowfin, a smaller tuna species that accumulates less mercury than the larger bigeye or bluefin tuna species typically prepared in restaurants.

Michael Gochfeld, MD, PhD, professor at the Environmental and Occupational Health Sciences Institute, Robert Wood Johnson Medical School, University of Medicine & Dentistry of New Jersey, Piscataway.

The Cleanest Fish

Fish with the lowest levels of contaminants but rich in *omega-3 fatty acids* are albacore tuna (from the US or British Columbia)... freshwater Coho salmon (farmed using tank systems in the US)...mussels (farmed)...oysters (farmed)...Pacific sardines (wild-caught)...rainbow trout (farmed)...and salmon (wild-caught in Alaska).

Report by Monterey Bay Aquarium's Seafood Watch, reported in *Environmental Nutrition*, 800 Connecticut Ave., Norwalk, Connecticut 06854.

2

Medical Manager

Treat *Me*...Not My Age! Getting the Best Medical Care as You Get Older

It is not surprising that older adults have more health problems than young people. What is surprising however is how poorly the older population is served by our health-care system.

This is partly due to medical ageism, a subtle type of age discrimination that makes it harder to navigate the health-care system as you get older. In a Duke University survey, nearly 80% of respondents older than 60 had been told at least once by their doctors that their ailments were due to age—the implication being that the ailment is simply a result of getting older, so the doctor isn't going to treat it.

Many of the conditions that get more common with age, such as pain, hearing loss and depression, are never fully investigated. Similarly, a doctor might feel that a little knee pain

or the leakage of urine is "normal" with older adults. This philosophy means that underlying problems might never be diagnosed.

Undertreatment is one consequence of medical ageism...*overtreatment* is another. Doctors who practice what is often called "cookbook medicine" tend to recommend the same tests and procedures for everyone.

Your doctor should treat you, not your age. Here's what to watch out for—and what to do to make sure that medical ageism doesn't hurt you or a loved one...

UNDERTREATMENT

Rationing health care is among the most common forms of medical ageism. A doctor looks at the patient's medical record, notes the birth date and then makes certain assumptions.

Mark Lachs, MD, MPH, a professor of medicine and co-chief of the division of geriatrics and gerontology at Weill Cornell Medical College in New York City. He also is the director of Cornell's Center for Aging Research and Clinical Care and director of geriatrics for the New York-Presbyterian Health System. He is author of *Treat Me, Not My Age* (Viking, *www.treatmenotmyage.com*).

Example: An older man who complained that he hurt his knee during a tennis match might be advised to take up a less physically demanding sport, such as golf. Or he might simply be told to "take it easy."

I know plenty of 70- and 80-year-olds who are in great shape and play a tough game of tennis, and a few 40-year-olds who are frail. The doctor's duty is to address the problem, not to simply ignore the problem with age-based assumptions.

Self-protection: Don't let your doctor brush off any health issue with a reference to age. Be wary if he/she performs a perfunctory exam or rushes through your history. You should be asked detailed questions such as, "When did your pain start?"…"How many days are there when it doesn't hurt?"…"How's your range of motion?" etc.

It's possible that there will not be an easy solution, or any solution, for your problem. If that is the case, make sure that your doctor tells you why. "You're just getting older" is not an acceptable answer.

OUTDATED EXAM

The traditional office exam is not effective for older adults. It was created more than 100 years ago, when people did not live as long. Information regarding blood pressure, reflexes, heart sounds, etc., is helpful, but it tells little about how well you function in daily life.

Example: The patient who appears perfectly healthy based on the standard medical exam might be falling every day at home.

Self-protection: Do not wait for your doctor to discover things. Make a list before you go in, which might include balance problems, declines in muscle strength, poor hearing or even social isolation, which can bring on depression. These and other functional problems often are more important for long-term health than what is revealed by an exam.

Ideally, your doctor also will perform tests to assess how you actually function. He might speak at different volumes to check your "real-life" hearing. You might be asked to walk or to stand up and then sit down. You might be given a list of words and numbers and asked to repeat them.

Helpful: Ask friends and family members if they've noticed things that you haven't. Maybe you keep turning up the volume on your television or asking people to repeat themselves. You might be getting tired more easily or forgetting names more often.

ARE YOU DEPRESSED?

Depression is common in the elderly, but doctors often fail to diagnosis it. This is partly because it takes time to perform a mental health evaluation, so most doctors don't routinely do it. It's also because older adults often experience different symptoms of depression than those who are younger.

Self-protection: Tell your doctor if you've been feeling more irritable lately…have been losing weight…or are eating less regularly. All of these are common signs of depression in older adults.

Important: If you're suffering from depression, ask for a referral to a gerontologist (an internist who specializes in treating older patients) or a geriatric psychiatrist. Medicines can be helpful, especially when used in conjunction with supportive psychotherapy, but older people respond differently to antidepressants. They may require different doses and/or durations of treatment than younger adults.

OVERCARE

Too much medical care is just as dangerous as too little, particularly for those who are taking multiple medications, have underlying health problems and generally are frail.

Example: The mother of a friend of mine has Alzheimer's disease and dementia, as well as diabetes. The doctors and nurses who care for her always are monitoring her blood sugar. This requires numerous daily blood pricks… which she thinks is a sign that they're trying to kill her, making her agitated and unhappy. For any patient like this, treating the diabetes this aggressively doesn't make a lot of sense.

And similarly, I would hesitate to subject an 82-year-old woman to the inconvenience and stress of a mammogram, particularly if she has had many negative mammograms in the past, no history of breast problems and no family history of breast cancer.

Self-protection: Don't agree to any test or procedure without asking your doctor if the results will change or improve your outcome. You also should ask questions such as, "What will happen to me if I do nothing?"…"Will the results of this test lead to more tests?"…"What are the side effects of testing?"

A patient might reasonably decide that he wants every possible test and treatment—it's just as reasonable to do the opposite in some cases.

AVOID THE ER

According to data from the National Center for Health Statistics, about 25% of Americans older than 75 went to the emergency room at least once that year. That's the last place that you want to be except in a real emergency.

In the ER, there's too much care—and too little. Examinations are rushed. There's often a lack of communication among doctors. Patients may be given tests that they don't really need. It's an extremely stressful environment.

My advice: Ask your doctor how you can contact him, or an assistant, at any hour. Certainly don't delay in getting to the ER if you have any serious symptoms, such as those of a stroke or heart attack, but other conditions might wait until the next day if you can get the over-the-phone OK from your doctor.

Is Your Surgeon Sleep-Deprived? What to Do…

Regulations limit working hours of doctors in training but not practicing physicians.

Recent study: Patients who had nonurgent surgery with surgeons who slept fewer than six hours the previous night while on call had an 83% higher risk for complications, including bleeding and damage to organs. Research shows that lack of sleep can impair surgeons as much as alcohol intoxication.

When you schedule a nonurgent surgery: Check to ensure that the proposed day is not following a night your surgeon will be on call.

Michael Nurok, MD, PhD, critical care physician, Hospital for Special Surgery, New York City.

Take a Peek at Your Doctor's Notes

Rebecca Shannonhouse, editor, *Bottom Line/Health*, Boardroom Inc., 281 Tresser Blvd., Stamford, Connecticut 06901.

When you visit your doctor, have you ever wondered what he/she writes in your medical file?

Problem: Many physicians either refuse to share these notes with patients or make it difficult for them to get copies even though federal law clearly states that patients have a right to see them.

Recent development: Tom Delbanco, MD, an internist at Harvard Medical School, is conducting a study to evaluate what happens when patients do get copies of their records. *He explains that potential benefits may include…*

•**Shared decision making.** Patients have unique insights about all their symptoms and how their bodies work. Doctors have specialized knowledge. Bringing these perspectives together should improve medical care.

•**More accurate diagnosis.** Patients aren't always honest about lifestyle factors, such as alcohol consumption. Someone who reads in the notes that his doctor is concerned about excessive drinking might be more forthcoming. Conversely, a patient who does not drink can explain to the doctor that alcohol can't be a factor.

•**Reminders.** Patients remember very little of what they're told in the doctor's office. A review of their records will help them keep track of what the doctor said as well as medication instructions, etc.

Important: Doctors *must* give you copies of records upon request (a charge might be applied). If your doctor refuses, ask to speak with a senior office manager—and consider changing doctors.

Medical Test Overdose: Are You Getting Too Much Radiation?

Mahadevappa Mahesh, PhD, associate professor of radiology in the Russell H. Morgan department of radiology and radiological science, and associate professor of medicine, division of cardiology, Johns Hopkins University School of Medicine, Baltimore. He is one of the authors of the National Council of Radiation Protection's report "Ionizing Radiation Exposure of the Population of the United States."

We worry about radiation from nuclear reactors, power lines and our cell phones. Yes, we get too much radiation—but not from any of those sources. The real demon is too many medical tests.

In America we're exposed to more radiation than individuals anywhere else in the world. In the early 1980s, the average American was exposed to 0.5 millisieverts (mSv, a dose measurement) of medical radiation annually. But today, the average is 3 mSv, a sixfold increase.

This corresponds to the increasing use of *computed tomography (CT) scans* (also called CAT scans) and other medical imaging tests. A typical CT scan delivers between 7 mSv and 10 mSv. That's between 70 and 100 times the amount of a typical chest X-ray. Scans that examine multiple parts of the body might deliver up to 25 mSv.

Too much radiation raises the risk for cancer. A single CT scan is not likely to increase anyone's odds of getting cancer, but patients who are exposed to repeated high amounts of radiation, whether from CT scans or other imaging tests, do face higher risks. This is particularly the case for patients under age 40 or 45. Radiation-induced cancers can take decades to develop. The younger person who gets excessive radiation faces a higher lifetime risk than someone who's much older.

Here's how to reduce your risk…

UNNECESSARY EXPOSURE

It's not known exactly how much medical radiation is safe. Most of the data is derived from studies of atomic bomb survivors. Their odds for cancer were found to increase after exposure to roughly 500 mSv of radiation. By comparison, a mammogram delivers less than 1 mSv…full-mouth dental X-rays deliver about 0.15 mSv.

Granted, atomic bomb radiation is different from the radiation used in medical scans, and the survivors received the radiation in an instant, rather than over years or decades. This probably put them at a higher risk. But high levels of radiation from any source clearly are unsafe.

The imaging tests that utilize radiation are an essential part of modern medicine. For the vast majority of patients, the benefits of these tests far outweigh the potential risks.

The problem is excessive medical testing. Most experts agree that about one-third of all diagnostic tests, including imaging tests, are unnecessary.

Example: It is not uncommon for heart patients to receive multiple CT scans after being admitted to the hospital, even though a single scan might be sufficient for some of these patients.

Be aware that one study found that physicians who owned CT scanners ordered about three times more radiological tests, on average, than physicians without a financial stake in the exams.

REDUCE YOUR RISK

The FDA, which regulates imaging devices, has begun investigating ways to reduce radiation exposure. These might include the development of lower-radiation scans or creating a national dose registry in which patients' total radiation doses would automatically be noted in medical files.

Because the danger from radiation accumulates with repeated exposure, patients should work with their doctors to keep total doses as low as possible.

What to do…

•**Question every scan.** Don't assume that you require an X-ray or CT scan just because your doctor ordered the test. Some scans that are ordered routinely are unnecessary.

Example: Patients having low-back pain or headaches might be given CT scans, even though the information that's provided by the tests rarely affects the diagnosis or treatment of these conditions.

Obviously, every patient is different. These tests might be essential, but don't just assume that is the case. Tell your doctor that you are concerned about radiation. Ask him/her if the potential benefits of the test outweigh the potential risks.

• **Keep copies.** Virtually every type of scan can be transferred to a CD. When you have an imaging test, ask for and keep a copy. This makes it easier to avoid duplicate scans.

Example: Suppose that you go into the hospital because of abdominal pain. Even if you've had a CT scan for this problem in the past, the records won't be available at a different hospital. The scan will have to be repeated unless you have a copy of the earlier test.

Even if you go into the same hospital, the doctor ordering the scan might not notice that you already have been tested. It's possible that you'll need a new scan to track recent changes, but don't assume that's the case.

Important: If the hospital or testing facility won't give you a CD of the scan (it might insist that test results are confidential), speak with an administrator. You own all your medical records, including scan results. You have a right to a copy, though you may be charged reasonable cost-based fees.

• **Try to avoid repeat scans.** Doctors often request multiple imaging tests. This might be done to confirm a diagnosis, provide additional views of an organ or detect changes that occurred after an initial scan. Repeating these tests sometimes is necessary, but not always.

Example: It is normal for kidney stone patients to have multiple stones and to suffer multiple attacks. These patients often wind up in the emergency room. Even if the emergency room doctor suspects that he/she knows what the problem is, CT scans might be ordered "just to be safe."

If you've already had one scan for a particular condition, don't agree to additional scans unless the physician can explain why they are necessary. As for routine tests, such as dental X-rays, ask your dentist or doctor to do only what is needed.

• **Ask about all alternatives.** The advantage of CT scans is that they provide highly detailed images, but this isn't always important, particularly when other, nonradiation tests—such as magnetic resonance imaging (or MRI) scans or ultrasound—will give equally definitive results.

Example: Pain in the upper-right part of the abdomen is a classic sign of gallstones. Ultrasound is effective at diagnosing this, and it doesn't expose the patient to radiation.

• **Avoid routine lung screening.** Smokers and previous smokers may be encouraged to undergo routine CT scans to detect lung cancer. While the screening tests do detect some cases of lung cancer, they also expose patients to unacceptable risks.

Researchers from the Mayo Medical School recruited several thousand smokers and past smokers and gave all of them chest CT scans. About half turned out to have nodules—abnormalities that might be cancer. However, all subsequent tests showed that the vast majority of these nodules were benign.

While a CT scan might be warranted for some patients, widespread screening isn't the answer. It would expose too many people to unnecessary radiation and could result in unnecessary surgeries—all without decreasing the number of lung cancer deaths.

• **Make sure that the facility is accredited.** The American College of Radiology (ACR) is one of the organizations recognized by the US government to accredit the advanced imaging tests, such as CT scans. ACR accreditation requires facilities to meet certain minimum standards with regard to clinical image quality and radiation dose safety. This helps to reduce the risk that you will get too much radiation from, for example, any equipment that is not working properly.

How to Fudge on Your Doctor's Orders

Julian Seifter, MD, associate professor of medicine at Harvard Medical School in Boston. A nephrologist at Brigham and Women's Hospital, also in Boston, he has practiced medicine for 30 years. He is the author of *After the Diagnosis: Transcending Chronic Illness* (Simon & Schuster).

If you're one of the more than 90 million Americans who suffer from a chronic illness, such as high blood pressure, diabetes, kidney disease or asthma, chances are your doctor has recommended that you take medication and/or change your lifestyle.

Following your doctors' orders isn't always easy, but a bit of judicious "cheating" is almost always OK.

Julian Seifter, MD, is a Harvard nephrologist (kidney specialist) who has diabetes himself. *He shares some advice based on his personal experiences…*

MY HEALTH CHALLENGES

As a nephrologist, I am an expert in all the complications of diabetes, but I've sometimes been unable to change my own habits to keep my diabetes under control. At different times, I've been out of shape and overweight and allowed my blood pressure and blood sugar to get too high. *What I've learned…*

WHY WE CHEAT

Being diagnosed with a chronic illness profoundly impacts your sense of identity. You may need to give up things that are important to you…forever. And doing what you're told by your doctor means that you're losing some control over your life.

It's only human that we often respond to these losses with denial. That's especially true if you don't feel particularly sick, as with high blood pressure. You can ignore dietary guidelines your doctor has given you or not take your medication—and if you're lucky enough to not suffer ill effects, this cheating lets you tell the world, and yourself, there's nothing wrong with you.

Even if you accept your illness, giving up favorite foods or pleasurable habits can hurt your quality of life. And allowing your illness to define you—becoming afraid to do activities you enjoy and worrying about everything you eat—isn't healthy either. Life has to be worth living, which requires compromise.

FIND THE RIGHT DOCTOR

Doctors shouldn't just serve as instruction givers…they should be problem solvers. They should meet their patients halfway and help them figure out how to do what is necessary for their health while maintaining their pleasure in life.

If your doctor is rigid and moralistic, this can create a communication barrier that makes matters worse. You will be tempted to lie or simply cancel your appointment if you haven't followed your diet lately or you stopped taking medication that was triggering uncomfortable side effects.

To find out if you can work with your doctor, say something like, "I am worried that I'll never be able to have corned beef (or a glass of wine…or a piece of pie) again. Is there any way we can compromise on my diet?" You also may want to ask about larger worries, such as how you can continue to travel or participate in your favorite sport.

STRIKE A BALANCE

It is almost always possible to build flexibility into a diet or medical regimen and still achieve a high level of care.

Example: Having a pastrami sandwich is not part of a low-fat or low-salt diet. But one every other week won't make much difference to most people's health, and if you love pastrami, it's likely to make you a lot happier with the whole eating plan.

If you are prescribed a low-salt diet for hypertension, can you indicate three salty foods that you would not mind giving up? And are there three foods that you would truly miss? Talk to your doctor about the foods you will miss most to see whether a compromise can be made. The "special foods" may need to be rotated or scheduled with appropriate portion sizes.

If you feel that you must cheat, work with your doctor to find a creative solution.

Example: When I told one of my patients drinking alcohol contributed to his high blood pressure, he insisted that he had to have his two martinis nightly. To compromise, I said he could have one martini every night but without the high-sodium olive.

FORGET YOU'RE SICK

With my diabetes, the turning point for me arrived after I collapsed, due to poorly controlled blood sugar that was compounded by anxiety, while visiting Paris with my wife.

What I realized: Ironically, cheating less could give me what I wanted most—to simply forget about my illness. Thereafter, I made it a habit to check my blood sugar before and after meals, as well as to exercise, take my blood pressure pills and eat the right foods.

I'm not perfect. But I make repeated efforts to get it right, and this has allowed me to live with increased confidence and freedom—and simply have more fun. I aim for the art of the possible and try to help my patients do the same.

Are Drug Companies Controlling Your Doctor?

Carl Elliott, MD, PhD, a professor in the University of Minnesota Center for Bioethics and the department of pediatrics at the University of Minnesota Medical School in Minneapolis. He is also a professor in the department of philosophy in the College of Liberal Arts. Dr. Elliott is the author of *White Coat, Black Hat: Adventures on the Dark Side of Medicine* (Beacon).

The strategies used by the pharmaceutical industry to influence doctors' prescribing and treatment practices have come under a great deal of scrutiny in recent years.

Now: A recent survey shows that doctors are less likely than in the past to accept gifts or other financial incentives from the drug or medical device companies, but there is still a lot of room for improvement.

The survey, which was completed by 1,891 primary care physicians and got published in *Archives of Internal Medicine*, indicated that a number of "relationship-building" incentives are still widely used. Overall, 83.8% of doctors reported some type of relationship with the industry in the year prior to the 2009 study. About 18% were reimbursed by drug companies for professional meetings and continuing medical education. In addition, 70.6% of all the doctors surveyed received food and beverages from drug companies.

To find out more about the pharmaceutical industry's continuing influence over physicians, we spoke with Carl Elliott, MD, PhD, a leading medical ethicist at the University of Minnesota, who has extensively studied drug companies' relationships with doctors.

• **How do drug companies inform doctors about their products?** As most people know, pharmaceutical companies employ armies of salespeople. Few people realize, however, the amount of influence that these drug reps can have over doctors. Many physicians are willing—and sometimes pleased—to spend time with these reps. They are typically young, personable, smart and fun to be with. They also tend to be very good-looking.

Drug reps show up at doctors' offices, hospitals and medical conferences. Their main job is to get a few minutes with as many doctors as possible to talk about their products. If the company rep is successful over a long period of time and persuades doctors to write a lot of prescriptions, the rep may even receive a bonus or commission.

During their brief meetings with doctors, the reps leave behind small gifts like coffee mugs, note pads, etc. Doctors do not prescribe a different drug because of free mugs, but they are often influenced simply because such gifts are one way of creating goodwill between drug reps and doctors.

• **How do we know this?** To test whether doctors are influenced by the pharmaceutical companies, researchers at the Cleveland Clinic had the clever idea to compare doctors' prescribing habits before and after they had gone on free trips sponsored by drug manufacturers. For one drug, the number of prescriptions written after a trip was awarded was 10 times higher than it was before.

• **What about the scientific studies that are conducted to determine a drug's effectiveness?** Doctors will tell you that they prescribe certain medications because studies prove that they're superior or because leading experts recommend them. But the drug reps are often the ones who provide the drug research to the doctors. And even the doctors may not realize that the expert opinions and the studies themselves may be tainted by hidden sales strategies.

● **What are some of these hidden strategies?** One is "ghost authorship," which could occur in articles that are published in some prestigious medical journals or research that is presented at medical conferences. In each case, the information is linked with the names of prominent physicians.

However, the famous name (or names) at the heads of these articles may have only reviewed the material and provided suggestions. The real author, known as a "ghost," isn't listed anywhere in the article. He was probably a medical writer who was paid by a pharmaceutical company.

This practice deceives readers because an article that appears to come out of, let us say, Harvard might in fact, come from a pharmaceutical company. Though some journals have become more stringent and created policies against this, the practice still goes on at some publications.

Additionally, when a drug company wishes to establish a market niche for its drug, it may do so by publishing articles about a competing drug's deficiencies.

For example, one of my colleagues was contacted to read over an article that would highlight the dangers of a popular blood-thinning medication. Later, she was sent the completed manuscript with her name on it. Only then did she realize that the company was developing a competing drug. Part of its marketing strategy was to insert negative references about the competition into the medical literature.

● **Are there any other ways that the drug companies influence scientific research?** Yes. With so-called "review articles," a doctor summarizes the status of knowledge regarding one particular drug therapy. The author—again, a well-known physician who is widely respected —uses information from studies.

What's interesting, however, is that some or even all of the background material for the review article may have been provided by the pharmaceutical company, which might leave out "negative" material about a specific drug.

The author may have been approached by a pharmaceutical company because he is known to have a point of view that's favorable to the company. As a "thought leader" in the field, this physician is in a unique position to influence the prescribing habits of other doctors.

● **Can't physicians detect—and resist—industry influence?** Most do try, but it is tricky. Just as the drug companies give small presents to doctors, the pharmaceutical companies also provide the vast majority of funding for scientific research. Without this money, medical researchers can't work—or get a salary. Industry influence is built into the system.

Even though grants from the National Institutes of Health and other government agencies are free from an industry influence, these grants—given current budgetary constraints— are especially hard to get.

In fact, as a stipulation of grants from some pharmaceutical companies, the studies might be designed by the drugmakers themselves, not by the researchers. There are many ways to design a study so that a new drug appears better than it really is.

For example, suppose that a pharmaceutical company is funding a study that will compare an older medicine with a new and "improved" drug. The study can be designed so that participants taking the older medicine are given a lower dose—this is known as "underdosing" the competition. The new drug will appear to have stronger effects.

Or suppose that a company has developed a new drug that will be advertised as having fewer side effects. Participants will be given a higher dose of the competing drug ("overdosing"), which will exacerbate its side effect profile.

● **Don't medical journals look out for such ploys when determining which research to publish?** They should—but you would be surprised at how many articles with questionable research are approved for publication in peer-reviewed journals. Studies can be manipulated in complex ways that require statistical expertise to spot.

• **What can medical patients do to protect themselves?** If you're ever concerned that your physician's prescribing practices could be influenced by drug companies, consider consulting ProPublica at *http://projects.propublica.org/doc dollars*. This is a not-for-profit organization that has assembled a database listing payments from pharmaceutical companies to doctors. Patients can search for the name of a doctor. Receiving payments isn't necessarily wrong, but it could indicate that a doctor may be biased in prescribing a certain drug.

• **Are there any specific questions you can ask a doctor to determine whether he has been influenced by the pharmaceutical industry?** You can ask your doctor whether he accepts payments or gifts from pharmaceutical companies, and if so, whether the payment has anything to do with the drugs he is prescribing you.

Remember: These influences are complex, and even your doctor may not be fully aware of how his decisions may be affected. But asking the question will prompt him to at least think about it.

Secret to Making Any Medication Work Much More Effectively

Murray Grossan, MD, otolaryngologist and head and neck surgeon with Tower Ear, Nose & Throat at Cedars-Sinai Medical Towers in Los Angeles. He has written about biofeedback for medical journals and is author of the e-book *Stressed? Anxiety? Your Cure Is in the Mirror.* Dr. Grossan's Web site is *www.grossan.com*.

The *placebo response* is the therapeutic benefit that many patients experience after taking a placebo (something that looks like a drug but does not contain any medicine).

In drug research, approximately one-third of patients who take placebos report an improvement in symptoms. Sometimes placebos work even better than that. A study of patients with acute sinusitis, published in *Archives of Internal Medicine*, found that patients taking placebos did just as well after one week as patients taking the active drug already proven to be effective.

I have found in my research that we can harness the placebo response to make actual medications work even better. I call this "medication enhancement." For patients taking medications, it can be used to improve the effects of these drugs. In some cases, medications can even be reduced or stopped (so it is important to be monitored by your doctor).

MINDFUL HEALING

It's not entirely clear why or how placebos work. We used to believe that placebos were mainly effective for subjective symptoms that aren't easily measured, such as pain. It's become clear, however, that placebos can affect virtually every bodily function, including respiration, heart rate and even the movement of immune cells to the sites of injuries.

Also, patients who reduce stress, think positively about getting well and take an active role in their recovery can experience a very strong enhancement of their body's natural healing factors. Patients who do these things and take medication usually respond better than those who merely take a pill a few times a day.

Patients who think positively about a treatment can change their internal chemistry so that it mimics the effects of some drugs. Consider antihistamines, which work by blocking a key chemical that causes nasal congestion. A patient with allergies who takes antihistamines—and who believes that the treatment is working—will produce higher levels of histamine-blocking chemicals than a patient who just takes the drugs.

To make all of your medications much more effective…

• **Know how the drug works.** I spend a lot of time explaining to my patients exactly what their medications do—how they work, what body systems they affect, how quickly they work and how different symptoms will respond. Once the patient understands how a drug works, the brain amplifies this information and produces additional positive effects.

Example: I might offer the exact same prescription antihistamine to two patients. The patient who takes the time to understand how the drug works will almost always get better results than the patient who tunes out the discussion and just takes the pills. This is difficult to prove scientifically, but every doctor I know reports the same thing.

• **Visualize it working.** A technique known as visualization therapy, in which patients visualize soothing mental images, very commonly is used to reduce stress. It also can enhance the effects of medication by altering how the body functions.

Example: Someone who takes a medication for hypertension can achieve further reductions in blood pressure by imagining that the medication is expanding blood vessels… reducing contractions of arteries…and causing blood to flow more smoothly.

Studies have shown that visualization exercises can change heart rate, respiration, blood pressure and the perception of pain. They also can reduce inflammation and swelling. I advise patients who take sinus medications, for example, to spend a minute or two every day thinking about how the drug is causing the swollen tissues to shrink and allowing more air to move through the nose into the lungs.

• **Imagine yourself as healed.** Every serious athlete is trained to visualize success—winning the tough race, making the free throw, hitting the ball.

Reason: Thinking about failure increases the odds that you will fail, because negative thoughts raise levels of hormones that impair performance. But positive thoughts will do the opposite.

The same is true when you're taking medications. Patients who tell themselves that the drug is working and imagine being completely healed tend to have better physiological responses than those who are skeptical.

• **Do-it-yourself biofeedback.** The so-called stress hormones, including *cortisol*, make just about every symptom worse. People who are highly stressed recover more slowly after surgery, experience more pain and respond less effectively to medications.

Stress control is such an important part of healing that most medical centers provide biofeedback machines to promote relaxation and reduce pain. These machines give patients feedback on how much muscle tension they have.

Try this: Use a mirror as a biofeedback machine. Once or twice a day, stand in front of a mirror and look at your face for a few minutes. Unclench your jaw. Let your lips relax and hang slightly apart. Feel the tension drain away from your cheeks and eyes. It's almost impossible to feel anxiety when your muscles are relaxed.

While you're doing the mirror exercise, pay attention to your breathing. Breathe in deeply for a count of four, then relax as you exhale for a count of six. Do this several times. This type of breathing and muscle relaxation shifts the *limbic system* (the part of the brain associated with stress) into a more relaxed mode.

Free Site Covers Latest Drug Recalls

To stay up to date about drug recalls, regularly check the Web site *www.recalls.gov.* The free site compiles information from federal government agencies that initiate or announce recalls, including the Food and Drug Administration…Environmental Protection Agency… US Department of Agriculture…and Consumer Product Safety Commission. You also can go to individual agency sites and sign up for e-mail alerts that will be sent directly to you.

Examples: www.fda.gov or *www.epa.gov.*

The e-mails may include safety advice in addition to recall announcements.

Donald L. Mays, senior director of product safety and technical policy, Consumers Union, Yonkers, New York, which publishes *Consumer Reports.*

Herb/Drug Dangers

Some dangerous supplement-medication interactions include…

• **Licorice,** taken for digestive problems such as heartburn, does not mix well with *diuretics* for high blood pressure—the combination can cause potassium levels to drop, interfering with normal heart rhythms.

Better: Ginger tea.

• **Turmeric,** taken for arthritis pain, can react with blood thinners, increasing the possibility of bleeding.

Better: Antioxidant-filled juices, like grape, pomegranate and cherry.

• **Feverfew,** a migraine remedy, also should not be taken with blood thinners.

Better: Get sufficient magnesium through supplements—people with low levels of it are more prone to migraines.

Note: Doses of more than 300 milligrams (mg) of magnesium a day can cause diarrhea.

Joe Graedon, MS, pharmacologist, Durham, North Carolina, and author of *Best Choices from the People's Pharmacy* (NAL Trade).

Meds Don't Mix with These Popular Juices

Orange juice and apple juice affect medicines. Grapefruit juice will often increase a drug's potency, but orange and apple juices can induce the opposite effect—drinking them within two hours of taking some medications could diminish the drugs' effectiveness. These medications include *beta-blockers* for blood pressure, the allergy treatment *fexofenadine*, the antibiotic *ciprofloxacin* and the anticancer drug *etoposide*.

Best: Avoid fruit juices for four hours before and after taking medicines. Drink a glass of water with medicines.

David G. Bailey, PhD, professor of clinical pharmacology, The University of Western Ontario in London, Canada, and leader of a study reported in *Tufts University Health & Nutrition Letter*.

Measuring Mishaps

Don't use ordinary kitchen spoons to dispense medicines. Using a regular spoon for medication dosages may lead to over- and underdosing. When study participants used a variety of kitchen spoons to take medication, they overdosed by 11.6% when using a larger spoon and underdosed by 8.4% when using a medium-sized spoon.

When dispensing liquid medicines: Use a proper measuring spoon, measuring cap or measuring dropper, available at pharmacies.

Study of 195 people by researchers at Cornell University, Ithaca, New York, published in *Annals of Internal Medicine*.

"Dirty" Drugs—Popular Meds with Nasty Side Effects

James Rudolph, MD, a geriatrician and the director of the Postoperative Delirium Service at the Veterans Affairs Boston Healthcare System and the Boston Geriatric Research Scholars Program. Dr. Rudolph is also geriatrician at Brigham and Women's Hospital and an assistant professor of medicine at Harvard Medical School, both are in Boston. Dr. Rudolph, with his colleagues, developed the "Anticholinergic Risk Scale," which was published in the *Archives of Internal Medicine*. The scale helps doctors to predict, and avoid, complications from the use of these medications.

If you are like most Americans, you have probably taken—or may currently take—an over-the-counter (OTC) allergy or cold drug, pain reliever or sleep aid containing *diphenhydramine*. This generic medication has become widely available without a prescription in such products as Benadryl, Excedrin PM and Tylenol PM.

What you may not know: These drugs, as well as dozens of others that are used by millions of Americans, block the action of *acetylcholine*, the *neurotransmitter* that controls several critical functions in the body ranging from body secretions to cognitive function.

Why is this a potential problem? Cells in virtually every part of the body have molecular openings (or *receptors*) that respond to acetylcholine. A drug that is used to treat a condition in one part of the body invariably affects receptors somewhere else.

Result: A high incidence of unintended effects. In some cases, people who take these so-called anticholinergic drugs suffer side effects such as constipation, urinary retention, blurred vision, dry mouth or even symptoms that mimic Alzheimer's disease.

"DIRTY" DRUGS

Medications that cause a high rate of unintended effects are known in the health-care community as "dirty" drugs. The same active ingredient that decreases bladder spasms, for example, might also cause constipation by reducing intestinal contractions or eye dryness by blocking acetylcholine at the receptors that control body secretions.

Important finding: A study published in the *Journal of the American Geriatrics Society* looked at 544 men with high blood pressure, some of whom were using the *anticholinergic* drugs for relatively minor conditions such as allergies. Over a two-year period, the men taking the drugs were significantly more likely to suffer impaired memory and other cognitive declines.

Most cognitive effects will clear once a person discontinues the drug, but total recovery is not a certainty, depending on your age and other health conditions. What's more, many of the anticholinergic drugs are taken indefinitely for chronic conditions.

COMMON USES AND ALTERNATIVES

Popular anticholinergic drugs…

• **Allergies.** Many of the older allergy drugs, including Benadryl, are effective for relieving red irritated eyes, sneezing and a runny nose. That's not surprising, since one of the biggest anticholinergic effects is to reduce mucus and other secretions. But the side effects, such as drowsiness and a dry mouth and eyes, are pronounced. Very few can take these drugs and function well the next day.

My advice: Take Benadryl or a similar drug only if you have occasional allergy symptoms and need to get a good night's sleep. To reduce daytime drowsiness, take such a drug only at bedtime.

Better: Avoid allergens in the first place. If this is not possible, take a nonsedating antihistamine, such as *fexofenadine* (Allegra) or *loratadine* (Claritin). These drugs produce relatively mild anticholinergic effects—most people can take them without experiencing side effects. If you suffer seasonal allergies, use one of these drugs daily throughout the allergy season. They aren't designed to control single flare-ups.

Also effective: Nasal steroids. Consult your doctor.

• **Depression.** Before the *selective serotonin reuptake inhibitor* (*SSRI*) *antidepressants* were developed, physicians frequently recommended *amitriptyline* (Elavil) for depression. This drug has fallen out of favor because it tends to cause strong anticholinergic side effects. But some of the newer drugs, including *paroxetine* (Paxil), the most anticholinergic of the SSRIs, produce similar effects.

My advice: If your doctor is going to prescribe an antidepressant, ask him/her about SSRI antidepressants with the least anticholinergic effects, particularly those with a shorter "half-life," like *sertraline* (Zoloft). These drugs are eliminated from the body more quickly, so they are less likely to cause side effects. This is particularly important for older adults, who metabolize drugs more slowly.

• **Insomnia.** Most of the OTC drugs taken for insomnia, including the allergy medication Benadryl and sleep aid Sominex, contain *diphenhydramine*. It can bring on constipation, difficulty concentrating, urinary retention and trouble with eye focus—and it stays active in the body for 12 to 18 hours, which can lead to next-day grogginess.

My advice: Avoid taking diphenhydramine for insomnia.

Better: Practice good sleep habits.

Examples: Get into bed at a reasonable hour, and maintain the same schedule every night. Exercise regularly but not within two hours of your bedtime, as it will make falling asleep more difficult. Take a warm bath before bed to help you relax.

Important: Make the bedroom a peaceful place—no TV, computer, etc. If you don't fall asleep within a half hour, get up and do something else until you're ready to try to sleep again. Avoid the computer and all electronics—their glow will delay release of the sleep-inducing hormone *melatonin*.

• **Motion sickness.** Lots of anticholinergic drugs prevent and/or relieve motion sickness. However, the doses needed to reduce motion sickness can also cause drowsiness or confusion as a side effect.

My advice: Avoid motion sickness drugs such as *dimenhydrinate* (Dramamine).

Better: Put on the prescription *scopolamine patch* (such as Transderm Scop). The active ingredient enters the body gradually and is less likely to cause side effects than oral dimenhydrinate. The patches deliver roughly 1.5 mg of scopolamine over three days. Apply the patch to a hairless area at least four hours prior to traveling/sailing.

• **Urinary incontinence.** People who suffer from an unusually intense and frequent need to urinate, known as *urge incontinence*, are often treated with an overactive bladder medication such as o*xybutynin* (Ditropan) or *tolterodine* (Detrol).

These drugs may cause dry mouth, blurred vision, constipation and/or impairment of cognitive function.

Adults age 65 and older have the highest chance for side effects. This is in part because the blood-brain barrier becomes more porous with age. These drugs are not supposed to enter the brain—but often do.

My advice: After discussing dosages and all potential side effects with your physician, you may want to consider taking one of these drugs if incontinence is preventing you from living a normal life. It may be better to cope with drug side effects than to become housebound due to fear of having an "accident."

Even better: Bladder training, in which a doctor or therapist teaches you to gradually increase the intervals between urinating by waiting longer than you think you can. Most people can gradually increase their "holding" time by several minutes to several hours.

If urgency/frequency occurs throughout the night, see your physician. Nighttime urination may especially be a problem for men with enlarged prostates, but incontinence drugs are unlikely to help—and may even be harmful.

Painkillers Can Kill: Even OTC Drugs Can Cause Heart Attacks…Stroke… Asthma…Ulcers

Amanda Risser, MD, MPH, an assistant professor of family medicine at Oregon Health and Science University (OHSU), Portland. She practices family medicine at OHSU Family Medicine at Richmond, a community health center in Portland.

Millions of Americans regularly use one or several of the *nonsteroidal anti-inflammatory drugs,* called NSAIDs. Drugs in this class include over-the-counter *analgesics* (painkillers), like aspirin and *ibuprofen,* as well as prescription medications, such as *celecoxib* (Celebrex), *indomethacin* (Indocin) and *diclofenac* (Cataflam).

NSAIDs are not as safe as people think. In 2004, an NSAID known as *rofecoxib* (Vioxx) was withdrawn from the market after it was found to increase the risk for heart attack and stroke. Other NSAIDs, including aspirin, have a high risk for side effects, including internal bleeding.

The occasional use of an NSAID is unlikely to cause serious problems. The risks begin to rise when people take these drugs too often or if people have certain risk factors. *Biggest dangers…*

CARDIOVASCULAR RISKS

Low-dose aspirin therapy (100 milligrams [mg] or less daily) has been shown to decrease the risk for heart attack and stroke in high-risk patients. Other NSAIDs don't fare so well.

Individuals who regularly take NSAIDs other than aspirin have an average increase in blood pressure of roughly five points. These drugs also can worsen congestive heart failure and increase risk for heart attack. The *COX-2 inhibitor* Celebrex is believed to increase these risks more than other NSAIDs.

Self-defense: Avoid Celebrex if you have cardiovascular risk factors, such as hypertension or high cholesterol, or if you've previously had a heart attack. With the other NSAIDs, I advise patients to check their blood pressure within a week or two after starting the drug. If blood pressure is going to rise, it usually does so during that time.

Also important: Don't exceed the dosage recommended on the label. People who take high doses of ibuprofen or *diclofenac*, for example, are more likely to have cardiovascular "events" than those who take the amounts recommended on the label.

While it would be easy to assume that the people who regularly use a nonaspirin NSAID may reduce cardiovascular risk by taking low-dose aspirin as well, studies have shown that this isn't the case and that this combination of medications is risky, especially for *gastrointestinal* (GI) complications.

ASTHMA

About 21% of adults with asthma experience a worsening of symptoms when they take aspirin. In rare cases, aspirin can cause respiratory problems, such as difficulty breathing, in people without a history of asthma.

Warning: People who experience respiratory problems when they take aspirin usually have a high cross-reactivity to similar drugs— they will experience similar symptoms when they take ibuprofen, indomethacin or another NSAID. The risk for aspirin-exacerbated asthma is highest in patients who also have nasal polyps and/or recurrent bouts of sinusitis.

Self-defense: In general, asthma patients should avoid aspirin and other NSAIDs, particularly if they also have polyps or sinusitis. These individuals can safely substitute *acetaminophen*. The asthma patients who require additional pain relief should ask their doctors about such prescription non–NSAID drugs as *gabapentin* (Neurontin) and *nortriptyline* (Aventyl, Pamelor).

KIDNEY COMPLICATIONS

Up to 2% of patients who regularly take NSAIDs will have to stop taking them because of kidney problems.

Self-defense: Patients who undergo dialysis or those with kidney disease should not take NSAIDs—acetaminophen is a better choice.

I advise patients with diabetes or other risk factors for kidney disease to have a baseline creatinine test when they start NSAID therapy and then subsequent monitoring. *Creatinine* is a metabolic by-product that indicates how well the kidneys are working. Patients can keep using NSAIDs if their creatinine remains stable.

Important: Patients who have developed kidney disease as a consequence of liver disease should never take NSAIDs, as they have a high risk for complications, including total kidney failure.

LIVER DISEASE

Some studies have shown that patients who take the painkillers *sulindac* (Clinoril) or diclofenac have an increase in liver enzymes circulating in the bloodstream. This increase is less likely to occur with other NSAIDs.

Self-defense: Stop taking NSAIDs if your doctor determines there's an increase in liver enzymes. The complications typically reverse when the drugs are discontinued.

Important: NSAID-related liver damage is rare. It usually occurs in patients who already suffer from a liver disease, such as *hepatitis C* or *cirrhosis*. (Liver problems are rare with acetaminophen as well, but be sure not to take too much—follow directions on the label.)

CENTRAL NERVOUS SYSTEM

Elderly adults who take NSAIDs will sometimes suffer central nervous system problems. Aspirin, for example, can cause or worsen *tinnitus* (a ringing or other sounds in the ears). *Indomethacin* has been linked with cognitive changes, including psychosis in rare cases.

Self-defense: Follow all the dosing instructions on the label. These disorders primarily occur when people take NSAIDs in excessive doses—and will resolve when the drugs are discontinued or are taken in a lower dose.

GI COMPLICATIONS

It's estimated that at least 10% to 20% of people who regularly take one or more NSAIDs experience GI irritation. Many eventually will develop ulcers in the stomach, duodenum (the part of the small intestine nearest the stomach) and/or esophagus.

What happens: The NSAIDs reduce levels of *prostaglandins*, the substances that help to maintain the protective linings of the digestive tract. These drugs also are acidic, so they can irritate tissues and potentially cause internal bleeding.

An analysis of data from the 1990s showed that NSAID-related bleeding was responsible for 32,000 hospitalizations and 3,200 deaths annually. The risk for bleeding is especially elevated among people 75 years old or older.

Self-defense: Older individuals, particularly those with ulcers, should avoid NSAIDs—so should anyone who also is taking an anticoagulant, such as *warfarin*. The risk for bleeding in those who take both types of drugs is five to six times higher than for those who are taking only an anticoagulant.

Patients with a high risk for NSAID-related bleeding can take acetaminophen. It seldom causes GI irritation. People with arthritis also might try the supplements *glucosamine* and *chondroitin* or *capsaicin* cream.

Help from the FDA...

Find out if doctors are reporting side effects from new medications at a Web site run by the Food and Drug Administration (FDA). The Postmarketing Drug Safety Evaluations site gives information about what the FDA has learned 18 months after a drug or vaccine is approved or after 10,000 patients have used it, whichever comes later. The list of currently available information is at *www.fda.gov* (click on "Drugs," then on "Drug-Specific Information").

Are Your Meds Making You Sick? Widely Used Drugs May Be Robbing You of Vital Nutrients

Hyla Cass, MD, a board-certified psychiatrist and nationally recognized authority on nutritional and integrative medicine. She is also the author of several books, including *8 Weeks to Vibrant Health* (McGraw-Hill) as well as *Supplement Your Prescription: What Your Doctor Doesn't Know About Nutrition* (Basic Health). Her Web site is *www.cassmd.com.*

When we think of drug side effects, what generally comes to mind are headache, dizziness, dry mouth and other such complaints.

Commonly ignored side effect: Many popular medications can deplete your body of crucial nutrients—an unintended side effect that could increase your odds for diseases ranging from cancer to heart disease. *What you need to know...*

ARE YOU AT RISK?

Nutrient depletion, which causes such symptoms as fatigue, muscle cramping and even a rapid heartbeat, can potentially occur within weeks after starting a medication.

More often, these symptoms come on gradually, during months or even years—and, as a result, often are dismissed by people taking the drugs as mere annoyances or mistaken for signs of aging.

In some cases, a hidden nutrient deficiency increases one's risk for other illnesses—for example, a deficiency of *folate* (a B vitamin) may raise your risk for cancer or cause physiological changes that can set the stage for heart attack or stroke.

Important: If you take one or more medications regularly, ask your doctor about nutrient depletion—and whether you should be tested. Doctors can do a basic blood screening profile for low blood levels of vitamins and minerals, such as B-12, folate, calcium, magnesium and potassium.

However, to more accurately measure your amounts of all the important nutrients, your physician should consider more sophisticated testing.

For example, the SpectraCell micronutrient test measures more than 31 vitamins, minerals, amino acids and antioxidants. Not all doctors are familiar with the test, but you can go to *www.spectracell.com* and click on "Find a Clinician" to locate a physician in your region who is. The panel costs around $325,* and insurance may pay some of the cost. Or try the Metametrix Nutrient and Toxic Elements Profile, which costs from $79 to $164, depending on the specific tests (800-221-4640, *www.meta metrix.com*).

Helpful: Be sure to eat foods that are rich in nutrients that may be depleted by your medications. To ensure adequate amounts of these nutrients, ask your physician about taking the supplements described below. *Drugs that can deplete nutrients…*

ASPIRIN AND OTHER NSAIDs

The *nonsteroidal anti-inflammatory drugs* (NSAIDs), such as aspirin, are commonly used to reduce pain and inflammation. Millions of Americans also take aspirin to "thin" the blood, reducing the risk for a heart attack or stroke.

Nutrients depleted: Folate and vitamin C. Insufficient folate is thought to increase the risk for a variety of cancers, including malignancies of the breast and colon. Lower folate also has been linked to elevated levels of *homocysteine*, an amino acid that can raise risk for heart attack and stroke.

People who are low in vitamin C get more colds, flu and other infections than those with normal levels. A deficiency of vitamin C also can impair the body's ability to produce and repair its cartilage—which may explain why people with osteoarthritis who regularly take an NSAID often suffer *more* joint pain in the long run.

My recommendation: Take 1,000 milligrams (mg) of vitamin C daily if you take an NSAID regularly. A Boston University study found that people who got the most vitamin C were three times less likely to develop osteoarthritis, or to have an increase in symptoms, than those who got lower amounts.

*Prices subject to change.

Caution: High-dose vitamin C can trigger loose stools in some people—if this occurs, reduce your dose to 500 mg daily.

In addition, take a 400-microgram (mcg) to 800-mcg folic acid (the man-made version of folate) supplement per day. Take vitamin B-12 (1,000 mcg daily) with folic acid—taking folic acid alone can mask a B-12 deficiency.

Also helpful: 1,000 mg to 2,000 mg of fish oil daily. One study found that 60% of people with osteoarthritis who took fish oil improved their joint pain within 75 days. Half improved so much that they no longer needed to take an NSAID.

CALCIUM CHANNEL BLOCKERS

When it comes to blood pressure medication, most people know that *diuretics* (water-excreting drugs) can deplete important nutrients, including potassium. It is not as well-known that blood pressure drugs known as *calcium channel blockers*, like *amlodipine* (Norvasc) and *nicardipine* (Cardene), can have the same effect.

Nutrient depleted: Potassium. People with low potassium may experience muscle weakness and fatigue. Their blood pressure also may rise, which offsets the drug's effectiveness.

My recommendation: Take a 100-mg potassium supplement every day. Because many foods contain significant amounts of this mineral, you can eat a single extra serving of a high-potassium food as an alternative. A medium baked potato with the skin, for example, provides 850 mg of potassium…and a large banana has 487 mg. Check with your physician if you have kidney disease—extra potassium can worsen the condition.

GEMFIBROZIL

People who cannot control elevated cholesterol with a statin, or who suffer muscle pain or other side effects when they take a statin, could be given a prescription for *gemfibrozil* (Lopid). This and similar drugs, known as *fibrates*, raise levels of HDL (good) cholesterol and decrease destructive LDL cholesterol and triglycerides.

Nutrients depleted: Vitamin E and the naturally occurring nutrient called *coenzyme Q10* (CoQ10). A deficiency of vitamin E, a potent antioxidant, can increase risk for cancer, heart disease and other conditions, such as nerve disorders. Inadequate CoQ10 often results in muscle pain and weakness…and can impair the heart's ability to beat efficiently.

My recommendation: 200 mg of CoQ10 and 100 mg of natural vitamin E (also called *mixed tocopherols*) daily.

METFORMIN

Metformin (Glucophage), the most popular of oral diabetes medicine, reduces blood sugar by making cells more responsive to insulin. It also causes less weight gain and fewer episodes of *hypoglycemia* (excessively low blood sugar) than other diabetes drugs.

Nutrients depleted: Vitamin B-12. A study in *Archives of Internal Medicine* found that patients taking metformin had average vitamin B-12 levels that were less than half of those in people who weren't taking the medication. Metformin also reduces levels of folate. A deficiency of these nutrients can cause fatigue, forgetfulness and depression.

My recommendation: Use about 1,000 mcg of vitamin B-12 daily. Since many multivitamins have under 200 mcg of B-12, you will have to supplement to reach the 1,000-mcg daily dose. For folic acid, take 400 mcg to 800 mcg daily.

Important: When increasing levels of vitamin B-12, people with diabetes may be more likely to experience episodes of hypoglycemia. Ask your doctor about getting an A1C blood test, which provides an estimate of blood sugar levels over many weeks rather than at a single point in time.

Are You a Cyberchondriac?

A cyberchondriac is a hypochondriac who goes on the Internet to self-diagnose himself/herself. If you use the Internet to find out what's wrong, be aware that it always is easier to find bad news than good.

University of California, Berkeley, Wellness Letter, 500 Fifth Avenue, New York City 10110, *www.wellness letter.com.*

What You Need to Know About Hospital Safety Now!

Charles B. Inlander, health-care consultant and founding president of the People's Medical Society, a consumer advocacy organization active in the 1980s and 1990s. He is the author of 20 books, including *Take This Book to the Hospital with You: A Consumer Guide to Surviving Your Hospital Stay* (St. Martin's).

Since medical mistakes in hospitals have been widely reported on for years, you would think that things would have improved by now. Well, they have not. In fact, a new study shows that your risk of being injured, receiving the wrong drug or acquiring an infection in the hospital is no less than it was in 1999.

Why haven't things improved? The research indicates that most hospitals have not implemented vital processes that are necessary to improve the safety of hospital patients, such as hand-washing guidelines for staff…computerized medication-monitoring and ordering systems…and electronic medical-record programs that help alert staff to possible mistakes before they occur.

But even if all hospitals are not yet doing things right, you can dramatically curb your chances of becoming the victim of a hospital mistake. *What to do the next time you or a loved one is hospitalized…*

• **Take control of all your medications.** In the US, more than 400,000 patients are seriously harmed each year by preventable hospital medication errors (such as wrong dosages and/or wrong drugs). Even though most hospitals currently check to see if you are the patient who is supposed to receive the drug and note in your file what drug is being administered, a more effective way to prevent errors is to ask the nurse to write down, on a sheet of paper that you bring and keep at your bedside, the drug being given, the time it is given and the dosage. If there are any changes, ask who ordered the change before you take the medicine.

Insider secret: You also have the right to bring your own meds from home to protect yourself against getting the wrong drug.

• **Make sure you don't get a used medical device.** Up to 10% of all hospital patients acquire infections during their hospital stays. That's why we've all been told to insist that no one touch us without washing his/her hands and changing gloves in our presence. However, some hospitals are also putting their patients in danger by reusing medical devices that are meant to be used only once, such as catheters, as a way to save some money. Hospitals clean these devices in between uses—but in many cases, the cleaning methods are not effective and could result in life-threatening infections. That's why you should ask whether any device that is about to be used on you is designed for "single use." If so, insist that it be taken out of the original package in front of you.

• **Use your case manager.** Mistakes tend to happen because hospital patients may not see the same nurse more than once during their stays. That's why all hospitals now employ case managers (a nurse, social worker or physician's assistant) who help oversee the consistency of patient care. Ask to meet your case manager when you are admitted to the hospital. Get his direct phone number, and call whenever you have a question that is not being answered. He can be your watchdog—and a great way to get in touch with your doctor very quickly.

How to Get Out of the Hospital Alive

Peter J. Pronovost, MD, PhD, professor in the departments of anesthesiology, critical care medicine and surgery at Johns Hopkins University School of Medicine in Baltimore. He is also the medical director for the Center for Innovation in Quality Patient Care, which helps to promote patient safety at Johns Hopkins Hospital. He is coauthor, with Eric Vohr, of *Safe Patients, Smart Hospitals* (Hudson Street).

H ospital-acquired infections are among the most common preventable causes of death due to medical mistakes, but hospitals still aren't doing enough to prevent these and other mistakes.

Recent research: One survey of hospitals found that 87% don't always follow infection-prevention guidelines—including basic hand-washing protocols.

Result: As many as one in 10 patients will acquire a potentially deadly hospital infection.

Most doctors know what they need to do to prevent unnecessary mistakes. The challenge is to *consistently implement* all proven safety measures. Until this happens, there are steps you can take to help protect yourself if you are hospitalized.

To learn more about risks in hospitals—and what patients can do to stay safe—we spoke with Peter J. Pronovost, MD, PhD, a patient-safety researcher at Johns Hopkins University School of Medicine.

• **You refer to the "toxic" culture in hospitals. What does this mean?** Most patients assume that medical care is guided by scientific principles—that doctors do things in a manner that is safe as well as effective.

But it's not that simple. Doctors are human. They often are overconfident and have strong personalities and big egos that cause them to do things that conflict with the patient's best interests.

Recent example: At our hospital, an otherwise healthy patient suffered serious complications after kidney surgery. It was clear that the patient needed to return to the operating room, but the surgeon refused because a CT scan done after indicated that there was nothing wrong.

We all know that test results can be misleading. Even though the patient had serious complications, the surgeon wouldn't admit the possibility of error. And surgeons often have complete authority in such cases.

As the intensive care physician on call, I explained the situation to another surgeon and she agreed to operate. It turned out that the first surgeon had accidentally cut the pancreas and intestine during the procedure—an error that could be lethal.

Surgery is not a perfect science—even the best of surgeons make mistakes. Had systems been in place to keep personality issues (such as a surgeon's insistence that he couldn't make a mistake in an operation) out of the equation, much of this patient's suffering could have been prevented.

• **What kinds of systems can help?** Teamwork is a big one. Johns Hopkins researchers did a study that looked at errors and liability claims at a number of hospitals. We found that in nearly 90% of cases, at least one of the team members knew that something was wrong but was either afraid to speak up or was ignored by the person in charge.

At Johns Hopkins, we created a system in which nurses need to attend rounds with the attending physician and head resident. This helps prevent subsequent errors in communication and has caused medication errors to drop to almost zero. It also cut the time that patients spent in intensive care units (ICUs) by about half.

Patients also should be active team members. Speak up and ask lots of questions if you do not understand something. Always ask all health-care practitioners who enter your room to please wash their hands.

• **You've pioneered the use of checklists. How do they help?** A checklist virtually eliminates the hierarchal mind-set that I discussed above. A doctor or surgeon can't get away with merely saying, "Because I said so." He/she is required to follow step-by-step procedures that have been shown to improve safety.

Example: About 31,000 Americans a year die from infections triggered by *central lines* (catheters placed in a vein in the neck, groin or chest). We examined data from the CDC in order to summarize the most important points in developing the checklist. Our checklist included things like hand-washing…cleaning the patient's skin with the disinfectant *chlorhexidine*…draping the patient…and the use of a surgical mask, hat, gown and gloves.

In Michigan, where the checklist was first instituted the incidence of central-line infections dropped by 66% within 18 months after the protocols were implemented—a reduction that has now been sustained for more than three years.

If you're planning a surgery: Ask what the hospital's rate is for catheter-related bloodstream infections—and be concerned if it is much beyond one out of every 1,000 catheter days. If you or a family member has a catheter inserted, ask every day whether it is still needed.

• **Should patients ask about checklists before choosing a hospital?** Absolutely. Virtually every procedure can be done more safely when the medical staff follows clear and consistent guidelines.

The checklists don't have to be complicated. Take hand-washing. It's among the most effective ways to prevent a hospital infection. Yet even doctors and other health-care employees in hospitals working on infection prevention do not do it about 30% of the times that they should. It is perfectly reasonable for a patient who is scheduled to undergo surgery to ask his surgeon whether he follows an infection-prevention checklist.

One other example: Wrong-site surgery. Nearly 3,000 times a year in the US, surgeons operate where they should not. There are cases in which the surgeon has operated on the wrong side of the body (such as amputating the left leg instead of the right) or even on the wrong patient.

The Joint Commission (a nonprofit group that regulates hospital standards and safety) now mandates that operating room teams perform a "time-out" before surgery. During this time, the surgeon marks the surgical site. The case is then reviewed both by surgeons and nurses to confirm the patient's name and the nature of the surgery.

If you're planning a surgery: Prior to the operation, ask your surgeon if he will use the time-out period. If so, ask him to perform the step before you're sedated so that you can participate. That way, you can confirm your name and other details. For example, your surgeon might touch your injured knee and say something like, "This is where we are operating today, right?" When you're awake, the risk for error is further reduced.

• **Hospital-acquired pneumonia is a huge risk for patients. What can patients do to prevent this?** If you spend time in the ICU, there's a very good chance that you'll be put on mechanical ventilation to help you breathe. We have found that elevating the head of the bed so that it is raised at least 30° will help mucus from the mouth and nose to drain into the stomach instead of the lungs. Yet the beds in ICUs are often kept in a horizontal position. Inhaling mucus is one of the main causes of ventilator-associated pneumonia.

Also important: A family member should ask each day whether mechanical ventilation is still needed for the patient.

• **How can patients who are allergic to latex—widely used in many hospitals—protect themselves?** We went latex-free at Johns Hopkins several years ago. Various hospitals, however, continue to use latex gloves during surgery even though about 1% of Americans are allergic and could experience a life-threatening anaphylactic reaction.

The allergy tends to occur in people who have had frequent exposure to latex in their past. This includes health-care workers (who often wear these gloves) or patients who have undergone multiple surgical procedures during which latex gloves were used.

My advice: Before having a procedure, tell your surgeon that you do not want to be exposed to any latex. Latex-free gloves are readily available—hospitals should use them.

Hospital Delirium Self-Defense

Hospital delirium is common. It affects 25% to 50% of older adults admitted to general medical wards, and 68% to 80% admitted to surgical floors or intensive care units. Patients with delirium have such symptoms as reduced ability to focus, disorientation and/or agitation. These patients remain hospitalized longer, are more likely to go into a nursing home or other institutional setting and have a higher risk for

death. Its cause is unclear, and there is no specific treatment to prevent delirium, although nondrug approaches may be helpful, including preventing sleep deprivation.

Noll L. Campbell, PharmD, FASCP, BCPP, a clinical specialist in geriatrics, Wishard Health Services, Indianapolis, and lead author of studies of hospital delirium, published in *Journal of Hospital Medicine*.

Urinary Catheters Often *Unnecessary*

Over a 12-week period, researchers examined 532 emergency room patients who received urinary catheters when admitted to hospitals.

Results: More than 30% were unnecessary. At highest risk for the unnecessary treatment were women age 80 or older—they were nearly three times as likely to have an unnecessary catheter as women age 50 or younger.

When a urinary catheter is recommended: Ask the doctor whether it is truly needed.

Mohamad Fakih, MD, department of medicine at St. John Hospital and Medical Center, Grosse Pointe Woods, Michigan.

Secret to Faster ICU Recovery

Patients recover more quickly with less sedation and more exercise.

Recent finding: Participants requiring mechanical ventilation who were given less sedation in the intensive care unit (ICU) were able to do mild exercise while in the ICU (30 to 45 minutes daily) and reduced their ICU stay by two days.

Exercise helps to prevent muscle weakness and shortens recovery time. Patients and families should talk with doctors about physical therapy, including mild exercise.

Helpful: A video on exercise in ICU care at *www.hopkinsmedicine.org/oacis* (click on "Videos and News").

Dale M. Needham, MD, PhD, associate professor at Johns Hopkins University School of Medicine in Baltimore. He led a study published in *Archives of Physical Medicine and Rehabilitation.*

More on ICU Recovery

After being discharged from intensive care units (ICUs), some patients develop *post-traumatic stress disorder* (PTSD).

Recent study: Among 352 adults with ICU stays longer than 72 hours, subjects given detailed, written accounts of their ICU stays (in the form of diaries that had been kept by nurses or relatives) one month after discharge were 62% less likely to develop PTSD than those not given these accounts.

Theory: Unlike patients' fragmented memories, which may include frightening hallucinations, diaries present factual evidence of what happened in the ICU.

If your loved one is admitted to an ICU: Keep a diary chronicling his or her illness and treatment.

Christina Jones, PhD, RN, nurse consultant, Critical Care Rehabilitation, Whiston Hospital, Liverpool, UK.

Do You Really Need Surgery?

Dennis Gottfried, MD, associate professor of medicine at the University of Connecticut Medical School, Farmington, and a general internist with a private practice in Torrington, Connecticut. He is the author of *Too Much Medicine* (Paragon House). His Web site is *www.drdennisgottfried.com.*

Up to 30% of surgical procedures in the US are unnecessary. This shocking statistic was recently released by the respected nonprofit, nonpartisan policy analysis group The Rand Corporation.

The analysis confirms why it is so crucial to request a second opinion from a physician who is not associated with your doctor before agreeing to any elective surgery.

Procedures that may not be necessary—and alternatives to consider…

STENTS

Each year, more than one million heart patients are treated with angioplasty and stents, which restore normal circulation to the heart and reduce *angina* (chest pain).

During *angioplasty*, a deflated balloon gets threaded into the coronary artery. It then gets inflated to flatten *plaque* (fatty deposits), and a metal stent is inserted to prevent arterial deposits from reblocking the opening.

Problem: Angioplasty and stents are overused. A study with more than 2,300 patients presented at one recent meeting of the American College of Cardiology found that patients who had stable angina, in which discomfort occurs in a consistent pattern (such as during exertion), who were treated with medications (such as *nitroglycerine* to dilate the blood vessels) had the same outcomes as those treated with stents—without the dangers of an invasive procedure.

Who is helped by stents: Patients with a recent worsening of chest pain (unstable angina). For people with a significant blockage in the left main coronary artery or with three coronary arteries blocked and a weakened heart muscle, bypass surgery (which involves grafting a vein from another part of the body to bypass the blockage) improves life expectancy.

Who is not helped by stents: People with stable angina. These patients generally should be treated with medications to control the pain and to reduce blood pressure and cholesterol. Medications are just as effective at preventing future heart attacks and preventing death as stenting in these patients—without all the risks of a surgical procedure. Stenting and bypass surgery should be used only in those patients for whom medication fails to adequately control chest pain.

CAROTID ENDARTERECTOMY

About 20% of all strokes are related to blockages in the carotid arteries in the neck. With a

51

procedure known as *carotid endarterectomy*, the blockages are surgically peeled away to improve circulation to the brain and potentially prevent a stroke.

Problem: Severe carotid blockages (generally blockage of 80% or more) occasionally can lead to "ministrokes"—*transient ischemic attacks* (TIAs), which often precede a full-blown stroke. But if a person has a severe obstruction and no TIA symptoms, the likelihood of having a major stroke is very small. Performing a carotid endarterectomy in those people decreases the chance of having a stroke by only 0.7%.

Who is helped by carotid endarterectomy: People with severe carotid blockage and TIAs have a 13% risk of suffering a disabling stroke over the next two years. When the carotid endarterectomy is performed, the risk is reduced to 2.5%.

Who isn't helped by carotid endarterectomy: People with a blockage of less than 60% even if they have a history of ministrokes. In this group, the risk for stroke is higher after surgery—perhaps because the risk of stroke-producing plaque becoming dislodged during the operation may exceed the patient's initial stroke risk.

In groups of people with severe obstruction and no symptoms of TIA, more than 140 endarterectomies must be performed to prevent one stroke. With obstructions of 60% to 79%, there is no convincing scientific evidence for surgery. Nonsurgical treatment, including the use of aspirin and cholesterol-lowering drugs, is preferable in all of these cases.

PROSTATECTOMY

Roughly 180,000 American men are diagnosed with cancer of the prostate every year and about 30,000 die from this disease. Surgical removal of the prostate (*prostatectomy*) often is recommended, but risks include infection, impotence and incontinence.

Problem: The majority of prostate cancers grow slowly. Most men with the disease would eventually die of an unrelated condition even if the prostate cancer weren't treated.

In one recent study published in *The New England Journal of Medicine*, older men with early prostate cancer who were treated with prostatectomy died at about the same rate as older men with similar cancers who had no surgery.

Who is helped by prostatectomy: Men who are in their 50s and younger with biopsy findings that show an aggressive form of prostate cancer are generally the best candidates for a prostatectomy.

Who isn't helped by prostatectomy: Men whose life expectancy is less than 10 years at the time of diagnosis. They're less likely than younger men to die of their cancer and face a high threat of surgical complications. Older men with prostate cancer often do better with hormone therapy and/or radiation.

BACK SURGERY

Surgery for a *herniated* (ruptured) disk is among the most commonly performed orthopedic procedures in the US.

Problem: A herniated disk that presses on a nerve can be excruciatingly painful. But in 80% to 90% of cases, enzymes secreted by the body break down disk material and the nerve pain disappears in time. This could take many months, so surgery promises faster relief.

Disk surgery, however, has serious potential risks, including nerve injuries, buildups of scar tissue, infection and chronic back pain. A recent study in the *Journal of the American Medical Association* compared the long-term outcomes of back patients who had surgery with those who did not. The likelihood of recovery was virtually the same.

Who is helped by back surgery: People with severe, intractable back pain that radiates into a leg (*sciatica*) or those with a progressive neurological deficit, such as foot weakness, or a loss of bowel or bladder control, which indicates compression of a spinal nerve, require prompt surgical treatment.

Who isn't helped by back surgery: People whose only symptom is low back pain. Studies have shown that individuals with local symptoms feel better using nonsurgical treatments, including anti-inflammatory drugs, acupuncture, massage therapy and physical therapy. For most people who have mild sciatica, the pain usually disappears within a few months as the disk breaks down.

KNEE REPAIR

You shouldn't assume that you need surgery if you suddenly develop pain, inflammation and swelling in one or both knees. Sometimes the pain comes from a medical problem such as gout or Lyme disease.

Problem: Even with knee injuries, so many surgeons want to repair or remove damaged tissue without waiting enough time to see if normal healing will take place.

Who is helped by knee surgery: People in whom a ligament or tendon is completely severed. For these patients, the knee will rarely heal well enough on its own to reinstate adequate function and reduce pain. For people who engage in intensive sports, *arthroscopic* surgery (using a "keyhole" incision) for lesser injuries often is recommended since they may not be willing to wait for healing to occur.

Who isn't helped by knee surgery: For most individuals with knee injuries, surgery—even arthroscopic—is the last resort. First, rest the leg, use anti-inflammatory drugs and try physical therapy and braces. Follow this approach for at least one to two months before considering knee surgery.

You're in Good Hands

Nurse anesthetists deliver anesthesia just as well as anesthesiologists, according to two recent studies. In the states that permit a nurse anesthetist to administer anesthesia without the supervision of an anesthesiologist or operating surgeon, there was no evidence of increased deaths or complications.

Jerry Cromwell, PhD, senior fellow in health economics, Research Triangle Institute, Research Triangle Park, North Carolina, and lead researcher on a study of Medicare data on anesthesia, published in *Health Affairs*.

Sutures vs. Staples

In one recent study, researchers reviewed six papers analyzing infection rates of 673 joint-surgery patients whose wounds were closed with nylon sutures or metal staples.

Result: Infection risk was three times higher after staple closure than after suture closure. In hip surgeries specifically, infections were four times more likely when staples were used instead of stitches.

If you're considering orthopedic surgery: Ask your doctor which closure method he/she recommends for your procedure.

Toby O. Smith, honorary lecturer, University of East Anglia, Norwich, UK.

Great Greenery

In a recent study, when 90 patients recovering from hemorrhoid removal stayed in hospital rooms with 12 potted plants or no plants, those surrounded by greenery had lower *systolic* (top number) blood pressure and much less pain and anxiety.

Theory: Plants and flowers have a calming effect (which lowers blood pressure) and make patients feel cared about (which distracts from pain).

Important: Do not bring flowers to anyone with lung problems…neither plants nor flowers should be placed in intensive care units.

Richard Mattson, PhD, professor, department of horticulture, forestry and recreation resources at Kansas State University, Manhattan, Kansas.

Hospital Patients' Bill of Rights

Marjory Abrams, president of Boardroom Inc., 281 Tresser Blvd., Stamford, Connecticut 06901.

After my mother's recent surgery (she's fine now), a friend told me that hospital patients can request to be treated by a full-fledged doctor rather than just a resident. Another friend informed me that hospital charts are no longer top secret—thanks to the *Health Insurance Portability and Accountability Act* (HIPAA), patients may ask for their own copies instead of trying to sneak a look. That got me thinking—what other rights do patients have that no one ever tells us about?

Trisha Torrey is a patient advocate and author of *You Bet Your Life! The 10 Mistakes Every Patient Makes* (*www.everypatientsadvocate. com*), and here are some of the rights that she and other advocates encourage hospital patients to assert…

• **You have the right to refuse to be observed, examined or treated by anyone** and to ask for someone else. For example, if a technician is not able to draw your blood after repeated attempts, ask for someone with greater expertise.

• **You have the right to refuse any treatment and to be told what the ramifications of refusal may be.** You can refuse any medication, too—but be sure to ask about possible consequences.

• **You (along with loved ones) have the right to receive an ethics consultation upon request**—for example, if family members disagree about life support. Ethics consults may include a physician, nurse, patient representative or additional professionals, along with the patient and/or family members.

• **You have the right to the visitors you choose.** A new federal regulation allows the patient to designate anyone he/she wants to visit, as long as you provide signed documentation to the hospital and your request complies with the hospital's visitors policy.

• **You have the right to be made as comfortable as possible.** If nighttime lighting is too bright for you, ask for it to be switched off or dimmed. People who aren't ready to walk should be helped into a chair for an extended sitting period several times daily.

• **You have the right to have an advocate by your side 24/7.** You may ask a friend or a loved one to fill that role or hire someone. You can find professional advocates at *www. advoconnection.com*.

• **You have the right to be moved to a different room** if and when the hospital has a vacancy if a roommate keeps you up at night or otherwise hinders your recovery.

Torrey urges patients and their loved ones to insist on their rights, when appropriate, as respectfully as possible rather than confrontationally. Try to reach a mutually acceptable solution. You don't want to create animosity, but you want to make sure—very sure—that you get what you need.

3

Fast Fixes for Common Conditions

Favorite Home Remedies From the Wilen Sisters

I love spending time with Joan Wilen and Lydia Wilen. These sisters have rediscovered thousands of amazing "cures from the cupboard," which they like to share through their best-selling books and appearances on TV. They recently shared the following favorite remedies with me. As with most home remedies, it is not always apparent why they work, but these are time-tested and safe to try.

• **Headache.** Swing your arms forward and back 100 times. This will redirect blood away from your head and release some *endorphins* to make you feel better almost instantly.

• **Heartburn.** Eat a few raw almonds or raw almond slivers—make sure to chew them thoroughly. (Do not try this if you are allergic to tree nuts!)

• **Burned fingertips.** If you sustain a minor burn while grabbing something hot, place your thumb on the backside of your earlobe and the burned fingertips on the front of your earlobe. Squeeze for one minute. (If you seriously burn your fingers, put them under cold water and seek medical help.)

• **Leg cramp.** Pinch the philtrum (the midline indentation under your nose and above your upper lip), and hold for a few minutes. (I wish I had known this when I was pregnant!)

• **To relieve anxiety.** Roll up 12 fresh basil leaves, chew on them for a few minutes, then swallow. If you live a chronically stressful life, do this twice a day.

Of course, no remedy helps everyone, but I'm almost looking forward to my next headache so that I can try swinging my arms. In the meantime, I plan to stock up on some raw almonds at home and at work, and I just bought

Marjory Abrams, president of Boardroom Inc., 281 Tresser Blvd., Stamford, Connecticut 06901.

some fresh basil (and will plant it again in our garden this year).

Steer Clear of Viruses: Six No-Fuss Germ-Fighting Secrets

Philip M. Tierno, Jr., PhD, director of clinical microbiology and immunology at New York University Langone Medical Center and a member of the faculty at New York University School of Medicine, both in New York City. He is the author of *The Secret Lives of Germs* (Atria).

During the fall and winter, we're all on high alert to avoid germs that cause colds and flu. But there are other microbes—some very dangerous—that we should also protect ourselves from all year long.

The majority of people know that *methicillin-resistant Staphylococcus aureus* (MRSA), an antibiotic-resistant organism that often affects hospital patients, is now infecting more and more people in community settings, such as health clubs, assisted-living facilities and other public places.

What you may not know: There's been a significant increase in the prevalence of MRSA in the noses of healthy adults and children, according to recent research published in *The New England Journal of Medicine*. Since anyone can harbor MRSA without becoming sick, this means that an infected individual could unknowingly pass on the dangerous bacterium simply by sneezing into his/her hand before touching a doorknob, for example, or another surface.

KNOW WHERE THE GERMS HIDE

Most people know that hand-washing with warm water and plain soap for at least 20 seconds is a highly effective germ-control strategy. However, there are valuable little-known secrets that you also need to be aware of to help protect yourself—and your family—from germs that cause colds or the flu or infection with MRSA or other dangerous bacteria...

Secret 1: **Opt for sanitizer wipes instead of gel.** Alcohol-based gels are effective, but sanitizer wipes (with 62% *ethyl alcohol*) are better because the friction caused by wipes helps remove bacteria and skin debris containing dead skin cells that can harbor infectious agents.

My advice: Keep sanitizer wipes in your bag or a shirt pocket, and use them whenever you've been out in public and can't get to a bathroom to wash your hands.

If you do use gel: Apply a dollop about the size of a quarter. Using less won't completely cover the hands.

Whether you are using a gel or wipe, use the product for at least 20 seconds. It takes this long to completely cover the hands, rub between fingers, etc. Let the sanitizing agent dry, do not wipe it off, and be sure to apply it under the fingernails, too.

Secret 2: **Use *triclosan* in certain situations.** If you or someone in the family is sick with a communicable illness such as the flu, a cold, stomach virus or any infection that can be transmitted, wash your hands with a soap that contains triclosan. It is an antimicrobial agent that kills both bacteria and viruses.

Important: Some researchers worry that soaps with triclosan might increase antibiotic resistance. This does not occur when people use products like Dial Complete liquid soap, which has a ratio of about 4:1 of *surfactant* (a detergent-like agent) to triclosan.

My advice: To help protect against bacteria and viruses when you or someone in your home is ill, use Dial Complete liquid soap.

Secret 3: **Bring your own reading material to the doctor's office.** Cold and flu viruses can survive up to 48 hours on the pages of magazines—longer if the reader has left behind any smudges of hand cream or makeup, which can help some organisms survive.

My advice: Bring your own magazine or book to read. If you do read one of the doctor's magazines, do not moisten your finger in your mouth when turning the pages—and keep your hands away from your eyes, nose and mouth until you've had a chance to wash your hands.

Secret 4: **Air-dry bath towels.** Most people, after using a bath or hand towel, fold it over and hang it neatly on a towel rod. This is the worst thing you can do because it traps moisture and makes it possible for germs to thrive.

A few staph bacteria deposited on a damp towel will increase to about 100,000 in four hours. Some organisms can live for several hours to days on a damp towel.

Danger: Suppose you have a cut on your skin, then wipe yourself with a staph-infected towel. Because of the bacterial "bloom," you'll be exposing the cut to very high concentrations of staph bacteria.

My advice: To avoid doing multiple loads of laundry, completely air-dry towels between uses by hanging them up in such a way that air can reach every part of the surface. If you follow this practice, it is fine to wash towels just once or twice a week. If someone in your home has a communicable illness, he should use a personal towel and keep it separate from other towels.

Secret 5: **Keep your toothbrush upright.** Like bathroom towels, a toothbrush that stays moist can accumulate enormous quantities of bacteria and cold and flu viruses in just a few hours.

My advice: Don't lay your brush down to store it—stand it up with the bristles at the top so that it will dry completely between uses. Also close the toilet lid before you flush. The flushing action in some toilets can spray invisible water droplets—which contain fecal and other disease-causing organisms—up to 20 feet. An exposed toothbrush is an easy target.

Also beneficial: Sanitize your toothbrush by submerging the bristles in a germ-killing mouthwash for about five minutes. Do this several times a week or with each use if you are ill.

Secret 6: **Use hotter water.** Everyone wants to save money on utility bills, but some people do this by turning down the thermostat on the water heater.

The risk: Undergarments and bath towels can contain enormous amounts of dangerous organisms—the *hepatitis A virus* (which gets transmitted primarily from human stool) and bacteria including *staph* and *Escherichia coli*. Washing clothes in cool or warm water will remove some of these germs, but it won't kill them. Hot water is needed to kill these organisms as well as cold and flu viruses.

My advice: Make sure that the water temperature in your washing machine is at least 150°F by checking it with a candy thermometer. This is hot enough to kill microbes. If your washer doesn't have a heating cycle that uses water this hot, raise the hot-water setting on your water tank—just be careful of scalding from tap water.

Helpful: Wash your underwear separately so that any surviving organisms will not be transferred to other clothes.

Also: Use bleach on all your whites—it kills microbes.

The Secrets of People Who *Never* Get Sick

Gene Stone, a journalist located in New York City who, in the process of writing about health, has undergone dozens of treatments, from hypnotherapy to Rolfing. He interviewed more than 100 healthy people for his book, *The Secrets of People Who Never Get Sick* (Workman, *www.secretsofpeople.com*).

W hy is it that some people hardly ever get sick? I wanted to learn their secrets. Some of these secrets are a bit unusual, but they do have a basis in scientific fact.

BREWER'S YEAST

Barbara Pritzkat, age 84, hasn't had a cold in decades. In 1983, at age 56, she started her second career as an archaeologist. She is still surveying archaeological sites, most recently in the Syrian Desert, where the temperatures can reach 110°F. She credits her good health to brewer's yeast, which she takes in a powder form dissolved in water every morning. She first learned about the health benefits of brewer's yeast in the 1940s when she attended a presentation by Adelle Davis, a pioneering nutritionist.

The science: Most commercially available brewer's yeast is extracted from the yeast that is used to ferment beer or wine. A single tablespoon contains the recommended daily allowance for most of the B vitamins, including folate.

Folate is one of the most important B vitamins because it breaks down and eliminates homocysteine, an amino acid, from the blood. Reducing *homocysteine* has been linked to a reduction in risk for stroke and heart disease. Folate also is thought to reduce the risk for a variety of cancers, including colon cancer.

Other B vitamins are needed for the maintenance of blood cells, nerves and the immune system. Brewer's yeast also contains a variety of minerals, including chromium, a trace mineral that decreases blood sugar and improves glucose tolerance. In addition, one two-ounce serving provides 8 grams (g) of protein, more than the amount in a large egg.

What to do: Take one to two tablespoons of brewer's yeast daily. You can dissolve it in water or sprinkle it on your cereal or yogurt. Some people may suffer adverse gastrointestinal reactions at first. Start by taking a small amount and increase it gradually.

Any brand should be fine—even buying from bulk bins. But look for a kind that's debittered—the taste is more palatable.

COLD SHOWERS

They're not very pleasant, but your shivering body may thank you.

Nate Halsey, age 38, got hooked on cold-water hydrotherapy a decade ago, when one of his friends explained that cold showers were the reason that he never got sick. Nate, who had been getting sick fairly often, gave it a try—and hated it. He still hates it, but he likes the energy boost. He also appreciates that he never gets sick anymore.

The science: Researchers have found that cold-water submersion increases levels of disease-fighting white blood cells. In one study, scientists found that people who took cold showers daily for six months had fewer colds than people in the control group. In another

study, year-round swimmers in Berlin, who took regular dips in freezing-cold water in the winter, suffered half as many chest infections as other people.

Exposure to cold water also may increase *glutathione*, one of the body's main antioxidants—the study of Berlin swimmers found that they had elevated levels of glutathione.

What to do: Ease into it. Turn on the cold water for 30 seconds or so. With the shower running, stick your head in to wet your hair. Turn off the water, shampoo your hair, then turn the water back on to rinse off the lather and get your skin wet. Turn off the water again, soap up your body, then turn the water back on to rinse off. The entire event should take about five minutes.

Caution: If you have a heart condition, Raynaud's disease or blood pressure issues, talk to your doctor first.

GARLIC

Even people who do their best to take care of themselves aren't immune to colds and flu. That was the experience of Susan Brown, age 51, a shiatsu massage therapist and the former owner of a health-food store. She got the flu year after year—until her boyfriend suggested garlic.

Now she cooks with garlic every day, adding it to every dinner, which often consists primarily of vegetables and some kind of starch, such as rice or pasta. She also squeezes raw garlic on top of the dish. If she feels like she's coming down with a cold, she eats garlic three times a day, and within 24 hours, she's fine. She hasn't gotten the flu since she started her garlic regimen more than six years ago.

The science: Garlic offers antibacterial and antiviral properties. Researchers from the University of Western Australia found that people who began using garlic were able to decrease their sick days by more than 50%.

Some of the active ingredients in garlic inhibit the ability of platelets to produce clots in the arteries—important for preventing heart disease and stroke. Individuals who eat garlic regularly can have drops in blood pressure of about 10 mm Hg (millimeters of mercury).

What to do: Chew a clove of garlic whenever you feel a cold coming on or you want to give your health a quick boost. It is better consumed raw, as cooking may destroy some of its health benefits. Most scientific studies are done with garlic supplements. However, some experts believe that the process of making the supplements destroys some of the health benefits.

Caution: If you're on a blood thinner or have a bleeding disorder, such as *hemophilia*, talk with your doctor before consuming large amounts of garlic.

PROBIOTICS

Tony Japour, MD, age 51, is a molecular virologist and a pharmaceutical researcher. His impressive credentials didn't keep him healthy. He would get an awful cold every year. The colds stopped six years ago when he started consuming a yogurt drink that contains live bacterial cultures.

The science: Many of the bacteria that live in the digestive tract have beneficial effects. Known as probiotics, these organisms have been shown to relieve many gastrointestinal conditions and to boost the body's immunity, reduce high blood pressure and decrease cholesterol.

Probiotics that reside in the intestine make it harder for disease-causing germs to take up residence. People who have low levels of probiotics—after taking antibiotics, for example—get infections a lot more often than those with healthy probiotic levels.

How to do it: Eat one or more servings of probiotic-rich foods every day. These include yogurt with live cultures, fermented soybean pastes (such as miso or tempeh), sauerkraut, probiotic-fortified soy milk and the fermented cheeses, such as cottage cheese.

If you are not eating probiotic-rich foods, you can take a supplement. Look for one that has a blend of probiotic organisms, such as *Lactobacillus (L.) acidophilus, L. rhamnosus* and/or *L. bulgaricus*, and follow all directions on the label.

pH BALANCE

Until about eight years ago, Thomas Appell, age 56, got a cold or the flu along with a sore throat at least two or three times a year. One of his healthier friends explained his personal secret—no sugar, no meat and a lot of vegetables. Appell followed the strategy and found that he stopped getting sick. He investigated why the strategy was working and discovered that the foods he was eating were predominantly *alkaline*. The traditional American diet is extremely acidic. It's possible that diseases thrive when the body's pH—a good measure of acidity/alkalinity—is out of balance.

The science: Proponents of the pH theory of health argue that our shift away from a plant-based, low-protein diet, which naturally keeps the body's pH at "neutral" levels, created epidemic levels of disease.

Several recent books, including one from medical anthropologist and certified nutritionist Susan E. Brown, PhD, have linked disease to metabolic acidosis, which can occur when the kidneys don't process acids fast enough.

What to do: Before you can achieve an optimal pH, you have to find out your baseline. You can buy pH test-strip kits at pharmacies and health-food stores. Basically, you hold a strip in your stream of urine, then look at the color. Most experts recommend testing first urine of the morning. A pH chart that comes with the kit explains the reading.

Most people will find that they are slightly acidic. To balance your pH, you will want to eat highly alkaline foods. These include most vegetables, legumes and olive oil. You also want to avoid foods that make your body more acidic, such as meats and processed foods. Thomas routinely checks his urine pH after a meal to see the food's effect on his balance.

Even critics of the pH balance theory agree that consuming more vegetables and less processed foods is important for good health.

A Surprising Way to Boost Immunity

Just looking at someone who is sick could boost your immune system.

Recent study: Participants viewed slides of people brandishing weapons and slides of people who were obviously sick. The blood levels of immunity-enhancing *interleukin-6* increased by 24% in people who viewed images of sick people versus an increase of 7% for those who viewed the slides of people with weapons.

Mark Schaller, PhD, professor, department of psychology, University of British Columbia, Vancouver, and coauthor of a study that was published in *Psychological Science.*

Avoid These Common Herbs When Taking Tamiflu

Some herbal products make Tamiflu less effective. *Oseltamivir* (Tamiflu) often is prescribed to prevent or treat flu.

Recent finding: Herbal products containing *echinacea*, *goldenseal* or the *Labrador tea plant* inhibit Tamiflu's ability to fight flu. So does *chai.*

Self-defense: If you take Tamiflu, avoid all herbal medicines and teas.

John Arnason, PhD, professor of biology and anti-infectives/natural products group leader, Centre for Research in Biopharmaceuticals and Biotechnology at the University of Ottawa, Ontario, Canada. He is coauthor of a laboratory study published in *Journal of Pharmacy & Pharmaceutical Sciences.*

A Humidifier Fights the Flu

Recent evidence indicates that raising the humidity in your home will cause the flu virus to die off and decrease person-to-person transmission. The humidity increase seems to deactivate airborne flu molecules, possibly by changing their size or shape. When using the humidifier, be sure to empty, dry and refill it every day to prevent the buildup of mold and bacteria.

Jeffrey Shaman, PhD, assistant professor, College of Oceanic and Atmospheric Sciences, Oregon State University, Corvallis, and leader of a study of the effects of humidity on flu mortality, published in *PLoS Biology.*

Don't Push It!

Don't push yourself when you are ill. *See why below…*

Recent finding: In a study of 11,838 adults, people who reported going to work despite being sick more than six times in the previous year were 74% more likely to take more than two months of sick leave during the next 18 months, compared with workers who stayed at home when sick. Among those who worked while sick were people with heavy workloads, senior-level employees and those in poor general health.

Theory: Taking sick days when needed enables individuals to rest and recuperate from job demands, preventing more serious health problems later.

Claus D. Hansen, PhD fellow, researcher, department of occupational medicine, Herning Hospital in Landevej, Denmark.

Blame It on the Alcohol

Alcohol increases allergy symptoms. Beer, wine and liquor contain *histamine* produced by yeast and bacteria during fermentation. Histamine often brings on allergy-like symptoms such as sneezing, runny nose and scratchy throat. Other foods that contain or release histamine include aged cheeses, pickled and fermented products and yeast-containing foods, such as bread, cider and grapes (yeast occurs naturally on the skin of grapes). Women are about twice as likely as men to suffer from allergies after drinking alcohol.

Best: Especially throughout allergy season, avoid alcoholic beverages and foods that contain yeast.

Martha V. White, MD, director of research, Institute for Asthma & Allergy in Wheaton and Chevy Chase, Maryland, *www.allergyasthma.us.*

Drug-Free Back-Pain Therapy

Among 701 people with lower back pain who received an advice session on how to reduce the pain, nearly twice as many of those who also underwent six 90-minute *cognitive behavioral therapy* sessions (to challenge destructive thoughts about pain and encourage exercise and relaxation) reported having *no* back pain as those in the advice-only group.

To ease lower back pain: Consider cognitive behavioral therapy. To find a practitioner near you, contact the Association for Behavioral and Cognitive Therapies, 212-647-1890 or *www.abct.org.*

Sarah Lamb, PhD, professor of rehabilitation, Warwick Medical School, University of Warwick, Coventry, UK.

First Aid for Sudden Back Pain

To remedy sudden severe back pain (often triggered by bending over or even sneezing)... Lie down immediately in a comfortable position on your bed or firm mattress placed on the floor. Then apply ice for 10 to 30 minutes—use either a soft gel ice pack or flexible freezer package, such as a bag of peas. Phone your doctor or chiropractor for advice. To get up from lying down, roll onto your side, lift your body while swinging your legs over the edge of the bed. If getting up from the floor, roll onto your side, then onto your knees and then get help rising to a standing position.

Caution: Do not sit on soft furniture, such as an overstuffed chair—this can make back pain worse, and you may have trouble getting up. If you must sit, use a straight-back chair with arms that will provide support when you need to stand.

Louis Sportelli, DC, chiropractor in private practice, Palmerton, Pennsylvania, and author of *Introduction to Chiropractic* (Practice Makers).

Natural Headache Therapy Better Than Meds

Acupuncture provides better headache relief than medication.

Recent finding: 62% of headache sufferers felt less pain after acupuncture...only 45% had less pain after taking medication such as aspirin, Advil or Vicodin.

Tong J. Gan, MD, professor and vice-chair, department of anesthesiology at Duke University, Durham, North Carolina, and leader of a study of 31 studies of acupuncture and headache, published in *Anesthesia & Analgesia.*

Migraine/Depression Link

Depression and migraines often go together. Twenty-five percent of patients with migraines also suffer from depression—versus only 13% of people who do not get migraines. Migraines are known to have a strong genetic basis—which may be linked with the genetic tendency to develop clinical depression.

Best: Migraine sufferers should discuss any signs of depression with their doctors.

Gisela M. Terwindt, MD, PhD, assistant professor, neurology, Leiden University Medical Centre, the Netherlands, and coauthor of a study of 2,652 people, including 360 with migraines, published in *Neurology.*

If You Get Migraines From Computer Use...

Alan Rapoport, MD, clinical professor of neurology, David Geffen School of Medicine at UCLA, Los Angeles.

Flickering lights, flashes of light, bright sun and light from some computer monitors can all trigger migraines or worsen such headaches. This may be because the visual cortex, which allows us to see, becomes overexcited in migraine sufferers.

To disarm light triggers: Reduce the intensity of computer-screen illumination...avoid all fluorescent lights (especially any malfunctioning ones that flash) and lights that blink or flicker ...use tinted contact lenses or glasses...use hats with visors or sunglasses outdoors on brighter days...and go to a completely dark room when migraines strike.

If severe attacks persist, ask your physician about taking the regimen of supplements that may help prevent migraines. This may include 200 milligrams (mg) of magnesium, 200 mg of vitamin B-2, 75 mg of butterbur, all twice daily...300 mg of CoQ10 once daily...and 3 mg of melatonin at night. Or ask about prescription drugs, such as the anticonvulsant *topiramate* (Topamax) or the antidepressant *amitriptyline* (Elavil)—both may help prevent migraines.

Contacts with Built-In Sun Protection

New contact lenses protect eyes from the sun's harmful rays.

Recent finding: Hats and sunglasses will not provide enough protection from the sun's *ultraviolet (UV) radiation*, which can damage the corneas and lenses of the eyes and eventually lead to cataracts.

Self-defense: UV-absorbing contact lenses, even for adults and children who don't need contact lenses to improve vision.

But: Absorption levels vary among brands of lenses. Talk to your doctor about contact lenses that will protect your eyes from the sun.

Heather Chandler, PhD, assistant professor, College of Optometry, The Ohio State University, Columbus, Ohio, and leader of an animal study published in *Investigative Ophthalmology and Visual Science.*

Eyelid Twitching? Quick Fixes

James Salz, MD, clinical professor of ophthalmology, University of Southern California, Los Angeles.

Involuntary eyelid spasms are most often caused by excessive fatigue, caffeine, alcohol or stress. Typically, they are painless, occurring every few seconds for several minutes, and can be accompanied by blurry vision and sensitivity to light. Eye twitches (*blepharospasm*) can occur intermittently for several days to months. Twitching usually stops on its own.

To help eliminate eye twitches: Get at least eight hours of sleep nightly...limit alcohol and caffeine...lubricate the eyes with artificial tear drops (such as Refresh and TheraTears) every four hours. Go to your eye doctor if twitching persists for more than one week, your upper eyelid droops, the eyelid completely closes up with the twitch or tics start occurring in other parts of the face. In rare cases, eye twitching may be a side effect from medications, such as *chlorpromazine* (Thorazine) and *prochlorperazine* (Compazine), or may indicate a brain or nerve disorder, such as *Bell's palsy* (in which facial muscles become temporarily paralyzed) or *Tourette's syndrome* (indicated by unusual movements called tics).

Longer Eyelashes Worth the Risk?

A drug that lengthens eyelashes has risks. Latisse, originally sold under a different name to treat glaucoma, is FDA-approved to develop longer and darker eyelashes. It costs up to $120* for a one-month supply and can take months to make lashes longer and darker. The effects continue only as long as the drug is used.

Downsides: Latisse can darken eyelids and make eye color darker—turning blue, green or hazel eyes brown. It can trigger eye redness and itching. Latisse may be useful for people who have lost eyelashes due to chemotherapy or illness, but for most people, mascara is less risky and much cheaper.

Consumer Reports, 101 Truman Ave., Yonkers, New York 10703, *www.consumerreports.org*.

*Price subject to change.

Fish Finding

Fish decreases risk for age-related hearing loss.

Recent finding: People over age 50 who ate at least two five-ounce servings of fish per week had a 42% reduced risk of developing hearing loss, compared with people who ate less than one serving of fish per week.

Possible reason: *Omega-3s* may help preserve circulation in the inner ear. Fish that are high in omega-3 fatty acids, such as salmon, sardines and mackerel, provide the greatest benefit.

Paul Mitchell, MD, professor, department of ophthalmology, University of Sydney, Australia, and coauthor of a study of 2,956 people, published in *American Journal of Clinical Nutrition*.

Common Vitamin Protects Against Hearing Loss

In an 18-year study of 51,529 men, those age 60 and older with the highest intake of the B vitamin folate (folic acid) had a 21% lower

risk for hearing loss than men of the same age who consumed the least folate.

To protect your hearing: Have folate-rich foods, such as spinach, chickpeas, sunflower seeds and fortified cereals, daily.

Caution: Consuming more than 800 micrograms (mcg) of folate daily has been linked to a higher risk for colon cancer. Researchers do not know why folate appears to protect hearing nor whether the nutrient would help prevent hearing loss in women.

Josef Shargorodsky, MD, otolaryngologist, Massachusetts Eye and Ear Infirmary, Boston.

Popular Drugs Linked to Loss of Hearing

Among 27,000 men who were tracked for 18 years, those age 60 and older who used *acetaminophen* (Tylenol) or *nonsteroidal anti-inflammatory drugs* (NSAIDs), such as *ibuprofen* (Advil) or *naproxen* (Aleve), two or more times weekly were 16% more likely to develop hearing loss than those who did not. Regular aspirin users had no increased risk.

Theory: Acetaminophen depletes *glutathione*, an antioxidant that protects the ears, and NSAIDs reduce blood flow to them.

Sharon Ellen Curhan, MD, clinical researcher, department of medicine, Harvard Medical School, Boston.

Nosebleed Know-How

To treat a nosebleed, sit upright, lean forward and pinch the soft part of your nose with your thumb and forefinger for five to 15 minutes.

To prevent recurrent nosebleeds: Humidify your living space and lubricate your nose with saline spray or a thin film of petroleum jelly. Also, talk to your physician—the blood vessel causing nosebleeds might need to be cauterized.

Caution: If a nosebleed doesn't stop after 30 minutes, go to the hospital. A doctor may have to insert packing material into the nostril or surgery may be needed.

Mayo Clinic Health Letter, 200 First St. SW, Rochester, Minnesota 55905, *http://healthletter.mayoclinic.com.*

Best Toothbrush for Receding Gums

Gums recede when tissue that covers the supportive structure of teeth (roots and bone) is lost. When this occurs, more of your teeth's surfaces become visible and/or increasingly sensitive to extreme temperatures. This could be a response to chronic inflammation, infection, irritation or trauma. Also, some dental products, such as hard toothbrushes that brush away the gums or overly abrasive toothpastes that erode tooth structure, often lead to receding gums.

To protect your gums: Use a soft-bristle toothbrush and a nonabrasive traditional fluoride toothpaste without harsh additives (I recommend Colgate or Crest without whitening).

Even better: An electric toothbrush (which has been shown to clean more effectively and apply less force to teeth than manual toothbrushes).

Brush two to three times daily, floss regularly and have a checkup with your dentist every six months.

Timothy Chase, DMD, dentist in private practice, SmilesNY, New York City, *www.smilesny.com.*

Better Mouthwash

Cosmetic mouth rinses do not kill germs or protect teeth. These rinses can help to temporarily diminish bad breath but do not treat the underlying cause.

Better: Purchase a therapeutic mouthwash approved by the American Dental Association (ADA), with the ADA logo on the label. Any ADA-approved mouthwash kills germs, helps reduce plaque and gingivitis and/or protects teeth against cavities.

Marvin A. Fier, DDS, executive vice president, adjunct professor and guest lecturer, American Society for Dental Aesthetics, Pomona, New York. His Web site is *www.rocklandnydentist.com.*

Simple Way to Tell If You Have Bad Breath

To figure out if you have bad breath, first wash your hands with an odorless soap. Then lick the back of your hand, and let the saliva dry for five seconds. Take a whiff. If you can smell the sulfur compounds of bad breath, brush your teeth, tongue and the back of your mouth. Do not rely on gum and mints—they cover odor only temporarily.

Harold Katz, DDS, founder, California Breath Clinics, treatment centers for occasional or persistent bad breath, Los Angeles, *www.therabreath.com.*

How to Prevent Dreaded Garlic Breath

Drinking milk *while* eating raw or cooked garlic neutralizes much of garlic's sulfur odor. Full-fat milk is more effective than skim milk—the fat seems to play a significant role in the deodorizing. Drinking milk *after* eating garlic is less effective.

Sheryl Barringer, PhD, professor, department of food science and technology, The Ohio State University, Columbus, and coauthor of a study published in *Journal of Food Science.*

Put an End to Chronic Bad Breath

If you have chronic bad breath, try the following advice…

In addition to brushing your teeth at least twice daily, also brush your tongue and floss at least twice daily, in the morning and before bed. Use a tongue cleaner (it's also called a tongue brush or scraper), available at drugstores, to remove food debris trapped on the back of the tongue near the tonsils. Ask your dentist about prescription mouthwashes containing *zinc chloride* and *sodium chlorite* or *chlorine dioxide*. Some of the blue-colored generic mouthwashes also contain zinc chloride.

Good brands: SmartMouth and ProFresh. If bad breath persists, ask your dentist to check for gum disease, sinus infection, chronic nasal drip or mouth breathing (which dries the oral cavity, making oral smells airborne).

Rarely, bad breath can signal acid reflux or a more serious condition such as diabetes or chronic lung infection.

Andrew Spielman, DMD, PhD, associate dean, academic affairs, and professor, basic science and craniofacial biology, NYU College of Dentistry.

Could the Toilet Seat Give You a Rash? What To Do Now…

Wooden toilet seats—especially the ones covered with varnishes and paints—can cause skin irritations after repeated use. Residues of harsh chemicals used to clean toilet seats also may cause irritation. Most cases are easily treated with topical *steroids*. Untreated cases can lead to pain, spreading inflammation and itchy skin eruptions.

Self-defense: Use paper toilet-seat covers in public restrooms…replace wooden toilet seats at home with plastic ones…try to avoid harsh cleaning products that contain irritants, such as *phenol* and *formaldehyde*.

Bernard Cohen, MD, director of pediatric dermatology, Johns Hopkins Children's Center in Baltimore, and leader of a study of five cases of toilet seat dermatitis, published in *Pediatrics*.

Wear These Colors for Sun Protection

When researchers dyed lightweight cotton fabrics different shades of blue, red and yellow and measured the amount of *ultraviolet (UV) radiation* that penetrated them, they found that darker, color-intense blue and red hues blocked more harmful UV rays than lighter yellow hues.

To protect skin from sun damage: Wear darker blue and red cottons.

Ascension Riva, PhD, engineer, Institute of Textile Research of Terrassa, Technical University of Catalonia, Barcelona, Spain.

Nature's Remedies for Sunburn and Bug Bites

Jamison Starbuck, ND, naturopathic physician in family practice in Missoula, Montana. She is past president of the American Association of Naturopathic Physicians and a contributing editor to *The Alternative Advisor: The Complete Guide to Natural Therapies and Alternative Treatments* (Time Life).

If you're tired of using the same old products to prevent or remedy sunburn, bug bites and other summertime skin problems, there are a number of natural remedies that I've found to be effective in my clinical practice.

My favorite natural remedies for…

•**Sunburn protection.** *Beta-carotene* is a naturally occurring pigmented compound that helps protect against sunburn—perhaps due to its powerful antioxidant properties. To prevent sunburn this summer, supplement your sunscreen use by loading up on beta-carotene–

rich foods. (This nutrient also improves general immunity, so it makes sense to have these foods year-round.)

Best food sources of beta-carotene: Most orange-colored vegetables and fruits (such as carrots, sweet potatoes, mangos, cantaloupe and apricots)…and green vegetables (such as broccoli, spinach and kale). Adults with fair, sun-sensitive skin may also reduce sunburn risk with a beta-carotene supplement (50,000 international units [IU] daily) June through September in North America.

A note: Some research has suggested that this dose of beta-carotene may be harmful to smokers. If you smoke, consult your doctor before taking beta-carotene. Even though beta-carotene helps protect against sunburn, you still need to wear sunscreen (check a natural-foods grocery store for a chemical-free product). The combination will provide even more protection than when either is used alone.

• **Sunburn relief.** If you do get a sunburn, *calendula* is one herb that may help soothe burned skin, reduce pain and speed healing. Calendula flowers (used to brew up a soothing tea) and calendula tincture and lotion are readily available wherever botanical medicines are sold. These flowers also can be easily grown in home gardens (most nurseries stock both plant starts and seeds). Use one tablespoon of fresh flowers or two teaspoons of dried flowers per cup of water for tea. Put calendula tea, tincture or lotion directly on sunburned skin three times daily until symptoms improve. You can splash the tea or tincture on your skin or dab it on with cotton balls.

Caution: Do not use calendula if you are allergic to plants in the daisy family.

• **Bee stings.** A homeopathic remedy made from the honeybee, *Apis 30C* reduces swelling and pain. Take two pellets (under the tongue) twice daily for one to three days.

Caution: Do not take Apis if you are allergic to bees. You can also use calendula tea, tincture or ointment topically for relief.

• **Insect bites.** Homeopathic *Lachesis 30C* relieves the pain from swollen, tender insect bites, such as those caused from green bottle flies and house flies. The typical dose is two pellets (under the tongue) twice daily for one to three days. *Echinacea* (the well-known cold and flu preventive) in tincture form can be applied directly on any insect bite, including one caused by a mosquito, to reduce inflammation and soothe irritation. Apply as needed.

Caution: Do not use echinacea if you are allergic to plants in the daisy family.

Poison Ivy *Not* Contagious Once You Do This

A poison ivy rash isn't contagious once the skin has been washed. Washing removes the plant's resin, which causes the itchy rash. Once the resin is removed, the rash will not spread.

Richard O'Brien, MD, spokesperson, American College of Emergency Physicians (*www.acep.org*). He is also attending emergency physician at Moses Taylor Hospital, and associate professor of emergency medicine, The Commonwealth Medical College of Pennsylvania, both in Scranton.

Pineapple Power

P ineapple pills can help healing. The compound *bromelain*, found in the stem and juice of the pineapple plant and taken in pill form, helps acute injuries, including cuts and bruises, to heal quickly. It improves circulation at the injured site by halting the production of prostaglandins, by-products of inflammation. Bromelain takes one to two days to work. Use only enteric-coated pills to be sure that the bromelain is not degraded by stomach acid.

Caution: Bromelain thins the blood—talk to your doctor before using it if you are taking a blood thinner.

Tieraona Low Dog, MD, director of the fellowship for the Arizona Center for Integrative Medicine, University of Arizona, Tucson. Her Internet site is *www.drlowdog.com*.

Best Coffee If You Have Tummy Trouble

Dark-roasted coffee is gentler on the stomach than light-roasted coffee. People who get heartburn or stomach irritation from most coffees often find dark roasts less bothersome.

Possible reason: Dark-roasted coffee contains more *N-methylpyridinium*, a compound produced in the roasting process that reduces stomach acid.

Veronika Somoza, PhD, professor and chair of the research platform of molecular food science at the University of Vienna and researcher of different coffee blends, presented at a recent meeting of the American Chemical Society.

Heartburn Helper

Sleeping on your right side worsens heartburn. People who sleep on their right side suffer reflux for longer periods than people who sleep on their left side. Left-side sleeping may keep the junction between the stomach and esophagus above the level of gastric acid, reducing heartburn symptoms.

Self-defense: If you have heartburn, sleep on an incline so that gravity helps keep stomach contents in place. And if you tend to sleep on your side, make it your left side.

Donald O. Castell, MD, professor, division of gastroenterology at Medical University of South Carolina, Charleston, and leader of two studies of acid reflux, published in *The Journal of Clinical Gastroenterology* and *The American Journal of Gastroenterology*.

Pardon Me!

Burping is your body's way of ridding itself of excess air in the stomach. It can be caused by swallowing too much air when you eat and drink. Acid reflux, in which stomach acid backs up into the throat or mouth, also can bring on burping. That is because people with this condition swallow frequently to get rid of the acid but often swallow too much air in the process.

To reduce air-swallowing: Limit carbonated beverages....avoid chewing gum and hard candy....eat slowly...and treat acid reflux.

Also helpful: Ease anxiety, which exacerbates air-swallowing, through deep breathing and/or relaxation techniques. If your abdomen distends (enlarges), promptly see your physician—this could be a sign of a condition such as irritable bowel syndrome or partial bowel obstruction.

Douglas A. Drossman, MD, codirector, UNC Center for Functional GI and Motility Disorders, University of North Carolina, Chapel Hill.

Tried Everything for Snoring? Solve This Problem Once and for All!

Murray Grossan, MD, an otolaryngologist and head and neck surgeon with Tower Ear, Nose & Throat at Cedars-Sinai Medical Towers in Los Angeles. He is the author of *Free Yourself from Sinus and Allergy Problems—Permanently* (Hydro Med). Dr. Grossan's Web site is *www.grossan.com*.

Anyone who snores—or who lives with a person who does—knows that it can literally wreck your own health or that of your partner if it robs either of you of too much sleep.

If you're lucky, your snoring will be temporary and due to something harmless such as nasal congestion caused by a cold. But for about one out of every four American adults, snoring is a chronic problem.

Good news: There are two little-known—some people might say quirky—therapies that work extremely well.

FIGHTING THE BATTLE

Snoring isn't always easy to correct, so people who suffer from this condition will do almost anything to get relief. Fortunately, some people can eliminate the snoring with surprisingly simple approaches, such as sleeping on their sides.

A trick that may help: Sewing a pocket on the back of your sleepwear and placing a tennis ball inside will help keep you off your back during sleep.

Wearing a mouth guard at night, which repositions the tongue to help stop the snoring, may also help.

For people whose snoring is due to *sleep apnea*, a condition in which breathing temporarily ceases during sleep, *continuous positive airway pressure* (CPAP) is often prescribed.

With this treatment, a small pump delivers air through a nasal mask to keep the airway open. However, many people find the CPAP mask uncomfortable and stop using it.

In severe cases, some people who snore resort to surgery to tighten and cut the excess tissues that cause snoring. Risks include infection and bleeding.

A problem: None of these therapies works well for all snorers.

Alternatives worth trying: Of the thousands of snoring patients I've treated over the past 40 years, I've seen the most remarkable results from two nonsurgical therapies. Both approaches can correct snoring by strengthening the loose, flaccid muscles of the tongue and throat that obstruct the airway, leading to the forceful breathing that causes snoring. Try one or both of these therapies to relieve your snoring.

BLOW A DIDGERIDOO

The *didgeridoo* (it is pronounced *did-jer-ee-DOO*) is an Australian trumpet—wooden or bamboo—that is approximately four feet long. Blowing it helps to tone the muscles of the tongue and throat, making snoring much less likely to occur.

Scientific evidence: A *BMJ* (*British Medical Journal*) study found that people with mild sleep apnea who practiced playing the didgeridoo for 30 minutes daily, six days a week, for four months had significant improvement in all their sleep apnea symptoms, including snoring.

In my practice, the didgeridoo has helped numerous snorers regardless of whether they had sleep apnea. I recommend playing it 20 minutes daily. To watch an instructional video,

go to *www.ehow.com* and search for "Basic Didgeridoo Articulation."

You can buy a didgeridoo for $20 to $30.*

My recommendation: The Didgeridoo Store, 866-468-3434, *www.didgeridoostore.com*…Australian Originals, 800-278-4287, *www.australianoriginals.com*.

EASY THROAT EXERCISES

Certain throat exercises also help to relieve snoring by strengthening both the tongue and throat muscles.

Scientific evidence: Study results published in the *American Journal of Respiratory and Critical Care Medicine* found that performing throat exercises, such as those described below, for 30 minutes daily for three months reduced snoring and improved sleep quality.

To reduce snoring, try each of the following exercises for at least five minutes daily…

• **Exercise 1.** Press your tongue against the roof of your mouth repeatedly—as hard as you can—for 20 seconds at a time.

• **Exercise 2.** While pressing your tongue against the roof of your mouth, say the vowel sounds—"a"…"e"…"i"…"o"…"u."

• **Exercise 3.** Place your tongue at the front of the roof of your mouth, pressing it against the back of your upper teeth. Then slide it all the way to the back of the roof of the mouth. As you do this, rapidly pronounce the vowel sounds.

• **Exercise 4.** While keeping your tongue pressed against the roof of your mouth, swallow repeatedly. (Do not try this with food in your mouth!)

It may take a few months to strengthen your tongue and throat muscles. Be patient—it will be time well spent if you finally stop snoring.

*Prices subject to change.

A Juice That Eases Insomnia

Fifteen adults with chronic insomnia drank 16 ounces of tart cherry juice per day over two weeks and then a placebo drink for two weeks.

Results: When participants drank the juice, they experienced 17 fewer minutes, on average, of awake time when they were trying to sleep than when they drank the placebo.

A theory: Tart cherries contain *melatonin*, which regulates the body's sleep-wake cycle.

If you suffer insomnia: Try tart cherries (dried, frozen or in juice). If you have prediabetes or diabetes, ask your doctor before increasing your intake of fruit juice.

Wilfred Pigeon, PhD, director of the Sleep and Neurophysiology Research Laboratory at University of Rochester Medical Center, New York.

Take Time for Tea

Drinking tea decreases stress. Stress levels of people who made and drank tea after taking a math quiz were 4% lower than their pretest levels. Those given water after the test saw a 25% increase in stress. While tea does have compounds that help combat anxiety, researchers believe that the act of preparing and drinking tea also soothes people.

Malcolm Cross, PhD, professor of psychology, City University London, England, and leader of a study of 42 people.

All-Natural Energy Booster

Quercetin boosts energy. This antioxidant and anti-inflammatory compound, found in berries, grapes, red onions and apple skin, increases energy and performance in healthy individuals.

Recent study: After taking 1,000 milligrams (mg) daily of the dietary supplement form of quercetin for seven days, the participants had a 13.2% increase in endurance.

Note: You can't achieve this dose by eating fruits and vegetables.

J. Mark Davis, PhD, director, Exercise Biochemistry Laboratory, University of South Carolina in Columbia, and leader of a study published in *International Journal of Sport Nutrition and Exercise Metabolism*.

Couldn't Sleep Last Night? How to Get Through the Day...

Consume small amounts of caffeine every few hours to keep going on little sleep. Low doses of caffeine throughout the day are more effective at maintaining alertness than a large cup of caffeinated coffee in the morning. Drink four to six ounces at a time to stay alert and think more clearly.

Health Magazine, 1271 Avenue of the Americas, New York City 10020, *www.health.com/health*.

Do You Smell? Solutions to Your Most Embarrassing Problems

Mark A. Stengler, NMD, naturopathic medical doctor and founder and medical director of the Stengler Center for Integrative Medicine in Encinitas, California...adjunct associate clinical professor at the National College of Natural Medicine in Portland, Oregon...the author of numerous books, including *The Natural Physician's Healing Therapies* and a coauthor of *Prescription for Natural Cures* and *Prescription for Drug Alternatives* (all Bottom Line Books, *www.bottomlinepublications.com*)...as well as author of the *Bottom Line/Natural Healing* newsletter.

Do you have a little medical problem that you're too embarrassed to talk to your doctor about? Maybe you worry that your breath is bad or you pass gas in public? *Here, natural solutions that work...*

BODY ODOR

A high-fat diet, or a diet that's high in processed foods, interferes with normal digestion and can cause a strong body odor. So can an overgrowth of fungus in the intestine. Fungus overgrowth can occur when antibiotics kill off bacteria in the intestines. High intake of sugar also can cause overgrowth.

Solutions: One teaspoon of liquid *chlorophyll* (available from health-food stores) taken orally once or twice daily with any meal. This plant pigment helps to remove odor-promoting toxins from your body. *Milk thistle*—200 milligrams (mg) to 250 mg daily, taken by mouth—also is helpful because it promotes healthier digestion. Any food that is high in *probiotics*, such as live-culture yogurt, can help restore a healthier balance of bacteria in the intestine, as can a probiotic supplement. Probiotics help control fungi.

FLATULENCE

The average adult passes gas between eight and 15 times daily. Normally gas doesn't smell, but it can be embarrassing when it does…and too much gas can cause pain and bloating.

Solutions: Ginger or *chamomile.* They can improve intestinal motility, the ability of the colon to move stools out of the body at a normal rate. They also reduce the amount of gas that forms in the intestine. Drink one cup of chamomile or ginger tea after meals or whenever you feel gassy.

Also helpful: Dandelion (*taraxacum*) supplements, 250 mg to 500 mg three times daily, taken with meals. Dandelion increases flow of bile from the liver to the intestines, which improves digestion and reduces gas.

COLD SORES

Caused by a herpes virus, cold sores can be unsightly and painful.

Solutions: L-lysine, 1,000 mg, taken three times daily between meals at the first sign of the tingling or burning that precedes an outbreak. It is an amino acid that aids in tissue repair, and it can help cold sores to heal more quickly.

Avoid foods that are high in the amino acid *L-arginine,* such as peanuts, almonds, whole wheat and chocolate. L-arginine makes it easier for the virus to thrive.

Also helpful: Apply *lemon balm* cream to the area four times daily at the first sign of an outbreak. One double-blind study found that

people who did this had less discomfort and fewer blisters during outbreaks than people who used a placebo.

CONSTIPATION

It's among the most common digestive complaints, yet many people are too embarrassed to discuss it with their doctors. This is unfortunate because it's usually simple to treat.

Solutions: Try ground *flaxseed* (one to two tablespoons per day with eight ounces of water). It adds to your daily fiber intake and also breaks down in the intestine to form mucilage, a soothing gel that promotes more frequent and more comfortable bowel movements.

An ancient remedy known as *Triphala* also stimulates digestion and promotes the passage of stools through the colon. Triphala, meaning "three fruits," is made from the fruits of three trees (*amalaki, bibhitaki* and *haritaki*) that grow throughout India and the Middle East. Add one-half teaspoon of Triphala to one cup of warm water, and consume it once or twice per day after a meal. Take it daily if you have chronic constipation. Triphala is available online and at health-food stores.

Surprising Ways to Use Coffee

Coffee has many little-known uses. *Try a few of these yourself…*

Neutralizes odor: Ground coffee absorbs moisture and replaces an offending odor with the smell of coffee. Hang a cheesecloth pouch filled with cooled used coffee grounds in the cabinet where the garbage is kept.

Stress buster: Inhaling the scent of roasted coffee beans eases stress and produces a natural relaxation response.

Skin exfoliant: Mix one cup of ground coffee, one-half cup of sugar and one-half tablespoon of jojoba oil. Apply the mixture to your body, and gently rub using a circular motion. Rinse and pat dry.

Health Magazine, 1271 Avenue of the Americas, New York City 10020, *www.health.com/health.*

4

Focus on Fitness

Time to Get Off the Couch! The Extreme Health Dangers of Sitting

Living like a couch potato has long been known to threaten a person's health. But now researchers are discovering that it is so *much more* dangerous than previously thought.

Troubling statistic: Americans spend more than half their waking hours sitting—primarily watching TV, driving and working at a desk.

Important recent finding: When Australian researchers recently tracked 8,800 men and women (average age 53) for about six years, they found that for every hour of daily TV viewing, risk for death due to cardiovascular disease increased by 18%. For those who watched TV four or more hours daily, the risk of dying from cardiovascular disease was 80% higher than for those who reported watching fewer than two hours daily.

Most surprising: A similar Canadian study of about 17,000 adults found that even among those people who are physically fit and have a normal body weight, prolonged sitting, for any reason, was associated with increased health risks, suggesting that sitting for long periods may cancel out some of the health benefits of regular exercise.

THE PROBLEM WITH SITTING

Our bodies are programmed to move. When we spend most of our waking hours sitting, our health suffers in various ways. *Examples...*

• **Sluggish central nervous system.** Sitting will cause your central nervous system to slow down, contributing to fatigue. Three weekly sessions of low-intensity exercise, such as walking at a leisurely speed, which stimulates the

James A. Levine, MD, PhD, head of endocrinology, University Hospitals Case Medical Center in Cleveland, and former director of the Non-Exercise Activity Thermogenesis (NEAT) Laboratory at the Mayo Clinic in Rochester, Minnesota. He is coauthor of *Move a Little, Lose a Lot* (Crown).

central nervous system, lowered fatigue by 65% after six weeks, according to one study.

•**Weakened muscles.** Sitting weakens your muscles (especially those that support posture and are used to walk) and stiffens joints, leading to a hunched posture and increased risk for back and joint pain.

•**Poor fat burning.** The walls of your capillaries are lined with *lipoprotein lipase,* an enzyme that helps break down certain fats in the bloodstream. Sit for just two hours, and these enzymes start switching off. If you sit all day, their activity drops by 50%.

•**Increased heart risks.** Sitting for long periods, even in people who have healthy body weight, will produce negative effects on blood sugar and blood fat levels, which may contribute to diabetes and heart disease.

THE "NEAT" SOLUTION

Fortunately, the dangers of prolonged sitting can be countered by engaging in simple, low-intensity movement throughout the day.

Thirty minutes or more of cardiovascular exercise (such as brisk walking, swimming or biking) several days every week is known to help promote good overall health. However, research at the Mayo Clinic has shown that the average American's biggest health problem is a deficit in activity when formal exercise is not being performed.

Non-exercise activity thermogenesis (NEAT) is the term that is used for the energy that is expended (calories burned) doing everyday activities.

While in previous generations our work and recreational activities involved regularly standing up and moving the body's muscles, today's world of cars, desk jobs, TVs and computers has reduced our daily NEAT dramatically.

The solution is to add small amounts of non-exercise-related activity into your daily routine. For example, simply standing up triples your energy expenditure compared to just sitting. And since a slow (1 mile per hour) walk triggers more than half the metabolic activity of a brisk (3 mph) walk, a leisurely hour-long stroll burns more calories than an intense 30-minute power walk.

Interesting: We burn just five calories an hour while sitting and 15 while standing.

TO COUNTERACT SITTING AT HOME

With a little forethought, it's possible to significantly raise your activity level without stepping foot in a gym. Not surprisingly, watching TV and long hours at the computer are among the biggest traps when you're at home. *To develop your own NEAT lifestyle in your home…*

•**Stand up and walk around.** Do this every time an advertisement comes on the TV.

•**Keep a stability ball handy.** Since sitting on this kind of large, inflatable ball requires you to shift slightly from side to side to keep your balance, it engages more muscles (especially those in your abdomen and back) than sitting in a regular chair does. Strong abdominal muscles help fight back pain and enhance stability and balance. Stability ball chairs are available at both Gaiam (877-989-6321, *www.gaiam.com*, $120*)…and Isokinetics, Inc. (866-263-0674, *www.isokineticsinc.com*, $65).

•**Place exercise equipment near your TV.** Good choices include a treadmill, stationary bike and/or elliptical trainer. If you watch TV, choose a half-hour program every day and begin using the equipment as the theme music comes on. Continue until the show ends.

Another option: Try the "mini stepper," a small device with two footpads that lets you step in place against a resistance. Stepper machines can be tucked away when not in use. These mini steppers are widely available from companies such as Stamina Products, Inc. (800-375-7520, *www.staminaproducts.com*, $40 to $220) and NordicTrack (*www.nordictrack.com*, 888-308-9616, $120).

•**Put your computer on an elevated surface,** such as a shelf or stand. This way, you can stand while typing or surfing the Web.

•**Choose action-oriented video games.** If you play video games, opt for an active game (including Wii, which enables you to mimic motions used in sports such as tennis) instead of more sedentary games.

•**Engage in "active intimacy."** Catch up with your spouse or other family members or friends by talking with them while you stroll around the neighborhood together.

*Prices subject to change.

TO COUNTERACT SITTING AT WORK

For a NEAT lifestyle at work…

•**Stand up when you answer the phone.** If possible, pace near your desk for the duration of the call.

•**Schedule "walking meetings."** This is ideal when you need to meet with just one or two people and don't need to take a lot of notes.

•**Cut back on phone calls and e-mails to coworkers.** When you need to speak to a co-worker, walk to his/her work space. Besides getting you out of your chair, this face-to-face communication style has been shown to improve relationships.

•**Adhere to the 10-minute rule.** Whenever you are working at your computer, get up for 10 minutes every hour to stretch your back and legs. Use this time to perform tasks that can be done while standing, such as making phone calls.

•**Take the stairs.** Avoid the elevator when going to and from your office floor.

•**Park your car a distance (half a mile, for example) from your office.** If you take mass transit, get off the bus or subway one or two stops before your destination.

•**Take a midday walk.** Use half your lunch hour for a stroll.

•**Use a standing desk.** This allows you to stand while working. Ernest Hemingway used such a desk. They can be ordered from such companies as Ergo Desk (800-822-3746, *www.ergodesk.com)* or Anthro (800-325-3841, *www.anthro.com).*

Cost: About $240 to more than $2,000.

Even better: Add a treadmill for less than $1,000 to your work space to create a "walking desk." Don't laugh—so many people who have done this (using it for four to 12 hours daily) have found that their productivity and concentration have improved along with their health.

A Little Bit of Exercise Helps a Lot

As little as one minute of standing and/or walking around can make a difference in waist circumference over time.

Example: Individuals who get up regularly and switch TV channels by hand, instead of using the remote, have, on average, a waist circumference of six centimeters less than those who stay seated.

People who do these small amounts of activity also have lower body mass indexes and lower glucose and triglyceride levels. Stand up to answer the phone…take a long route back to your desk…do some stretches before reading a new e-mail.

Genevieve Healy, PhD, Population Health, The University of Queensland, Herston, Queensland, Australia, and leader of a study of 169 adults, published in *Diabetes Care.*

Women Need This Much Exercise to Avoid Weight Gain

To avoid gaining weight over time, older women at a healthy weight need roughly one hour of moderate-intensity activity *every day.* This can include going for a brisk walk, riding a bicycle, playing golf, gardening and playing with grandchildren.

I-Min Lee, MD, an associate professor, department of medicine, Brigham and Women's Hospital, Harvard Medical School, Boston, and leader of a study involving 34,079 women, average age 54, published in *The Journal of the American Medical Association.*

Best Time to Exercise

There's no scientifically established optimal time to exercise. You may, however, have a personal preference based on your body's *biorhythms.* For instance, certain people have more energy in the morning and enjoy starting the day with a workout. For others, energy levels peak in the evening, and they enjoy exercising to wind down the day. You may want to modify your workout slightly based on your preferred exercise time.

For morning exercise: Your body temperature is lower during this time, so spend additional time warming up (20 minutes instead of the typical 10 minutes) to loosen muscles and avoid injury.

For evening exercise: Leave at least two hours between your workout's end and your bedtime to slow heart rate, metabolism and breathing enough so you can fall asleep.

What is even more important than timing, though, is consistency. Pick a time that works best for you and stick with it.

Wayne Westcott, PhD, fitness research director at South Shore YMCA, Quincy, Massachusetts.

How to Combat Germs At the Gym—Deadly Bacteria on the Rise

Steven Zinder, PhD, ATC, a certified athletic trainer and assistant professor of exercise and sports science at University of North Carolina, Chapel Hill. He is lead author of the National Athletic Trainers' Association position paper on the causes, prevention and treatment of skin diseases in athletes, published in *Journal of Athletic Training.*

Even the cleanest health club provides an ideal environment for a variety of skin diseases. That's unfortunate because an estimated one-third of American adults has some type of skin disease at any given time. And more than half of all infectious diseases among athletes are contracted *cutaneously*, or through the skin.

The problem with health clubs is that they provide plenty of heat and humidity, along with the secretions from hundreds of perspiring bodies.

Result: Fungi, bacteria and viruses survive and may even proliferate on floor mats, towels, hand weights, treadmills, weight machines and on other equipment. Viruses and bacteria may survive for hours on metal and other gym surfaces—some fungi can live for years. And the skin chafing that occurs during workouts makes it easy for these organisms to penetrate the body's defenses.

MAIN RISKS

Most skin infections, such as athlete's foot and jock itch, are an annoyance and easy to treat. They're unpleasant but unlikely to pose a serious threat.

A very dangerous exception is *community-acquired methicillin-resistant Staphylococcus aureus* (CA-MRSA). This is a potentially life-threatening antibiotic-resistant bacteria that's increasingly found in exercise settings.

One study published in *The New England Journal of Medicine* showed that 42% of nasal swabs from professional football players tested positive for MRSA, even if the players did not have active infections.

Fortunately, most MRSA and other gym-acquired skin infections can be prevented. *How to protect yourself…*

WASH GYM CLOTHES AFTER EVERY WORKOUT

Many people keep their exercise clothes in a duffel bag or backpack. They change into them at the gym and then pack them up and take them home, but they wear them repeatedly before putting them in the wash.

Unwashed athletic clothing—even when you did not break a sweat—serves as a reservoir for disease-causing microbes. Wearing these clothes repeatedly increases the risk that the organisms will colonize and/or penetrate the skin. And if you wear clothes repeatedly and don't change them before you leave the gym, it spreads the organisms to other areas, such as the seat of your car, where you or someone else can get infected.

Solution: Don't wear your exercise clothes out of the gym. Take them off as soon as you're done with your workout, and wash them when you get home. A normal wash cycle with hot water and detergent will eliminate virtually all germs.

It's just as important to wash the bag that you use to carry your gym clothes. Put it in the washing machine if it's washable. The easiest thing to do is use a mesh bag that you can throw in the washer with your clothes. If your bag is not washable, you can swab the inside with a solution made from one part bleach and 10 parts water. Never stuff your gym clothes into your briefcase or purse.

Also, wash your reusable water bottle when you get home.

SHOWER AFTER YOUR WORKOUT

The longer infectious organisms stay on the skin, the higher the risk for infection.

Solution: Take a shower after all gym workouts—and when you work out at home. When you shower, wash every part of your body including the bottoms of the feet, between the toes, the groin area and the lower and upper legs. Also, wear shower shoes, such as flip-flops, in the shower and locker room—but be sure to still wash your feet.

Use an antimicrobial liquid soap. Soap bars, even when they are antibacterial, can harbor germs long enough to spread them from one part of the body to another—or, when a bar of soap is shared, from person to person.

Make sure the liquid soap is labeled antimicrobial, not just antibacterial. Antimicrobial soap kills a broader spectrum of pathogens. An antibacterial soap kills only bacteria.

WASH YOUR HANDS BEFORE AND AFTER

Because MRSA can live indefinitely in nasal secretions, and we all touch our noses very frequently, the organism is readily transferred from one person to another.

Solution: Wash your hands—vigorously, for no less than 30 seconds, using an antimicrobial soap—when you arrive at the gym (in case you are bringing in germs) and again when you're done with your workout.

USE ALCOHOL WIPES

Many people who exercise at health clubs carry a hand towel as they work out. They use this to wipe down exercise bars, the seats on rowing machines, etc. This is not effective for preventing infection. It only removes sweat/moisture left by the previous user—it does not eliminate microbes and can, in fact, transfer them to other surfaces.

Solution: If your gym provides you spray bottles of disinfectant and paper towels, use those to clean every piece of equipment—the handles, bars, seats, etc.—before you use it, or bring along a package of alcohol wipes. You can reuse the same wipe for multiple areas as long as it's still damp with alcohol. I also recommend bringing your own floor mat (if you use one) and wiping it down with disinfectant or an alcohol wipe after each use.

STAY DRY

Tinea pedis (or athlete's foot) is among the most common gym-acquired infections. Others include *tinea cruris* (jock itch) and *tinea capitis* or *tinea corporis* (ringworm).

These fungi tend to thrive in the areas of the body that accumulate moisture, such as the feet or the groin.

Solution: Dry your feet and groin thoroughly after showering. Don't put on your clothes until your entire body is completely dry.

Helpful: After your feet are dry, dust them with any moisture-absorbing powder—regular baby powder works well.

AVOID "COSMETIC" SHAVING

Those who shave more than just the face, legs and armpits are more likely to get a skin infection than those who shave only these traditional areas. Studies have shown that people who shave their "tender" regions, such as the chest or pubic area, are up to six times more likely to get MRSA than those who don't. Even a smooth, comfortable shave can create micronicks in the skin that make you vulnerable to bacterial infections.

Solution: Ideally, shave only your face, legs and/or underarms. And be sure to wash your entire body with an antimicrobial soap immediately after workouts. Never use a shared razor—if you shave at the gym, bring your own shaving gear.

Running Safety Tip

Running when angry increases likelihood of injury. Stress and anxiety reduce energy levels and make it harder to use muscles efficiently and react quickly. Previous research has shown that elite athletes are more likely to be injured if they compete while upset or fatigued or dealing with even a minor life issue. Stress can increase muscle tension, which can decrease reaction time, situational awareness (for potholes, traffic, signs) and muscle coordination.

Self-defense: Use more caution when running if you're stressed.

Buz Swanik, PhD, an associate professor of sports medicine, University of Delaware, Newark, Delaware, quoted in *Runner's World*.

An Olympic Trainer's Secret to Improving Your Balance—Takes Just 10 Minutes a Day

Joel Harper, a New York City–based personal trainer who designs equipment-free workouts for Olympic athletes and business executives. His exercises have been featured in the *You* book series (Free Press) by Mehmet C. Oz, MD, and Michael F. Roizen, MD, including *You: Raising Your Child*. The exercises described in this article are included in his DVD *Fit Pack: Better Balance*, available at *www.joelharperfitness.com*.

Health experts have always advocated doing aerobic exercises and strength training on a regular basis, but a new type of activity is now being added to that prescription—*balance training*.

Startling statistic: Declining balance skills as people age are thought to be a major factor in the 450,000 hospitalizations that occur in the US each year due to falls. Research suggests that up to half of those falls could be prevented with the help of balance exercises.

Good news: Five easy exercises will begin to improve your balance, ankle flexibility, leg strength and overall agility—within days for many people. For best results, spend about 10 minutes performing these exercises every day. If the basic exercises seem too easy, try the advanced versions.

BETTER BALANCE WORKOUT

You can strengthen all the key muscles that are critical to your overall sense of balance by simply using the force of your body weight.

When beginning these exercises, stand next to a sturdy chair for added support when necessary. Keep your stomach taut throughout, pretending there's a string pulling up from the top of your head and lengthening your spine. This helps center your body and engages and strengthens all your stabilizer muscles (which support your trunk, limit movement in joints and control balance). Be sure to breathe naturally rather than holding your breath, which can throw off your balance. Also, it's ideal to do the exercises barefoot in order to use the muscles in your feet.

Note: These exercises, designed by leading fitness expert and Olympic trainer Joel Harper, are unique in that they help decrease the imbalance that most of us have—we all carry more tension in one side of our bodies—but also simultaneously strengthen all the muscles that support our skeletal structure.*

THE HIPPIE

Purpose: Stretches the hips and hamstrings (that run along the back of the thighs).

What to do: Stand with your feet together and bend forward at your waist as far as you comfortably can. Let your arms hang down. If your lower back is stiff or your hamstrings are tight, place your hands on your hips instead of letting them hang down. Let your head hang down to help release tension.

Next, alternate bending one knee slightly for about 15 seconds while keeping the other leg straight (keeping both feet flat). Perform a total of three bends per leg. If you feel light-headed from the blood rushing to your head from this position, put your hands on the ground and look straight ahead.

QUAD SWAYS

Purpose: Strengthens your core (abdominal and back muscles) and quadriceps (located at the front of the thighs).

*Consult your doctor before starting this or any other exercise program.

What to do: Stand up with your left palm flat on your stomach and the top of your right hand resting on your lower back. Next, lift your right knee in front of you until your thigh is parallel to the floor—if this is too hard, simply lift it as high as you comfortably can.

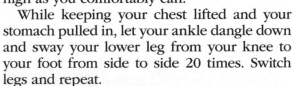

While keeping your chest lifted and your stomach pulled in, let your ankle dangle down and sway your lower leg from your knee to your foot from side to side 20 times. Switch legs and repeat.

Advanced version: Do this with your eyes closed.

TIGHTROPE

Purpose: Improves mental focus. For this exercise, use a stretched-out, 10-foot string or some other straight line on the floor that you can easily feel and follow with your bare feet, such as a line of tile grout.

What to do: Stand with your arms out to your sides at shoulder height, palms up. Next, walk along the line, imagining that you're walking along a tightrope. Try to look straight ahead the entire time. Walk to the end of the line, then turn and walk back, keeping the line in the middle of your feet. With each step, focus on not shifting your body weight until you feel the string below your foot. Don't move forward until you are centered on the line. Do five times.

Advanced version: Perform this exercise walking backward or with your eyes closed.

NORTH AND SOUTH

Purpose: Strengthens your legs and core.

What to do: With your arms out to your sides at shoulder height and palms facing down, lift your left leg in *front* of you as far and as high as you can while holding it straight and keeping your toes pointing forward. Second, without contacting the ground, sweep your leg under your body

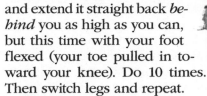

and extend it straight back *behind* you as high as you can, but this time with your foot flexed (your toe pulled in toward your knee). Do 10 times. Then switch legs and repeat.

Advanced version: Reach out your arms and your hands at shoulder height directly in front of you while simultaneously reaching a leg directly in back of you. Switch directions. Aim to be horizontal while balancing on your supporting leg.

FLOATING CHAIR

Purpose: Helps strengthen lower abdominals, hip flexors (muscles that bring the legs and trunk together in flexion movement) and quadriceps.

What to do: Sit on the floor with your knees bent and your feet flat on the ground. Place your hands underneath your legs behind the backs of your knees. Next, pull in your stomach and lift your feet off the ground so that you're balanced on your buttocks. Hold for 30 seconds, keeping your back straight and breathing normally.

Advanced version: Perform this exercise with your palms facing up, one inch from the sides of your knees.

Sore Shoulders, Knees Or Elbows? Try the Pain-Relieving Technique Pro Athletes Use

Warren I. Hammer, DC, a chiropractor who's been in private practice in Norwalk, Connecticut, for more than 40 years. Dr. Hammer lectures both nationally and internationally on the treatment of soft-tissue problems and is the author of the textbook titled *Functional Soft-Tissue Examination and Treatment by Manual Methods* (Jones & Bartlett Learning). His Web site is *www.warrenhammer.com.*

I f you stepped inside the practice facilities of various pro baseball and football teams, you'd be likely to see the teams' physical therapists, chiropractors or trainers using a variety of curved, stainless steel instruments to work on their athletes' sore shoulders, knees, elbows, backs and other body parts.

These instruments are part of an innovative therapy known as the *Graston Technique*, which is used to treat and heal connective soft tissue that's become stiff and inflexible due to injury or overuse.*

When administered by a trained practitioner (usually a chiropractor or physical therapist), this approach can be highly effective at relieving joint and muscle pain and improving flexibility. This therapy often gets people back to activity faster and with longer-lasting results than other treatments.

As a chiropractor, I have used the technique for more than nine years and have achieved consistently helpful results with my patients. Nearly 7,300 clinicians in the US practice this technique.**

WHO CAN BENEFIT FROM THIS APPROACH?

Any person who suffers from musculoskeletal pain of almost any kind can potentially benefit from this treatment. It is particularly effective for chronic joint, muscle or tendon problems that never seem to fully heal, such as a sprained ankle, a sore Achilles tendon, a painful knee, tennis elbow or recurring back pain due to injury, repetitive overuse and/or chronic poor posture.

HOW IT WORKS

When a person suffers from tendon, joint or muscle pain, the cause can often be found in the connective tissue, especially in the fascia, a type of soft tissue that covers all our organs, muscles, nerves and blood vessels.

Reason: Healthy connective tissue supports our muscle-tendon system. But when connective tissue gets injured, fibrous adhesions form and make it stiff.

These adhesions prevent nearby joints or muscles from moving freely—and eventually may lead to pain even in distant parts of the body.

*The Graston Technique is a registered trademark and the instruments are patented.

**To locate a practitioner formally trained and certified in this treatment, go to *www.grastontechnique.com* and click on "Locate a Provider."

Therapeutic massage has been used for centuries to treat this type of pain. The Graston Technique, conceived in the early 1990s by athlete and machinist David Graston, is based on similar principles but uses six patented stainless steel instruments that are molded to adapt to the various tissue, shapes and curves of the body. This protocol is supported by research that has gotten published in peer-reviewed journals, including the *Journal of Bodywork and Movement Therapies* and the *Journal of Manipulative and Physiological Therapeutics*.

When the Graston Technique is applied to a ligament, tendon or section of muscle that is bound up with fibrous adhesions, the practitioner is doing more than simply "breaking up" the scar tissue. In fact, microscopic changes in the tissue are being caused so that the tissue becomes more pliable and elastic.

How it works: Normally, the connective tissue in our ligaments, tendons and muscle is being renewed all the time thanks to the activity of cells called *fibroblasts*, which continuously manufacture the chemical building blocks that allow new connective tissue to form. This process also generates new collagen, which is essential to keeping connective tissue pliable and elastic.

If connective tissue gets damaged, however, this process of renewal no longer takes place. Applying pressure on the damaged tissue with Graston instruments triggers the production of fibroblasts in the treated tissue.

Important finding: When imaging studies were used to study the Graston Technique, researchers found that the heavier the pressure, the greater the production of fibroblasts. These fibroblasts generate the growth of new, elastic collagen in the injured area.

The degree of pressure used will depend on the type of injury being treated. A recent, acutely painful injury should be treated with light pressure, which helps promote the production of anti-inflammatory chemicals.

An older, chronic condition is best treated using heavier pressure, which will speed up the renewal process by producing minor inflammation on a microscopic level to help the body heal.

Before the treatment even begins, the practitioner performs muscle testing and passive stretching to identify areas with painful adhesions. Each treatment session starts out with warm-up movements (to increase circulation to the affected area) and ends with stretching and strengthening exercises and ice to help repair the connective tissue. These exercises should also be performed at home (typically two sets of 15 repetitions twice daily).

Many of my patients have reported some reduced pain and increased mobility after one treatment. For others, it can take three or four treatments to achieve a positive response. For serious joint or muscle problems, eight to 12 treatments may be required. Patients typically have two sessions per week.

A number of insurance companies will cover treatment with the Graston Technique. The therapy is generally safe and can be used on most people—exceptions include those with open wounds, *thrombophlebitis* (inflammation of veins, usually in the legs) and uncontrolled high blood pressure.

It is common to experience minor discomfort during treatment and some bruising afterward. This is a normal response and part of the healing process. Bruising seldom lasts for more than three days.

Are the New Shape-Up Shoes for You?

Wendy Bumgardner, certified marathon coach and a walking expert for About.com, located in Vancouver, Washington. Bumgardner has walked seven marathons and thousands of miles.

Recently there have been many advertisements for the new shape-up shoes with curved soles that profess to burn more calories, tone muscles and relieve back pain. Are they any good?

These shoes will help some people, but they are not for everyone. Skechers Shape-Ups and Chung Shi shoes can provide a greater range of motion while walking, exercising muscles on both sides of the legs, burning more calo-

ries and toning muscles. Some people say that these shoes have cured their back pain—but others say that they have caused it. If you are considering these shoes, which cost $100 to $250,* plan to spend time getting used to them. Start out by wearing them for about five minutes of activity and build up gradually. Do not put them on and immediately do your normal walking routine.

Be especially cautious if you have biomechanical issues, such as a long-standing knee injury or scoliosis. Buy only from a store with a liberal policy for returns in case you develop aches, pains or backaches, and only wear the shoes indoors until you are sure that you want to keep them.

*Prices subject to change.

Coconut Water: Healthy or Hype?

Sari Greaves, RD, spokesperson, American Dietetic Association, Chicago.

Coconut water is all the rage now. But is it actually healthy? Somewhat, but it's not a cure-all. This clear liquid extracted from not-yet-ripe coconuts typically contains a single pure ingredient—coconut water. Without artificial flavors or coloring, it is more healthful than sugar-laden sodas and various juices and sports beverages. Because it is low-calorie (about 45 calories per eight ounces), low-fat and rich with the electrolyte potassium (about 480 milligrams [mg]), it has been hailed as a natural alternative to sports drinks. But when you sweat, you lose more sodium than potassium. While most sports drinks contain more sodium than potassium (110 mg and 30 mg per eight ounces, respectively), the reverse is true for coconut water (28 mg and 480 mg), making it an alternative for people who perform light and moderate exercise.

As for the claim that coconut water has antiaging powers, there is no convincing scientific evidence to back this. Potassium is crucial to healthy heart function, and adults who get adequate amounts (4,700 mg daily) have lower stroke risk. However, it may not be advisable to drink coconut water—due to its potassium content—if you have kidney disease. Consult your doctor first if you have this condition.

Yes, You Can Be Too Thin! It's a Bigger Health Risk Than Most People Realize

Gretchen E. Robinson, RD, LD, an adjunct professor at Ohio Northern University, in Ada, Ohio, and a committee member of the American Dietetic Association work group for the development of "Unintended Weight Loss in Older Adults Guideline," available at *www.adaevidence library.com*. She also is a private-practice corporate consultant to several long-term-care facilities.

The obesity epidemic in the US receives so much attention these days that few people realize just how risky it can be when a person is underweight.

While roughly 72 million American adults are considered to be overweight or obese, almost five million don't weigh enough.

Important finding: Underweight people —defined as having a *body mass index* (BMI) of less than 18.5—have an increased risk of dying from infections, postsurgical complications and other conditions than people who are a normal weight, according to an analysis of statistics from the National Health and Nutrition Examination Surveys. According to the BMI categories, any person who is five-foot-eight-inches tall, for example, and weighs 120 pounds would be considered underweight.*

WHAT IS UNDERWEIGHT?

Genes play a role in an individual's ability to gain weight, lose weight or remain thin. In some cases, however, people are too thin because of unintentional weight loss—often due to underlying health issues.

*To calculate your BMI, go to the National Heart, Lung and Blood Institute Web site, *www.nhlbisupport. com/bmi*. Discuss your BMI with your doctor—there are other measurements that also may be appropriate to help determine a healthy weight.

Examples: Depression, chewing and/or swallowing disorders, or chronic conditions, including Crohn's disease and celiac disease, that lead to digestive and malabsorption problems. Commonly used medications, including diuretics, certain painkillers, antidepressants and antibiotics, also can cause unintentional weight loss.

Important: Weight loss that's unintentional should always be evaluated by a doctor.

HEALTHY WAYS TO GAIN WEIGHT

People who are underweight should try to gain weight. This is mainly achieved by consuming more calories. To put on one to two pounds a week, a person who is underweight may need an additional 500 to 1,000 calories daily beyond what his/her body requires for weight maintenance. *Helpful...*

•**Get more fat in your diet.** Millions of Americans wisely limit their consumption of dietary fat. But that's generally not as important for people who are underweight.

My advice: To gain weight, consume more energy-dense foods, such as milk shakes made using whole milk, peanut butter, noodles and dense cereals such as granola. Foods that are high in fat have nearly twice as many calories as carbohydrates. Although it's not healthy for most people to eat foods high in fat, it could be essential for older adults and younger individuals who are underweight. If you have a chronic condition such as heart disease or diabetes, consult a registered dietitian for advice on specific food choices.

•**Drink food-supplement beverages.** They taste good, and most provide about 250 calories per eight-ounce serving—more if you use a powdered form and mix it with whole milk. High-quality protein beverages also contain a mix of nutrients that can improve immunity and wound healing.

My advice: Use these products in addition to your regular diet. Aim for two to three daily servings (an hour before or after meals). Good products include Ensure Plus, Boost High Protein, Carnation Instant Breakfast and Resource Health Shake.

•**Add flavor whenever you can.** It's normal for people to lose some taste buds with age.

Foods will often taste "flat" unless the flavors are heightened. That's why it's important to make every bite of food as appetizing as possible when you're trying to gain weight.

My advice: Season foods generously with salt-free seasonings, including fresh or dried bay leaves, basil, celery seed, garlic powder, lemon juice or Mrs. Dash, a salt-free seasoning blend.

•**Snack often.** It's generally a good idea for underweight adults to have at least six meals a day—three large meals plus three high-calorie snacks.

My advice: Snack on some breakfast cereal (use only whole milk or half-and-half), crackers with cheese, graham crackers and a glass of milk, or a sandwich that's made with two tablespoons of peanut butter and jelly, chewy granola bars, etc.

Keep plenty of healthy snacks readily available in your kitchen—this makes it easier to take in more calories daily.

•**Make mealtimes an event.** Research has shown that people who are involved in meal preparation—choosing foods and recipes, adding seasonings, etc.—consume more calories than those who have their meals prepared for them. Improving the ambiance of your dining area with good lighting and a pleasant table setting also will encourage you to eat more.

•**Dine with others.** People who eat alone may consume up to 50% fewer calories than those who dine with company. When people make eating a social event, they spend more time at the table, enjoy their food more and consume more calories.

•**Stop smoking.** Smoking suppresses the appetite and allows people to satisfy the normal "mouth function" with a cigarette rather than from eating. Many people who quit smoking put on an average of five to eight pounds within a few months.

•**Treat depression.** It is among the main causes of weight loss in adults from all ages. Those who are depressed often lose interest in many of life's pleasures, including eating.

My advice: Get professional help if you experience any of the signs of depression, which include changes in eating or sleeping habits, difficulty concentrating or feelings of hopelessness or other mood changes.

•**Start moving.** Exercise is among the most powerful of strategies for gaining weight. Even though exercise burns calories, you will make up for it with increased appetite, improvement in mood (which also increases calorie intake) and greater muscle and bone mass.

My advice: Start slowly by throwing a ball for your dog, for example, or just flexing your muscles when you sit in a chair. Work up to walking at least 30 minutes daily and, if possible, add strength and flexibility exercises a few times per week. Quite often, people will start eating more and gaining weight within a few weeks of beginning regular exercise.

Before You Start That Diet...

Older people who are overweight live longer than those of normal weight.

Recent finding: People age 70 and older who were overweight but not obese had 13% lower risk for death from all causes.

Theory: Extra fat provides a metabolic reserve, which older people need to help them recover from illness.

Leon Flicker, PhD, director, Western Australia Centre for Health and Ageing, The University of Western Australia, Perth, and leader of a study of 9,240 people, published in *Journal of the American Geriatrics Society*.

"Forbidden" Foods That Promote Weight Loss

Do not ban foods you like when dieting. Putting specific foods off limits creates a constant craving for them and makes a diet more likely to fail.

Also: Many foods that dieters try to avoid may help with weight loss.

Examples: Some breads contain complex carbohydrates, which increase brain chemicals that reduce overeating…pasta's high fluid content keeps you feeling fuller longer…potatoes contain a fiber that burns fat…dark chocolate satisfies a common craving, so eating moderate amounts can make a binge less likely.

Bottom line: Portion control and a focus on nutrient-rich foods lead to successful weight loss.

D. Milton Stokes, MPH, certified registered dietitian-nutritionist, One Source Nutrition, Stamford, Connecticut, quoted in *Prevention*.

The Tea Diet

Tea may help men lose weight. In a recent finding, men who drank more than two cups of tea a day had trimmer waistlines, on average, than men who drank coffee or other beverages.

Danielle R. Bouchard, PhD, School of Kinesiology and Health Studies, Queen's University, Kingston, Ontario, and leader of a study of 3,823 people.

A Juice for Weight Loss

Vegetable juice aids weight loss. In a recent finding, overweight adults with *metabolic syndrome*—characterized by excess fat in the midsection, high blood sugar and high blood pressure—who followed a diet rich in fruits, vegetables and whole grains lost an average of four pounds during 12 weeks when they also drank eight ounces of low-sodium vegetable juice daily. People who did not drink vegetable juice lost an average of one pound.

Possible reason: The juice—usually tomato juice mixed with juices from a variety of vegetables—may fill you up so that you eat less.

Study of 81 adults with metabolic syndrome by researchers at Baylor College of Medicine, Houston, presented at an *Experimental Biology* meeting.

Popular Snack Food Curbs Appetite

Popcorn can curb your appetite. In a recent finding, people who ate one cup of low-fat popcorn (15 calories) 30 minutes before lunch consumed 105 fewer calories throughout their meal than those who had one cup of potato chips (150 calories).

Reason: Popcorn contains more fiber and carbohydrates than potato chips, which may make it more filling.

James Rippe, MD, chairman, Center for Lifestyle Medicine, University of Central Florida, Orlando, and leader of a study presented at an Experimental Biology conference. His Web site is *www.rippehealth.com*.

Use Your Imagination

Imagine those M&Ms and you won't eat as many. A recent study found that people who imagine eating certain foods before indulging will eat less of them.

Science, www.sciencemag.org.

Powerful Peppers

Peppers may aid weight loss. In one recent study, when 33 people on a month-long liquid-meal diet took a supplement containing *dihydrocapsiate* (DCT), a substance found in sweet chili peppers, or a placebo after meals, the supplement group burned more calories (up to 160 daily).

Theory: DCT signals the brain to accelerate fat-burning.

To boost weight loss: Eat three to four sweet chili peppers daily or use chili seasoning. Or ask your doctor about DCT supplements.

David Heber, MD, professor of medicine and public health, UCLA Center for Human Nutrition, David Geffen School of Medicine at UCLA, Los Angeles.

Olive Oil vs. Butter

Did you know that olive oil has more fat than butter? Also, it has 20% more calories per tablespoon.

But: Olive oil has less unhealthy saturated fat than butter.

Bon Appétit, 4 Times Square, New York City 10036, *www.bonappetit.com*.

Study Says Junk Food as Addictive as Drugs

Junk food can be as addictive as cocaine. Rats given unlimited access to healthy foods and high-calorie snacks quickly developed a preference for the snacks and became obese. The obese rodents also had decreased levels of a *dopamine* receptor that provides a feeling of reward—similar to that found in humans addicted to nicotine, cocaine and other types of drugs.

Paul Kenny, PhD, associate professor, department of molecular therapeutics, The Scripps Research Institute, Jupiter, Florida, and researcher involved in an animal food study that was published in *Nature Neuroscience*.

Healthy Flavor Boosters

To make food taste better without adding fat or salt…

• **Use citrus**—lemons, limes and oranges—to bring out food flavors.

• **Cook with herbs**—then sprinkle on fresh herbs just before serving.

• **Try unusual spices,** such as cumin and cloves—alone or in combination—to produce varied flavors.

• **If a salad dressing or cooking liquid tastes a little flat,** add dried or fresh herbs to the dressing as well as an acid, such as lemon or vinegar, to brighten the cooking liquid.

Linda Gassenheimer, an award-winning author and food columnist in Coral Gables, Florida, *www.dinnerinminutes.com*.

Getting Thick Around the Middle? What to Do…

To prevent fat around your middle, eat a snack containing protein, fat and low-glycemic carbohydrates every day between 3 pm and 4 pm—perhaps a protein bar, such as the Simply Bar or ProteinFusion Bar…or one serving of high-protein low-fat cheese and 12 almonds. This type of snack boosts metabolism and balances blood sugar—keeping the body's insulin level lower. A lower insulin level helps protect against midbody weight gain.

Natasha Turner, ND, naturopathic doctor in Toronto, Canada, and author of *The Hormone Diet* (Rodale, *www.thehormonediet.com*).

A Vitamin That Boosts Weight Loss

In a recent study, researchers measured the blood levels of vitamin D in 38 overweight men and women before and after an 11-week diet in which they consumed 750 fewer daily calories than their estimated total caloric needs.

Result: Higher amounts of *25-hydroxycholecalciferol* (a marker of vitamin D status) were associated with greater weight loss while following the diet.

Shalamar Sibley, MD, MPH, assistant professor of medicine, division of endocrinology and diabetes, University of Minnesota Medical School, Minneapolis.

Calorie Count Deception

Do not believe calorie counts on restaurant menus or frozen meal labels.

Recent study: At 10 chain restaurants, calories in 29 meals averaged 18% higher than listed on menus. For 10 frozen supermarket meals, calories were about 8% more than labels said.

Reasons: Variations in ingredients and portion sizes.

Example: The amount of mayonnaise may vary from sandwich to sandwich.

Self-defense: Use nutrition labels as guidelines, but do not consider them to be scientifically precise.

Susan B. Roberts, PhD, professor of nutrition and professor of psychiatry, Tufts University, Boston, author of *The "i" Diet* (Workman) and leader of a study published in *Journal of the American Dietetic Association*. For more, go to *www.instinctdiet.com*.

Menu Magic

We eat less when fast-food menus include calorie counts. When calories are posted with the recommended daily caloric intake for the average adult (2,000 calories), consumers cut the calories they ate across a dinner meal and an evening snack by 14%.

Christina A. Roberto, MS, MPhil, doctoral student, department of psychology/department of epidemiology and public health at Yale University in New Haven, Connecticut, and lead author of a study of 303 people, published in *American Journal of Public Health*.

It Has How *Many* Calories?

Rebecca Shannonhouse, editor, *Bottom Line/Health*, Boardroom Inc., 281 Tresser Blvd., Stamford, Connecticut 06901.

Not long ago, when I was stuck at an airport, I stopped for a cup of coffee and a donut. I don't usually eat donuts, but I was desperate and the "old-fashioned cake" donut didn't have frosting, so it seemed a little more healthful than the other choices.

Not so! The nutritional information that was posted indicated that the old-fashioned cake donut actually had more calories and fat than the more indulgent-sounding frosted Bavarian cream-filled version that I winded up getting (and eating only half of)—320 calories versus 270…and 22 grams (g) of fat versus 15 g.

Starting this year: New federal legislation requires restaurant chains having 20 or more outlets to post such nutritional data, but not all restaurants have done so yet.

"Considering how much food we eat away from home, this action is long overdue," said Sandra Woodruff, RD, a Tallahassee, Florida–based nutritionist and author of *The Complete Diabetes Prevention Plan* (Avery Trade).

When you see this nutritional data posted for the first time, you may be very surprised by some of it. *For example, a…*

• **Burger King Veggie Burger** has 1,020 milligrams (mg) of sodium—almost half the recommended daily amount for a healthy adult.

• **Starbucks Tazo Green Tea Crème Frappuccino** (16 ounces) has 440 calories—about twice as many as in the same size Coke.

• **Taco Bell Fiesta Taco Salad** has 42 g of fat. For comparison, a typical pack of brownie minis has about 16 g of fat.

With these kinds of numbers, it's definitely worth looking before you buy.

Weight Gain While You Sleep

Even just a little light at night is related to weight gain.

Recent finding: Persistent exposure to dim light at night caused mice to gain 50% more weight than mice in a standard cycle of light and total darkness.

Theory: Mice exposed to nighttime light ate at times they normally would not eat, and their bodies did not metabolize food efficiently.

Laura Fonken, doctoral student in neuroscience at The Ohio State University in Columbus, and leader of the mouse study published in *Proceedings of the National Academy of Sciences*.

5

Natural Health Now

Learn a Word a Day and Other Fun Ways to Add *Healthy* Years to Your Life

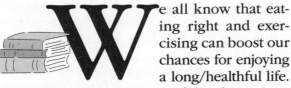

We all know that eating right and exercising can boost our chances for enjoying a long/healthful life. But sometimes it seems as if the changes we have to make to live a healthier life are simply too overwhelming. The good news is that just a few little changes can have a significant impact on our health. *Here, the fun, little changes that can make a big difference...*

• **Learn a word a day.** Pick a word out of the paper or dictionary every day. Or have a word e-mailed to you daily (*http://dictionary. reference.com/wordoftheday*). Put it on an index card and drill yourself. This type of cognitive calisthenic keeps your brain sharp.

The brain continues to regenerate nerve cells throughout life. This process, known as *neuro-genesis*, helps older adults to improve memory and other cognitive functions as they age.

Example: A 2006 study published in *The Journal of the American Medical Association* compared two groups of older adults. Those in one group were given training in memory, reasoning and mental processing. After just 10 sessions of 60 to 75 minutes each, these participants had immediate and long-lasting improvements, compared with those who didn't get the training.

If learning a word a day doesn't appeal to you, pick an activity that you enjoy and find mentally challenging.

The late Robert N. Butler, MD, president and chief executive officer of the International Longevity Center-USA. Dr. Butler was a professor of geriatrics at Brookdale Department of Geriatrics and Adult Development at Mount Sinai Medical Center in New York City. He was author of *The Longevity Prescription: The 8 Proven Keys to a Long, Healthy Life* (Avery) and won the 1976 Pulitzer Prize for his book *Why Survive? Being Old in America* (The Johns Hopkins University Press).

Examples: Reading history books, learning chess or memorizing poems. When the activity starts getting easier, move on to harder challenges.

People who do this can regain as much as two decades of memory power. In other words, someone who begins at age 70 could achieve the memory of the average 50-year-old.

•**Take a trip.** Go on a cruise or take a bus tour. Go to a reunion. All of these are wonderful ways to connect with people. Why bother? Because emotional connections add years to your life.

Example: Studies published in the last 10 years show that people in happy marriages have less heart disease and live longer than those in unhappy relationships or who are divorced or widowed. Being happily married at age 50 is a better predictor of good health at age 80 than having low cholesterol.

These same benefits happen when people maintain any close relationship—with friends, children and even pets. People who are emotionally bonded with others suffer much less depression. They also tend to have less stress and lower levels of disease-causing stress hormones. And inviting new people into your life can help you cope with the dislocations—due to death, divorce, retirement, etc.—that occur over time.

Emotional connections don't just happen—people have to work at them. Think of all the friendships that are important to you. If you are like most people, maybe a few of these relationships are active, but others have gone dormant for a variety of reasons. Ask yourself why some relationships have lapsed and what you can do to reinstate them. If you have lost touch with someone special, send an e-mail or pick up the phone.

We all have "relationship opportunities" that we can take advantage of. Talk to the stranger next to you at a concert or a sports event. If you volunteer, invite one of your coworkers for coffee.

•**Take a nap.** It's a myth that older people need less sleep than younger adults. They often do sleep less, but this is mainly because they're more likely to have physical issues, such as arthritis or the need to use the bathroom at night, that interfere with restful sleep.

People who don't get enough sleep often have declines in immune function, which can increase the risk for cancer as well as infections. They also have a higher risk for hypertension and possibly prediabetes.

A short nap—no more than 20 to 30 minutes—can make up for a bad night's sleep. But beware of excessive napping. A long nap or more than one short nap every day can ruin a good night's sleep. Napping late in the day, say, after 3:00, also can interfere with a night's sleep.

•**Climb the stairs.** It takes very little time but is a great way to get your heart and lungs working. Most exercise guidelines recommend at least 20 to 30 minutes of exercise most days of the week. That much exercise, or more, is clearly beneficial, but short amounts of activity can have a significant impact.

In a study of 5,000 people over age 70, all the participants had some physical limitations, but those who got even minimal exercise (defined as the equivalent of walking a mile at least once per week) were 55% less likely to develop more serious physical limitations (defined as severe joint pain or muscle weakness) that could compromise independence.

•**Watch the birds.** For many people, contact with the natural world has a restorative effect. Just a few minutes observing birds at a feeder or watching a sunset can restore our equilibrium. The natural world has a pace that reminds us that life does not have to be lived in a rush.

Taking a few moments to destress is worth doing because an estimated 60% of all doctor visits are for stress-related disorders.

Connecting with nature also can boost our performance. A study at Kansas State University gave 90 women a five-minute typing assignment. The researchers noticed that those who worked with a bouquet of flowers nearby outperformed those with no flowers.

•**Watch a funny movie.** A good guffaw is more complicated than most people imagine. Laughter involves 15 facial muscles, along with the lungs, larynx and epiglottis. It even seems to protect against heart disease.

A study at Loma Linda University School of Medicine found that volunteers who watched one humorous video had decreased levels of the stress hormones *cortisol* and *epinephrine*. These and other stress-related chemicals have been linked with increased inflammation and an elevated risk for heart disease and many other conditions.

Boredom May Be Lethal

When 7,524 people reported their boredom levels and were then monitored by researchers for 10 years, those with high boredom levels were 37% more likely to have died (mostly of heart disease).

Theory: Chronically bored people tend to be less happy and fulfilled. This may lead to smoking, overeating and/or drinking—all of which increase heart disease risk.

Self-defense: Consider traveling, gardening or other fulfilling pursuits. Find engaging activities near you at *www.meetup.com*, a Web site listing community groups and events.

Annie Britton, PhD, senior lecturer in epidemiology, University College London, UK.

Don't Go It Alone

Being socially isolated may be just as dangerous as obesity or smoking. This was among the conclusions of researchers who reviewed 148 studies that compared participants' frequency of social interaction with health status over an average of 7.5 years. Strong relationships with family, friends and coworkers increased likelihood of survival by 50%.

To live longer: Organize a weekly event at home…join a club…or do volunteer work.

Julianne Holt-Lunstad, PhD, associate professor of psychology, Brigham Young University, Provo, Utah.

Study Proves Praying Works

Praying helps others to heal, especially if the person praying is physically near the person being prayed for.

Recent discovery: When people with impaired vision or hearing were prayed for by individuals who were standing or sitting close enough for physical contact, their vision and hearing improved significantly.

Candy Gunther Brown, PhD, associate professor in the department of religious studies, Indiana University, Bloomington, and Michael McClymond, PhD, associate professor, theological studies, Saint Louis University, St. Louis, and coauthors of a study of proximal prayer, published in *Southern Medical Journal*.

A Top Doctor's Natural Cures: Proven to Lower Cholesterol 30%…Reduce Cancer Risk 68%…and That's Not All!

Brent A. Bauer, MD, director of the complementary and integrative medicine program and a physician in the department of internal medicine at Mayo Clinic, Rochester, Minnesota. He's also professor of medicine in the College of Medicine, Mayo Clinic, and medical editor of *Mayo Clinic Embody Health* newsletter. And, he is medical editor of *Mayo Clinic Book of Alternative Medicine* (Time Inc. Home Entertainment).

We now have hundreds of supplements and health foods to choose from. Most have not been thoroughly researched in large quantitative trials, but a few have been tested and found to work effectively—and, in many cases, without the side effects of drugs.

If you are interested in using any of these natural approaches, first talk with your doctor. He/she can help you make informed decisions based on your unique health needs.

Caution: If you are already taking a prescription medicine, don't stop taking it without your doctor's OK.

Here are the best natural remedies that the medical community has found effective...

• **Garlic,** which lowers cholesterol...and may reduce heart attack risk.

Fresh garlic as well as garlic supplements help decrease cholesterol. Many older studies found that garlic reduced both total and LDL (bad) cholesterol within four to 12 weeks, usually by about 10%. Ten percent is a modest reduction in cholesterol, but it might be enough to allow someone with slightly elevated cholesterol either to avoid medication or to take a lower dosage. However, more recent studies haven't been able to confirm these results.

Even so, studies suggest that long-term use of garlic can slow the development of *atherosclerosis* (hardening of the arteries). At least one study seems to suggest that regular use of garlic may help arteries remain more pliable as we age. And for the most part, garlic generally is considered safe. The one caveat is that it could inhibit the *aggregation* (clumping) of blood platelets, so taking garlic and an *antiplatelet* drug (such as aspirin) or an *anticoagulant* drug (such as *warfarin*) is discouraged because of a risk for bleeding.

Because garlic may inhibit the aggregation of blood platelets, it could potentially reduce the risk for heart-damaging clots—but this effect hasn't been established.

Typical dosage: Research usually involves 600 milligrams (mg) up to 900 mg of supplemental garlic daily, divided into three doses. The World Health Organization recommends two to five grams (about one to two cloves) of fresh garlic daily.

• **Green tea,** which reduces heart disease and cancer risk.

Green tea is a highly concentrated source of antioxidants, particularly *polyphenols*, such as *epigallocatechin gallate* (EGCG). Most studies show that people who drink three or more cups of green tea daily are between 25% and 35% less likely to develop heart disease than those who don't drink tea.

Tea (both green and black) also seems to protect against a variety of cancers. Researchers at the University of Minnesota School of Public Health tracked 35,369 postmenopausal women. Those who drank two or more cups of tea daily reduced their risk for digestive-tract cancers by about 68% and their risk for urinary-tract cancers by about 40%.

Asians, who typically consume much more green tea than Americans, often have significantly reduced cancer rates. It is possible that substances in tea protect DNA from carcinogenic changes and/or promote the death of cancer cells. Also, people who consume plenty of tea are not drinking as much soda and other unhealthy beverages.

Typical dosage: Three or more cups daily. Green tea also is available in extract form.

• **Probiotics,** which help prevent infections, including colds and flu.

The good bacteria that inhabit the large and small intestines do more than just aid digestion—they play an important role in immunity. These very beneficial organisms, known as *probiotics*, are thought to alter the signaling mechanisms in the intestinal wall and "switch off" inflammation throughout the body. This is important for preventing infections, including colds and flu.

In an 80-day Swedish study, volunteers given daily doses of the probiotic *Lactobacillus reuteri* were less than half as likely to require sick days (for either respiratory or gastrointestinal illnesses) as those who were taking placebos. A study of children in day-care settings showed a similar benefit.

There are many different types (and subtypes) of probiotics. The ones that have been most studied include the Lactobacillus and *Bifidobacterium* organisms.

Typical dosage: Many individuals find that food-based sources, such as the Activia and DanActive brands of yogurts and beverages, are a convenient way to try probiotics. You also can get probiotic supplements—follow directions on the label.

• **Ginger,** which fights nausea from motion sickness and chemotherapy.

A study funded by the National Cancer Institute found that patients undergoing chemotherapy experienced 40% less nausea when they took ginger. It also reduces motion sickness.

Although ginger has been used to ease the discomfort of morning sickness, I don't recommend the use of any medicinal herb during pregnancy.

Typical dosage: The optimal dosage is not known. People sometimes chew on a slice of fresh ginger. Ginger candies and ginger teas may work. Most ginger ales don't have enough ginger.

• **St. John's Wort,** which eases depression.

Some studies indicate that this herb is as effective for mild-to-moderate depression as prescription antidepressants.

New finding: A large meta-analysis, which combined the results from previous studies, found that *St. John's wort* also may be effective for severe depression.

St. John's wort is less likely than prescription antidepressants to cause side effects, although some patients may experience stomach upset, dizziness, a dry mouth, anxiety and/or sexual dysfunction.

Warning: Don't use St. John's wort and a prescription antidepressant at the same time.

Typical dosage: Most studies used 900 mg to 1,800 mg daily.

• **Fish Oil,** which lowers triglycerides...stabilizes heart rhythms...relieves arthritis.

Even many mainstream doctors now consider fish oil a first-line treatment for high triglycerides, harmful blood fats that are linked to heart disease. Most people who take fish oil for this use will have a reduction in triglycerides of 20% to 30%.

Fish oil also helps stabilize heart rhythms and has anti-inflammatory effects, which can help to reduce joint pain from arthritis.

Fish oil has a bad reputation because it is known for causing fishy-tasting burps. It also is a blood thinner. However, we have learned that these side effects tend to occur only when people take extremely high doses.

Typical dosage: 1 gram (g) to 3 g daily. Good dietary sources include cold-water fish, such as salmon, mackerel, herring, sardines and trout.

ARTHRITIS RELIEF

There are several natural remedies for joint pain. I recommend trying the combination of *glucosamine* and *chondroitin* for eight to 12 weeks. If it relieves your symptoms, continue indefinitely. If not, add *devil's claw* or *SAM-e* as a second approach. There is no strong evidence to suggest that one is superior to the other.

• **Glucosamine/chondroitin.** Glucosamine, produced from the skeletons of shellfish, and chondroitin, made out of *shark/cow cartilage* or *bovine trachea*, have been shown to work as well as *ibuprofen* and *acetaminophen* for joint pain.

Typical dosage: 1,500 mg daily of glucosamine...1,200 mg daily of chondroitin. If you are allergic to shellfish, don't take glucosamine until you talk to your doctor.

• **SAM-e.** *S-adenosylmethionine* (SAM-e) is a synthetic form of a compound naturally present in the body. SAM-e can potentially interact with antidepressants—talk with your doctor before using it if you're taking an antidepressant or St. John's wort.

Typical dosage: 600 mg to 1,200 mg, divided into three doses daily.

• **Devil's claw.** The root from this African plant contains *harpagosides*, anti-inflammatory substances that also have painkilling effects. Some patients experience stomach upset, but this is rare.

Typical dosage: 600 mg to 1,200 mg daily, with doses standardized to provide 50 mg to 100 mg of harpagosides. Take between meals.

Craving a Burger? Or Chocolate? What Your Body May Be Trying to Tell You

Fred Pescatore, MD, an internist who practices nutritional medicine in New York City and the author of *The Hamptons Diet* (Wiley). He is president of the International & American Associations of Clinical Nutritionists, *www.iaacn.org.*

It can strike when you least expect it—an overwhelming desire to satisfy a food craving. You may be desperate for a burger, cake, chocolate, pizza or some other specific food.

Even though food cravings seem harmless enough, they are often a red flag that a person's diet needs attention. Strong food cravings generally don't occur unless the body is crying out for particular nutrients—ones that can almost always be found in more healthful foods than what we may initially desire.

Five common cravings—and what each may mean...*

• **Burgers and steaks.** A craving for red meat is often a sign that you are lacking iron and/or *conjugated linoleic acid* (CLA), a fatty acid that helps your body burn stored fat.

A healthful alternative: To satisfy your body's need for iron, try dark leafy greens, such as spinach or Swiss chard. These vegetables may be a more healthful option if your diet is high in fat and carbohydrates.

An occasional steak (once per week) is OK, but try incorporating small amounts of red meat into your regular diet so you don't go overboard when you indulge this craving.

Consider adding small amounts of lean beef into your vegetable soup or a sprinkle of lean ground beef into a bean chili. Vegetarians can get CLA in butter and low-fat milk.

• **Baked goods.** If you're desperate for a rich, gooey brownie, a piece of cake or a glazed donut, your blood sugar (*glucose*) levels are probably fluctuating, often in response to surges of the stress hormone *cortisol*. Too much cortisol triggers the release of glucose, thereby causing the blood sugar–regulating hormone insulin to spike then drop precipitously.

Because baked goods are essentially sugar and carbohydrate, they provide a quick boost in energy and *serotonin* (a brain chemical that brings on feelings of happiness) when blood sugar levels are waning.

Healthful alternative: Try a piece of fruit or one glass of antioxidant-rich pomegranate juice. These natural sources of sugar provide

*If you continue to crave a certain food, consider getting tested for deficiencies in vitamins A, B-12, D and folic acid (these tests have been clinically proven, whereas the accuracy of other types of nutritional deficiency tests is questionable).

nutrients that baked goods can't, such as vitamin C. To stem your craving for carbohydrates, consider trying the dietary supplement *chromium picolinate* (200 micrograms [mcg], three times daily).

Caution: Discuss with your doctor if you have diabetes. Chromium picolinate may alter drug requirements.

Physical activity, such as walking, also will allow your body to use up some of the excess cortisol. Exercise activates the body's relaxation response to maintain healthy cortisol levels.

• **Chocolate.** People who yearn for chocolate may be deficient in *phenylalanine*, an essential amino acid that's found in chocolate that the body converts into yet another amino acid, *tyrosine*. Tyrosine plays a key role in the production of the brain chemicals *dopamine* and *serotonin*, which enhance mood and reduce pain. You may also crave chocolate when you need an energy boost.

Healthful strategy: Eat dark chocolate or cocoa powder with at least 75% cacao. Limit amounts of lighter chocolates, which contain more sugar and less cacao. Avoid all chocolate if you have *phenylketonuria*, a condition in which the body cannot process the phenylalanine found in chocolate.

Another option: Mix unsweetened cocoa powder with skim milk to taste (or follow the instructions on the cocoa powder container). Add the all-natural sugar substitute stevia and/or top with a small amount of whipped cream.

• **French fries.** A craving for fries usually means your body is lacking sodium and/or *serotonin* or experiencing a blood sugar imbalance caused by high levels of *cortisol*.

The simple carbohydrates in potatoes break down into glucose, boosting your energy and serotonin levels. The salt used on fries satisfies your need for sodium, and the oil used for frying helps keep you satiated.

Healthful alternative: Consuming about 20 salted nuts (two ounces)—such as almonds, pecans or walnuts—each day provides healthful omega-3s and sodium. (People with high blood pressure should only eat unsalted nuts.) Nuts also provide a sustained glucose boost that helps stabilize blood sugar. A diet rich in proteins, vegetables, fruits and whole grains will naturally keep cravings for greasy, high-fat foods at bay.

•**Pizza.** A craving for pizza usually means that you could be low in calcium (which is found in the cheese) and/or lacking in essential fatty acids (which are found in the cheese and olive oil).

Healthful alternative: Create your own pizza with a whole-grain crust, organic low-fat cheese, fresh tomatoes and veggies. Try adding to your diet more foods that are rich in essential fatty acids, including walnuts, avocado, flaxseed and fatty fish, such as salmon.

What Body Odors Reveal About Your Health

Kevin Wilson, ND, a naturopathic physician in private practice in Hillsboro, Oregon. He is an adjunct professor of naturopathic medicine at the National College of Natural Medicine in Portland and vice-speaker of the House of Delegates for the American Association of Naturopathic Physicians.

Almost everyone has an occasional bout with bad breath, body odor or awful-smelling flatulence. While these odors can be embarrassing, they usually are not a sign of a serious health problem.

But in some cases, body odors are symptoms of a health problem and warrant medical attention—especially if the smell is new or offensive to yourself or others.

Five common body odors you should not ignore…

EXTREMELY SMELLY SWEAT

Sweating eliminates toxins from your body, so it's normal for it to cause some odor. However, particularly bad-smelling sweat may be due to problems digesting dietary fats (causing a rancid odor) or a magnesium deficiency (producing a locker-room smell). In some people, the odor may be related to a yeast or bacterial infection of the skin (causing a yeasty or sickeningly sweet smell).

Kidney or liver failure may cause sweat to smell like ammonia.

My advice: Boost your overall intake of vegetables and other high-fiber foods, such as flaxseed meal or apples. Fiber soaks up toxins and helps eliminate poorly digested fats that can cause body odor.

To improve levels of magnesium, increase your intake of green vegetables, such as broccoli and kale, and reduce your consumption of sugar. Too much sugar not only decreases magnesium, but also feeds any odor-causing yeast that may be lurking in your body. Stress and alcohol also can deplete magnesium, so try to minimize both. If you believe that you may need more magnesium, ask your doctor about taking a magnesium supplement.

If these steps don't help within a few days, see your doctor.

BAD BREATH

Coffee and garlic, as well as poor dental hygiene, are known to cause bad breath. Dehydration or a dry mouth also can be the culprit.

In some people, bad breath occurs when stomach acid is depleted due to a deficiency of zinc or *thiamine* (vitamin B-1). Even being very anxious or nervous—which triggers the release of stress hormones, such as *cortisol*—can make your breath smell bad.

Very few people realize that acid-suppressing drugs, such as *esomeprazole* (Nexium) and *omeprazole* (Prilosec), can result in breath that smells putrid. Without enough stomach acid, food ferments in the gut. People with lactose intolerance also have bad breath if they consume dairy products.

Bad breath with a fruity smell may be a sign of diabetes. The fruity scent occurs because fats and protein are burned rather than glucose.

Breath with a fishy smell may indicate liver failure, while breath that smells like ammonia may occur in late stages of kidney failure.

My advice: Brush your teeth twice a day and floss daily. If your gums are swollen, red or tender, you may have gum disease, so be sure to see a dentist.

Also, make sure that you're drinking enough water, so that you don't get dehydrated.

To determine how much water you need: Divide your body weight in half and convert it to ounces. For example, someone who weighs 150 pounds should drink 75 ounces of water daily.

If you suspect a zinc or thiamine deficiency, eat more zinc-rich foods, such as lean meats, seafood and pumpkin seeds, as well as foods that contain thiamine, such as oatmeal, oranges and green peas.

For occasional bad breath: Drink green tea—it contains plant compounds known as polyphenols, which help fight the odor.

If you've been taking an acid-suppressing drug, talk to your doctor about using digestive enzymes or apple cider vinegar (one teaspoon to one tablespoon in a few ounces of water) with meals.

If these steps don't improve your bad breath within a few days, talk to your doctor. If your breath has a fruity or fishy smell, visit your doctor immediately to rule out diabetes and liver failure, respectively.

FOUL-SMELLING FLATULENCE

Extremely foul-smelling flatulence may be due to poor absorption of dietary fats. This is most often caused by insufficient amounts of pancreatic enzymes or a lack of bile to help with the digestive process.

In people who take acid-suppressing medication for heartburn, the odor may be due to a lack of stomach acid, since food takes longer to work its way through the digestive tract and may not even fully digest.

The smell also may be a sign of *dysbiosis*, an imbalance of bacteria in the intestines caused from the use of antibiotics or by the ingestion of contaminated foods, such as poorly cooked meats. Taking antibiotics kills the good and bad bacteria in the body, allowing bacterial infections when the bad bacteria overwhelm the good.

My advice: When you eat, chew your food until it's essentially liquefied. The *amylase* produced in your saliva from chewing enhances

the breakdown of food so it is more likely to be thoroughly digested.

Also, ask your doctor about taking an over-the-counter pancreatic enzyme that contains amylase, *protease* and *lipase*. These enzymes help the body break down food much more effectively.

To restore stomach acid, try taking 180 mg of the digestive aid hydrochloric acid with each meal or drink a vinegar-and-water mixture.

If you're on an antibiotic, ask your doctor about taking one to four probiotic capsules (such as *lactobacillus acidophilus* and/or *bifidobacterium bifidus*) daily for at least a week after completing the antibiotic course to restore the healthful bacteria to your gut.

If these solutions don't work within a few days, see your doctor. A stool analysis may be necessary to rule out a bacterial infection.

STRANGE-SMELLING URINE

If your urine doesn't smell normal, it may be due to a ***urinary tract infection*** (UTI).

Note: Eating asparagus causes a harmless and temporary change in the smell of urine.

My advice: For urinary tract infections, I sometimes prescribe antibiotics or recommend herbs, such as *uva ursi*, *goldenseal*, *echinacea*, *Oregon grape* and/or *usnea* in a combination product (usually 250-milligram [mg] to 500-mg capsules) taken four times daily. Cranberry extract, two capsules taken three to four times a day, also helps.

To help prevent UTIs, I recommend taking *D-mannose*, a nondigestible sugar that inhibits disease-causing bacteria from adhering to urinary tract cells, and/or cranberry capsules. Make sure that you also drink enough water.

BAD FOOT ODOR

Smelly feet often result from a bacterial or fungal infection, such as athlete's foot.

My advice: Bacterial infection may require an antibiotic, while a fungal infection might clear up with the use of an over-the-counter antifungal cream containing *miconazole*, or, if that doesn't work, a prescription antifungal.

See your doctor if the skin on your feet is broken, scaly or inflamed (a red color may be present). These may be signs of a foot infection. If wounds don't heal, you may have diabetes.

Home remedies that help eliminate foot odor: Soak your feet in a quart of lukewarm water that contains one tablespoon of vinegar. Soaking your feet for at least 30 minutes a day for a few weeks will usually take care of the problem.

Another option is to rub your feet with a menthol vapor rub, such as Vicks Vaporub, which contains essential oils with antiseptic properties.

If the smell persists after a couple of weeks, talk to your doctor.

Grill Safely to Reduce Cancer Risk: A Simple Marinade Can Reduce Toxins by 90%

Karen Collins, RD, a registered dietitian, syndicated columnist and nutrition adviser to the American Institute for Cancer Research, Washington, DC. She was the expert reviewer for the Institute's international report, "Diet, Nutrition, Physical Activity and the Prevention of Cancer: A Global Perspective." Her online site is *www.karencollinsnutrition.com.*

Grilling can be among the healthiest of cooking types because it gives foods a delicious flavor while using little or no added fat. But grilling also can produce toxic compounds.

Recent study: Researchers from University of Minnesota analyzed data on the cooking methods, amount of meat eaten and the doneness of meat for nearly 63,000 participants. They reported that those who preferred their steaks well-done and who used grilling and other high-heat cooking methods were about 60% more likely to develop pancreatic cancer than those who cooked their meat at a lower temperature and/or for less time.

Other studies have confirmed that the high heats used in grilling increase the risk for a variety of cancers, including cancers of the colon and rectum.

Example: A recent study based on data from the Ontario Cancer Registry found that people who ate well-done red meat more than twice a week had a 57% higher risk of developing colon cancer than those who ate their meat medium or rare.

To reduce cancer risk, it is always wise to limit your intake of red meat to no more than 18 ounces (cooked) each week and minimize consumption of processed meats, such as hot dogs, bacon and sausage. *There also are simple steps to take to reduce grilling dangers...*

TOO HOT, TOO LONG

Grills that burn gas, briquettes or hardwood charcoal easily can climb to temperatures of 500°F or more...covered ceramic grills can exceed 1,000°F. High heats are ideal for searing meats and sealing in the juices, but prolonged cooking at high temperatures produces dangerous chemical by-products. *These include...*

• **Heterocyclic amines (HCAs),** which form when animal proteins, including the proteins in meat, chicken and fish, are cooked at very high temperatures for extended periods. "The Report on Carcinogens," produced by the National Toxicology Program, now lists IQ (one type of HCA) as a compound reasonably anticipated to cause cancer.

• **Polycyclic aromatic hydrocarbons (or PAHs),** which are formed when the fat from cooking meat drips onto a heat source (such as hot coals or metal or ceramic "smoke bars") and creates a smoky flare-up. Like HCAs, PAHs are thought to be potent carcinogens.

• **Advanced glycation end products,** chemical compounds that might increase the risk for cancer. They are produced at higher levels when foods are cooked at hot temperatures for prolonged periods.

SAFER GRILLING

Take the following steps to reduce risk...

• **Marinate.** Meat that is marinated for as little as 15 to 20 minutes prior to grilling produces up to 90% less HCAs than unmarinated meat. We do not know why this happens. It might be because the acidic ingredients used in marinades, such as lemon juice and vinegar, change the molecular structure of meat protein and inhibit HCA production.

• **Season with spices.** Meats that are coated with antioxidant herbs and spices, such as rosemary, turmeric, ginger and cumin, as well as garlic, produce fewer HCAs during grilling than unseasoned meats. Again, we're not sure why.

• **Cook cooler.** For cancer prevention, the temperature of your grill is more important than the time on the grill. One study found that meats cooked at a lower-than-usual temperature, but for two minutes longer, had only about one-third of the HCAs as meat that was cooked at a higher temperature for a shorter time and to the same doneness.

After searing the meat, move it to a cooler part of the grill...or raise the grill rack a few inches so that the meat is farther from the heat. With gas grills, you can use the high-heat setting to quickly sear the meat, then lower the flames for slower cooking.

• **Minimize the cooking time.** All meat that is cooked rare, medium-rare or medium will produce significantly lower amounts of HCAs than meat that is well-done. When grilling a medium-rare steak, the internal temperature should be 145°F—that's hot enough to kill disease-causing microorganisms but cool enough to limit the production of HCAs.

A steak cooked to medium-doneness will be 160°F inside.

Important: Always cook poultry to an internal temperature of 165°F to kill salmonella and other organisms.

You also can shorten cooking time by precooking in a microwave or an oven. Do this with foods such as chicken and ribs. I wouldn't recommend it for burgers or steak, though, because precooking removes some of the juices that make these foods flavorful.

• **Cut meat into small pieces before grilling.** Chunks of beef and pork (when making kebabs, for example) will cook more quickly than a whole steak or roast, which will reduce the level of HCAs.

• **Cook lean to avoid flare-ups.** Slicing off all the visible fat from meats before grilling reduces fatty flare-ups and the production of

PAHs. Also, avoid fatty cuts of meat (such as rib-eye steak), and select lean beef when making hamburgers.

• **Avoid smoking foods.** People often use mesquite or other types of wood chips when grilling and smoking meats. The smoke that's produced by these chips may increase cancer risks.

• **Use more vegetables.** HCAs are produced only when animal proteins are subjected to high-heat cooking...and PAHs are produced by fat drippings.

You can avoid both risks by grilling vegetables, such as onions, broccoli, mushrooms, zucchini, eggplant and peppers. A little olive oil brushed on veggies before grilling is fine.

By shifting the balance in a meal to a smaller portion of meat, fish or poultry and adding more vegetables, there are two benefits—less meat automatically means less of meat's cell-damaging compounds, and more plant foods means more of the protective phytochemicals that inactivate those compounds.

A Sweet Cancer Fighter!

Sweet potatoes contain *carotenoids*, including *beta-carotene*, which help lower risk for cardiovascular disease.

Also: According to a study, a diet including three or more servings a week of carotenoid-rich vegetables, such as sweet potatoes, is associated with as much as a 57% reduced risk for stomach cancer. Sweet potatoes are rich in dietary fiber...and they are a good source of vitamins A, B and C.

Best: Store sweet potatoes in a dry, unrefrigerated bin. Scrub them and trim woody portions before baking, broiling, roasting or microwaving.

Environmental Nutrition, 800 Connecticut Ave., Norwalk, Connecticut 06854, *www.environmentalnutrition. com*.

Berries Can Reduce Cancer Risk Up To 40%

Lab animals exposed to carcinogens and then given berry extracts were 25% to 40% less likely to develop cancer than animals given their normal diets.

Cancer Prevention News, www.cancerpreventionnews. com.

Medical Marijuana: When It May Help

Donald I. Abrams, MD, a professor of clinical medicine at the University of California, San Francisco, School of Medicine, chief of hematology and oncology at San Francisco General Hospital and president of the Society for Integrative Oncology. He has conducted clinical research on medical marijuana and other integrative approaches for treating cancer-related symptoms. He is the editor, with Andrew Weil, MD, of *Integrative Oncology* (Oxford University).

While the medicinal use of *cannabis* (more commonly known as marijuana) remains controversial in many parts of the US, researchers are discovering more about the plant's ability to help improve a variety of conditions.

Most recent development: Early in 2011, Delaware joined 15 states and Washington, DC, in approving medical marijuana for individuals with chronic or debilitating diseases that cause pain, nausea, vomiting, loss of appetite and other serious symptoms.*

What you need to know...

MARIJUANA AS MEDICINE

Medical marijuana is not the same as the prescription drug *dronabinol* (Marinol), which is derived from one of the plant's active compounds, *delta-9-tetrahydrocannabinol* (THC).

*Marijuana is approved for medicinal use in Alaska, Arizona, California, Colorado, Delaware, Hawaii, Maine, Michigan, Montana, Nevada, New Jersey, New Mexico, Oregon, Rhode Island, Vermont, Washington and Washington, DC.

Marinol was approved by the FDA in 1985 for cancer patients whose nausea and vomiting did not respond to conventional treatments. In 1992, the drug was approved for loss of appetite due to AIDS wasting syndrome.

Though Marinol is widely available now, it contains just *one* of marijuana's estimated 70 compounds known as *cannabinoids*. And for this reason, some researchers believe that it is important to investigate the medicinal use of marijuana—its many other cannabinoids may offer significant benefits beyond those conferred by THC alone.

However, marijuana has also been widely utilized as a recreational drug, and it remains illegal or "decriminalized" (regulated but not banned) in most parts of the world when used for this purpose.

Even now, when state laws permit the use of medical marijuana, federal law does not. Because of this, physicians can recommend marijuana for certain medical conditions (such as cancer, chronic pain and glaucoma) for which medicinal use of the plant has been approved by state legislatures. In these cases, the physician will generally write a letter that permits patients to access medical marijuana from the dispensary.

The legal and political issues surrounding medical marijuana have prevented it from being studied in the same ways that other medications are researched in the US. However, the Institute of Medicine (IOM), an independent organization that provides unbiased scientific opinions to government agencies, did issue an important analysis on medical marijuana.

Landmark report: The IOM concluded in 1999 that chemical compounds in marijuana, particularly cannabinoids, seem to have therapeutic value in treating...

•**Appetite loss, nausea and pain.** Cancer sufferers who undergo chemotherapy frequently experience nausea, pain, insomnia and/or depression. All of these symptoms can be treated separately using prescription drugs, but combining the drugs often results in drug-drug interactions. With marijuana, some patients have relief without this risk.

•**Nerve-related pain.** Research published in the *Journal of Pain* found that patients who smoked marijuana had less nerve-related pain from spinal cord injuries or other conditions.

•**Neurological conditions.** Some patients with multiple sclerosis who smoke marijuana report that they have less pain and fewer/less intense muscle spasms. Patients with seizure disorders may do better when they combine marijuana with antiseizure medications.

•**Glaucoma.** Marijuana has been found to help reduce eye pressure caused by glaucoma and is approved for this purpose in several of the states that permit its use.

USING MARIJUANA SAFELY

Marijuana is unlikely to cause serious side effects—but, like any drug, it's not appropriate for everyone. *Marijuana may...*

•**Decrease blood pressure and increase heart rate.** For this reason, it may not be appropriate for people with a medical history of heart problems.

•**Produce unwanted sedation.** The use of marijuana might increase confusion in older adults with cognitive difficulties. Similarly, it shouldn't be used when driving or operating machinery.

Many people do wonder about the potential health risks of smoking marijuana, but there's no evidence that the small amounts used for medicinal purposes are likely to increase the odds for lung cancer and serious respiratory diseases.

Best ways to use marijuana...

•**Choose your method of delivery wisely.** Some patients choose to eat marijuana—in the form of brownies or other prepared foods—rather than inhale it. However, there are some potential problems when marijuana is eaten.

Taken by mouth, marijuana takes two hours or longer to reach peak concentrations in the blood. Patients who don't feel the effects right away tend to eat a little more—and then discover that they have taken too much. Signs of taking too much include confusion, paranoia and dizziness.

Caution: When it's eaten, the patient's liver creates a *metabolite* that can accentuate the plant's *psychoactive* effect.

Inhaled marijuana, on the other hand, reaches peak levels in the bloodstream within two to two-and-a-half minutes. Because the effects happen so quickly, patients can readily adjust the dose by inhaling more or less.

•**Consider using a "vaporizer."** Some patients use devices that heat, but don't actually burn, marijuana. Vapors go into a bag and can be extracted only through the mouthpiece. We've found in studies that fewer noxious gases are inhaled when marijuana is vaporized as opposed to smoked.

•**Be cautious with dosing.** Go slowly. Because the potency varies by plant, marijuana can't be standardized in the same ways that medications are standardized in a laboratory. In addition, a patient's sensitivity to marijuana will partly depend on his/her genetic make-up. I recommend patient-titrated dosing—try a small amount...see how you feel...then increase/decrease the dose as needed.

Eat Your Way to Low Cholesterol: Surprising Superfood Cuts Heart Attack Risk 35%

Kenneth H. Cooper, MD, MPH, founder of The Cooper Institute, Dallas. A leading expert on preventive medicine and the health benefits of exercise, he is author of *Controlling Cholesterol the Natural Way* (Bantam). For more, go to *www.cooperaerobics.com*.

If you have high cholesterol, your primary objective should be to find a way to lower it without drugs and their side effects. The good news is that just eating the right foods often can reduce cholesterol by 50 points or more.

Most people know to eat a low-fat diet, but there are certain foods that can help lower cholesterol that may surprise you...

MACADAMIA NUTS

Macadamia nuts are among the fattiest of plant foods on the planet, about 76% total fat by weight. However, practically all of the fat is *monounsaturated.* This type of fat is ideal because it lowers LDL (bad) cholesterol without depressing HDL (good) cholesterol.

A team from Hawaii University found that study participants who added macadamia nuts to their diets for just one month had total cholesterol levels of 191 milligrams/deciliter (mg/dL), compared with those eating the typical American diet (201 mg/dL). The greatest effect was on LDL cholesterol.

Macadamia nuts are higher than other nuts in monounsaturated fat, but all nuts are high in vitamin E, omega-3 fatty acids and other antioxidants. Results from the Harvard Nurses' Health Study found that participants who ate at least five ounces of any kind of nut weekly were 35% less likely to develop heart attacks than those who ate less than one ounce per month.

Caution: Moderation is important because nuts—macadamia, in particular—are high in calories. Limit your servings to between one and two ounces daily—about a small handful a day.

RHUBARB

Rhubarb is ideal for both digestive health and lowering cholesterol because it contains a mix of soluble (see "Oats" later in this article) and insoluble fibers.

A study reported in *Journal of the American College of Nutrition* reported that participants who ate a little less than three ounces of rhubarb daily for four weeks had an average drop in LDL cholesterol of 9%.

This tart-tasting vegetable isn't only an ingredient in pies. You can cut and simmer the stalks and serve rhubarb as a nutritious side dish (add some low-calorie strawberry jam for a touch of sweetness).

RICE BRAN

It's not as well-known for lowering cholesterol as oats and oat bran, but rice bran is just about as effective and some people do enjoy it more. A six-week study at University of California, Davis Medical Center found that people who ate three ounces daily of a product with rice bran had drops in total cholesterol of 8.3% and a reduction in LDL of 13.7%.

You can buy rice bran in most supermarkets—it's prepared like oatmeal. Or you can try prepared rice-bran breakfast cereals, such as Quaker Rice Bran Cereal and Kenmei Rice Bran.

RED YEAST RICE

Made from a yeast that grows on rice, red yeast rice contains *monacolins*, helpful compounds that inhibit the body's production of cholesterol.

One study found that people who took red yeast rice supplements and did nothing else had drops in LDL of 23%. When the supplements were combined with healthy lifestyle changes, their LDL dropped by about 42%.

Red yeast rice may be less likely than statins to cause the side effect *myopathy* (a painful muscle disease).

Recommended dose: 600 milligrams (mg), twice daily. It is available online and at health-food stores.

GREEN TEA

Green tea is a concentrated source of polyphenols, which are among the most potent antioxidants. It can lower LDL cholesterol and prevent it from turning into plaque deposits in blood vessels. In one study, men who drank five cups of green tea daily had total cholesterol levels that were nine points lower than men who didn't drink green tea.

Three to five cups daily are probably optimal. Black tea also contains polyphenols but in lower concentrations than green tea.

VITAMINS C AND E

These vitamins help prevent cholesterol in the blood from oxidizing. Oxidized cholesterol is more likely to cling to artery walls and promote the development of *atherosclerosis*, the cause of most heart attacks.

I advise patients with high cholesterol to take at least 400 international units (IU) of *d-alpha-tocopherol*, the natural form of vitamin E, daily. You might need more if you engage in any activities that increase oxidation, such as smoking.

For vitamin C, take 1,000 mg daily. People who get the most vitamin C are from 25% to 50% less likely to die from cardiovascular disease than those who get smaller amounts.

THE BIG THREE

In addition to the above, some foods have long been known to reduce cholesterol, but they are so helpful that they bear repeating again…

• **Cholesterol-lowering margarines.** I use Benecol every day, a margarine that contains *stanol esters*, cholesterol-lowering compounds that are extracted from plants such as soy and pine trees. About 30 grams (g) of Benecol (the equivalent of about three to four pats of butter) daily will lower LDL by about 14%.

Similar products, such as Promise Buttery Spread, contain sterol esters. Like stanols, they help block the passage of cholesterol from the digestive tract into the bloodstream. We used to think that sterols weren't as effective as stanols for lowering cholesterol, but they appear to have comparable benefits.

• **Oats.** They are among the most potent of *nutraceuticals*, natural foods with medicine-like properties. Both oat bran and oatmeal are high in soluble fiber. This type of fiber dissolves and forms a gel-like material in the intestine. The gel binds to cholesterol molecules, which prevents them from entering the bloodstream. A Harvard study that analyzed the results of 67 scientific trials found that even a small amount of soluble fiber per day lowered their total cholesterol five points. People who eat a total of 7 g to 8 g of soluble fiber daily typically see drops of up to 10%. One and a half cups of cooked oatmeal provides 6 g of fiber. If you don't like oatmeal, try homemade oat bran muffins. Soluble fiber also is found in such foods as kidney beans, apples, pears, barley and prunes.

Also helpful: *Psyllium*, a grain that's used in some breakfast cereals, such as Kellogg's All-Bran Bran Buds, and in products such as Metamucil. As little as 3 g to 4 g of psyllium daily can lower LDL by up to 20%.

• **Fish.** People who eat two to three servings of fish a week will have significant drops in both LDL and triglycerides, another marker for cardiac risk. One large study found that people who ate fish as little as once a week reduced their risk for a sudden, fatal heart attack by 52%.

I have salmon, tuna, herring and sardines. Other good sources of omega-3 fatty acids include walnuts, ground flaxseed, tofu and canola oil.

Fish-oil supplements may provide similar protection, but they are not as effective as the natural food, which contains other beneficial nutrients as well.

Low-Carb vs. Low-Fat: What's Best for High Cholesterol?

Low-carb diets are better for reducing cholesterol than low-fat ones.

Recent finding: People on either a low-carb or a low-fat diet lost about 15 pounds—but those on the low-carb regimen had a 23% increase in HDL (good) cholesterol, compared with a 12% improvement for those on the low-fat diet. The low-carb group was allowed as many calories as they desired from fats and protein, but their carb intake was limited to 20 grams (g) per day in the form of low-glycemic-index vegetables, gradually increasing by 5 g per week. They also were allowed fruits and small quantities of dairy. The low-fat diet consisted of a limited caloric intake of up to 1,500 calories each day for women and 1,800 per day for men, with no more than 30% of calories from fat.

Gary Foster, PhD, director of the Center for Obesity Research and Education, Temple University, Philadelphia, and leader of a study of 307 adults, published in *Annals of Internal Medicine.*

Tasty Nuts Reduce Cholesterol

Pistachios contain healthy fats and are rich in plant *sterols*, which inhibit cholesterol absorption. These nuts also are high in antioxidants—even higher than other nuts. Substituting one or two one-and-a-half-ounce servings of pistachios a day for fatty meats or other sources of saturated fat can lower LDL (bad) cholesterol by 10% to 12%.

Penny M. Kris-Etherton, PhD, Distinguished Professor of Nutrition, department of nutritional sciences, Penn State University, University Park, Pennsylvania, and leader of a study published in *The Journal of Nutrition*.

Natural Alternative to Statins Works Just as Well

Ram Y. Gordon, MD, cardiologist, Chestnut Hill Hospital, Flourtown, Pennsylvania.

In one recent study of 62 adults (average age 61) who had stopped taking their cholesterol-lowering statin medication (such as *atorvastatin* [Lipitor], *rosuvastatin* [Crestor] or *lovastatin* [Mevacor]) because of muscle aches (one possible side effect from statins), patients took supplements of red yeast rice (three 600-milligram [mg] capsules twice daily) or placebo capsules for six months.

Result: LDL "bad" cholesterol levels dropped by an average of 35 milligrams/deciliter (mg/dL) in the red yeast rice group (a reduction comparable to that typically provided by a low-to-moderate dose statin), compared with an average decrease of 15 mg/dL in the placebo group.

Theory: Red yeast rice contains statin-like compounds that can inhibit production of LDL cholesterol in the liver and may be better tolerated than statin drugs. Side effects of red yeast rice are rare but include headache, dizziness, intestinal gas and bloating.

Self-defense: If you have experienced muscle pain due to statins, ask your doctor whether red yeast rice supplements would be appropriate for you. Do not take red yeast rice if you have liver disease, are pregnant or have a history of inflammatory muscle disease, a disorder that causes muscle weakness and pain.

Salt Is Even Worse Than You Thought: Just a *Little Less* a Day Can Help You Live Longer

Mark Houston, MD, associate clinical professor of medicine at Vanderbilt University School of Medicine, director of the Hypertension Institute and staff physician at the Vascular Institute of Saint Thomas Hospital, all in Nashville. He is a member of the American Heart Association Council on Atherosclerosis, Thrombosis and Vascular Biology and author of *Handbook of Hypertension* (Wiley).

You know salt is bad for you, but you may not realize just how unhealthful it can be.

Fact: A diet that is high in salt is almost guaranteed to raise blood pressure. Hypertension is a leading trigger for heart disease, kidney disease and stroke. And even in people with normal blood pressure, excessive salt stiffens the arteries and increases the odds for heart enlargement, heart failure and other cardiovascular and kidney diseases.

The problem is that salt attracts water. A high-salt diet will pull water into the bloodstream. This increases the blood volume and forces the heart to pump harder.

A NATIONAL THREAT

In January 2011, the American Heart Association urged federal officials to adopt a new recommended upper limit for salt of 1,500 milligrams (mg) a day. Most Americans consume more than double that amount. Some Americans consume up to 10,000 mg daily.

Also, the American Heart Association, along with health agencies in New York City and elsewhere, is promoting a campaign (the National Salt Reduction Initiative) to reduce the amount of salt in packaged and restaurant foods by 25% over five years. That is a good start, but it's far from enough.

LIVE LONGER

The average adult who reduces his/her salt intake to the recommended level can expect to have a reduction in *systolic blood pressure* (top number) of six to seven points and a reduction in *diastolic pressure* (bottom number) of three to four points. For patients who have mild-to-moderate hypertension, that might be enough by itself to achieve healthy blood pressure. For those with higher pressure who are taking medication, a lower-salt diet could allow them to take a lower dose.

A recent study conducted by researchers at Harvard Medical School and other institutions found that people with slightly elevated blood pressure who reduced their salt intake by 25% to 30% were about 25% less likely to have a heart attack or stroke 10 to 15 years later than those who didn't curtail salt. On average, the participants who reached healthier blood pressure reduced their salt intake by only about one teaspoon daily.

HOW MUCH DO YOU NEED?

To be clear, we all need some salt. It contains sodium, an *electrolyte* that aids in the transmission of nerve impulses, it controls muscle contractions and it helps maintain healthy hydration and blood pressure. The body doesn't make salt, so you need to get it from foods.

However, no one needs more than 500 mg of sodium per day. In other words, the recommended amount is the *upper limit*. The less sodium you consume, the better—it would be very difficult in the US to consume too little salt. The kidneys are very efficient at retaining sodium—a little goes a long way.

SALT SENSITIVITY

An even lower sodium intake is essential for those who are salt-sensitive. About 26% of Americans with normal blood pressure, and up to 58% of people with hypertension, exhibit rapid rises in blood pressure even when they have small amounts of salt. These people should try to consume less than 1,500 mg of sodium daily.

There isn't a test for sensitivity to sodium. Those who are most likely to have it include people 55 years old or older…African Americans…and those with metabolic syndrome, a combination of disorders that includes insulin resistance, a high waist circumference (central obesity) and other factors.

POTASSIUM HELPS

One way to reduce the effects of a high-sodium diet on blood pressure is to consume more potassium. It can lower blood pressure almost as much as decreasing sodium.

Try to get at least two times more potassium in your diet than sodium. If you take in 2,000 mg of sodium a day, aim for 4,000 mg or more of potassium. In societies with a higher potassium-to-sodium ratio—where people consume three or even four times more potassium than sodium—the rate of hypertension is far lower than in the US.

High-potassium foods include fruits, vegetables, beans and low-fat dairy products.

Examples of potassium-rich foods (these are one-cup servings unless otherwise noted)…

- **Apricots (dried) 10 halves, 407 mg.**
- **Banana (raw), 594 mg.**
- **Beans (baked), 752 mg.**
- **Beets (cooked), 519 mg.**
- **Cantaloupe, 494 mg.**
- **Milk, skim, 407 mg.**
- **Orange juice, 496 mg.**
- **Potato (one average potato, baked), 1,081 mg.**
- **Raisins, ½ cup, 544 mg.**
- **Spinach (cooked), 839 mg.**
- **Tomato sauce, 909 mg.**

Caution: If you have kidney disease, talk to your doctor about the amount of potassium that is safe for you.

HOW TO CUT BACK

About 70% of the salt in our diets comes from packaged foods and foods prepared in restaurants. The McDonald's Double Cheeseburger, for example, contains 1,150 mg of sodium. A typical frozen dinner contains nearly 800 mg, and even a bowl of raisin bran might contain more than 340 mg. The most effective strategy is to avoid processed foods and prepare low-salt meals at home.

About 30% of the salt that Americans consume is added at the table or during cooking. Some people can train their taste buds to enjoy less salty foods, but many people can't.

My advice: Use potassium chloride instead of the usual sodium chloride. Different brands, such as NoSalt, are available. The taste is very close to regular table salt.

Bonus: The potassium helps counteract the effects of sodium elsewhere in the diet.

IS SEA SALT HEALTHIER?

Companies promote sea salt as a healthier choice than table salt. Don't believe it. Regular table salt is almost pure sodium chloride. Typical sea salt contains about 55% chloride, 31% sodium, 4% magnesium and 1% potassium, along with trace amounts of other minerals. That sounds healthier than table salt, but it's still 86% sodium chloride. The difference is insignificant.

EXERCISE IS NOT AN EXCUSE

Many people think that they need more salt when they exercise or on hot days when they perspire heavily. The sports-beverage industry has made a fortune from this widespread belief. It is not true. During exercise, the body actually retains sodium in the sweat glands. The minerals that are lost in perspiration are mainly potassium and magnesium, not sodium. You don't need a sodium-spiked beverage to replace fluids. Just drink more water.

Wonderful Walnuts

Walnuts lower blood pressure. In a recent finding, after consuming 18 walnut halves and taking one tablespoon of walnut oil daily during six weeks, study participants had lower pressure when exposed to a variety of stressors than participants who did not consume walnuts and walnut oil. Healthful *omega-3 fatty acids* in walnuts are likely responsible for lowering the body's stress response.

Sheila G. West, PhD, associate professor of biobehavioral health and nutritional sciences, Pennsylvania State University, University Park, and leader of a study published in *Journal of the American College of Nutrition.*

The Whey to Lower Blood Pressure

Seventy-one adults with hypertension who drank a beverage containing 28 grams (g) of powdered *whey* (a by-product from cow's milk) daily for six weeks had an average six-point drop in blood pressure.

Theory: Whey protein can increase production of *nitric oxide,* a compound that expands blood vessels.

If you have high blood pressure: Ask your doctor about whey protein powder (available at health-food stores). Try adding it to smoothies or sprinkling it on cereal or yogurt.

Susan Fluegel, PhD, nutritional biochemist, department of food science and human nutrition, Washington State University, Pullman.

Whole Grains Linked to Lower Blood Pressure

Researchers who reviewed health and nutrition reports for 31,684 men found that those who consumed the most whole grains (about 52 grams [g] daily) were 19% less likely to develop high blood pressure than those who consumed the least whole grains (about 3 g daily).

Best sources: Oatmeal (instant or cooked)—one cup, 30 g to 35 g...popcorn—one cup, 10 g to 12 g...whole-wheat bread—one slice, about 15 g...and bran cereal—one cup, 5 g to 10 g.

Alan Flint, MD, DrPH, research scientist, department of nutrition, Harvard School of Public Health, Boston.

Mineral Magic

Mineral water may help lower blood pressure substantially.

Recent finding: After consuming one liter of mineral water every day during one month, people between the ages of 45 and 64 with borderline *hypertension* (high blood pressure) experienced a significant decrease in blood pressure.

Theory: Most mineral waters contain significant amounts of magnesium and calcium, both of which help to reduce blood pressure.

Study of 70 people by researchers at Gothenburg University, Gothenburg, Sweden, published in *BMC Public Health*.

Is Your Personality Harming Your Heart?

When researchers gave 5,614 adults personality tests, individuals who were antagonistic (aggressive, competitive, manipulative or quick to express anger) were about 40% more likely to develop *thickening of arteries* (a risk factor for heart attack and stroke) than those who were least antagonistic. To help manage anger and antagonism, consult the American Psychological Association Web site, *www.apa.org* (click on "Anger" under "Psychology Topics"). Or consider seeing a therapist for more strategies.

Angelina Sutin, PhD, postdoctoral fellow, National Institute on Aging, Baltimore.

Beans Lower Blood Sugar as Well as Meds

In a recent finding, diabetics who ate one-half cup of beans a day—garbanzo, black, white, pinto or kidney beans—had significantly lower fasting glucose, insulin and *hemoglobin A1C*, a marker of long-term glucose control. When eaten as a regular part of a high-fiber, low-glycemic-index diet, beans lower hemoglobin A1C

by an average of 0.48%, about as much as medications such as *metformin* (Glucophage).

Cyril Kendall, PhD, research scientist, department of nutritional sciences, University of Toronto, and the Clinical Nutrition and Risk Factor Modification Centre, St. Michael's Hospital, Toronto, and leader of research analyzing 41 studies regarding the effects of beans on blood sugar levels, published in *Diabetologia*.

Magnesium Wards Off Diabetes

When researchers studied 4,497 healthy adults' diets over 20 years, people who consumed the most magnesium (roughly 200 milligrams [mg] per 1,000 calories) were 47% less likely to develop diabetes than those who consumed the least (about 100 mg per 1,000 calories).

Theory: Magnesium enhances enzymes that help the body process blood sugar.

Self-defense: Eat magnesium-rich foods like almonds (one-quarter cup roasted, 97 mg) and spinach (one-half cup cooked, 77 mg).

Ka He, MD, associate professor, departments of nutrition and epidemiology, University of North Carolina, Chapel Hill.

Just a Spoonful of Vinegar Helps the Blood Sugar Go Down

Adding vinegar to a meal slows the *glycemic response*—the rate at which carbohydrates are absorbed into the bloodstream—by 20%.

Reason: The acetic acid in vinegar seems to slow the emptying of the stomach, which decreases risk for *hyperglycemia* (high blood sugar), a risk factor for heart disease, and it helps people with type 2 diabetes to manage their condition.

Ways to add vinegar to meals: Use malt vinegar on thick-cut oven fries...marinate sliced tomatoes and onions in red-wine vinegar before adding the vegetables to a sandwich...mix two parts red wine vinegar with one part olive oil, and use two tablespoons on a green salad.

Carol S. Johnston, PhD, RD, director, nutrition program, Arizona State University, Mesa, and coauthor of a study published in *Diabetes Care.*

Popular Drinks That Decrease Risk for Diabetes 25%

Coffee and tea lower diabetes risk. People who drank three or more cups of coffee daily had a 25% lower risk for type 2 diabetes than subjects who drank two or fewer cups. Similar results were shown for tea and decaffeinated coffee, indicating that the effect is not entirely due to caffeine but is likely to include other compounds present in these beverages, such as magnesium.

Rachel Huxley, DPhil, director of the nutrition and lifestyle division and associate professor in the faculty of medicine, University of Sydney, Australia, and lead author of a meta-analysis of 18 studies involving more than 450,000 people, published in *Archives of Internal Medicine.*

Red Wine Mimics Diabetes Drug

A recent finding indicated that compounds in red wine bind to cellular receptors that regulate blood sugar. In fact, just a half glass (2.5 ounces) contains up to *four times* the cell-binding activity as a dose of the diabetes drug *rosiglitazone* (Avandia).

Note: By November 2011, Avandia can only be prescribed in limited circumstances and by approved physicians because it increases risk for heart attack.

Food & Function.

Dogs for Diabetics

Dogs can detect drops of blood sugar in diabetics. Trained dogs can detect a faint odor that's emitted by humans as much as 20 minutes before blood sugar drops to a critical level. These drops can cause diabetics to collapse or go into a coma if they do not receive medication immediately. A trained dog is valued at $20,000, but Dogs4Diabetics and other providers often require only $150* for people in need.

Dogs4Diabetics, Nylabone Training Center, Concord, California, *www.dogs4diabetics.com.*

*Price subject to change.

Promising New Way to Fight Glaucoma

Experimental contact lenses infused with vitamin E may release glaucoma medications up to 100 times longer than current lenses, according to new animal studies. Clinical trials of these new contact lenses could begin within one to two years.

University of Florida, Gainesville, *http://eye.ufl.edu.*

Supplements That Protect Against Skin Cancer

Shield your skin from the inside out. Dietary supplements that contain *beta-carotene* or *mixed carotenoids* (beta-carotene plus *lycopene* and *lutein*) help protect skin from harmful UV radiation.

Dosage: 24 milligrams (mg) of beta-carotene daily or 25,000 international units (IU) of a mixed carotenoid.

Alternative: FernBlock, an oral supplement made from fern extract and herbs. Take two capsules daily, in the morning, 30 minutes prior to sun exposure. Take an additional capsule at noon.

Important: Supplements should be used in addition to sunscreen, not as a replacement.

Mark A. Stengler, NMD, naturopathic medical doctor and founder and medical director of the Stengler Center for Integrative Medicine, Encinitas, California. He is also adjunct associate clinical professor, National College of Natural Medicine in Portland, Oregon, and author of the *Bottom Line/Natural Healing* newsletter. For more, go to *www.drstengler.com*.

Surprising Natural Cures For Arthritis

Jamison Starbuck, ND, naturopathic physician in family practice in Missoula, Montana. She is past president of the American Association of Naturopathic Physicians and a contributing editor to *The Alternative Advisor: The Complete Guide to Natural Therapies and Alternative Treatments* (Time Life).

I've got a strong family history of osteoarthritis and have suffered several sports-related knee injuries. Although conventional wisdom would say that osteoarthritis is inevitable for me, I disagree. I do not have arthritis and am very physically active despite my history. Arthritis can be prevented, and if you've already got it, you can keep it from becoming worse—if you're willing to do some self-care.

Conventional care for osteoarthritis is pain medication, rest and sometimes surgery. The first-line approach usually includes *nonsteroidal anti-inflammatory drugs* (NSAIDs), such as *ibuprofen* (Advil) or *naproxen* (Aleve). In the short term, these medicines are effective at reducing the pain, but they don't help very much in the long term. NSAIDs can actually speed up the process of joint destruction and damage the intestinal lining, causing gastritis and ulcers.

To fight arthritis, the main goal is to reduce the inflammation that triggers it. To do this, you need to identify the root cause of the inflammation. This varies from one person to another, but common sources include poor diet, allergies to food or something in the environment, the accumulation of heavy metal in the body (such as mercury and lead), a chronic illness, insomnia and hormonal imbalance. Naturopathic physicians and holistically minded MDs can test for these inflammatory factors.

In addition, I advise my patients who have arthritis or want to prevent it to...

• **Strive for a healthy digestive tract.** People with arthritis often suffer from indigestion, constipation or irritable bowel syndrome—all of which inflame and irritate the gastrointestinal tract.

Good natural remedy: The amino acid *glutamine*, which helps to strengthen the lining of the gastrointestinal tract. Glutamine is abundant in cabbage and okra and can be taken as a supplement—dose is 1,000 milligrams (mg) in powdered form added to four ounces of water and taken three times a day, between meals.

• **Get positive.** You might be surprised to learn that in arthritis patients, 85% or more of their 50,000 or so daily thoughts are negative, critical and self-defeating. To reduce thoughts that increase pain perception and worsen joint stiffness, aim to become more self-supportive through counseling, meditation, biofeedback or stress-management counseling.

• **Watch out for all "trigger" foods.** Coffee, sugar, alcohol, red meat, dairy products and processed foods often promote inflammation, increasing risk for painful joints. To prevent arthritis, cut back or eliminate these foods and increase your intake of the anti-inflammatory foods—for example, vegetables, fruits, plain water and healthful oils (such as those from fish and olives).

• **Move your body.** All physical activity improves circulation and sends nourishing nutrients to joints and surrounding tissue. It also helps to keep body weight under control—an important factor in fighting joint pain. Regular movement will not worsen arthritis. Start slowly with simple stretches or walking. Consult a physical therapist if you need help setting up an exercise program that's right for you.

The Power of Happiness

Arthritis sufferers have less pain when they are happy.

Recent finding: When people with osteo-arthritis were asked questions about their pain and psychological states once each week over 12 weeks, subjects with the lowest scores on a mental health scale had twice the number of pain flare-ups as participants with the highest scores.

Theory: Treatment for mental health issues could effectively lessen arthritis pain.

Barton L. Wise, MD, assistant professor, general internal medicine, UC Davis School of Medicine, Sacramento, California, and lead author of a study of 266 people, published in *Osteoarthritis and Cartilage*.

The Real Secret to Curing Depression

Zindel V. Segal, PhD, the Cameron Wilson Chair in Depression Studies in the psychology department at the University of Toronto, in Ontario, Canada, and head of the Cognitive Behavior Therapy Unit at the university's Centre for Addiction and Mental Health. He is coauthor of *The Mindful Way Through Depression: Freeing Yourself from Chronic Unhappiness* (Guilford). For more, go to *http://mbct.co.uk.*

Most people who experience depression—or even simply a bout of the blues—try to "fix" it with an antidepressant or something else to make them feel better.

A different but highly effective approach: Do not try to fix the uncomfortable feelings. That's a crucial aspect of mindfulness—which involves paying special attention to what's going on in our minds and bodies in a nonjudgmental way. With this approach, many people who have battled depression or sadness have experienced significant improvement in their symptoms.

For anyone who has ever suffered the pain of depression or down moods, this approach may sound wrongheaded. But the truth is it works. Of course, there are instances in which antidepressants may be called for. However, when people stop taking the drugs, depression often returns.

Important finding: People with a history of depression who used mindfulness in an organized program had half as many recurrences as people not on the program.

Here's what you need to know to use mindfulness to cope with sadness or depression...*

THE OLD WAY DOESN'T WORK

Most people do not realize that it's not the sad thoughts and/or feelings that cause us to spiral downward. It's what we do about them that matters. Two of the most common coping mechanisms to get out of a bad mood—trying to think our way out of a problem or trying to avoid painful feelings—actually trap us in the darkness.

The reasons...

• **Why thinking doesn't help.** We are accustomed to believing that we can think our way out of any problem. So it's only natural to regard a dark mood as a problem to be solved. When we're in this dreary state, we might ask ourselves questions such as Why do I feel this way? How can I change my life? What should I be doing differently? We believe that if we think hard enough, we'll find a solution.

But the opposite is true. Dwelling on how terrible you feel, on the distance between the way things are and the way things should be, just reinforces your mood. Your mind begins running in an endless circle—and it seems as though there is no way out.

• **Why ignoring feelings doesn't help.** We often think that if we ignore painful feelings, they will go away. When we try to push away these strong emotions, they rebound, stronger than ever.

Think about it this way: If someone told you not to think about the white bear, guess what you would do? You could not help but think about a white bear or how you shouldn't think about it. Suppressing thoughts or feelings doesn't work.

WHAT TO DO INSTEAD

The practice of mindfulness enables you to look at your thoughts and feelings in a different way. Instead of dwelling on how bad you feel and struggling to do something about it, you simply experience what's going on.

*Consult a doctor before trying this approach if you have experienced suicidal thoughts or your depression interferes with your ability to perform daily activities.

Mindfulness encourages you to be aware of your emotions, thoughts and bodily sensations without judging or interpreting them. You simply "watch" them…identify them…and acknowledge them instead of lingering over each one.

To get an idea of what mindfulness feels like, apply it to an ordinary activity that you do every day. While washing the dishes, for instance, observe how the warm water feels over your hands…how your hands and arms feel as you turn a dish over and rinse it off. Make washing dishes the full focus of your attention, not a task to get past. If your mind wanders, bring your focus back to the dishes. What you've done is to bring physical sensations into the realm of mindfulness.

Next, bring thoughts and feelings into the realm of mindfulness. Being aware of all your thoughts/feelings without actually reacting to them is the key to keeping negative emotions from cascading. This can be particularly challenging, which is why it's helpful to begin as though thoughts are sounds that you are simply listening to.

Here's how: While sitting quietly, let your attention shift to your hearing. Open up your mind to the sounds from all directions, near and far, subtle as well as obvious sounds. Be aware of all these auditory sensations without thinking about where they're coming from or what they mean. Notice the way they appear and fade. When you realize that your attention has drifted, note where it has gone and gently come back to the sounds.

After trying this a few times with sounds, change your awareness to your thoughts. Let your mind "hear" them as if they were coming from outside, noting how they arise, linger and move on.

Helpful: Imagine your thoughts projected on a screen at the movies…or see them as clouds passing across a clear sky. When any thought provokes strong emotions or physical feelings, notice this as well but only notice it, without trying to draw any conclusions from it.

Acknowledge if a feeling is particularly unpleasant. Does it cause any physical sensations or discomfort? Instead of ignoring the thought or the discomfort because it's unpleasant and you don't want to deal with it, sit with it for a little while. This can be difficult to do.

Helpful: Notice your thought patterns. If you are feeling—*I'll never be happy again* or *I feel like a failure*—you can say to yourself, *There's that "never-be-happy-ever" feeling again.*

How often to practice: It is recommended that you put aside just 30 minutes each day to practice mindfulness. You can do this in a variety of ways—lying on the floor comfortably and focusing on your breathing…or walking and focusing on how your legs and arms feel as they move.

Even incorporating mindfulness for merely five minutes at a time into your routine daily activities—such as showering…brushing your teeth…or taking out the garbage—can help. The point is to be able to focus on what you are doing when you are doing it.

When you practice mindfulness regularly, it makes it easier to use the technique when you need it most—when you are anxious because you are stuck in traffic…are in the middle of a heated argument…or begin to feel a bout of depression coming on.

Finally…The Truth About Alzheimer's Prevention

Marwan Sabbagh, MD, a geriatric neurologist and founding director of the Cleo Roberts Center for Clinical Research under the umbrella of the Sun Health Research Institute in Sun City, Arizona, one of 29 NIH-sponsored Alzheimer's Disease Centers in the US. He is author of *The Alzheimer's Answer* (Wiley).

Of course, all of us desire to do everything that's possible to avoid developing Alzheimer's disease.

The problem: Experts disagree on whether anything we do to change our lifestyles will actually help.

The news media has recently reported a statement made by a panel of 15 scientists in the *Annals of Internal Medicine* that there is not enough evidence to recommend any particular lifestyle habits to prevent Alzheimer's.

HOW COULD THEY MAKE SUCH A STATEMENT?

What the headlines missed: There is, in fact, a large body of scientific evidence suggesting that certain strategies help protect against Alzheimer's disease—it's just that these interventions have not yet been definitively proven in clinical settings. Instead, all the evidence we have at this time is basic scientific research, such as cellular and animal studies, as well as epidemiological research that analyzes large groups of people to discover factors that may be linked to increased or decreased risk for Alzheimer's.

Clinical research, which tests one specific agent such as medication along with a placebo, always lingers behind basic and epidemiological research because it is expensive and difficult to conduct.

My advice: Follow well-known Alzheimer's prevention strategies. To begin, eat healthfully—preferably a Mediterranean diet that emphasizes brain-healthy omega 3–rich fish and antioxidant-loaded fruits, vegetables and nuts. And get regular aerobic exercise to stimulate blood flow to the brain. The most recent research links 45 to 60 minutes four days a week to reduced Alzheimer's risk. Pace yourself, and consult your doctor before starting any exercise program. *In addition, keep pace with the latest research, and consult your doctor about incorporating simple, underrecognized strategies such as those described below…*

AVOID COPPER

Current evidence: In basic research on animals and on the brain cells of people who have died of Alzheimer's, scientists from the University of Rochester Medical Center in New York recently found that copper damages the molecule that shuttles *beta-amyloid* out of the brain. Beta-amyloid is a protein that produces toxic chunks (plaque) in the brains of people with Alzheimer's, and it may play a key role in the development of the disease. This research builds on a decade of research linking excessive levels of copper in the body to Alzheimer's.

What to do: According to recent research published in *Chemical Research in Toxicology*, people over age 50 should avoid all nutritional supplements that contain copper…take a 15-milligram (mg) zinc supplement daily, as zinc helps the body to remove excess copper…limit intake of red meat, which contains a lot of copper…and use an effective filtering system to remove copper from drinking water.

My personal approach: Depending on the water source, tap water may contain significant amounts of copper even if the water isn't flowing through copper pipes. For this reason, I've stopped drinking unfiltered tap water. To remove copper from my drinking water, I use a reverse osmosis water filter to separate the water from potentially harmful substances.

Reverse osmosis filtration systems are found at the home-improvement stores and online in tap or under-the-sink models (about $150*) or whole-house models (up to $3,000).

GET ENOUGH VITAMIN E

Vitamin E has been studied for Alzheimer's for more than a decade, with a landmark study in *The New England Journal of Medicine* in 1997 showing that high doses of vitamin E were more effective than a placebo at delaying specific outcomes of Alzheimer's disease, such as nursing home placement. Now, a recent new study links high dietary intake of vitamin E to a reduced risk for the disease.

Current evidence: In one 10-year study involving more than 5,000 individuals, those with the highest dietary intake of vitamin E were roughly 25% less likely to develop Alzheimer's than people with the lowest intake, reported Dutch researchers in *Archives of Neurology*.

What to do: Eat vitamin E-rich foods, which supply the full range of vitamin E nutrients. Most vitamin E supplements do not provide the entire class of these nutrients. The reports now clearly support dietary sources of vitamin E over supplements. Aim to get 15 mg of vitamin E daily.

Best sources: Wheat germ oil (20 mg per tablespoon)…almonds (7 mg per ounce)…sunflower seeds (6 mg per ounce)…and spinach (4 mg per cup, boiled).

*Prices subject to change.

BEWARE OF HOSPITALIZATION
AND ANESTHESIA

Doctors have long known that some older adults devclop Alzheimer's symptoms soon after being hospitalized.

Current evidence: Researchers conducted a six-year study involving nearly 3,000 people age 65 and older who did not have dementia (cognitive decline most commonly caused by Alzheimer's). As was reported in *The Journal of the American Medical Association*, people who were hospitalized for noncritical illness, such as broken bones, had a 40% higher risk of developing dementia.

The researchers speculated that several factors might play a role in increasing dementia after hospitalization, such as hospital-acquired infections...general anesthesia, tranquilizers and painkiller meds used while in the hospital... and the blood pressure and blood sugar problems that frequently come up during hospitalization. Research has linked each one of these factors, in varying degrees, to the development of Alzheimer's disease.

What to do: If you are hospitalized, try to stay in the hospital for as short a period as possible. If you need anesthesia and have a choice between general anesthesia or local or spinal anesthesia, opt for the local or spinal. As much as possible, minimize the use of optional psychoactive medications, such as tranquilizers and sleeping pills.

Apple Juice for Alzheimer's Symptoms

Apple juice may help curb some types of Alzheimer's symptoms.

Recent study: Twenty-one adults (ages 72 up to 93) with moderate-to-severe Alzheimer's disease who consumed eight ounces of apple juice daily for one month showed a 27% improvement in behavioral and psychotic symptoms (including decreased anxiety, agitation and delusions).

Theory: Apple juice may boost production of the *neurotransmitter acetylcholine*, which declines as a result of Alzheimer's.

If a loved one suffers from Alzheimer's: In addition to prescribed medications, try giving apple juice to enhance his/her comfort.

Thomas Shea, PhD, professor and director, Center for Cellular Neurobiology and Neurodegeneration Research, University of Massachusetts Lowell.

Fish Oil Fights Deadly Infection

Among 23 people who had life-threatening *sepsis* (body-tissue damage from bacterial infection), those fed fish oil intravenously (6.4 grams [g] daily) for five days recovered and were discharged in 28 days, on average, compared with 82 days for those not given fish oil.

Theory: Fish oil's inflammation-decreasing effect may curb uncontrolled inflammation in critically ill sepsis patients.

To reduce inflammation: Have *omega-3-rich fatty fish* several times per week, or ask your doctor about fish-oil supplements.

Philip Calder, PhD, professor of nutritional immunology, School of Medicine, University of Southampton, England.

Best Time to Take Your Vitamin D

Take vitamin D with your largest meal of the day. Taking vitamin D with a big meal increases absorption by 57%, possibly because large meals have more fat content to boost the absorption of this fat-soluble vitamin. Vitamin D may help prevent cancer and diabetes, boost immunity and protect against back pain.

Angelo Licata, MD, PhD, endocrinologist, Cleveland Clinic, Ohio, and coauthor of a study published in *Journal of Bone and Mineral Research*.

Dehydration—The Surprising Cause of Many Health Problems

Ann Grandjean, EdD, associate professor of medical nutrition education at the University of Nebraska Medical Center in Omaha. She is coauthor of *Hydration: Fluids for Life*, published by the International Life Sciences Institute, *www.ilsi.org.*

We all know that water is essential for human life and dehydration is dangerous. But there are some surprising effects of even mild dehydration.

Little-known risks: In addition to impaired cognitive function and lethargy, dehydration is associated with an increased risk of falls, gum disease and bladder cancer.

What you need to know about water's effect on your mental and physical well-being...

HOW MUCH DO YOU NEED?

It's difficult to pinpoint exactly how much water we need.

Problem: Depending on activity levels, metabolism and environmental factors, such as heat and humidity, one person may require up to eight times as much water as someone else.

Solution: Even though we often hear that most people should consume eight glasses of water each day, there isn't really any scientific evidence to support this approach. The first official recommendation for water consumption was issued in 2004 from the Institute of Medicine, the health arm of the government-sponsored National Academy of Sciences. This so-called *adequate intake* (AI) for males age 19 and older is 15 eight-ounce cups daily...for females of the same age group, 11 cups daily.

Sound like a lot of liquid? Remember this represents total intake of water, including all the water that comes from food—and for most people, this amounts to roughly 20% to 25% of the total. When focusing on water alone, the AI includes about 13 cups of beverages, including water, for males age 19 and older...and nine cups for females of the same age group.

Important: Contrary to what many people believe, there is no evidence to show that coffee, tea and other caffeinated beverages contribute to dehydration. So it's fine to count these beverages as part of your daily fluid intake.

Since it's so difficult to establish strict guidelines for water consumption, the most convenient indication may be your urine.

Simple self-test: If you urinate at least four times daily and the urine is colorless or pale yellow, you are probably well-hydrated.

Note: Some vitamin supplements, such as B vitamins, can cause urine to be yellow even if the person is hydrated.

DANGERS OF DEHYDRATION

The first symptoms of dehydration usually are dry mouth and thirst. If the dehydration progresses, headache, dizziness, sleepiness and muscle weakness may occur.

Dehydration that produces a 2% decrease in body weight (due to water loss via sweat, vomiting, diarrhea, etc.) is associated with declines in the short-term memory, attention and other mental functions. Similar levels of dehydration can lead to fatigue and reduce strength and endurance. *Chronic low-water intake can increase risk for illnesses, such as...*

• **Urinary tract infection.** When female factory workers significantly increased their water intake and urination frequency by three times or more during their shifts for two years, the rate of urinary tract infections dropped from 9.8% to 1.6%.

• **Bladder cancer.** Not all research findings agree, but one large study that followed 47,000 men over 10 years found that people with the highest levels of fluid consumption (10.6 cups daily) had half the risk for bladder cancer as men who had the least fluids (5.5 cups).

WHEN YOUR RISK IS HIGH

Some people are at higher risk for acute and chronic dehydration. *Key risk factors...*

• **Age.** The sensation of thirst gets blunted as we age, so "drink when you are thirsty" becomes a less reliable guide. For many people, appetite also lessens with age, so you can end up getting less water from food.

Other indirect age-related factors also may come into play. For example, people troubled by incontinence often limit water intake.

• **Exercise.** During exercise, you lose more water through your sweat. So make sure that you drink enough water when you exercise— generally one to two cups before…one to two cups during…and one to two cups after your workout. This is especially important in hot and humid weather or at high altitudes.

• **Illness.** So many chronic illnesses (diabetes and kidney disease are among them) raise the odds for dehydration. Diarrhea and vomiting can present an acute danger of dehydration— and water alone won't replace the minerals, such as sodium and potassium, that you lose. If either is severe or prolonged, or if you can't keep liquids down, consult your doctor.

TREATING DEHYDRATION

When dehydration is mild to moderate, the treatment is simple—drink more liquids.

Severe dehydration is a medical emergency that requires *immediate* medical help. Some symptoms are the same as those for mild dehydration but greatly magnified (extreme thirst, profound sleepiness or lethargy and very dry mouth). Sweating and urination come to a virtual halt.

Older adults especially may experience irritability and lethargy, while severe dehydration also may lead to delirium (marked by disorientation and delusions) or unconsciousness.

If you experience or witness any of these symptoms, contact a doctor.

The Healthiest Juices

Nutrition Action Healthletter, 1875 Connecticut Ave. NW, Washington, DC 20009, *www.cspinet.org*.

The supermarket is full of fortified juices. Which ones live up to their promises… and which aren't worth the money?

AVOID JUICES FORTIFIED WITH…

• **Vitamins and/or minerals.** Juice contains merely 10% to 25% of the recommended daily values for vitamins and minerals, so don't give up your multivitamin.

• **Fiber.** Fiber added to juices often is in the form of a type of sugar called *maltodextrin*, which is absorbed poorly.

• **Glucosamine.** *Glucosamine* in juice does not protect joints according to a recent study.

• **Antioxidants.** All juices naturally contain *antioxidants* (vitamins, such as C and E) that could help ramp up your immune system, but there's no evidence that juices with added antioxidants are better for you than regular juices.

CONSIDER JUICES WITH…

• **Omega-3s.** Eight fluid ounces of Tropicana Healthy Heart has 50 milligrams (mg) of *omega-3 fatty acids*—far less than in a serving of salmon but still beneficial for your heart.

• **Plant sterols.** In one finding, two eight-ounce glasses a day of a plant sterol–fortified drink, such as Minute Maid Heart Wise orange juice, lowered cholesterol by 7%.

Healthier Tea

Tea in a bottle contains fewer antioxidants than green or black tea brewed at home. Some bottled tea includes so few cancer-fighting *polyphenols* that you would have to drink 20 or more bottles to have as many as are in one cup of homemade tea. Also, bottled teas often are high in sugar—and more costly.

Shiming Li, PhD, an analytical and natural-product chemist at WellGen, Inc., North Brunswick, New Jersey.

Top Antioxidant Source

Cooked black rice provides you more antioxidants than blueberries—with less sugar and more fiber. The *anthocyanin* antioxidants in black rice are believed to fight heart disease and cancer. Black rice is used mainly in Asia. You may be able to find it in Asian markets, some gourmet shops and specialty stores.

Zhimin Xu, PhD, an associate professor, department of food science, Louisiana State University Agricultural Center, Baton Rouge, and leader of a black rice study.

6

Private and Personal

Super Sex *Every Time*: Natural Cures for Impotence, Low Desire, Dryness, More

Couples who enjoy having sex regularly tend to live longer than couples who seldom or never have sex. Sexual activity can cleanse congestion from the prostate gland and relieve pain by stimulating the release of *endorphins*, "feel-good" chemicals in the brain.

Yet millions of Americans struggle to have satisfying sex, or any sex, because of physical limitations. Medications can assist with problems such as an inability to have erections or vaginal dryness, but they don't always work—and can carry the risk for side effects.

Better: Natural remedies that improve energy and libido as well as sexual performance. In my 40 years of specializing in herbal medi-

cine, I have found them to be quite effective for many people. (The herbs and supplements noted here are readily available at most health-food stores and online.)

LUBRICATION

Vaginal dryness can be as problematic for a woman as erectile dysfunction is for a man. Women naturally produce less moisture (in the vagina, as well as in the eyes, skin and other parts of the body) as they get older. But it's one of the easiest sexual problems to correct—and without the use of store-bought, chemical-filled lubricants. Try one of the following remedies. If that doesn't work, try another until you find what works best for you.

Brigitte Mars, herbalist, a founding member of The American Herbalists Guild and instructor at Naropa University, Bauman College and Boulder College of Massage Therapy, all in Boulder, Colorado. Mars has been practicing and teaching herbal medicine and nutrition for more than 40 years. She's also author of *The Sexual Herbal: Prescriptions for Enhancing Love and Passion* (Healing Arts). Her Web site is *www.brigittemars.com*.

●**Barley water.** *Barley water* is an emollient that also nourishes and strengthens vaginal tissues. Cook two cups of light pearled barley in 10 cups of water for two hours. Strain, and reserve the water. Drink one glassful three or four times per day between meals for at least three weeks. If it helps, continue doing it. It can be kept in the refrigerator for up to three days. (You can use the leftover barley in soups and salads.)

●**Acidophilus.** Dryness is sometimes caused by an overgrowth of vaginal yeast. Before going to bed each night, insert a capsule of *acidophilus* into the vagina. It inhibits yeast and helps the vagina produce more lubrication.

Important: Do not use an enteric-coated capsule—it won't dissolve readily. Use an acidophilus gel capsule.

●**Chemical-free lubricant.** Mix one ounce of softened *cocoa butter* with one tablespoon each of powdered *dong quai* (an herb in the parsley family), *licorice root* and *marshmallow root*, along with one tablespoon of powdered *wild yam* and two tablespoons of *vitamin E oil.*

Optional: Two drops of essential oil of rose for a pleasant aroma.

Form this mixture into suppository shapes about the size of your little finger. Store them in a glass jar in the refrigerator for up to six months. Insert one in the vagina daily before bedtime.

LOW LIBIDO

If your sex drive is lower than you (or your partner) would like…

●**Eat black foods.** According to Traditional Chinese Medicine, the kidneys govern sexual vitality. Foods with natural black color, such as *black olives, black sesame seeds, chia seeds* and *black beans,* strengthen the kidneys and improve sexual energy and performance.

Bonus: Black olives and chia increase the production of *mucilage,* important for sexual lubrication.

●**Muira puama.** This is a South American herb that traditionally is used as an aphrodisiac and to improve erections as well as orgasms in men and women. It's a warming herb that increases circulation. If you have cold hands and/or feet, you probably have impaired circulation to the genitals as well. *Muira puama* can help.

Dose: One-half cup of muira puama tea…or 10 to 30 drops of tincture, mixed with an inch of water or taken straight, three times daily. It's also available in capsules. Natives of South America sometimes apply the cooled tea directly to the genitals as a sexual stimulant.

●**DHEA,** an over-the-counter hormonal supplement that gets converted to testosterone in the body, can increase both libido and sexual responsiveness in women and men.

Important: Improper dosing can bring on acne, the growth of facial hair in women and other side effects—including an increased risk for some cancers. Take DHEA only under the supervision of a doctor.

ERECTILE DYSFUNCTION

The arteries that carry blood to the penis are just slightly wider than the head of a pin. Even slight buildups of plaque (*atherosclerosis*) can impede circulation and make it difficult for a man to get and/or maintain an erection.

The same things that improve overall cardiovascular health, such as lowering cholesterol and blood pressure, can improve a man's ability to achieve an erection. *Also helpful…*

●**The Deer.** This is a Taoist exercise that removes energy blockages, stimulates hormone production and improves erections. Sit on the edge of the bed, and rub your hands to warm them. Hold the scrotum with one hand. With the other hand, massage right below the navel in a circular motion. Do it 81 times, then switch hands and rub in the other direction 81 times.

Follow this up with 36 Kegel exercises, in which you tighten and then release the *pubococcygeus muscles*—the same muscles that you would use to stop urine in midstream.

●**Foot massage.** Once or twice a day, massage the entire foot, paying particular attention to the sides of the heels. The *meridians* (energy pathways) that support sexual potency run through this part of the foot.

●**Yohimbe.** *Yohimbe bark extract* is among the most effective natural products for improving erections. It increases flow of blood to the genitals while at the same time impeding the flow of blood out of the penis—important for keeping an erection.

Dose: One cup of yohimbe tea…or 30 drops of tincture, mixed with an inch of water or taken straight, 30 minutes to an hour before sex. Also available in capsules.

Caution: Yohimbe can elevate blood pressure and cause insomnia. It also interacts with many common drugs, including antihypertensives and heart and diabetes medications. Use it only under the supervision of a doctor and never more than twice a week.

•**Omega-3 fatty acids** enhance circulation and help the nervous system function better. Eat fish (such as salmon, tuna, sardines) twice per week or supplement with fish oil (follow directions on the label).

BETTER ORGASMS

Men and women who eat well, exercise regularly and are comfortable with their bodies experience better and more frequent orgasms. *Also helpful…*

•**Arginine.** An amino acid called *L-arginine* is a *vasodilator*, which means it helps to widen or open up blood vessels. Arginine cream can be applied to the clitoris or penis before having sex to increase arousal and the intensity of orgasms. You also can take an oral capsule form to increase blood flow to sexual organs. Follow directions on the label.

The Fun Exercise That Promotes *Much* Better Sex

Forty healthy women who practiced a series of yoga poses one hour daily for 12 weeks reported significant improvements in sexual functioning (including increased arousal, lubrication and frequency of orgasm).

Theory: Yoga improves functioning of the hormone secretion glands and strengthens pelvic muscles—both of which can lead to satisfying sexual activity.

To enhance sex: Consider a yoga class. To find a certified teacher, visit the International Association of Yoga Therapists Web site, *www. iayt.org*, or phone 928-541-0004. Consult your physician before trying yoga.

Vikas Dhikav, MD, research officer, neurology department, Guru Gobind Singh Indraprastha University, New Delhi, India.

Make a Great First Impression

To look your best on matchmaking Web sites…

Photos taken at twilight are more attractive—the angle of beams from the setting sun makes faces appear better and may increase romantic associations for those viewing your photo. A shallow depth of field—in which you are in focus in front of a fuzzy background—seems to make viewers feel more comfortable. Late-night photos also are effective, possibly because subjects are dressed up or because they look more relaxed, perhaps after a glass of wine.

Survey of users of online matchmaker OkCupid at *www.okcupid.com*, reported in *Psychology Today*.

Tasty Aphrodisiac

Women who drank red wine in moderation had more sexual interest and lubrication than ones who drank little or none.

Possible reason: The antioxidants and alcohol in the wine may increase production of nitric oxide, a gas that helps artery walls relax—increasing blood flow to genitals.

Caution: Drink no more than one to two glasses of red wine a day—any more decreases sexual response.

Study of 798 women by researchers at University of Florence, Italy, published in *The Journal of Sexual Medicine*.

Scents More Arousing Than Perfume

The combined scent of lavender and pumpkin pie can boost blood flow to the penis by 40%…popcorn with butter by 9%…cheese pizza by 5%. The scent of perfume increases blood flow by only 3%.

Alan Hirsch, MD, director, Smell & Taste Treatment and Research Foundation in Chicago, *www.smelland taste.org,* and leader of a study published in *Medical Aspects of Human Sexuality.*

A Powerful Color

Men who wear red appear more powerful to women. And women view powerful men as more attractive and sexually desirable. They also view men in red as wealthier and more likely to climb the social ladder.

Andrew Elliot, PhD, professor of psychology, University of Rochester, New York, and author of the study of 313 people, published in *Journal of Experimental Psychology: General.*

More Housework Leads to More Sex

For both husbands and wives, doing more work around the house increases the likelihood of having sex together.

Possible reasons: Spouses who divide the housework have more time and energy to have sex…and working hard may signal a commitment to the home and marriage.

What to do: Share household work as well as other tasks in a manner that satisfies both partners.

Constance Gager, PhD, assistant professor of family and child studies, Montclair State University, Montclair, New Jersey, and leader of a study of 6,877 married couples, published online in *Journal of Family Issues.*

A Viagra Caution

Use of Viagra may lead to long-term hearing loss.

Recent finding: Men who indicated that they had hearing problems were twice as likely to have used Viagra or another *erectile dysfunction* (ED) drug than men who said they did not have trouble hearing. The FDA already requires labels on Viagra and other ED drugs, such as Cialis and Levitra, to include warnings about possible hearing loss.

Possible reason for the side effect: In addition to increasing blood flow to the penis, ED drugs may increase blood flow to the ear, causing damage.

Gerald McGwin, PhD, professor of epidemiology, University of Alabama at Birmingham School of Public Health, and leader of a study of 11,525 men, published in *Archives of Otolaryngology—Head & Neck Surgery.*

Skip the Receipt!

Scientists reported that *bisphenol A*, a chemical in some plastics that has been linked to sexual dysfunction in men, also can be found on cash register receipts and readily passes through the skin and into the bloodstream.

Chemosphere, www.elsevier.com/locate/chemosphere.

Walk Your Way to Better Sex

Men who walked briskly for 30 minutes a day, four times a week—or did equivalent exercise—were two-thirds less likely to report sexual dysfunction than men who were sedentary. Exercise may increase blood flow in all regions of the body—including the penis—making it easier to get an erection. And men who work out tend to feel better about themselves, which may improve their sexual performance.

Erin McNamara, MD, urology resident, Duke University Medical Center, Durham, North Carolina, and leader of a study of 178 healthy men, average age 62, presented at a recent meeting of the American Urological Association.

If You Don't Like Your Body...

People who hate their bodies have different activity patterns in areas of the brain devoted to visual processing than people with normal views of their bodies. *Body dysmorphic disorder* (BDD), the syndrome in which people become overly focused on a perceived body defect, is estimated to affect about 1% to 2% of Americans. Treatment includes a combination of drug treatments and cognitive behavior therapy.

Jamie D. Feusner, MD, director, BDD Research Program, David Geffen School of Medicine, University of California at Los Angeles.

Nonhormonal Remedy Reduces Hot Flashes 50%!

Hot flashes can be decreased with a *nonhormonal* treatment. A small dose of the prescription antidepressant drug *escitalopram* (Lexapro) can decrease hot flash frequency by nearly 50% and diminishes the severity of the hot flashes that do occur. Possible side effects include short-term dizziness, fatigue, insomnia and/or nausea.

Ellen Freeman, PhD, research professor of obstetrics and gynecology and psychiatry at University of Pennsylvania School of Medicine in Philadelphia, and lead researcher of a study of 205 menopausal women, which was published in *The Journal of the American Medical Association*.

Popular Surgery Linked To Heart Disease

Hysterectomy is linked with cardiovascular disease.

Recent finding: Women who have hysterectomies before age 50 are nearly 20% more likely to develop coronary artery disease or heart failure or have strokes than women who have not had hysterectomies.

A possible reason: Removal of the uterus disrupts blood flow to the ovaries, decreasing heart-protective estrogen. A link has not been made between hysterectomy and heart disease in women over age 50.

Daniel Altman, MD, PhD, associate professor of medical epidemiology and statistics, Karolinska Institute in Stockholm, Sweden, and senior author of a study with 824,484 women, published in *European Heart Journal*.

Common Drink Fights Endometrial Cancer

When researchers studied the diets and health of 23,356 women (ages 55 to 69), those who drank at least 2.5 cups of coffee daily had a much lower risk for endometrial cancer than those who drank no coffee over a 20-year period. Decaffeinated coffee is believed to offer the same benefit.

Theory: Coffee helps to metabolize sugar—thus fighting obesity, which plays a role in endometrial cancer.

If you're at risk for endometrial cancer (due to such factors as obesity and diabetes): Ask your doctor about drinking a few cups of coffee daily.

Stefano Uccella, MD, researcher, department of obstetrics and gynecology, University of Insubria, Varese, Italy.

Easy Way to Cut Breast Cancer Risk 40%!

Women who used calcium supplements daily for five years had 40% lower risk for breast cancer than those women who did not take calcium...women who took a multivitamin daily had 30% lower risk.

Jaime Matta, PhD, professor of pharmacology and toxicology, Ponce School of Medicine in Ponce, Puerto Rico, and coauthor of a study of 725 women, presented at the American Association for Cancer Research's 2010 annual meeting.

Breast Cancer Vaccine On the Horizon

A breast cancer vaccine could be available in the next decade. An experimental vaccine that targets a protein in most breast cancers was found effective in preventing the disease in mice. Researchers need funding and permission from the FDA for clinical trials.

Vincent K. Tuohy, PhD, professor, department of immunology, molecular medicine and pathology, Cleveland Clinic's Lerner Research Institute, and team leader of an animal study, published in *Nature Medicine*.

Better Breast Cancer Detection

In a recent study, researchers analyzed one mammography clinic's records after it had switched to digital mammography from traditional film screening.

Result: The detection rate rose from 4.3 to 7.9 breast cancers per 1,000 women screened.

Theory: Digital mammography, in which images are directly transmitted to a video monitor, shows more detail than film.

To find a digital mammography provider: Look for a facility designated as a "Breast Imaging Center of Excellence" at the American College of Radiology Web site, *www.acr.org*.

Fred S. Vernacchia, MD, medical director, San Luis Diagnostic Center, San Luis Obispo, California.

Mammograms May *Increase* Breast Cancer Risk Among These Women

In a recent finding, women who had five or more exposures to low-dose radiation, such as during mammograms or chest X-rays, before age 20 were twice as likely to develop breast cancer as women who had not been exposed. Even though mammograms use low-dose radiation, the exposure from annual screenings at young ages may add to breast cancer risk in women with genetic mutations or a family history of breast cancer. MRI screening might serve as a good alternative. Further research is necessary.

Marijke C. Jansen-van der Weide, PhD, epidemiologist, University Medical Center Groningen, the Netherlands, and the leader of an analysis of seven studies involving 10,000 high-risk women in the US and Europe, presented at a meeting of the Radiological Society of North America.

Insist on *This* Before Your Next Mammogram

Shield your breasts from CT scans to reduce exposure to radiation. The shield—a thin piece of heavy metal—can decrease radiation by at least 30%, lowering odds for radiation-caused cancers in breast tissue in men and women. Many doctors, however, will not use them because these shields can cause streaks and lines on the scans.

Reality: These markings do not cause experienced technicians to miss abnormalities—and the markings can be limited by elevating the shield with towels or foam about two centimeters above the chest.

Terrance T. Healey, MD, director of thoracic radiology and clinical assistant professor, Warren Alpert Medical School of Brown University, and a radiologist at Rhode Island Hospital, both in Providence. He led a study presented at a recent meeting of the Radiological Society of North America.

Why Breast Cancer Survivors Should Lift Weights

Breast cancer survivors who lift weights are less likely to develop arm and hand swelling. That condition, *lymphedema*, occurs after women undergo breast cancer surgery. In the past, physicians told women not to lift weights—or even to carry children or bags of groceries—after breast surgery, to avoid making symptoms worse.

Recent finding: Women who lifted weights regularly after surgery, first under the guidance of trained fitness instructors and then on their own, developed stronger arms and were less likely to have lymphedema.

Kathryn Schmitz, PhD, MPH, associate professor of epidemiology and biostatistics, University of Pennsylvania School of Medicine, Philadelphia, and leader of a study of 141 breast cancer survivors with lymphedema, published in *The New England Journal of Medicine*.

If Your Partner Has Breast Cancer...

Men whose partners suffer from breast cancer are at risk for mood disorders serious enough to require hospitalization. All the stress of dealing with a partner's sickness, and the deprivation of emotional and/or social support that it brings, makes men more likely to develop major depression, bipolar disease and other serious mood-related conditions.

Self-defense: All men whose partners have breast cancer should be screened for depressive symptoms and treated before their conditions become bad enough to require hospital care.

Christoffer Johansen, MD, PhD, head, department of Psychosocial Cancer Research, Institute of Cancer Epidemiology, Copenhagen, Denmark, and the leader of a 13-year study of 20,538 men whose partners were diagnosed with breast cancer, which was published online in *Cancer*.

Hernia or UTI?

What seems like a hernia in men might be a *urinary tract infection* (UTI). Typical UTI symptoms include frequent urination, burning on urination and fever—but men can have deep pain within the pelvis or pain radiating to the groin or testicles. These are similar to hernia pains, although pain from a hernia usually happens during lifting or straining. If pain continues for more than one day or two, see your doctor—and if the pain is constant or accompanied by fever, see the doctor immediately. UTIs are treated with antibiotics.

Peter N. Schlegel, MD, professor and chairman, department of urology, The Weill Medical College of Cornell University, New York City.

Men at Risk for Breast Cancer, Too

Among 28 men with at least one maternal relative with breast cancer, 80% did not know that they themselves were at increased risk for the disease.

Self-defense: Men, not only women, should discuss a family history of breast cancer with their physicians and be aware of lesser-known breast cancer symptoms—nipple discharge or inversion, breast swelling and/or reddening or dimpling of the skin or nipple.

Eileen Thomas, PhD, RN, assistant professor, College of Nursing, University of Colorado Denver, Aurora.

Popular Pill Fights Prostate Cancer

Prostate cancer patients were less likely to die when they were given an *anticoagulant,* such as aspirin, in addition to standard treatment (surgery or radiation).

Possible reason: The body's natural tendency is to cover cancer cells with platelets in the blood. The platelet covering protects cancer cells from the immune system, making it easier for the cells to survive. Anticoagulants interfere with this platelet function.

Kevin Choe, MD, PhD, assistant professor of radiation oncology at University of Texas Southwestern Medical Center at Dallas and leader of a study of prostate cancer, presented at a meeting of the American Society for Radiation Oncology.

Prostate Surgery Warning: Safer Options Few Men Are Told About

Mark Scholz, MD, executive director of the Prostate Cancer Research Institute, at www.prostate-cancer.org, a nonprofit research and education organization in Los Angeles, and medical director at the Prostate Oncology Specialists practice in Marina del Rey, California. He is coauthor, with Ralph H. Blum, of Invasion of the Prostate Snatchers: No More Unnecessary Biopsies, Radical Treatment or Loss of Sexual Potency (Other Press).

With all of the controversy now surrounding testing and treatment for prostate cancer, it's no wonder that men are confused.

When should the *prostate-specific antigen* (PSA) test be repeated or a biopsy given? And when is surgery indicated for prostate cancer?

For answers, we recently spoke with Mark Scholz, MD, one of about 100 medical oncologists across the US who specialize in treating prostate cancer…

•**What do you believe is the biggest misconception surrounding prostate cancer?** Even with all the discussion about so-called "watchful waiting" (or active surveillance) and other treatment options for men with prostate cancer, far too many of them still assume that they need surgery. But that is not true. Research shows that out of 50,000 radical prostatectomies (removal of the prostate) that are performed every year in the US, more than 40,000 are unnecessary. In other words, these men would have lived just as long with as good a quality of life had they not had surgery.

•**Why is this so?** Prostate cancer is different from other cancers. It generally grows more slowly and rarely spreads to vital organs. It can be detected early and monitored in most cases. Treatments for prostate cancer also are typically more effective than for other cancers.

•**But what about the roughly 30,000 men in the US who die of prostate cancer each year?** Prostate cancer is not just one disease. Men with a low-risk malignancy should have mild treatment or no treatment. Patients with aggressive disease should get aggressive treatment. We have learned to be very good at telling the difference through testing (described below).

Sadly, however, surgery for prostate cancer causes impotence up to half the time, which is a very good reason to be more selective!

•**Is screening a good step toward being more selective?** The PSA test, which is used to screen for prostate cancer, provides useful information. But some doctors may overreact to the results, leading to unnecessary biopsies. I recommend starting PSA testing at age 40 to determine your normal baseline, then testing every two to three years (assuming PSA remains low). Then, after age 50, men should switch to annual testing.

Biopsies are also tricky. If you were to perform biopsies on all men, you would find that 30% of men age 50 and 70% of those beyond age 80 have at least microscopic evidence of a malignancy. And once prostate cancer is diagnosed, I've observed that fear drives most men into immediate radical treatment whether they need it or not.

•**When do you think a man should have a biopsy?** If a man's PSA is elevated (typically 4 ng/mL or above), the PSA test should be repeated. Labs do make mistakes, and false positives can occur as a result of factors such as prostate infection or even recent sexual activity—that is, ejaculation within the past 24 to 48 hours.

A different test, for PSA density—a quotient calculated by dividing PSA by prostate volume as determined by ultrasound—gives a better idea of whether significant cancer is likely. So does PSA velocity—a calculation of the rate at which PSA has risen over a given period of time. Any steep rise over previous PSA results should be taken more seriously. The decision to proceed with a biopsy is based on a consistently elevated, or a consistently rising, PSA after repeated testing while weighing the impact of an enlarged prostate if one is present.

A relatively new genetic test, known as PCA-3, which measures urine levels of a compound that is overproduced by prostate cancer cells, can reflect size and aggressiveness of tumors. PCA-3 is widely available and is about as accurate as a properly interpreted PSA, but because prostate size does not have to be taken into account, it is easier for the doctor to interpret.

A suspicious nodule felt during a digital rectal exam also deserves a biopsy.

•**If cancer is detected in the biopsy, then what?** The first step is to determine the cancer type, which will aid decision-making on treatment options. Prostate cancer is categorized as low, intermediate or high risk, referring to the likelihood that cancer will return after surgery or radiation. Its treatment should be chosen accordingly. The standard calculation takes into account the Gleason score (one measure of the tumor's aggressiveness)…percentage of biopsy samples that were positive…PSA level, density and velocity…and the presence of nodules found with a digital rectal exam. About 40% of prostate cancers are low risk, 40% intermediate risk and 20% high risk.

It's low-risk cancer where you see the most overtreatment. About 94% of men who have this type of prostate cancer opt to have their prostate removed (largely for peace of mind), even though it extends life in only one out of 100 cases. The whole prostate gland needs to be removed because scarring caused by surgery makes it impossible to remove residual disease on a second attempt.

The better alternative is active surveillance. This involves quarterly PSA testing and repeat biopsies every one to three years. Other testing may include sophisticated imaging and genetic tests. If these tests indicate detectable tumor growth, then it's time to start treatment.

•**How would you treat intermediate- and high-risk prostate cancer?** High-risk cancer demands aggressive treatment, such as radiation combined with "seeds" (implants placed directly within cancerous tissues and tumors that deliver radiation treatment) and hormone therapy. Even though all these treatments do have side effects, they are typically preferable over surgery, since surgery often leaves some cancer behind, which then requires radiation and hormone therapy.

Intermediate-risk cancer is the most difficult to treat because in this case, a variety of treatment options are available, so it is difficult to choose one. Active surveillance alone may be a good option, but there is a 5% chance that during the next 10 years, the cancer could progress rapidly enough to need more aggressive treatment than it would have originally or will no longer be curable. One other possible treatment is a year or more of hormone therapy to shrink the tumor, followed by active surveillance. Or, as an alternative, radiotherapy with implanted seeds can be used.

Both the approaches have downsides—hormone therapy, which lowers testosterone levels, causes temporary loss of libido and may include several side effects such as hot flashes and weight gain, plus the uncertainty of waiting and a possible need for further treatment. Lasting impotence follows seed implants one-third of the time, and painful urination may persist. Bowel side effects, including diarrhea and rectal irritation, may occur and last two to six weeks. I tailor my recommendations for intermediate-risk patients based on individual characteristics, with surgery usually at the bottom of the list.

• **When is surgery the best choice?** Rarely, in my opinion. Surgery (whether open or laparoscopic) is no more effective than radiotherapy and more likely to trigger impotence or incontinence. Surgery may be indicated to remove a prostate that is too big to irradiate properly or for someone with a history of urinary tract problems that could be worsened by radiation.

• **How can a man with prostate cancer get the best care?** Don't just follow the advice of your urologist. Urology is a surgical specialty, so these doctors typically think that surgery is the best approach.

A medical oncologist, whose philosophy is geared toward the use of medicines rather than surgery to treat cancer, may help you consider more of your options in a relatively unbiased way. The best place to find a medical oncologist is at a university medical center or comprehensive cancer center. If possible, see an oncologist who specializes in prostate cancer.

Another Great Reason To Start Thinking Positively!

Testicular cancer patients who had positive thoughts showed improved mental health, in contrast to men who thought negatively or neutrally about their disease. The men who showed improvement wrote positively about their cancer in a journal for five weeks, writing things such as how the cancer had made them appreciate life more.

Men with testicular cancer often become depressed and/or anxious because chemotherapy and radiation treatment for the disease may temporarily interfere with sexual performance and fertility. Expressing positive feelings about the experience can help to improve the quality of life, especially since this disease usually

strikes younger men who will live a long time afterward.

Mark T. Morman, PhD, associate professor of communication studies and graduate program director, Baylor University, Waco, Texas, and coleader of a pilot study of 48 men with testicular cancer, presented at the International Communication Association Conference.

Chronic Constipation?

Brian Lacy, MD, PhD, director, Gastrointestinal Motility Laboratory, Dartmouth Medical School, Hanover, New Hampshire.

A low-fiber diet or medications that slow up gastrointestinal movement, including *calcium channel blockers*, *diuretics* and *Parkinson's drugs*, are among possible causes of chronic constipation.

My advice: Schedule daily bathroom times, such as 30 minutes after breakfast or dinner, when gut activity increases and prompts the bowel-movement urge. Consume roughly 30 grams (g) of fiber daily from fiber-rich foods, such as fruits, vegetables and whole grains, including brown rice and wheat germ. To avoid bloating and gas, slowly increase your fiber intake to this level.

If you have difficulty getting enough fiber into your diet, try taking one to three tablespoons daily of the natural high-fiber laxative *flaxseed*, crushed or mixed with juice. Drink eight ounces of water with flaxseed or any fiber supplement to help it add bulk to stool. Lastly, do not ever ignore the urge to have a bowel movement—you could eventually lose this sensation. Rarely, constipation can signal cancer. See a doctor if it's coupled with unintentional weight loss and/or blood in the stool and symptoms last longer than three weeks.

This Bread May Ease Constipation

When 51 constipated patients added rye bread into their diets for three weeks, they had better bowel function than people who added non-whole-grain wheat bread or took laxatives. Rye eaters had 23% shorter total intestinal transit times (how long it takes food to travel through the digestive tract) and 1.4 more weekly defecations. Rich in dietary fiber, magnesium and vitamin B-1, rye bread also lowers cholesterol and helps prevent diabetes and heart disease.

To ease constipation: Eat two slices of rye bread daily.

Reetta Holma, PhD, researcher, Institute of Biomedicine, University of Helsinki, Finland.

Probiotic Alert

Be wary of labels on probiotic supplements. When 13 supplements containing probiotics were analyzed, only two (Advocare ProBiotic Restore and Udo's Choice Adult's Probiotic) actually had the amount of healthful bacteria that was listed on their labels. Probiotic supplements might contain just 7% to 58% of the amount of bacteria indicated on the package by the time they are purchased.

Theory: Viable organisms in probiotic supplements may die off before the products are sold.

Self-defense: Buying probiotics from refrigerated cases and refrigerating them at home reduces the chances that the healthful bacteria will die.

Tod Cooperman, MD, founder, ConsumerLab.com, an independent supplement testing company in White Plains, New York.

Fiber Facts

Products fortified with fiber aren't as healthy as foods that naturally contain fiber.

A possible reason: The health benefits of naturally fiber-rich foods, such as fruits, vegetables and whole grains, are partially the result of the fiber's synergy with other naturally occurring nutrients—that synergy doesn't occur with so-called functional fiber, found in fiber-fortified products.

But: The added fiber in some fortified products can help relieve constipation and boost immune health.

Runner's World, 33 E. Minor St., Emmaus, Pennsylvania 18098, *www.runnersworld.com*.

Breakthrough: Antibiotic Relieves IBS

The antibiotic *rifaximin* can relieve *irritable bowel syndrome* (IBS) symptoms, such as bloating, abdominal pain and diarrhea, for up to 10 weeks after patients take it for two weeks. It is equally effective in men and women. Rifaximin was not tested in patients whose IBS causes constipation.

Mark Pimentel, MD, director of the GI Motility Program at Cedars-Sinai Medical Center, Los Angeles, and principal investigator in a study of rifaximin use, published in *The New England Journal of Medicine*.

Fun Way to Fight Diverticulitis

Vigorous activity fights off diverticulitis in men. Diverticulitis is the inflammation of pouches in the large intestine.

Recent finding: Men who exercised vigorously (the equivalent of three hours of running a week) had a 34% lower risk for diverticulitis and a 39% reduced risk for diverticular bleeding, compared with men who walked or did not exercise.

Lisa L. Strate, MD, MPH, assistant professor, division of gastroenterology at University of Washington School of Medicine in Seattle, and leader of a study of 47,228 men, published in the *American Journal of Gastroenterology*.

Better Colonoscopy Prep

When 116 patients took the complete dose of the colon-cleansing solution *polyethylene glycol electrolyte* the morning of a colonoscopy or split the dose between the night before and the morning of a colonoscopy, far more polyps were found in the morning-only group. This group also reported better sleep quality the night before having the procedure and less abdominal pain.

Before having a colonoscopy: Ask your doctor about possibly getting it in the afternoon with a morning-only colon prep. Morning doses are consumed seven hours, and then four hours, before the colonoscopy.

David Kastenberg, MD, associate professor of medicine, division of gastroenterology and hepatology, Jefferson Medical College, Philadelphia.

Colonoscopy That Provides More Accurate Cancer Detection

Doctors performed a standard colonoscopy on 1,000 adults, followed immediately by a colonoscopy only on the right side of the colon using the newer *retroflexion technique*, which involves turning the tip of the scope around inside the colon for increased visibility. Recent studies have shown colonoscopy to detect cancer less effectively in the right side of the colon—perhaps because colon prep is typically less thorough there.

Results: Retroflexion increased the number of polyps found by 14%.

When having a colonoscopy: Ask your doctor about retroflexion.

Douglas Rex, MD, distinguished professor of medicine at the Indiana University School of Medicine in Indianapolis.

Quick Colon Test Could Save Thousands Of Lives

A recent study found that a single *flexible sigmoidoscopy* test around age 60 could cut risk of colon cancer by about one-third. It is cheaper than a colonoscopy (important for people without insurance), takes an average of five minutes and involves no anesthesia. A tiny camera is used to detect any abnormal tissue in the lower-left side of the colon—where about two-thirds of all colon cancers occur—and assist in the removal of precancerous polyps. This colon test does require a night-before bowel preparation.

Wendy Atkin, PhD, MPH, professor of surgery and cancer, Imperial College London, England, and lead author of an 11-year study of 170,038 people ages 55 to 64, published in *The Lancet*.

Simple Pill Raises Colon Cancer Survival Rate 47%!

In a recent study, patients who started taking aspirin regularly for the first time after their colon cancer diagnoses had a 47% lower risk of dying from the disease than patients who did not take aspirin. Aspirin was most effective against the variety of colon cancer that overproduces an enzyme called *COX-2*.

Andrew T. Chan, MD, MPH, assistant professor of medicine at Harvard Medical School, Boston, and leader of a study of 1,279 colon cancer patients, published in *The Journal of the American Medical Association*.

7

Money Moves

When *Not* to Trust Your Gut—First Instincts Can Be Wrong...

We all make decisions at one time or another that can leave us wondering, *What was I thinking?* Even the most intelligent, cautious, well-informed people are not immune to occasional blunders. And those mistakes can be incredibly costly.

Example: Stephen Greenspan, the well-regarded clinical professor of psychiatry from University of Colorado, who studies gullibility and wrote a book back in 2008 called *Annals of Gullibility: Why We Get Duped and How to Avoid It*, lost 30% of his retirement savings in Bernard Madoff's Ponzi scheme.

Interestingly, whether our decision-making errors occur in our personal, professional or financial lives, they tend to follow predictable patterns. People who learn to recognize these patterns—and to spot salespeople, financial advisers and scammers who try to take advantage of the patterns—are likely to make fewer bad decisions.

Six common decision-making mistakes and how to do better...

Mistake 1: **We trust stories over statistics.** A 2004 study published in *Journal of Clinical Psychology in Medical Settings* found that individuals tend to opt for treatments that are accompanied by stories of other patients' successful recoveries—and avoid treatments that are accompanied by stories of patients who did not recover—even when the patients are informed that statistically the treatment linked to the negative anecdote is far more likely to be successful. The human brain simply finds it

---

Michael J. Mauboussin, chief investment strategist at the Baltimore-based investment company Legg Mason Capital Management. He is an adjunct professor of finance at Columbia Business School, New York City, and author of *Think Twice: Harnessing the Power of Counter-intuition* (Harvard Business). His Web site is *www.michaelmauboussin.com*.

easier to understand and believe stories than statistics.

Example: You are about to buy a Honda because of its high scores in vehicle-reliability surveys when a friend tells you about the problems he had with his Honda. Would you buy a different make of car instead? Many people would, though the experiences of the tens of thousands of vehicle owners summarized in vehicle-reliability surveys should mean much more than the opinion of the single car owner with whom you happened to talk.

What to do: Remind yourself to place more weight on statistical evidence than on any one person's story. If an anecdote proves too powerful to ignore, seek out additional anecdotes that point in the opposite direction, to get balance. Consumer-feedback Web sites generally provide a wide range of conflicting personal anecdotes.

Mistake 2: **We often think of ourselves as the exceptions.** From our own biased perspectives, we are special and not like everyone else. Thus our minds sometimes believe that the statistics and tendencies that apply to everyone else do not apply to us. That means that most of us are pretty good at judging the likely outcomes of other people's decisions. We run into trouble, however, when we try to predict the likely outcomes in our own lives.

Example: Most people know that kitchen renovations almost always run over their budgets and schedules, and yet very few home owners adjust their own renovation budgets and schedules to allow for overages. They're confident that they'll get everything done as planned—even if no one else does.

What to do: When you need to construct a schedule, budget or financial plan, pretend you are offering advice to a friend, not doing it for yourself.

Mistake 3: **When we hear a number, our mind becomes anchored to that number.** That may severely impede our ability to produce a truly objective numerical estimate or counteroffer.

Example: A group of people were asked to write down the final four digits of their phone numbers. Then they were all asked to

guess how many doctors there are in New York City. Those with phone numbers whose final four digits formed figures below 3,000 (for example, 555-2200) tended to come up with significantly lower estimates than those whose phone numbers formed figures above 7,000 (such as 555-9200). Their brains were unconsciously influenced by the phone number figure, even though they knew that it was completely unrelated to the guess they were striving to make. (*Correct amount:* There are about 20,000 doctors in New York City.)

This anchoring tendency can result in costly consequences. If a real estate agent says a home in our neighborhood recently sold for $600,000, our minds start to believe that the value of our home must be close to $600,000, even if the two properties are very different. If a broker tells us that a stock recently sold for $50 a share, its current $30 share price might seem like a tremendous value, even if it isn't.

What to do: There is no way to escape anchoring entirely. We can strive to anchor our minds to a relevant figure, however. Do some research before making a major purchase, producing a numerical estimate or setting a quantitative target. If you can focus on a useful figure or two—the wholesale cost of the product you wish to buy…the average price paid by other consumers…the price-to-earnings ratio (P/E) of other stocks in the sector—you are less likely to be anchored to an irrelevant figure.

Mistake 4: **We let subtle smells, sounds and background visuals influence our decisions.** A 2007 study found that 73% of shoppers selected a German wine from a display featuring both German and French wines when German music played…while French wines were the choice 77% of the time when French music played. Similar studies have found that retailers can influence our decisions on purchasing with smells and background images.

What to do: Be aware of your surroundings when deciding and, if possible, consider your decision under different conditions.

Mistake 5: **We tend to seek out information that confirms our beliefs, but we ignore any information that suggests we might be wrong.** When we make a decision, we also make an emotional investment in that decision being correct. Once we've done that, our minds try to protect us emotionally by deflecting any evidence that the decision might be incorrect.

Example: Salespeople sometimes try to convince customers to put down small deposits on large purchases. The salespeople know that once a deposit is made, customers' minds will steer them away from any evidence that completing the purchase would be a mistake. Questioning the purchase would obligate the customer to admit that making a deposit was a mistake.

What to do: Before settling on your favorite and making a deposit, list all your options on a sheet of paper, along with the pluses and minuses of each. Constantly entertain alternatives, including those that don't square with your view.

Mistake 6: **"We have always done it that way."** We often consider that a valid reason to continue doing something a certain way. Sometimes this makes sense—there isn't time to reconsider every preference, habit, choice. Trouble is, we often assume that our previous choices must still be the right choices, rather than just the easy choices.

What to do: When you catch yourself about to do something in the same way that you've done it before, pause to reflect on whether it's a good time for a reevaluation. Your priorities might have changed since you made the initial decision or new and better options might have appeared.

Found Money

The IRS has nearly $164.6 million in unclaimed refund checks. There are nearly 112,000 taxpayers who haven't received their tax refunds from 2009 due to mailing address errors. The average amount is $1,471. If you are missing a refund, update your address at *www.irs.gov*.

Internal Revenue Service.

Simple Money Savers Nobel-Prizewinning Economists Use

George Akerlof, PhD, Koshland Professor of Economics at University of California, Berkeley. He won the Nobel Prize in Economics in 2001. He is coauthor of *Identity Economics* (Princeton University).

Edward C. Prescott, PhD, the W.P. Carey Chair of Economics at Arizona State University's W.P. Carey School of Business, Tempe. He won the 2004 Nobel Prize in Economics. Prescott is coeditor of *Great Depressions of the Twentieth Century* (Federal Reserve Bank of Minneapolis).

Betsey Stevenson, PhD, assistant professor, The Wharton School, University of Pennsylvania, Philadelphia. She also is a faculty research fellow with the National Bureau of Economic Research and a visiting scholar with the Federal Reserve Bank of San Francisco.

Tahira K. Hira, PhD, a professor of personal finance and consumer economics, department of economics at Iowa State University, Ames, and creator of its Financial Counseling Clinic.

John Caskey, PhD, professor of economics and former chair of the department of economics, Swarthmore College in Swarthmore, Pennsylvania. He previously was economist with the International Monetary Fund. He is author of *Fringe Banking: Check-Cashing Outlets, Pawnshops, and the Poor* (Russell Sage Foundation).

Economists spend a lot of time exploring weighty subjects ranging from gross domestic product and stagflation to trade balances and yield curves. But when experts crunch numbers at home, the challenges they face and the solutions they find are not that different from what the rest of us often deal with. Learning how economists manage their money can help all of us to spend less, save more and invest more wisely, so we asked five prominent economists to reveal money-saving strategies that they use in their own lives...

GEORGE AKERLOF, PhD
University of California, Berkeley

Take out a 15-year mortgage. Back in the mid-1980s, I refinanced my 30-year mortgage to a 15-year mortgage. The shorter mortgage gave me thousands of dollars less in interest payments—and the higher monthly mortgage payments gave me experience living on a tight budget. That made it easier for me to continue to save aggressively even after my mortgage was paid off. (Recently, the average interest for a 30-year mortgage was 4.19%,* versus 3.43%

*Rates as of mid-August 2011.

125

for a 15-year loan, a savings of almost $50,000 for every $100,000 borrowed.)

Mortgages provide automatic savings discipline. We must make our mortgage payments each month or we could lose our homes. Thus, money needed to make mortgage payments is less likely to be misspent than money that is earmarked for bank and investment accounts.

EDWARD C. PRESCOTT, PHD
Arizona State University

Do not wait for a "better time" to invest. I don't get caught up in trying to time the markets. There is no wrong time to save and invest. When stocks are struggling, I tell myself, *Good—I can buy bargains*. When stocks are up, I say to myself, *Good—investing is paying off for me*. I don't get caught up in worrying about which investments to buy, either. I just put all of my savings into low-expense stock index mutual funds and in various exchange-traded funds (ETFs).

BETSEY STEVENSON, PhD
The Wharton School
University of Pennsylvania

Make sure your gifts are worth the cost. The rules of etiquette warn us not to arrive at a party empty-handed—but gift giving often is economically inefficient. The gift that costs us $40 might hold only $20 in value for its recipient. Like most people, when I'm in a situation that requires a gift, I usually bring a bottle of wine. It is not the most unusual or memorable gift, but if I select a wine that I know offers good quality for the price, my gift is likely to hold approximately as much value for its recipient as I paid for it, and it doesn't matter that he/she likely already owns bottles of wine.

If the recipient does not value wine, it is one of the easiest gifts for him to give to someone else. Economists tend to be less sensitive about such "regifting" than most people.

TAHIRA K. HIRA, PhD
Iowa State University

Set your spending priorities, and stick to them. Unfortunately, most people spend money on things that are not particularly important to them, which leaves them unable to afford things that would hold greater value.

In the early 1980s, when my husband and I were assistant professors who earned modest salaries, we decided that owning a home was high among our priorities. To afford the down payment, we willingly sacrificed—for instance, cutting back from two restaurant meals each week to an average of one or fewer. When we met with a real estate agent, we were encouraged to buy a larger home than we had saved up for because we could qualify for a larger mortgage. But my husband and I decided that we'd much rather have a modest home and enough assets left over to travel than a large home that consumed most of our resources. Because we had prioritized all our wants, the agent could not talk us into overspending.

JOHN CASKEY, PhD
Swarthmore College

Make it easy to save and hard to spend. The easier it is for us to spend our money, the more likely it is that we will do so. I build up almost all of my savings by having money automatically withdrawn from my paycheck and invested. That money never even makes it to my bank account, so it is difficult for me to spend it.

And with the case of tax-advantaged retirement accounts, there is a penalty for taking out money early, so that is an additional deterrent to spending.

Throw Out the Old Rules About Money— What to Do Instead

Ric Edelman, chairman and CEO of Edelman Financial Services LLC, a financial advisory firm that manages more than $6 billion in assets, Fairfax, Virginia. *Barron's* has chosen him for seven straight years as one of America's 100 top independent financial advisers, ranking him number one in both 2009 and 2010. Edelman has written seven books, including *The Truth About Money* (Harper-Business). His Web site is *www.ricedelman.com*.

When it comes to finances, the conventional wisdom often is your enemy. What everyone knows to be true is typically what trips you up.

The advice I give to my clients often is unconventional—it sounds and feels unfamiliar and is typically in sharp contrast to what they commonly hear—but I believe it is exactly the right thing to do in these turbulent times, and it has paid off for my clients over and over…

MORTGAGE MYTH

Conventional mortgage wisdom: Pay off your home mortgage as soon as possible using extra payments.

My unconventional wisdom: Keep a long-term mortgage, typically 30 years, regardless of your age or income, even if you can pay it off sooner.

Why it's smarter: Owning your home outright saddles you with some pretty significant disadvantages nowadays, such as a lack of liquidity. Every dollar you give to the bank is one that you will never get back until you sell your home. You may need that money if you lose your job unexpectedly or run into a costly medical expense. Making extra payments is like stuffing money into a mattress—it doesn't reduce the interest rate on the mortgage. All it does is reduce the amount of time that you will be sending in payments and the amount of interest you end up paying (assuming that you do not sell the home or refinance before the mortgage runs out). And the less that you are paying in interest, the less you can claim for tax deductions.

Instead, put that money to work in a diversified investment portfolio, possibly one composed of a mix of passively managed "index" funds to keep expenses low.

RETIREMENT PLANNING NO-NO

Conventional IRA wisdom: Convert your traditional IRA to a Roth IRA. Although you have to pay income taxes on the money you convert now, your withdrawals in retirement, including your gains, will be tax-free.

My unconventional wisdom: Forget about Roth IRAs, which are designed to get you to pay taxes earlier.

Why it's smarter: Converting to a Roth IRA does nothing to increase your finances. For example, I had a client in the 25% federal income tax bracket with a $100,000 IRA. If he converted the IRA to a Roth, he would have to pay tax and would be left with $75,000. Say the Roth doubled in 10 years thanks to shrewd

investments. It would then be worth $150,000. Instead, say this same person sticks with the traditional IRA and it doubles in a decade to $200,000. After paying taxes, my client would wind up with $150,000, the same amount but without the hassle, assuming that he still is in the same tax bracket at the end of those 10 years.

Also, Congress might decide to tax Roth IRA withdrawals in the future or make them subject to Alternative Minimum Tax (AMT).

WRONG PENSION CHOICE

Conventional pension wisdom: When you retire with a pension, always take the "joint and survivor" option that companies often offer. It pays you income for as long as you live and keeps paying after you die for as long as your spouse lives.

My unconventional wisdom: Set up your own "joint and survivor" plan.

Why it's smarter: Accepting the "joint and survivor" option means that you get as much as 25% less in each monthly pension payment. Instead, opt for the highest monthly pension payout or an up-front lump-sum payout, and purchase a life insurance policy, naming your spouse as beneficiary. If your spouse dies first, you can cancel the insurance and keep collecting the higher payout for the rest of your life.

LONG-TERM-CARE CAUTION

Conventional long-term-care advice: Purchase long-term-care (LTC) insurance with lifetime benefits, which pays for at-home health care or nursing home or assisted-living care as long as you live. It's very expensive, but you won't have to rely on family members for care or spend down your assets, so your children will inherit more.

My unconventional wisdom: Opt for five years of LTC benefits rather than benefits for lifetime.

Why this is smarter: The average nursing home stay is less than three years, and fewer than 12% of people who enter a nursing home stay more than five years. I have found that a policy offering five years of benefits often (but not always) is sufficient, and premiums are as much as 50% less.

Consider adding on a shared-care rider. This lets you use the benefits offered by your spouse's policy if you exhaust your own benefits.

FLAWED INFLATION FIGHTER

Conventional inflation-fighting wisdom: Treasury Inflation-Protected Securities (TIPS), whose principal is adjusted based on inflation, are the ideal investment to help protect your portfolio from inflation.

My unconventional wisdom: You cannot rely on TIPS to protect your portfolio from inflation.

Why it's smarter: If inflation soars, no one knows whether TIPS actually will succeed as an effective hedge. We have never experienced a prolonged inflationary situation since TIPS were introduced a little more than a decade ago. If interest rates rise more quickly than the inflation rate rises, that would increase the yield offered by new Treasury bonds, possibly making them more attractive than TIPS and possibly driving down returns on TIPS mutual funds. Plus, there's no guarantee that inflation will spike in 2011 or even 2012. High unemployment continues to stifle one of the main drivers of inflation—rising wages. If inflation remains low in 2011, you actually could lose money in TIPS this year.

529 PROBLEM

Conventional college-savings advice: The best way for grandparents to contribute to a grandchild's education is a 529 college savings plan. These state-operated plans are designed to help families set aside funds for future college costs by offering tax breaks.

My unconventional wisdom: Most grandparents should skip 529 plans.

Why it's smarter: There's no assurance that your grandkids will require the money. They might win scholarships or not go to college at all. What's more, their parents might incur problems of their own, such as divorce or job loss, causing them to raid the account that you helped fund. One other drawback is that 529 plans limit options for investing money. Most important, you may need that money yourself for health-care or other expenses.

Better: Talk to your estate-planning attorney about setting up a tax-free trust for your young grandchild, and stipulate that it remain untouched until the child reaches retirement age. In the long run, that will serve the child much better than your contributions to a college fund.

Strapped for Cash? How to Raid Your Retirement Accounts

Rick Meigs, founder and president of 401kHelpCenter.com, based in Portland, Oregon. He is coauthor of *Your 401(k) Survival Guide* (Authorhouse) and cohost of *The Retirement Hour* on a Portland radio station.

The number of individuals raiding their retirement accounts has soared despite the substantial drawbacks of doing so. If you have already exhausted the other ways to raise money, such as home-equity loans or college loans, here's what you need to know about drawing on 401(k)s and similar tax-advantaged accounts...

401(K)s

Federal regulations require that 401(k) hardship withdrawals be used only for "immediate and heavy financial need," such as staving off a foreclosure or paying unreimbursed medical bills, college tuition or funeral expenses for a family member. If you are under age 59½, you typically have a 10% early-withdrawal penalty for hardship withdrawals, in addition to having to pay income tax on them for that year. If you are age 59½ or older, you still pay the taxes but not the penalty. You also may qualify for a penalty-free withdrawal under some circumstances (see below).

Note: Not all employers choose to permit hardship withdrawals.

• **Determine whether you qualify for a penalty-free early withdrawal.** If you're under 59½, the IRS specifies very limited circumstances that allow you to avoid the penalty, although you're still liable for taxes.

Examples: You are in debt for medical expenses that go beyond 7.5% of your adjusted gross income...you become totally disabled... you are required by a court order to give the money to your divorced spouse, a child or a dependent.

More information: Check out *www.irs.gov/publications/p575.*

Important: If you are at least age 55 and leave your job, the early withdrawal penalties do not apply.

Drawbacks: Once you've taken a hardship withdrawal—with or without a penalty—you can't just put back those funds when you have the money. However, you can continue to contribute new money to your 401(k) account as long as you remain employed by the 401(k) sponsor.

• **Borrow from your 401(k).** Most, but not all, plans allow workers of any age to borrow up to half of the vested balance in their accounts, up to $50,000, without any withdrawal penalties or taxes. Unlike hardship withdrawals, there are no IRS rules regarding what the money must be used for. And unlike many kinds of loans, there are no credit checks and minimal paperwork is involved.

Annual interest rates usually are one percentage point above the prime rate, which is 3.25%,* and most employers deduct monthly loan payments, with interest, from your paycheck. (Of course, you are paying interest to yourself, which reduces the sting.) You need to repay the loan back to your account within five years.

Exception: If you borrow the money to buy a primary residence, you have up to 15 years.

Drawbacks: If you lose your job or switch jobs, the remaining balance of the loan typically becomes due within 60 days. Should you not meet this deadline, the balance is considered an early withdrawal subject to taxes and a 10% penalty if you are under 59½.

IRAs

• **Take early distributions from your IRA.** You typically must pay a 10% early-distribution penalty if you take money from a traditional IRA before age 59½. This is in addition to the

*Rates as of mid-August 2011.

income tax you pay on withdrawals from IRAs funded with deductible contributions. Federal rules do allow you to make early withdrawals (prior to age 59½) from an IRA without penalties if you withdraw equal amounts once a year over a minimum of five years...or equal annual amounts until age 59½ if that would extend the withdrawals to a later date.

You pay income tax on these equal annual withdrawals, which are called 72(t) distributions. This route is best if you are within a few years of retirement so that you don't have to spread the withdrawals over a prolonged period. (Similar rules apply to 401(k)s, but additional hurdles are involved, so this type of distribution is not often used for those accounts.)

Drawbacks: You'll be assessed a 10% early-withdrawal penalty on all withdrawals if you don't strictly adhere to the required schedule of withdrawals.

Special circumstances: Under certain circumstances, you can withdraw IRA money early without the five-year schedule and without the penalty. *These circumstances include...*

• If you are buying any home for the first time or at least two years after you last owned one, you can take a distribution up to $10,000 to use for expenses, including closing costs.

• If you have lost a job, you can withdraw enough to pay medical insurance premiums... and/or unreimbursed medical expenses that exceed 7.5% of your adjusted gross income.

• If you need to pay qualified higher-education expenses, like tuition, fees and books for college, university or vocational school for yourself or an immediate family member.

• If you are disabled or become disabled as a result of a mental or physical problem.

• **Take from your Roth IRA.** Because the money you contributed to Roth accounts was taxed before you made the Roth contributions, you are permitted to make early withdrawals of those contributions at any age, though not earnings on those contributions, without paying penalties or taxes. You also pay no taxes on the account's earnings after age 59½ as long as it is at least five years since you made your first Roth contribution.

Pawnshop Primer

Eric Modell, executive vice president of Modell Financial, Inc., which has eight pawnshops in Manhattan, Brooklyn and Queens. Modell is on the board of directors of the National Pawnbrokers Association. His Web site is *www.gmodell.net.*

Gone are the days of pawnshops as places to unload stolen goods. In many municipalities, pawnshops are required to provide law enforcement with a daily list of all pawned items, along with descriptions including serial numbers (if applicable).

A pawnshop's primary role is to offer small, short-term loans using merchandise as collateral—though you also can buy and sell items at most pawnshops. The top five categories of pawned items in the country are jewelry, electronics, musical instruments, tools and guns.

The time within which the borrower has to repay a loan is called the hold period—it is set by each state and varies throughout the country, anywhere from 30 days up to six months. Interest rates on the loan also are set by each state and generally range from 2% to 25% per month.*

If you don't pay back the loan and the interest, you lose your collateral, but it does not impact on future loans as it would with an unpaid bank loan—and there are no credit score issues to haunt you.

*Rates subject to change.

Find Lost Money On the Web

There are Web sites where you might find missing money. MissingMoney.com is one database of unclaimed property, such as bank accounts, stocks, bonds and insurance policies. PBGC.gov, it's run by the Pension Benefit Guaranty Corporation, tracks pensions owed to retirees who have worked for organizations with defined-benefit plans. IRS.gov compiles a list of unclaimed tax refunds. TreasuryDirect. gov's "Treasury Hunt" can find out if there are savings bonds that you have not claimed. And Unclaimed.org looks for abandoned checking and savings accounts, uncashed dividend and payroll checks and more.

What to do: Visit all the sites—there is no charge for any of them. Be prepared to type in plenty of identifying information, including name and maiden name if applicable, states where you have resided, and Social Security number at government-run sites.

Geoff Williams, author, *Living Well with Bad Credit* (HCI), writing at WalletPop.com.

Smarter Debt Payment

Pay off your smallest debt first to be motivated to continue paying off your debts. Most financial advisers do recommend paying your largest debts and those with the highest interest rate first, but that can take time, which can be frustrating. Paying off the smallest debt completely makes you feel that you really are making progress.

Caution: Be sure that you continue to make at least minimum payments on larger obligations, such as car loans, credit card bills and student loans.

Dave Ramsey, financial counselor, Brentwood, Tennessee, *www.daveramsey.com,* and author of *The Total Money Makeover* (Thomas Nelson).

Your Rights When Defaulting on Debt

If you default on a credit card bill or other debt, your debt could be sold to multiple collection agencies, resulting in repeated calls from several firms.

Reason: The debt-buying business is largely unregulated.

If you get calls: You can ask for proof that the organization has the right to collect your debt—it must send you verification within five days of receiving your request. You also can investigate your state's statute of limitations—you may not have to pay past a certain date.

Important: Respond quickly to any court notice—if you do not, your wages could be garnished or your bank accounts frozen.

Gerri Detweiler, credit adviser for the credit education Web site Credit.com, president of Ultimate Credit Solutions, *www.ultimatecredit.com,* and author of *Debt Collection Answers* (available from the author).

More from Gerri Detweiler...

Best Time to Negotiate Debt

Try to negotiate debt settlements by year-end. In December, credit card issuers and collection agencies are most willing to accept less than the full amount owed because they want to bring in whatever cash they can to improve balance sheets. Their balance sheets are in particularly bad shape this year because so many borrowers are unable to repay their debts.

Stash Your Cash Online To Get the Best Rates on Savings and Checking

Allan S. Roth, CFP, CPA, president of Wealth Logic, LLC, a financial advisory firm in Colorado Springs. He has made tens of thousands of extra dollars investing in online bank accounts and believes that a "dull" portfolio may be the best kind. He's the author of *How a Second Grader Beats Wall Street: Golden Rules Any Investor Can Learn* (Wiley). His Web site is *www.daretobedull.com.*

It is probably time to dump that money-market mutual fund if you haven't already. Sure, these funds were convenient when they had decent yields a few years ago...and they can be handy if you might want to shift the money into the stock market at very short notice. But yields today are miniscule—you typically get less than 0.2%, or $20, in interest annually on every $10,000—and there is no sign that yields will get much better any time soon.*

*Rates as of mid-August 2011.

You can find yields one or more percentage points higher with very little effort by using online-bank savings and checking accounts and online-bank certificates of deposit (CDs), which have lower expenses than accounts at bank branches. And you can easily shift the money electronically to and from other accounts within a few days.

Important: Make sure that your online accounts are covered by the Federal Deposit Insurance Corporation (FDIC), as all the bank accounts listed in this article are. Also, don't invest more than the insured limit, which is generally $250,000 per depositor, at any one institution. Credit union accounts have similar coverage.

HIGH-YIELD SAVINGS ACCOUNTS

The average annual percentage yield (APY) for bank savings and money-market accounts around the country is just 0.6%, but you can get nearly double that online with very little or no minimum balance requirement. Based on the Federal Reserve rules, consumers are allowed to make up to six free withdrawals or transfers from a savings account per month. However, it's up to the banks to set their own rules within those limits, and many allow only two to four withdrawals per month without a penalty. Exceed that number, and you may be hit with a fee of $3 to $10 per transaction. It's also helpful to look for offers that give you bonuses for signing up and/or maintaining a certain account balance. *My favorite easy-to-use online savings accounts...*

For consistently high rates...

• **Capital One InterestPlus Online Savings.** APY is 1.01% on balances of at least $1,000. If your balance is at least $10,000 every month in a quarter or you use a Capital One credit card at least once a month, you earn a 10% bonus on interest. *www.capitalone.com/directbanking.*

Note: Capital One offers a 1.15% APY if you are a Costco member and make a $5,000 minimum initial deposit.

For moving money from savings into top-paying CDs...

• **Discover Bank Online Savings.** APY is 1.10%. Discover offers simple online transfers into CDs with maturities ranging from three months up to 10 years, and the CD rates are consistently above the national average. *www. discoverbank.com*.

For savings with regular contributions…

• **SmartyPig Savings Account.** APY is 1.1% on balances up to $50,000…0.5% on balances over $50,000. This is not a typical savings account. It's an online savings service affiliated with BBVA Compass. *www.smartypig.com*.

How it works: You set up a goal that you would like to achieve, make an initial deposit and agree to make monthly deposits to meet that goal. The minimum requirement for a savings goal is $250. There are no fees to join, save or withdraw. Minimum initial deposit is $25.

INTEREST CHECKING ACCOUNTS

In general, look for online checking accounts that have no minimum balance and no monthly fees…and that offer free paper checks and overdraft protection. *My favorites…*

For consistently high rates…

• **Capital One Interest Online Checking.** APY is at 1.01%. Reimbursement of up to $25 each statement cycle for ATM fees charged by other banks. Go to *www.capitalone.com/direct banking*.

• **Heritage Bank NA eCentive.** APY is 1.71% on balances up to $25,000. *www.heritagebank na.com/ecentive*.

• **Avidia Bank eChecking.** It recently yielded 2.01%. *www.avidiabank.com*.

• **Bank of Internet USA Rewards Checking.** It recently yielded 1.25%. *www.bankofinternet. com*.

For a *combination* of online checking and savings…

• **Ally Interest Checking.** APY is 0.9% for balances of $15,000 and up…0.5% below that. Ally Financial, formerly called General Motors Acceptance Corp. (GMAC), refunds ATM fees charged by other banks. No-fee overdraft protection linked to savings. **Ally Online Savings Account.** APY is 1.0%. *www.ally.com*.

If you don't want to mail in your deposits…

• **EverBank Yield Pledge Checking.** APY is 0.51% during the first year on balances under $10,000…0.61% from $10,000 up to $24,999… 0.85% from $25,000 to $49,999…0.95% from $50,000 to $99,999…and up to 1.01% beyond that. (After the first year, the ongoing APYs range from 0.51% to 1.01%.) An inconvenience of most online checking is having to mail in your checks for deposit or deposit checks at your local bank and then initiate an electronic transfer. EverBank permits you to make a deposit by scanning in your check at home and e-mailing the scan, utilizing the bank's secure Web site. *www.everbank.com*.

For higher yields, if you don't mind all the requirements of Rewards Checking…

These types of accounts may offer high APYs, but typically they are brimming with fees, penalties and requirements, such as having to make 20 debit card purchases.

CERTIFICATES OF DEPOSIT

Be sure to read the full disclosure for any hidden fees in the CDs that you get. *My favorites include…*

For consistently high rates…

• **Six-month CD: Ascencia Bank.** APY is 1.02%. *www.ascenciabank.com*.

• **One-year CD: Ally Bank.** APY is 1.16%. *www.ally.com*.

• **Three-year CD: Discover Bank.** APY is 1.70% and offers BJ's Wholesale Club members a BJ's gift card for $75. *http://bjs.discover bank.com*.

• **Five-year CDs: Discover Bank.** APY is at 2.35%. *www.discoverbank.com/cd.html*.

Runner-up: Sallie Mae Bank. APY is 2.09%. *http://go.salliemae.com/bank*.

• **Seven-year CD: Pentagon Federal Credit Union seven-year CD.** APY is 2.75%. Most investors are not able to take advantage of attractive credit union CD rates because membership is restricted. But anyone can receive entry to this credit union just by becoming a member of the National Military Family Association. The $20 fee for the first year is worth it—and once you are a Pentagon Federal Credit Union member, you don't have to requalify. *www.pen fed.org*.

• **My favorite adjustable-rate CD: The Ally Raise Your Rate two-year CD.** APY is 1.34%. Also known as a "bump-up" CD, this allows you to increase your interest rate once without extending the length of the CD if interest rates rise. *www.allybank.com*.

Runner-up: **The USAA Bank three-year adjustable-rate CD.** APY is at 0.51% for balances of $1,000 to $94,999…0.56% for $95,000 to $174,999…0.71% for $175,000 and up. *www.usaa.com.*

•**No-penalty CD: The Ally No Penalty 11-month CD.** APY is at 1.1%. It has no early-withdrawal fees. You can cash out your entire balance plus all interest earned any time after the first six days. *www.ally.com.*

Also: If the rate Ally offers on this CD rises within 10 days after you open it, you automatically get the higher rate.

•**Long-term CD with low early-withdrawal penalties: Ally five-year CD.** APY is 2.2%. Ally penalizes early withdrawals with just 60 days' worth of interest on the amount that is withdrawn. *www.ally.com.*

Just Say No! to High Penalties

Say "no" to high-penalty overdraft protection. Under new federal rules that took effect in summer 2010, if you try to make a debit card purchase or ATM withdrawal for more than is in your account, the bank will deny the transaction unless you've agreed to overdraft protection. That protection could trigger penalties of $30 or more.

Instead: Sign up for a version of overdraft protection that has smaller penalties because it is linked to your savings account or to a line of credit.

Greg McBride, CFA, a senior financial analyst for Bankrate.com, which tracks interest rates and other trends at banks and other lending institutions, North Palm Beach, Florida, *www.bankrate.com.*

Checking Accounts For Teens

Checking accounts for teenagers are being offered by banks to youths as young as 13. Some banks provide online tools and educational material to help teens learn about managing money. A parent usually is co-owner of a teen checking account, with full access to it.

What to do: Shop around for an account with minimal fees—and have your teen help as part of his/her financial education. Review your teen's account regularly online. Because banks usually let parents monitor the account, consider initially establishing withdrawal limits and increasing them as your teen shows financial responsibility.

Tanya Breeling, vice president at Young Americans Bank, a division of Young Americans Center for Financial Education, based in Denver, *www.yacenter.org.*

Banks That Have Your Back

Identity theft affected more than 8.1 million Americans in 2010. Javelin Strategy & Research reviews financial institutions' online security protocols and uses "mystery shoppers" to ask banks security-related questions to evaluate how well the banks are protecting their customers. Among the safest banks in the recent annual survey, starting with the safest, are Bank of America…US Bank…Citibank…PNC Bank…Wells Fargo…HSBC Bank…and USAA. Consumers also can take steps to make sure that their identities are protected. Find out if your bank sends alerts when suspicious transactions are posted. See if your bank will let you ask and answer your own security question to verify your identity instead of relying on standard identifiers, such as your mother's maiden name. Monitor your bank balances and credit card activity at least once per week by phone, online or at an ATM so that you can spot and deal with any problems quickly.

James Van Dyke, president of Javelin Strategy & Research, Pleasanton, California, *www.javelinstrategy.com.*

Why You Should Know Your Credit Score—How Even a Small Dip Now Can Hurt You

John Ulzheimer, president of consumer education for SmartCredit.com, a credit information Web site in Costa Mesa, California. He previously worked with credit rating organizations Fair Isaac (FICO) and Equifax.

Turbulence in the economy and the financial industry has probably affected your creditworthiness, even if you have not lost your work or forgotten a single loan payment. Some lenders have taken steps that lowered their customers' credit scores—even though many of those customers did not do anything wrong. The industry's changes may have made it harder for you to borrow money for a car or house, obtain the best credit cards and even get the best insurance terms.

Here's what you need to know about your creditworthiness so that you are in control of your borrowing options. *You may be surprised by some of the ways that your credit score can be hurt, and how a lower score can hurt you...*

HIGHER BAR FOR LOW RATES

In 2007, a credit score of 680 (out of 850) would have qualified a borrower for the most attractive credit card, mortgage and car-loan terms. Today lenders consider that same 680 score closer to subprime than grade A.

Interest rates currently are very low by historical standards—but those attractive rates are available only to borrowers with extremely high credit scores...

•**Mortgage rates.** Rates as low as 3.9%* are available now on 30-year fixed mortgages but only to borrowers with credit scores of at least 760. A once-respectable score of 620 is more likely to receive a rate of 5.5%. That is a difference of around $86,000 over the life of a $250,000 30-year mortgage.

•**Auto loans.** Rates as low as 4.3% are available on 48-month new-car loans from independent lenders. Dealership financing departments occasionally feature rates as low as 0%, but only

*Rates as of mid-August 2011.

buyers with credit scores of at least 720 receive these terms. With a score of 680, the best available interest rate from independent lenders is likely to shoot up to 7.8%—resulting in more than $1,500 in extra payments on a $20,000 four-year car loan.

•**Credit cards.** Aside from short-term teaser rates, the lowest interest rates currently offered by credit card issuers are around 9.9%. You will need a credit score of at least 740 to be approved for those rates, however. If your score is closer to 680, you'll be lucky to find a 17.9% rate—and you might not do better than 19.9%. That's an extra $700 to $1,200 per year for each $10,000 in revolving debt.

•**Insurance.** Many vehicle insurance and homeowners insurance companies now check credit scores of policyholders and applicants. A low score could mean higher premiums or a rejected application—even for those who have never made an insurance claim. Also, the utility companies check credit scores to determine security deposit requirements.

HOW SCORES GET HURT

Lower credit limits: Issuers of credit cards have been slashing credit limits even for responsible cardholders, not just for those who miss payments. Lower limits don't just mean less spending power—they can also result in a substantially lower credit score. How? When credit limits drop, the percentage of available credit used rises, even if your spending does not increase. "Credit-utilization ratio" is a crucial factor in credit scoring.

Example: A man who has one credit card uses just 5% of his card's available credit line. He has an excellent credit score of 780. If the man's card issuer decreases his credit limit by 50%, then his credit-utilization ratio increases sharply and his credit score could plummet all the way to 650—subprime—even though this man has done nothing wrong.

In spite of the recent credit card industry reforms, card issuers are not required to warn customers when their credit limits are lowered.

If you have many credit cards, one card issuer slashing one credit limit might have only a small effect on your credit score—but cuts on credit limits can often snowball. When your other lenders see that your credit limit and credit score have fallen, they might get jittery and cut the credit limits on their cards, too.

Strategy for fixing the problem: Check your credit card account statements each time you pay your bills. If the credit limit on any of your cards is lowered, ask the lender to reconsider the decision. Also, immediately request increases from other lenders, and do everything possible to pay down all of your cards.

To maximize this component of your credit score, you must use less than 10% of the overall credit limit. Strive to boost your limit high enough so that you rarely exceed this percentage, even if that means hanging on to or adding credit cards that you'll seldom use. (Debit cards have zero effect on your score because they automatically draw on your accounts to pay expenses.)

Mortgage arrangements: Many people do not realize that some of the alternatives to a foreclosure can damage their credit scores just as much as foreclosure itself would. *These can include...*

●**Selling the home through a short sale.** With this arrangement, the lender agrees to accept less than the full amount owed on the home.

●**Deed-in-lieu of foreclosure.** In this case, property is handed over to the lender to satisfy the mortgage. There is no foreclosure proceeding, and the home owner is released from any further financial obligations.

Either of these actions is likely to result in a drop of 100 to 200 points or even more to the home owner's credit score—just as a foreclosure would.

Strategy for fixing the problem: There is no quick way to erase from your credit report the negative effect of a mortgage gone bad. It sometimes is possible to return a credit score to respectability, however. Pay off all of your credit cards until you are using less than 10% of your available credit limit. This sometimes adds as many points to the credit score as a mortgage problem subtracts.

More from John Ulzheimer...

Best Ways to Check Your Credit Score

By far the most important piece of information about your creditworthiness is your FICO credit score. Today's lenders and insurance companies rarely dig into the details of a credit report. They typically just check the FICO score—which can fluctuate somewhat depending on which credit-reporting agency's data is used—and judge the applicant based on this score. Even though there are tricks to getting estimated FICO scores and alternative credit scores at no cost, there are only three places to obtain your actual FICO score, and not one of them is free...

●**Fair Isaac,** which compiles the FICO score (800-319-4433, *www.myfico.com,* $19.95 for your FICO score and credit report*).

●**Equifax** (866-493-9788, *www.equifax.com,* select "Equifax Products," click the "Single Use Products" tab, then click on "Complete Report" $39.95).

●**TransUnion** (800-888-4213, *www.transunion.com,* click "Personal," then "3-Bureau Credit Report," $29.95).

The financial industry overhaul bill signed by President Obama in July 2010 requires that consumers get a free look at their credit scores when they are rejected for a loan, credit card, insurance rate or apartment because of their scores.

Meanwhile, several free online credit score estimator tools can give you a reasonable idea where your score likely stands, including...

●**Bankrate.com** (*www.bankrate.com/calculators.aspx,* select "FICO Score Estimator" from the "Credit Card Calculators" section).

●**Credit.com** (*www.credit.com/calculators,* select "Credit Score Estimator").

●**Quizzle.com** (*www.quizzle.com*).

Be skeptical of all "free credit score" offers. Many of these contain hidden costs...and the score provided is unlikely to be a FICO credit score. Each of us is entitled to receive a free copy of a credit report (which does not include a credit score, but it does give details of your

*Prices subject to change.

credit history) every year from AnnualCredit Report.com. To help protect yourself from identity theft and incorrect information, scan your report for listings that you don't recognize or that don't seem accurate.

Stricter Requirements For Retail Credit Cards

Store credit card issuers now consider applicants' income and ability to repay before giving out cards. Be prepared to provide financial information as you would with a bank to which you are applying to get a credit card. The retail card application may ask for it...or the lender might judge the applicant according to income estimation models, based on card application information, credit bureau data and information from employment and IRS databases.

Chi Chi Wu, staff attorney, National Consumer Law Center, Washington, DC.

Beware: Unactivated Credit Cards Can Hurt Your Score

A credit card that has not been activated still affects your credit score. Credit scores treat activated and unactivated cards the same way—which means that canceling a card that you never activated is considered an account closure, which could hurt your credit score.

What to do: Apply only for credit cards that you intend to activate and use.

Barry Paperno, consumer operations manager for FICO, the organization that creates the credit-scoring model, Minneapolis.

Instant Fraud Warnings For You

Combat credit card fraud with new *instant alerts*. These alerts are transmitted in seconds, via text message or e-mail, rather than taking up to 48 hours to reach cardholders, as with older services. Visa recently launched the free Rapid Alerts service with Wells Fargo. MasterCard's version is called inControl. Check with your card issuer about the availability of this service.

Bill Hardekopf, founder and CEO of LowCards.com, a credit card information site.

Make the Most of Your Credit Card Rewards

Not all credit card rewards are worthwhile. Catalog products tend to require more rewards points than the items are worth. Saving points for airline travel usually is a bad idea because card issuers often raise points required for tickets.

To maximize the value of rewards: Take them in cash if possible. For travel, use a credit card that allows you to use rewards points at multiple airlines and a variety of hotels. If you cannot get cash rewards and want retail items, use your rewards to buy a retailer's gift card instead of buying items through a points catalog.

CBS MoneyWatch.com.

Smart Credit Cards Coming Soon

Smarter credit cards are pending. The *Citi ThankYou Prestige 2G Card*, this is being tested with select customers, will let its users decide whether to charge a purchase or pay with rewards points by pushing a button on the card. Another design allows one card to be used for two separate accounts, such as a personal and a business account. And a third card is designed to prevent identity theft—it displays only partial account numbers until the user enters the PIN.

Kiplinger's Personal Finance, 1729 H St. NW, Washington, DC 20006, *www.kiplinger.com.*

Credit Card for Your College Student

Credit card options for college-age children are limited now. Under a new law, adults age 18 to 20 must have an independent source of income or a co-signer to open a new credit card account.

Alternatives: Authorized user cards with credit limits add a student to a parent's card at a lower limit than the parent has. The parent remains liable for all charges. Debit cards are easy to get and widely accepted. They are limited to the money in the account to which they are tied. Secured credit cards require up-front deposits—and that amount becomes the card's spending limit. Consider choosing a secured card that will convert to a regular, nonsecured card after a year or two of responsible spending.

CreditCards.com.

Savvy Home Buying Secret

Buy a home in a top school district even if you don't have school-age children. Houses in areas with good public schools gain value in up markets and sell faster and at higher prices in down markets. If costs and taxes are too high in an area with top-rated schools, re-

search test scores, teacher credentials, funding and community support in other areas to find school districts that are improving but where homes do not yet sell at premiums.

David N. Figlio, PhD, professor of education and social policy, Northwestern University, Evanston, Illinois, who has studied the relationship between home prices and schools.

Buying a New Home? Take Note of These Red Flags

Poor water pressure could indicate plumbing problems...doors that are tough to close, swing open by themselves or don't open fully could point to structural problems...multiple extension cords could mean that the electrical system is inadequate...a porch, patio or driveway that slopes toward the house could lead to water in the basement.

What to do: When having a home professionally inspected before you buy it, go with the inspector to make observations and ask questions.

Kathleen Kuhn, president of HouseMaster, a home-inspection company, Bound Brook, New Jersey, *www.housemaster.com.*

Should You Recast Your Mortgage?

Recasting your mortgage can let you reduce monthly payments for a small fee—without applying for a new loan or paying for a reappraisal. Recasting—also called reamortizing—can be done only with certain existing fixed-rate loans. Ask your lender if yours qualifies. If it does, you can pay down a substantial portion of the outstanding mortgage principal to reduce the monthly payments, including the amount of interest, for the remaining loan term. If you have cash, want to reduce monthly payments and can't refinance (perhaps because you had a loan that required no employment, income or asset verification), recasting may be an inexpensive option—a bank may charge only $150 or $250* for it. But there might be investment and tax consequences.

What to do: If your mortgage is eligible, ask your financial adviser if recasting makes sense for you.

Keith Gumbinger, vice president at HSH Associates, Pompton Plains, New Jersey, which provides mortgage and consumer loan information, *www.hsh.com.*

*Prices subject to change.

Short Sale Can Wreck Your Credit

The company Fair Isaac, which creates the FICO credit score, considers a short sale of a home the same as a foreclosure because the sale involves transferring the home for less than the amount required to pay off all mortgages on it. This appears on your credit report as a "settled" debt and can reduce your credit score by 200 to 300 points.

Mary Hunt, editor, DebtProofLiving.com, based in Paramount, California.

Home-Remodeling Projects That Boost Value

A steel entry-door replacement will cost an average of $1,218*—but you can get back 102.1% of the cost when selling. Garage-door replacement can cost $1,291 and returns about 84% of that at sale. A wood-deck addition can cost $10,973 and returns roughly 73% at sale. Minor kitchen remodeling costs $21,695 and returns about 73% at sale. These numbers are

*Prices and rates subject to change.

national averages and vary widely by region and type of material.

Remodeling Magazine and the National Association of Realtors 2010–2011 "Remodeling Cost vs. Value Report," which compares construction costs with resale values for 35 remodeling projects in 80 markets in the US.

Best College Values for Your Money

Below are public and private colleges that give you a lot for the cost...

Public colleges and universities: University of Virginia in Charlottesville...City University of New York–Hunter College in New York City...New College of Florida, Sarasota...Florida State University, Tallahassee...University of Colorado, Boulder.

Private colleges and universities: Swarthmore College in Swarthmore, Pennsylvania... Harvard College, Cambridge, Massachusetts... Wesleyan College, Macon, Georgia...Princeton University, Princeton, New Jersey...Yale University, New Haven, Connecticut.

Schools are rated on their ability to fulfill financial-aid needs for students (whether in-state or out-of-state in the case of public institutions)...and the quality of the academics.

David Soto, director of content development, The Princeton Review in New York City, *www.princeton review.com.*

Tuition-*Free* Colleges

Tuition-free colleges provide a quality education—usually for the cost of fees, room and board, textbooks and various other expenses. At military colleges, there may be no charges, but graduates must agree to serve a term in the military.

Tuition-free nonmilitary colleges: Berea College in Berea, Kentucky (which specializes in liberal arts)...College of the Ozarks in Point Lookout, Missouri (Christian school)...Cooper Union in New York City (architecture and the arts)…Webb Institute in Glen Cove, New York (naval architecture and marine engineering). You do not have to be a resident of the institution's state to attend these schools.

Tuition-free military colleges also include room and board among other costs: US Air Force Academy in Colorado Springs…US Merchant Marine Academy, Kings Point, New York …US Military Academy, West Point, New York …US Naval Academy, Annapolis, Maryland… US Coast Guard Academy, located in New London, Connecticut.

Princeton Review study, reported in *USA Today*.

How to Get *More* Financial Aid

To get more college financial aid, be prepared to provide the school evidence that does not appear on your federal student-aid form, such as high medical bills. Or show a significant change in your family's circumstances, such as a job loss.

If you do not have major issues such as these: Look for something specific to request, such as a winter-clothing allowance if you live in a warm climate and the school is in a cold one.

What to do: Write a two-to-three-paragraph letter requesting additional aid. Send it as soon as possible—aid is often given on a first-come, first-served basis. If your aid appeal is rejected, look into options such as awards offered through specific college departments and private scholarships with later deadlines.

Consensus of college financial-aid administrators, reported at Bankrate.com.

Cash Bonuses for 529s

Cash bonuses for 529 college savings plan contributions are being offered by several states. Parents can get $500* in Maine and $100 in Rhode Island for opening a 529 prior to a

*Amounts subject to change.

child's first birthday. About a dozen states match at least part of 529 plan contributions, usually for low- and moderate-income families.

What to do: Analyze 529 plans not just for bonuses but for expenses, investment options and tax breaks.

Mark Kantrowitz, publisher of FinAid.org, Chicago, and the author of *Secrets to Winning a Scholarship* (CreateSpace).

Can't Pay Back a Student Loan? What to Do…

Margaret Reiter, attorney, San Francisco, and coauthor of *Solve Your Money Troubles* (Nolo).

Default charges on federal student loans have skyrocketed, reaching 13.8%* for borrowers who began paying off their loans in 2008. A student loan is considered in default if you fail to make payments for 270 days (perhaps longer, depending on the specific repayment schedule). Not only will your credit be damaged if the loan gets handed over to a collection agency, the government can garnish your wages without going to court. If you are struggling to pay a loan, contact your lender to discuss your options.

•**Apply for a deferment for up to three years.** Deferments are available if you're still in school, are currently unemployed or are experiencing economic hardship.

•**Ask about an income-based repayment,** which enables borrowers to have their payments capped based on their income. Learn more about the program at *www.ibrinfo.org*.

•**Ask for forbearance,** which could allow you to postpone payments or to pay a smaller amount, although interest will continue to accrue. Other options include extended repayment plans and loan consolidation. More information is available from *www.ed.gov* and *www.student loanborrowerassistance.org*.

*Rate subject to change.

Little-Known Student-Loan Traps

If you skip your payments and use rescue programs, such as deferrals and forbearance (where you are allowed to stop making payments because of illness, financial hardship or other circumstances), the total amount owed can double in size because of extra interest and fees. If you default and your loan goes to collection, the monthly charge can be up to 25% more than the principal and interest due. Loans for students cannot be discharged in bankruptcy. The government and collection agencies can use tactics not allowed for other loans—including seizing tax refunds, garnishing up to 15% of your disposable income and taking part of your Social Security, all without a court order. Anyone who cosigns a student loan is liable if the borrower does not pay.

Self-defense: For a detailed list of all your options, check the Student Loan Borrower Assistance Project, run by the National Consumer Law Center.

Jane Bryant Quinn, personal-finance columnist, writing online at CBS MoneyWatch.com. Her Internet site is *http://janebryantquinn.com.*

The Unmarried Couple's Guide to Financial Security

Sheryl Garrett, CFP, founder of Garrett Planning Network, a large international network of fee-only financial advisers in Shawnee Mission, Kansas. Garrett has been recognized several times by *Investment Advisor* as one of the most influential people in financial planning. She is author of *Money Without Matrimony: The Unmarried Couple's Guide to Financial Security* (Kaplan Business). Her Web site is *www.garrettplanningnetwork.com.*

Frederick Hertz, JD, an attorney and mediator based in Oakland, California, who specializes in advising unmarried couples. He is coauthor of *Living Together: A Legal Guide for Unmarried Couples* (Nolo, *www.nolo.com*).

Hundreds of federal and state laws pertain to married couples, and they cover everything from taxes and Social Se-

curity benefits to child custody, real estate and inheritance.

But if you are not legally married to your partner, there are so many potential gaps that could leave one or both of you financially vulnerable. *Consider these steps to make sure that you're both protected...*

WRITE TWO CONTRACTS

If unmarried partners split up and the parting isn't amicable, disputes can turn into costly court battles. *Avoid that risk by preparing two documents...*

•**A property agreement should list jointly and separately owned nonfinancial assets** and contain provisions for how they will be divided if the relationship ends.

Real estate is the most important item in a property agreement. Unlike a spouse, a non-spouse partner can't keep living in a shared home without title. Make sure that your agreement provides for what happens to shared real estate if you and your partner separate.

Example: Amanda and Tim, both retired and affluent, decide that they want to build a house and live together. Before moving in, they develop a property agreement stipulating that if they do part ways, Amanda will buy out Tim so that she can continue to live in the house.

You don't need to list every pair of socks, but in addition to assets with high monetary value, such as a home or car, you should include any possessions that have significant sentimental value, such as music collections and picture albums.

•**A cohabitation agreement should spell out each partner's financial rights and obligations,** addressing what you want to happen if the relationship ceases. An unmarried partner has no statutory right to financial support, even if one person has been supporting the other for years or if one person has given up a career to raise a family. Cohabitation contracts protect the dependent partner from being left financially destitute. For example, you might include in your agreement that you are setting up an investment account whose income would go to your partner if you should break up.

Caution: Almost all states enforce written contracts between unmarried partners. However, in Georgia, Illinois and Louisiana, the courts may hold that living together without matrimony is "immoral," so contracts between unmarried partners aren't valid. Also, in most states, common-law marriage does not entitle couples to all the same rights as partners who are married, so you still need to protect yourselves. A simple contract drawn up by a lawyer typically costs $800 to $1,500,* depending on where you live.

KEEP THINGS SEPARATE

Unmarried couples do have some advantages over married couples. Partners aren't liable for each other's debts unless they have cosigned on a loan, such as a mortgage or car financing. And unless they share assets, their individual credit scores stay separate. Because your credit score primarily determines how much interest you have to pay on mortgages and other consumer loans, it's important to keep the number high. (A good FICO score is 720 or above.)

What to do: Keep your bank, credit card, investment and retirement accounts separate. But, maintaining a joint checking account for household bills is OK.

Also, if you want your assets to go to your partner when you die, consider a payable-on-death bank or investment account. It would let you keep financial assets in your own name and under your control while you are alive, then transfer them to your partner when you die while avoiding the lengthy court process called probate. The beneficiary needs to bring a certified copy of the death certificate to the bank or brokerage.

LEAVE A WILL

Unless you make legal provisions for your partner in case of your death, your property will go by default to close relatives—children or grandchildren, parents or siblings, nieces or nephews. If you do not have such relatives, it will go to the state.

What to do: Update both of your wills as soon as you make a long-term commitment to each other. A simple will should cost around $400 for a lawyer to prepare, or you can prepare

*Prices and rates subject to change.

a basic, state-specific will online at *www.nolo. com* for $59 (except in Louisiana).

Better: Set up a living trust. Trusts cost about twice as much as wills to establish, but they have three advantages. They are not subject to probate, which saves you money and protects your privacy because they are not examined in court…they can address what happens not just after you die but in the event that you become disabled…and they allow you to write in restrictions regarding where assets should go when your partner dies.

Example: Jonathan sets up a living trust leaving his entire net worth, which includes inherited wealth, to his partner, Barbara, during her lifetime. The trust stipulates that when Barbara dies, any remaining assets pass on to Jonathan's nephew and niece.

Note that beneficiary designations on retirement accounts take precedence over wills. If you want your partner to inherit your IRA and 401(k) assets, be sure to name him/her as the beneficiary on each account.

MONITOR YOUR TAXES

By filing their tax returns as singles, unmarried partners sometimes can claim more individual deductions and pay less income tax than if they had filed as a couple (the so-called marriage penalty). If there's a big disparity between two partners' incomes, the low-earning partner will pay less in taxes if the couple files singly—because he/she will not be pulled up into the partner's higher bracket.

Married couples, however, have the advantage when it comes to gift and estate taxation. They can give or bequeath each other unlimited assets without incurring taxes. In contrast, not married partners are subject to the same taxes on gifting to each other as total strangers are. In 2011, they may give each other (and anyone else) $13,000 per year without having to report it. Amounts above that count against the $5 million lifetime exemption from any tax on gifts.

Example: You add your partner's name to the title of your house, the equivalent of giving your partner half the house's value. If your partner's share is worth $100,000, it reduces your $1 million lifetime exemption by $87,000 ($100,000 minus $13,000).

PREPARE FOR INCAPACITY

If you want your partner to make medical decisions for you should you be not able to make them for yourself, you need a legal document that says so. Otherwise, under state rulings, the duty will fall to a family member. Some hospitals even keep nonspouse partners out of emergency rooms and intensive care units on the grounds that they have no legal right to be there.

What to do: Write a health-care directive that specifies all your own wishes regarding any medical intervention and end-of-life care. Then designate your partner as the person to carry out those wishes in a document called a durable power of attorney for health care (or health-care proxy). You can obtain these forms, which vary from state to state, for free in hospitals. State-specific forms also can be downloaded free from *www.caringinfo.org*. In some states, the two documents are combined as a single form.

Important: Name a backup agent in case you and your partner are in an accident together.

BUY LIFE INSURANCE

Unlike married couples, unmarried partners are not entitled to each other's Social Security benefits when one partner dies. Older unmarried couples should consider buying some life insurance as a replacement for Social Security income, especially if one partner is financially dependent on the other, and even to cover funeral costs. Most insurance companies will accept the designation of an unmarried partner as the beneficiary, but some may take issue with it. Check in advance, and choose another insurer if there is a problem.

New Measures of Financial Health

These new tools can help you get a more complete picture of your financial health and identity security. The *debt score* offered by Oweing.com grades debt relative to your income and other factors…the *identity risk score* from Credit.com rates how likely you are to become a victim of identity theft. Unlike credit scores—which lenders will use when making loans—the new scores are aimed only at consumers. The scores are offered for free, but the sites that sponsor them often try to get visitors to upgrade to paid services.

John Ulzheimer, president of consumer education, SmartCredit.com.

Always Fighting About Money? Mend Your Marriage in Just One Week

M. Gary Neuman, a licensed psychotherapist and rabbi. He has a private counseling practice in Miami, Florida, and was a frequent guest on *Oprah*. He's coauthor, with his wife of 23 years, Melisa Neuman, of *In Good Times & Bad: Strengthening Your Relationship When the Going Gets Tough and the Money Gets Tight* (Wiley). They have five children. For more, see *www.mgaryneuman.com*.

Money troubles often lead to relationship troubles. Couples who are coping with losses in investments, unemployment and/or debt may turn on each other out of frustration and anxiety…or they might turn away from each other, internalizing their problems and drifting apart.

As horrible as life can seem when your finances are a mess and you are at odds with your spouse, there is some good news. If the strains on your relationship are largely the result of financial stresses—not from deeper unresolved issues—you and your partner likely can make major strides toward repairing the relationship in just one week…and have fun doing so.

ONE WEEK?

Wondering how one week can really make a difference? You start by attacking the problems, not each other. The turnaround is quick because the love that existed before your money problems almost certainly still is there. The focus of the relationship has simply shifted away from your love for each other and onto your finances. Your task is to shift it back.

Doing so could be the first step to overcoming your financial problems. When we are upbeat and working as a team, our minds have an easier time finding solutions to our problems.

Here's how to mend your marriage in one week and tackle your money problems in the process…

SUNDAY: THE INITIAL CONVERSATION

The biggest mistakes couples make is not discussing the financial struggles and putting their love life on hold while hoping things will change.

When money is a source of stress in a relationship, money-related conversations between partners tend to degenerate into bickering and finger-pointing. Dial down relationship stress before trying to talk money.

Begin by reaffirming your love for your partner and expressing a desire to work together to solve the problems. *To do this without accidentally setting off another argument…*

• **Request a few minutes of your partner's time to discuss something.** Explain that this is very important to you, and ask your partner not to respond until you are done.

• **If your relationship has been strained lately,** mention this, then add, "But our marriage is too important for us not to get back to a good place quickly."

• **Set aside the blaming by saying whichever of the following seems most appropriate**—"I don't want to blame anyone, and I'm genuinely sorry for the times I have hurt your feelings"…"I do not want to be blamed anymore, and I am genuinely sorry for what I've done"…or "Can we please be done with the blaming?" Whichever you choose, follow it with, "I just want us to stop wasting our energy on what's gone wrong and instead move forward and work together toward solutions."

• **Remind your partner that your marriage has not been all bad.** Say, "Just look at what our love has given us," then mention your children…your past happiness…or the aspects of your life together that continue to provide happiness.

• **Express confidence that you can get through your financial troubles together.**

• **Reduce the odds that this conversation will deteriorate into an argument by keeping it under 10 minutes**…gently taking your partner's hand and continuing to hold it…and selecting a moment when both of you are well-fed, rested and not distracted. This is the moment to commit to doing things differently.

MONDAY: DATE NIGHT

You and your partner probably fell in love because you enjoyed spending time together. Tonight set aside your problems and remind yourselves that that hasn't changed. If spending time with your partner no longer seems enjoyable, that's likely because you spend too much time together discussing life stresses, such as money, work and kids. Ban these topics from date night.

Choose a date destination or activity that is both affordable and likely to provide a topic of conversation. This could be a museum or art gallery…a lecture or public music performance…or an auto show or flower show. You also could go for a walk or a bike ride. Avoid dinner dates. Nice restaurants tend to be too expensive for those with financial problems, and sitting across the table from each other for an entire meal creates too much pressure to come up with nonstressful conversation.

TUESDAY: BRIEF MONEY TALK

Today you will talk with your partner about your family's financial realities. Remind each other that you're not out to lay blame, but that you are on a fact-finding mission together as a team. Put all of the facts on the table—how much money is coming in, how much is going out, debts and upcoming outlays. Brainstorm some ideas for improving the situation. Often, getting it all out at once is cleansing and sends the message that you are going forward with an attitude of maturity and partnership. Give each other permission to be creative.

Examples: Where could we slash spending? Could we obtain lower interest rates on our debts? Can we come up with any potential sources of additional income?

Make a list of all actions that you and your partner could take and avenues you should explore, then divide these tasks between you and agree to get to work on them as soon as possible. End the meeting by expressing satisfaction that you are now confronting the situation. Keep this meeting under 30 minutes. Then try to share a relaxed dinner together.

If you have children still living at home, make this a family dinner. Eating together is a great way to remind ourselves that family is what matters most. With young children in the house, you may want to have the money talk in a private room, door closed, after the kids are asleep or settled.

WEDNESDAY: FUN HOUR

It likely will take more than one date and one dinner to rebuild the sense of unity that you and your partner have lost. Spending relaxed, enjoyable time together must become routine. Find an hour or more today to spend with your partner doing something fun and interactive. Avoid talk of money, work or kids. You could play a game, such as Scrabble or backgammon, or take a walk or bike ride together.

THURSDAY: MORE DISCUSSION

Your initial money talk likely raised questions that required some research before they could be answered. Now is the time for you and your partner to report what you've learned thus far.

Example: "I checked out credit card rates, and we might be able to save as much as $100 every month by transferring our balances to a lower-rate card."

Also, discuss any new ideas you have had about how to confront your money problems. Keep this conversation to less than 20 minutes.

If there are kids in the house, it is time to let them know about your financial situation if you haven't already—you can do this with kids as young as age six or seven. Children often sense when something is wrong, and they worry less when they are kept in the loop. You don't have to share every detail—just explain that money is tight for a while, but that the family will get through it together.

If your kids are grown and out of the house, inform them of your financial situation if it affects them.

Examples: "We are not going to be able to afford to visit this year"…or "We can't help with the grandkids' tuition this year."

Then have another relaxed dinner, with no talk about money.

FRIDAY: FAMILY NIGHT/COUPLE TIME

Take a vacation from stress as a couple or a family. Do something interactive that you all enjoy.

Examples: Play a board game…do a puzzle…start a craft project.

Once the kids are sleeping, have sex with your partner or at least snuggle. Our bodies send positive messages to our brain about our relationship when we're physically intimate.

SATURDAY: DATE NIGHT

Shut out the rest of the world, and explore anew how wonderful it feels to spend time with your partner.

When you wake up on Sunday, commit to weekly money discussions and date nights and to eating dinner together as a family as often as possible. Remind each other how powerful you are as a couple when you focus on your love and solve problems together.

Did You Know?

America's most financially capable citizens live in New York, New Jersey and New Hampshire. Residents from those states show the greatest knowledge of personal finance and managing their financial futures. Residents of Kentucky and Montana ranked lowest. States' financial capability was measured by such factors as whether households spent more money than their income and whether they had funds for emergencies.

Survey of 28,146 people conducted from June to October 2009 by the Financial Industry Regulatory Authority's Investor Education Foundation, Washington, DC, *www.finra.org*.

8

Inside Insurance

New Health-Care Benefits for *You*

**D**espite all the negative public opinion of the health-care reform bill passed in March 2010, there are several benefits that have not received much publicity, some of which will probably be helpful to you now or in the near future. In case you're wondering, the money to pay for all the new benefits, according to the US Congressional Budget Office, will come out of cost savings (from prevention of fraud, for example), taxes, requirements on private insurance and pharmaceutical companies and premium revenues. *New benefits…*

•**Gender discrimination is banned.** Until now, health insurance companies in most states have been able to charge higher premiums to women even if they had no preexisting conditions or were well beyond their childbearing years. That is now banned. This means that women buying or already holding individual policies cannot be charged more than men of equal risk. This may save women hundreds of dollars per year.

•**Medicare pays 100% for preventive services.** As of January 2011, Medicare beneficiaries no longer have to pay copayments of 20% or deductibles for preventive services, such as cholesterol screening and immunizations (including flu shots).

One possible side benefit: With no out-of-pocket costs for designated preventive services, some individuals may see their Medicare supplemental insurance ("Medigap") rates go down or remain steady in coming years because these plans often paid for part of such preventive services.

Charles B. Inlander, health-care consultant and founding president of the People's Medical Society, a consumer advocacy organization active in the 1980s and 1990s. He is the author of 20 books, including *Take This Book to the Hospital with You: A Consumer Guide to Surviving Your Hospital Stay* (St. Martin's).

• **Insurers cannot drop people who are sick.** Beginning in September 2010, no health plan can drop your coverage when you get sick—a practice that many insurers have used to lower expenditures and raise profits.

• **Insurance cannot be denied due to a pre-existing condition.** Since September 2010, no child can be declined insurance coverage due to a preexisting condition. By 2014, it will be unlawful for anyone to be denied coverage due to a preexisting condition, but the policyholder may have to pay a higher premium than a healthier person. However, for the first time, that higher rate will be regulated by the government and, as a result it will be more affordable.

• **The "donut hole" will begin to close up.** If you purchase private Medicare drug insurance, the gap in that coverage (known as the "donut hole") will be eliminated gradually over the next nine years. Under current law, if your drugs cost more than $2,840 per year in 2011, you must pay the next $3,607.50 out of your own pocket until the total outlay (the policy's and yours) reaches $6,447.50 (when the plan kicks back in). The new legislation stipulates that drug companies will be required to lower prices of all their brand-name drugs by 50% when you reach the donut hole.

Even better: After the donut hole closes in 2020, Medicare drug plan members will pay 25% of the cost of both brand-name and generic drugs.

More from Charles Inlander...

How to Not Get Bogged Down by Insurers

We all know that it's difficult and frustrating to try to navigate the insurance system. But when you're dealing with more than one insurer at a time, the process can become downright mind-boggling. For example, if you suffer an injury in an automobile accident, you need to deal with your auto insurer, the other individual's auto insurance company and your health insurer to determine which policy covers basic medical services. Since it is so time-consuming to keep track of everything that an insurer may want or need, many people give

up and don't get the services and benefits to which they are fully entitled.

To get all the insurance benefits that are due to you...

• **Create your master list.** Before you ever have an issue, it's good to have a master list of phone numbers, policy numbers and other relevant information for all the insurance policies you own or under which you are covered. You would be astounded to learn how few people have such a list. The list may include a private health insurer, Medicare and Medigap supplemental insurance (private insurance that helps pay for what Medicare does not fully cover) or Medicaid...long-term-care (LTC) insurance... specific disease–type insurance (such as cancer or heart disease insurance coverage)...and any other applicable coverage, including auto and homeowners insurance. Keep the list current by writing down the policy number...the date the latest premium was paid (if applicable)... the name of the insurance agent (if there is one)...and the phone number you should call if you have questions or need to file an insurance claim.

• **Secrets to success on the phone.** When calling any type of insurer, one of the more frustrating problems is being put on hold or being transferred from person to person. I have found that the earlier in the day you contact an insurer, the shorter the hold time. I have also found that hitting the numeral "0" on the phone will often switch you to a live person when you are stuck in recorded messages. Always ask for the name of the person to whom you are speaking and his/her direct phone number in case you get cut off or need to call back. This may sound basic, but most of us never ask for the representative's name. If your call is being transferred, ask the name of the person to whom it is being transferred and if there is a direct line to that department. If the person refuses to give you a name or number, insist on speaking to a supervisor.

Also helpful: If you still don't get answers to your problem, call the headquarters of the company and ask to speak to the customer-service director. If you cannot get through, ask for the president's office and ask whoever answers to help resolve your problem.

• **Play "hardball."** Every private insurer is regulated by state insurance departments. If you have a disagreement about what should be covered or how you are being treated, call your state's insurance department (check your phone book's government listings) for details on how to file a complaint or an appeal. This is sometimes the best way to fight for all the benefits you deserve.

Also from Charles Inlander...

What to Do If Costly Medicine Isn't Covered by Insurance

If you take expensive medicine not covered by your health insurance, there are three approaches you can take...

First, have the doctor who prescribed this medicine write a letter of appeal to the insurance company. If the doctor makes a strong case that only this medicine is effective for you, the insurer may make an exception to its formulary of covered drugs.

Second, contact the medicine's manufacturer and find out whether the firm has any special deceased-cost program for which you might qualify (ask your pharmacist or doctor, or call directly). Even individuals who have employer-provided insurance can be eligible for these need-based programs—depending on income level.

Finally, contact your state health department. Many states provide special programs to subsidize the cost of needed medications that residents cannot afford.

Easier Health Insurance Appeals

New regulations under the federal health-care overhaul now guarantee consumers the right to appeal denials of health insurance claims. Denials can be appealed to the insurer and, if necessary, to an independent external review board. Decisions made by the external review board will be binding for the health plan. Previously, the appeals process varied by each state and insurer, and only certain states honored the external review. These new rules apply to any new plan created after March 23, 2010, and are expected to affect more than 40 million Americans. For more information, go to *www.healthcare.gov.*

Erin Moaratty, chief of external communications at Patient Advocate Foundation, a nonprofit foundation that helps patients with the appeals process, based in Hampton, Virginia, www.patientadvocate.org.

Save on Health Care Without Putting Your Health at Risk

High-deductible, low-cost health plans are becoming popular as consumers look for more ways to save money. About 20 million people have plans with deductibles of at least $1,000—triple the number who had them four years ago. But some people are trying to save more by avoiding preventive procedures such as blood tests and colonoscopies—jeopardizing their health and increasing the chance of more serious illness.

What to do: Tie a high-deductible plan to a *health savings account* (HSA), which lets you set aside tax-deductible money for medical expenses. Use HSA funds to pay for preventive procedures and tests.

The Los Angeles Times, www.latimes.com.

Check Medical Bills for Coding Mistakes

Look out for coding errors on medical bills. Mistakes in *current procedural terminology* (CPT) codes can change your diagnosis and lead to higher charges both for your insurance company and for you.

What to do: Carefully examine the explanation of benefits or Medicare summary notice you receive when bills are processed. If these charges or procedures seem wrong, phone the provider or your insurer for their explanation. Check CPT codes for accuracy by searching online for the letters CPT and the code number.

Consumer Reports Money Adviser, 101 Truman Ave., Yonkers, New York 10703, *www.consumerreports.org*.

Is Your Insurer Checking Up on You?

Insurers are using social media Web sites to search for evidence of false claims.

Example: A woman on medical leave for depression lost benefits after she posted photos on Facebook showing herself having fun on a beach.

Insurers claim these sites help them detect fraud, which costs the US $30 billion a year. Insurers look for postings that are at variance with claims—for instance, someone claiming a disabling back injury who writes on Facebook about running. Insurers say information from the sites is not enough by itself to prove fraud, but some consumers say it has been used that way.

What to do: Assume that your insurer—along with your employer and others interested in your behavior—will see everything posted on social-networking sites.

Frank Scafidi, spokesman for the National Insurance Crime Bureau, a nonprofit organization that investigates suspect claims for insurance firms, Des Plaines, Illinois, *www.nicb.org*.

Steer Clear of Health-Care Credit Cards

Some medical practitioners offer these cards as an easy payment plan for such services as vision correction, cosmetic procedures, dental work and chiropractic services. Often, the

cards feature low or even 0% interest rates for promotional periods, such as six or 12 months. But bills not paid in full inside of that period and late payments incur hefty interest charges that can date back to the time of purchase. Moreover, some card users have been charged for services before they've received them—or when they've never gotten them. Amid a barrage of complaints, New York State's governor Andrew Cuomo has been investigating the financial arrangements between health-care card issuers and providers, probing potentially deceptive or misleading practices.

Better: If you need to pay a medical bill upfront but don't have the means, try to negotiate the fee with your doctor or dentist or seek an extended-payment plan.

Mark Rukavina, executive director, The Access Project, a nonprofit health advocacy group, Boston, *www.accessproject.org*.

New Warnings About Long-Term-Care Insurance: Watch Out For These Traps...

Bonnie Burns, a training and policy specialist with California Health Advocates, a nonprofit organization in Sacramento, California, *www.cahealthadvocates.org*. Burns is also consumer representative for the National Association of Insurance Commissioners. Burns coauthored the report "Comparing Long-Term-Care Insurance Policies: Bewildering Choices for Consumers" for the AARP Public Policy Institute in 2006.

Long-term-care insurance is supposed to help protect us from the ever-increasing costs of nursing home and in-home care. But the policies are complex and typically are purchased decades before their benefits are needed. That makes it difficult for consumers to know what they will need and what will and won't be covered.

Adding to the confusion is a new federal program to be funded by individuals' automatic payroll deductions at businesses that choose to participate—part of the government's health-care insurance overhaul. The program—whose premiums and many other details have yet to be decided—is meant to help consumers pay for some features of long-term care.

Here, several potential pitfalls surrounding long-term-care coverage…

Trap: **The new uncertainties.** Until the US Department of Health and Human Services reveals all the premiums and rules for the new federal program, possibly in October of 2012, there is no way to know whether it's a good deal. (The US Congressional Budget Office estimates premiums could range from $61 to $123 a month.)

The program, officially called the *Community Living Assistance Services and Supports Act* (CLASS), will be required to accept participants regardless of their age or health. Add up the potential costs, and it is possible, though not certain, that healthy people might be able to obtain better deals on long-term-care coverage from private insurers. On the other hand, people living below the poverty line will have to pay a premium of only $5 per month.

Even if the program does provide attractive terms…

• **It won't be available for enrollment to those who are already retired or about to retire**—the program will be tied to employment, much like Social Security. If your employer offers the program, you will be enrolled in it automatically unless you opt out. Also, you must pay premiums for five years before you can collect benefits.

• **It won't pay any benefits before 2018,** and its benefits might be insufficient to fully cover nursing home costs. The Congressional Budget Office estimates that its benefits might average around $75 per day—enough to help pay for a home health aide but it's well below nursing home costs, which currently average $200 per day and are climbing fast.

The program might turn out to be best used in conjunction with a private long-term-care policy…or with some future insurance product designed specifically to supplement the federal program.

What to do: If it makes sense for you to obtain private insurance now to protect your assets, do so. Otherwise you might find yourself in need of long-term care before the government program is up and running.

Trap: **Soaring private insurer premiums.** Don't purchase a private long-term-care insurance policy unless your retirement budget has enough flexibility to handle a 50% premium increase.

That is because premiums—which are not locked in when you obtain the policy—have been soaring. Policyholders who can't or don't want to pay the higher rates often abandon their policies.

What to do: If you want to buy a policy, do so through an independent insurance agent who sells policies issued by more than one company. Such an agent is far more likely to provide frank opinions about which insurers strive to limit increases in rates. Many of these agents can be found through the Web site of the Independent Insurance Agents & Brokers of America, a trade organization (*www.iiaba. net*), or the National Association of Professional Insurance Agents (*www.pianet.com*). Your agent should have at least 10 years of experience selling long-term-care insurance in the community. As a rule of thumb, choose a policy from one of the top six to eight companies selling long-term-care insurance. They are less likely to increase rates dramatically than those that do little long-term-care business. Contact your state insurance department to find one of these companies.

Trap: **Continuing premiums.** Some policies now continue to charge premiums even when they are paying people benefits. Traditionally, long-term-care policies stop charging premiums when they begin paying out benefits. That's an important feature since long-term-care policies rarely pay 100% of long-term-care expenses, and many retirees cannot afford to pay both their out-of-pocket care expenses and the insurance premiums.

What to do: Make sure that the policy includes a "waiver of premium" clause, either as a basic feature or as a rider, before signing a contract.

Trap: **No inflation protection.** Insurance agents sometimes encourage their customers to skip inflation riders, which increase benefits to keep pace with the cost of care, in favor of less expensive policies that include "future purchase options." These options give policyholders the right to buy additional coverage later, regardless of their age or health—but they don't guarantee that the added coverage you can buy in the future will be affordable.

What to do: Insist that your policy include a rider that covers annual inflation of at least 5%, compounded, in particular if you are younger than 60. It could be decades before younger people require long-term care, which means it is likely to be more expensive than it is today.

Trap: **No nursing home coverage.** A policy covering only in-home care is not a good one even if in-home care is what you want. As much as seniors want to remain in their homes, failing health sometimes means they cannot.

What to do: Do not buy a policy unless it provides coverage for in-home care, nursing home care and assisted-living facilities—all at levels sufficient to pay most or all of the bills charged for these care options in your area.

Trap: **Language tricks.** Crucial words and phrases frequently are not noticed, or they are misinterpreted.

Examples: One policy defined an "assisted-living facility" as having at least 10 beds. A policyholder received no benefits when he entered a facility with only six beds.

If you retain a family member rather than a professional caregiver to care for you, it is unlikely to count toward your "exclusion period"—the period before you can start getting benefits for a preexisting condition.

What to do: Read the "definition of terms" section of your policy thoroughly. If you are uncertain how to interpret something in your policy, contact your agent or your state's agency on aging or insurance department to ask for help. Seek an exclusion period of no more than three months.

LTC Rates Soaring— What to Do...

Companies including AIG, MetLife and Lincoln National have applied for or received approval to increase long-term-care (LTC) rates anywhere from 10% to 40%.

Example: John Hancock has recently increased rates by an average of 40%. The exact increase will depend on a policyholder's age and when the policy was purchased. Increases will not apply to Leading Edge or Custom Care II Enhanced policies or to federal workers, whose premiums already rose 25%. Rates were last raised in 2008, by 13% to 18%. The companies say that the number and length of claims have been higher than expected, increasing costs.

What to do: Keep your existing policy if you can afford the rate increase. If not, consider reducing the benefit period to keep premiums about the same.

The Kiplinger Letter, www.kiplinger.com and *The Wall Street Journal, www.wsj.com.*

You Probably Have the Wrong Amount of Life Insurance: Find Out *Now*

Timothy J. Maurer, CFP, vice president at The Financial Consulate, a fee-only financial management firm in Hunt Valley, Maryland, *www.financialconsulate.com.* Maurer is an adjunct faculty member teaching financial planning at Towson University in Towson, Maryland, and coauthor of *The Financial Crossroads: The Intersection of Money and Life* (Companion).

When was the last time you gave your life insurance a good tune-up? Even if you once purchased an appropriate amount of life insurance, your insurance needs probably have changed as your life has progressed. If you used the popular 10-times-current-income formula to gauge your needs, the accuracy of your estimate will depend on when it was made. Do this calculation early in your career, when earnings are low, and you usually end up with too little insurance. Do it during peak earning years, and you usually end up with too much.

Example: We require much more coverage when we have young children and a new home than we do when the college bills and mortgage are nearly paid.

Here's how to estimate how much life insurance you need—and when to reevaluate those needs...

THE FAST FORMULA

Add up the following four figures to arrive at a reasonable estimate of your life insurance needs...

1. Total up all your debts, including your mortgage, car loans, credit card balances and college loans.

2. Calculate your children's remaining or future college expenses, if any, and their potential wedding expenses if you plan to pay for those. Subtract any money you have saved specifically for these expenses and any college financial aid you expect to get.

3. Add in $15,000 to cover your funeral expenses.

4. Divide your current annual income in half, then multiply that figure by the number of years remaining until you retire, up to 20.

The result of adding together figures from the four steps above should provide enough income replacement for your spouse or family to live comfortably if you die prematurely.

The goal of insurance buyers is to give survivors the kind of lifestyles that they would have seen if the insurance buyers were still living and bringing in annual income. When savings are great enough to handle all future expenses, the need for insurance lessens. (See the savings section on the next page.)

FOR NONWORKING SPOUSES

Nonworking spouses do not need to use the four-step formula. Instead, they typically should have around $500,000 in life insurance coverage if the family's children are preschoolers...around $250,000 if the children are in elementary school...and around $100,000 if the children are still at home but too old to need a nanny. These amounts should be sufficient to help the surviving working spouse cover the additional costs of child care in most regions, although the ages of the spouses, where they live and other factors could affect their needs. The amounts also should provide a bit extra to cover any reduction in wages experienced by the surviving spouse if he/she temporarily cuts back on work hours to spend more time with the kids.

EIGHT LIFE CHANGES

Our life insurance needs change frequently, but often the best response to these changes is none at all. It can be impractical and expensive to make minor adjustments to your coverage. Applying for new policies means paying the higher rates associated with a higher age. *However, certain events do mean it is time to review your insurance...*

• **You divorce or are widowed.** If you no longer have a spouse and your kids are grown, you may no longer need life insurance.

Action: Canceling insurance is one option, but consult with a fee-only financial planner first. (Unlike other consultants, some of whom may try to sell you extra insurance no matter what your goal, fee-only planners won't earn a commission by selling you insurance.) Your life insurance still could be useful for estate planning. Also, some divorce agreements require previous spouses to continue life insurance coverage.

• **You remarry.** New marriages often bring new life insurance needs, such as new children and/or estate-planning complications.

Action: If you're in your 40s or older when you remarry—but additional children do seem likely—consider applying for additional term coverage immediately, before your advancing age or an unexpected health problem makes the cost of life insurance prohibitive. If property you intended to bequeath to children from your first marriage now appears likely to remain in the hands of your new spouse after your death, an insurance policy that indicates your children as beneficiaries could serve as a substitute inheritance. If new children and inheritances are not issues and your new partner is not financially dependent on you, additional insurance might not be necessary.

• **You endure an extended period of un-employment or underemployment.** A long stretch of lower income typically means more debts and less saved. Less savings means that your spouse would be even more dependent on your insurance money if you passed away. Unfortunately, people who use the 10-times-income estimate will often mistakenly conclude that their lower income means less life insurance is required. The loss of a job also might have ended any group insurance from an employer's benefits package.

Action: Don't cancel life insurance except as a last resort. Instead add coverage, if possible. Sometimes it's possible to increase coverage without increasing bills by canceling an existing permanent life insurance policy and buying cheaper term life insurance instead.

• **Your employer stops heavily subsidizing group life insurance.** Employers frequently offer limited amounts of group term life insurance through their benefits packages. But many employers have cut back on those subsidies recently, something employees often do not fully take into account.

Action: If your employer still offers free or heavily subsidized group life insurance, absolutely sign up. If your employer does not provide this or cuts way down, shop around for comparable or reduced term-life premiums on the open market. Individual term coverage is really preferable to group coverage if the costs are comparable, because the premiums on individual policies usually are fixed for a decade or longer and you won't lose coverage if you change jobs or lose your job.

• **You acquire a big new expense, possibly a new mortgage,** a new child or a small business loan.

Action: Add enough coverage to pay off the debt or pay for your child's college tuition.

• **You develop a serious health problem.** A major health issue might make it impossible to obtain affordable life insurance in the future.

Action: If you currently possess term life insurance with a fixed-premium period that will expire before your life insurance needs end, dig out your insurance contract. Does the policy have a conversion clause that allows it to be swapped for a permanent insurance policy without a new physical? Is that conversion period still open? If the answer to both questions is yes, strongly consider converting. Otherwise, you'll find it difficult to get additional coverage at an affordable price.

• **Your savings grow to the point where they are sufficient to cover your financial obligations and a comfortable retirement.** If you're confident that you have enough saved to pay the bills for the rest of your partner's life, you might no longer need life insurance.

Action: Canceling policies is an option, but speak with a fee-only financial planner first to confirm that this is your best option. Double-check that you actually have enough saved to provide income for your partner's future retirement needs even if investment returns are weak and inflation surges.

• **All of your kids graduate college.** Life insurance needs often drop dramatically once the last of the college bills have been paid—but not always.

Action: Wait until your kids have secure careers before reducing coverage. You may be able to cancel coverage outright if your savings are sufficient to cover remaining expenses and the cost of retirement.

HOW TO ADD COVERAGE

Boosting life insurance coverage typically means taking a physical and paying the rates associated with your current age and health. That can be prohibitive for those in their 50s or older. If it makes sense to add coverage at this stage of life, shop for a term policy with a fixed premium period of just 10 years. Such policies can have premiums that are 50% lower than 20-year fixed-term policies.

How to Earn 5% Tax-Free!

Consider making additional premium payments into your whole life insurance policy even if the policy is considered paid up.

Safe investments such as CDs and short-term bond funds currently yield less than 2%.* If you have a "participating" whole life insurance policy—a policy that pays out dividends—your insurance contract likely permits you to route your dividends back into the policy as "paid-up additions" to coverage. Those additions not only increase the policy's death benefit—they typically earn 5% to 6% annually, tax-free and virtually risk-free, and they can be withdrawn in as little as a year. (If you choose to withdraw your dividends, those funds may be subject to taxation.)

Some universal life policies offer similar investment opportunities. Review your policy or consult a qualified financial planner or insurance consultant.

Glenn Daily, fee-only insurance consultant, based in New York City, *www.glenndaily.com.*

*Rates as of mid-August 2011.

Life Insurance Companies Demand Full Disclosure

Disclose health conditions fully when applying for life insurance. Policies can be canceled—usually within the first two years—for misrepresentation or fraud.

Example: Omitting something relevant to the risk that the insurer is assuming—such as having a serious disease at the time you apply.

What to do: Give honest information about your health when applying—even if you are concerned about being considered higher risk because, for example, you used to smoke. After you get a policy, request a policy review if you make positive changes in your health, such as controlling high blood pressure—you may get a lower premium.

Bankrate.com.

Changes in Your Lifestyle May Provide Insurance Savings

Review insurance policies annually to see if any lifestyle changes you have made recently might get you improved coverage or a better price.

Examples: You might be eligible for an auto insurance discount if you are taking public transportation or driving less than 10,000 miles a year. You might get a discount on life insurance if you lowered your cholesterol. Call your insurer and ask what discounts are available.

Sam Belden, former vice president, Insurance.com, the nation's largest online car insurance agency.

Home Insurance Warning: Hidden Gaps That Can Cost You Big

Robert D'Amore, who has worked 43 years in the insurance industry as an adjuster, supervisor, claims manager and, for the past 25 years, a public adjuster licensed by New York and Connecticut to represent policyholders against insurance companies. He is vice president of the New York State Association of Public Adjusters and previously served as claims manager for several insurance companies in New York State. He is based in Mohegan Lake, New York, *www.damoreadjusters.com.*

You may think that your homeowners insurance is adequate, but potentially costly gaps often are overlooked—including a few that have developed in recent years as insurers have tried to decrease their liability.

Some of these gaps are well-publicized. If you live in an area that is prone to floods or earthquakes, for example, you likely already know that you're not covered for those risks unless you buy special flood or earthquake insurance. And most home owners know that they need to purchase "umbrella coverage" if they want liability coverage in excess of that provided by their homeowners and automobile insurance policies.

153

But that still leaves gaping holes, and many home owners do not learn of them until insurers deny a claim. That's a shame, because there are various steps that home owners can take to minimize or eliminate many of the gaps.

For instance, insurers often provide specific endorsements (add-on provisions for extra coverage) that close some of the gaps for an extra cost. Or you could opt for a so-called high-end policy (also called "super deluxe" by some insurers) that fills in some of the gaps and compensates for full-replacement costs rather than depreciated values.

Read your policy to see whether your home is covered for...

THEFT

•**Off-premises theft.** It used to be standard practice for a homeowners insurance policy to cover the theft of personal property even when items were stolen from somewhere other than the home. That off-premises theft protection has become much less common in recent years. Possessions stolen from cars generally are not covered by auto insurance, either.

Solution: An off-premises theft endorsement typically can be added to a homeowners policy for as little as $20 to $30 per year.* It's worth having if you frequently carry expensive items, such as computers or cameras, or wear high-end clothing or jewelry outside the home and if those items are worth significantly more than your policy's deductible.

•**Theft of valuable jewelry, watches and furs.** Most homeowners policies provide very limited coverage when jewelry and furs are stolen, often just $1,000 or $2,000.

Solution: There are two ways to increase your theft coverage for jewelry, watches and furs. You could pay your insurance provider to get a scheduled personal property endorsement that increases the policy's coverage for these particular items...or you could purchase a floater that covers easily movable property, such as jewelry and furs.

The scheduled personal property endorsement usually is the better choice because it typically costs a fraction of the price of a floater per dollar of coverage provided.

*Prices subject to change.

A floater makes sense if your insurer will not increase your jewelry, watch or fur coverage limit as high as you would like...or if you wish to be covered against all potential losses, not just theft. The scheduled personal property endorsement will cover only the "named perils" specifically covered by the policy—things such as fire and theft—while a floater covers all losses except those specifically excluded. A floater usually will pay when a gem falls out of its setting and is lost, for example.

DAMAGE

•**Sewer backflow and sump pump overflow.** It can cost you thousands of dollars to clean out the mess, remove the smell and replace your damaged possessions when a sewer line backs up into a home. Yet coverage for backflows is specifically excluded from most homeowners policies. Damage triggered from overflowing sump pumps is similarly excluded. However, all waste and/or water overflows caused by clogs within the home's plumbing typically are covered.

Solution: Most insurers provide add-on endorsements for perhaps $30 to $50 a year that cover sewer and sump pump backflow. That may be money well-spent, particularly if your home is at the bottom of a hill or near a body of water, locations where backflows and overflowed sump pumps are most common. However, certain insurers sometimes word these endorsements in ways that limit their usefulness. Look at your endorsement carefully—and make sure that you understand all of its terms, including coverage limits, before agreeing to it. If the endorsement seems excessively limited, it might be time to switch to a different insurer.

•**Flood damage to basement possessions.** Even flood insurance will not cover all of your flood losses. It typically does not cover damage to possessions that are in the basement at the time of the flood.

Exception: Basement possessions usually are covered if the home is built into a slope and one side of the basement is at or above ground level. The expense of replacing plaster walls also is not covered—if you have plaster basement walls that are ruined in a flood, expect to receive only enough to replace them with Sheetrock.

Solution: The insurance industry offers no good way to fill these gaps. Flood insurance is provided under a federal government program, and the government is not interested in offering extras and endorsements. If your home is in a region prone to floods, do not keep expensive furniture, high-end electronics and other valuables in the basement. If this cannot be avoided, at least put these items up on shelves or blocks.

• **Mold coverage stemming from a covered event.** Most home owners already know that mold remediation usually is not covered by homeowners insurance. But there always has been one exception—mold remediation typically is covered when the mold was triggered by a covered event, such as the water that the fire department used to put out a fire.

In the past few years, some insurers have quietly started minimizing coverage for this mold damage as well, restricting it at perhaps $20,000, nowhere near enough money to pay for major mold-remediation projects.

Solution: Ask your home insurance agent whether your policy restricts coverage for mold remediation related to covered events. If so, it is time to look for a new insurer, particularly if the cap is below $100,000.

• **Aquarium leaks.** Aquariums at home can provide great pleasure but also potential damage that is not covered by insurance.

Homeowners policies usually cover losses stemming from accidental discharge of water from plumbing, heating and air-conditioning equipment, appliances and sprinkler systems, but not damage to personal possessions from aquariums.

Solution: If you own an aquarium, do not position it above anything valuable, such as an expensive Oriental rug. Monitor the area below the tank regularly for moisture.

Is Your Home Over-Insured?

Your home may be over-insured if it has lost value because of the housing slump.

What to do: Obtain an estimate of its current value at *www.zillow.com* or *www.cyber homes.com*. If your insurance is for more than the current value, contact your insurance company and negotiate a lower premium. Your policy usually is based on the replacement cost— what you would pay to rebuild or repair your home—based on current construction costs.

Better Homes and Gardens, 1716 Locust St., Des Moines 50309, *www.bhg.com*.

Cheaper New-Car Insurance

Decrease the cost of new-car insurance by checking car models and features carefully before buying. Sports cars and two-door versions of family sedans cost more to insure than four-door sedans. Many bigger cars cost less to insure than many smaller ones, but the largest SUVs will cost extra because they can cause more damage to smaller cars in an accident. Higher-horsepower cars and ones with manual transmissions usually cost more to insure. And rates can vary for seemingly similar vehicles because of their safety ratings and likelihood of being stolen.

What to do: Compare insurance costs for similarly equipped versions of multiple competing models at *www.edmunds.com* (click on the "True Cost to Own" tool under "New Cars" or "Used Cars"). Then phone your insurance agent or use a free online quote service, such as InsureMe.com, before you make your final decision.

Bankrate.com.

What You Need to Know About Accident-Free Policies

Accident-forgiveness auto policies guarantee that premiums won't be increased because of one or more at-fault accidents. Some insurers—but not all—provide these policies, often marketing them to parents of teenage drivers.

Caution: These policies usually cost more than standard policies, and not everyone is eligible—you may need to have been a policyholder for a minimum number of years and have a good long-term driving record.

What to do: Compare the prices, terms and conditions of accident-free policies from several insurers, then decide whether the extra charge for this policy is worthwhile for you.

Consumer Reports Money Adviser, 101 Truman Ave., Yonkers, New York 10703, *www.consumerreports.org.*

Most/Least Expensive Car Insurance

Car insurance is most expensive in Michigan. This is the only state that guarantees unlimited personal injury protection to anyone injured in a car accident. Insurers pay up to $480,000 per claim plus up to three years of lost wages. The expense of those settlements is passed on to insurance customers.

Least expensive state: Vermont.

For states and premiums, log on to *www. insure.com/car-insurance* (click on "Car Insurance rates—by state").

Amy Danise, senior managing editor, Insure.com, which analyzed insurance rates for more than 2,400 vehicles based on 10 zip codes per state.

The Best Auto Insurance For Your Money

J.D. Howard, executive director of the Insurance Consumer Advocate Network, an insurance consumer advocacy organization, *www.ican2000.com.* He has worked in the insurance industry since 1965.

Nearly every auto insurer claims to beat its competitors' prices. How could that be possible?

Any auto insurance company can legally claim to offer the lowest rates if it offers the lowest rates to drivers in at least one demographic subset.

Example: The company might offer the lowest rates to married men in Maryland ages 30 to 39 who have spotless driving records.

Auto insurers that brag about low rates also tend not to mention that they offer low rates by providing less valuable coverage. Perhaps the company's policies require the use of aftermarket replacement parts or low-quality repair shops.

Rather than focus on which auto insurer is cheapest, search for the insurer that will offer you the lowest rate for quality coverage, which will vary depending on your driving record, credit score, age, region and other factors.

A good first step is to contact your state's department of insurance and ask which auto insurers have the fewest consumer complaints, or check the annual auto insurance customer satisfaction ratings compiled by research firm JD Power and Associates (*www.jdpower.com,* click the "Insurance" tab, then click "Auto Insurance Provider Ratings").

Hybrid Insurance Now High

Insurance discounts for hybrid vehicles have disappeared. Owners of hybrids today pay about $100 more per year* for insurance than owners of other cars. The original discounts of about 10% were based on the notion that hybrid owners would be more responsible on the road than average drivers, but as hybrids became more popular, the number of tickets and accidents rose—and hybrids cost an average of 6.5% more to repair than other cars.

What to do: If considering a hybrid, look into insurance costs before buying.

SmartMoney, 1211 Avenue of the Americas, New York City 10036, *www.smartmoney.com.*

*Rates subject to change.

9

Tax Tune-Up

Tax Return Rules Are More Confusing Than Ever! Five Common (And Costly) Mistakes

 **C**hanges in federal tax law and health-care law will add to the annual confusion facing taxpayers this year. The result for taxpayers could be higher-than-necessary tax bills or unwanted attention from IRS auditors.

Mistakes to avoid this tax season…

Mistake: **Ignoring the state sales tax deduction.** Congress has reinstated the rule that offers taxpayers who itemize on their returns the option of deducting state and local sales taxes rather than state and local income taxes. In previous years, this has been among the most overlooked and underclaimed of all deductions. Taxpayers likely to benefit reside in states that do not impose a state income tax,

but those who live in states with income taxes occasionally benefit, too.

Example: Retirees who have limited taxable income but who make major purchases, such as cars, boats or furniture, sometimes find that their sales tax—and thus their sales tax deduction—exceeds their state income tax.

One reason that many taxpayers fail to take advantage of the sales tax deduction is that they don't want to add up the sales tax they paid on every purchase they made that year. This is not necessary. For run-of-the-mill purchases, the IRS offers taxpayers the option of using an estimate from the sales tax table rather than adding up their actual taxes. Sales taxes from major purchases, such as motor vehicles, can be added to this estimate. See the

Dustin Stamper, manager of the Washington, DC, national tax office of Grant Thornton, LLP, a leading global accounting and tax advisory firm based in London, *www.grantthornton.com.* He is responsible for preparing technical analysis of US tax legislation and regulatory developments for the firm.

Instructions for Form 1040, Schedule A, Item-ized Deductions, line 5.

Mistake: Not deducting any job-search expenses. The unemployment rate has been high, leaving many Americans with reduced income and significant job-hunting expenses. Yet many filers fail to take advantage of the job-search deduction. Some do not even realize that these expenses can be deducted. It is easy to over-look—this deduction doesn't even get its own line on Schedule A. Taxpayers need to refer to the instructions for this form to learn that job-search expenses can be grouped in with "Unre-imbursed employee expenses" on line 21.

Other taxpayers give up striving to deduct job-search expenses when they find out that these are deductible only to the extent that they exceed 2% of their adjusted gross income (AGI), the figure reported on line 38 of Form 1040. But this 2%-of-AGI hurdle is far easier to clear than it seems. It applies not just to job-search expenses but to the total of all "Job ex-penses and certain miscellaneous deductions" that are grouped together on lines 21 through 23 of Schedule A. In addition to job-hunting expenses, this encompasses unreimbursed em-ployee expenses (both from your old job and your new job if you have secured work—and from your spouse's work if you are married)... fees for tax preparation...membership dues in professional organizations...trustees' charges for IRAs...depreciation on home computers used to earn income...certain legal bills...and safe-deposit-box rent.

See IRS Publication 529, *Miscellaneous De-ductions*, for more details and additional de-ductible expenses. Job hunters often discover that they get over the 2% hurdle with room to spare, particularly if an extended stretch of un-employment has lowered their AGI.

Tax-deductible job-search expenses include professional preparation of résumés, outplace-ment agency fees and travel costs. These ex-penses can be deducted even if you have not yet landed a new job. If you move, your mov-ing expenses likely will be deductible if you land a job more than 50 miles away from your former workplace, but these should be report-ed to the IRS on Form 3903 and Form 1040,

line 26, not grouped in with your job-search expenses on Schedule A.

Warning: Your job-search expenses aren't tax deductible if you are looking for your first job or for a job in a different sphere than the one you are currently in...or if you have been out of the workplace for a "substantial" period of time.

Mistake: Forgetting 2009 and 2010 when taking a tax credit for 2011 home energy-efficiency improvements. If you purchased and installed energy-efficient windows, doors, a water heater, insulation or central air-condi-tioning equipment for your primary residence in 2009 and 2010, you might have been eligi-ble for tax credits worth 30% of the purchase price (and in some cases, the installation cost), up to a maximum credit of $1,500.

Exception: The $1,500 limit did not apply to a separate 30% tax credit available to those who purchase geothermal heat pumps, wind turbines and/or solar energy systems.

The tax credit for energy efficiency recently was extended to the 2011 tax year—but with less attractive terms. Rather than providing a 30% credit up to $1,500, it will provide just a 10% tax credit up to $500. And if you claimed the energy-efficiency tax credit in 2009 and/or 2010, those tax credits count against this now-lower cap. (The separate credit for geothermal, wind and solar energy systems is unchanged for 2011.)

See the instructions to Form 5695, *Residen-tial Energy Credits*, for additional details.

Mistake: Underdeducting all your medical expenses. The *Healthcare Act of 2010* makes medical expenses more difficult to deduct, but not in 2011. Under the new law, medical ex-penses will be deductible only to the extent that they go over 10% of your AGI, but that rule doesn't take effect until 2013 (and not un-til 2017 for people 65 and older). Until then, medical expenses must exceed simply 7.5% of AGI to be deductible, same as in years past. With medical costs rising much faster than in-comes these days, that threshold, unfortunate-ly, can be easy to reach.

What's more, the IRS definition of medical ex-penses is broader than many taxpayers realize. In addition to obvious out-of-pocket health-care and prescription drug costs, deductible expenses include health insurance premiums…certain types of elective medical procedures, including Lasik eye surgery…most bills for dental…travel costs related to medical treatment…eyeglasses or contact lenses…hearing aids…improvements made to homes to accommodate family members with health problems…premiums paid for Medicare Part B or D…and certain premiums paid for long-term-care insurance. See IRS Publication 502, *Medical and Dental Expenses*, for additional deductible expenses and rules.

Mistake: **Miscalculating the Roth conversion tax.** New rules that took effect in 2010 eliminated income limits on conversion.

Reporting Roth conversions to the IRS is relatively straightforward. Just complete Form 8606, *Nondeductible IRAs.* Tax mistakes are common, however, when taxpayers who have made deductible *and* nondeductible—that is, after-tax—contributions to traditional IRAs attempt to make Roth conversions.

The good news: You do not need to pay income tax at all on those nondeductible contributions when you convert a traditional IRA to a Roth IRA—you already paid those taxes.

The bad news: You cannot choose to convert only the nondeductible portion of your traditional IRAs and pay no taxes on the Roth conversion. The IRS expects you to pay them income taxes on a percentage of the amount you convert that is equal to the percentage of your total traditional IRA assets that have not yet been taxed.

Example: If the total value of your traditional IRAs is $100,000, including $10,000 (10% of the total) in nondeductible contributions, you will have to pay income tax on 90% of the amount you convert.

The instructions to Form 8606 will walk you through the math. If you did a Roth conversion in 2010, you will have to do these calculations on this year's Form 8606, even if you elect to defer resulting taxes until 2011 and 2012.

What Your Accountant Won't Tell You: A Top CPA Answers the New Tax Questions

Gregg R. Wind, CPA, a partner with Wind & Stern, LLP, a Los Angeles–located accounting practice, *www. wscpas.com.* Wind has 25 years of experience as a CPA and is former vice-chair of the California Society of Certified Public Accountants.

Among the common, crucial and potentially confusing questions that tax preparers are hearing lately…

•**I sold some mutual fund shares and the resulting capital gains are a lot larger than I expected. Is there anything I can do to lower the capital gains tax?** You can do two things. First, confirm that you are including reinvested dividends in the cost basis that you used to calculate your profit. For example, if you bought the shares 10 years prior for $5,000… reinvested $1,000 in dividends over the ensuing decade…then sold the shares for $8,000, your taxable profit is not $3,000—it is merely $2,000. That's because you already paid tax on the $1,000 in dividends along the way. Investors often overlook this and overpay their taxes. A phone rep at the mutual fund company should be able to help you figure this out.

Second, refer back to your 2010 tax return to see if you had any capital losses that can be carried forward. This would have been reported on line 14 of your 2010 Schedule D. Many investors endured significant losses during the market's declines late in the last decade—more than they could claim on their returns during those years. Those losses could be used to offset 2011's capital gains. See the "Capital Loss Carryover Worksheet" in IRS Publication 550, *Investment Income and Expenses.*

•**I went back to college in 2011 because I lost my job and couldn't find a new one. Do I qualify for an education tax credit?** If you're an undergraduate, you may qualify for the American Opportunity Tax Credit, which offers up to $2,500 per year to help offset the cost of college, but it can be applied only to expenses incurred during the first four years of postsecondary education. This credit has no age limit, so you can claim it whether you're paying your child's college bills or your own.

You won't qualify for the full credit if your modified adjusted gross income (MAGI) is beyond $80,000 ($160,000 for joint filers), and you won't qualify at all if your MAGI is above $90,000 ($180,000 for joint filers). Up to 40% of this credit is refundable, meaning that you can claim it even if the amount of the credit exceeds your tax liability.

If you are in graduate school, check out the Lifetime Learning Credit. See the instructions to Form 8863, *Education Credits*.

•**My wife is unemployed, but I have a job. Can I make Roth IRA contributions for 2011 for both of us?** Yes. While people without earned income usually are not allowed to make Roth contributions, the IRS will allow a working spouse to make a Roth contribution for a nonworking partner, assuming that the couple files a joint tax return and does not exceed income limits.

•**My 26-year-old daughter lost her job and her home last year and moved back in with me. Can I claim her as a dependent?** Possibly. You generally can claim an adult child of any age as a dependent as long as you provided more than 50% of that child's financial support during the year and the child earned less than $3,700.

The same rules apply to any other relatives, including parents, grandparents, siblings, uncles, aunts, nieces, nephews and in-laws. You even can claim nonrelatives as dependents if they meet all the income and support criteria listed above and they were full-time members of your household—assuming that having this nonrelative living in your home does not violate any state or local laws. Each dependent you can claim is worth a deduction of up to $3,700, regardless of your income—beginning with the 2010 tax year, there is no phaseout for high earners.

•**I bought a home in 2011. Do I qualify for a home buyer tax credit?** Perhaps. Members of the military and certain other federal employees who served overseas for at least

90 days between December 31, 2008, and April 30, 2010, had until April 30, 2011, to enter into a contract to buy a home, and until June 30, 2011, to close on your purchase. You do not qualify if the home cost more than $800,000 or if your MAGI was above $145,000 ($245,000 for joint filers). You'll qualify for only a partial credit if your MAGI was below those figures but above $125,000 ($225,000 for joint filers).

Your home ownership history also could affect your eligibility. "First-time home buyers"— those who did not own a home for at least the previous three years—qualify for a tax credit of 10% of the purchase price of the home, up to $8,000. "Long-term residents"—people who previously owned and lived in one residence for at least five consecutive years during the prior eight years—qualify for a credit of 10% of the purchase price, up to $6,500. If you do not fit either of these categories, you do not qualify for a home buyer credit. Check the instructions to IRS Form 5405, *First-Time Homebuyer Credit and Repayment of the Credit*.

A $500 Tax Credit...and Other Ways the Tax Law Can Save You Money

Blanche Lark Christerson, JD, LLM, managing director, Deutsche Bank Private Wealth Management, New York City. She is author of *Tax Topics*, a monthly commentary on current legislation and other tax issues.

Johanna Sweaney Salt, CPA, a partner from Kaufman, Schmid, Gray & Salt, LLP, Claremont, California. She focuses on energy tax issues and has used $900 worth of energy tax credits for her personal residence. See *www. ksgcpas.com* for more.

John W. Roth, JD, LLM, senior tax analyst at the tax information service CCH Inc., Riverwoods, Illinois. He is also a contributing author to CCH's *US Master Tax Guide...CCH Essentials...Federal Tax Guide...Federal Tax Compliance Guide...*and *1040 Express Answers*. For more, go to *www.cch.com*.

The tax law, signed by President Obama in late 2010, goes way beyond extending federal income tax cuts and unemployment benefits and instituting new estate tax rules for 2010 and 2011. It contains many little-noticed provisions and implications that may save you lots of money.

Here are some of the important ways the new tax law may affect you, explained by experts on estate taxes, energy tax credits and more...

ESTATE TAX OPTIONS
Blanche Lark Christerson, JD, LLM

Even though the federal estate tax temporarily disappeared in 2010, for some beneficiaries the 2010 rules meant a deeper reduction of their inheritances than if there had been an estate tax.

Reason: The rule that allowed adjusting the "cost basis"—the basis for calculating taxable gains on assets such as stocks, mutual funds and real estate—also disappeared temporarily in 2010.

Normally, when someone dies, the current value of each asset in his or her estate at that time becomes the asset's new cost basis—this is the "step-up" rule. That means that when the estate and/or heirs eventually sell those assets, any taxable gains on the assets are calculated based on that new cost basis. Generally, that means less in declared capital gains for the heirs and, as a result, less in taxes.

But with the 2010 rules, the executor would determine the cost basis for a variety of assets based on original value of the assets (adjusted for reinvested dividends). The executor would then increase those cost basis amounts by a total of up to $1.3 million (plus an additional $3 million for assets inherited by a spouse).

If inherited assets had gained a lot in value since the decedent acquired them, that could mean hefty capital gains taxes for the heirs.

What's new: The new tax law reinstates the step-up rule retroactively.

Possible drawback: Under 2011 rules, beyond a $5 million exemption for an individual (see below), the federal tax on any part of the estate that is not passing to a spouse or charity would be imposed at the new estate tax rate of 35%.

What to do: If you are the executor of a 2010 estate, you are required to follow the 2011 rules unless you choose the 2010 rules.

Have your accountant run the numbers both ways, and then determine which year's rules would result in the smallest tax bite.

How the recent rules affect estate-planning strategies...

●**Less need for trusts.** Taxpayers with net worths of $1 million or more often utilize a variety of trusts in their estate plans. Bypass trusts, for example, are used to help married couples eventually use the maximum allowable federal estate tax exemption.

Under the recent law, not only does the individual exemption increase from $3.5 million in 2009 up to $5 million this year (and $5 million plus an adjustment for inflation in 2012), but any unused portion of the exemption becomes "portable," allowing it to transfer to the surviving spouse without the need for a bypass trust.

However, that does not necessarily eliminate the usefulness of the bypass trust if the state where the person lived imposes its own hefty estate tax.

And even though trusts may be less necessary for tax planning than previously, they still may serve a valuable purpose. If you are concerned that an heir will not handle an inheritance smartly, for example, or a spouse will pass money on to a new family rather than to your children if he/she remarries, then leaving money in a trust with restrictions may be prudent. And trusts can offer protection against creditors. Assets in a trust with language that places those assets beyond the reach of trust beneficiaries also are beyond the reach of the beneficiaries' creditors.

In addition, if you expect to have an estate in excess of $5 million ($10 million for a couple), some types of trusts can save on gift and estate taxes. *Grantor-retained annuity trusts* (GRATs), for example, permit you to remove any future appreciation of current assets from your taxable estate with little or no gift tax. Despite fears that Congress would issue new rules reducing the appeal of GRATs, the new tax law does not alter the rules, so GRATs remain attractive for many taxpayers.

●**Less need for life insurance.** Under one common strategy for estate-planning, a person could rely on life insurance proceeds for paying the estate tax. Then other estate assets, such as real estate and IRAs, could remain intact.

If you expect to owe little or no federal estate tax as a result of the new law, you might not need as much insurance as you have now. So this is an excellent time to review your coverage to determine whether you can reduce the life insurance premiums you are paying.

HOME ENERGY CREDITS
Johanna Sweaney Salt, CPA

Before Congress acted, a tax credit for improvements in home energy efficiency was set to expire December 31, 2010. That tax credit now has been extended—with some new limits—through December 31, 2011.

The tax credit covers purchases of qualified insulation, windows, doors, roofing, the heating and air-conditioning systems and more. But this credit is now 10%, reduced from the 30% offered in 2009 and 2010. If you spend $1,000 on qualified purchases in 2011, for example, you will get a $100 tax credit and thereby reduce your tax bill by $100. For 2011, you can use up to $500 of tax credits, down from a total of $1,500 in 2009 and 2010.

The recent law's $500 credit is a "lifetime" tax credit, meaning that if you used, say, $300 worth of home-energy-efficiency tax credits in 2009, you now can claim no more than $200 worth of new credits.

For certain purchases, there are individual caps on tax credits you can take. *Maximum tax credits...*

• **$50 for each "advanced main" air-circulating fan installed in a furnace.**

• **$150 for each qualified natural gas, propane or oil furnace or water heater.**

• **$200 total for exterior windows.**

• **$300 for a heat pump.**

When you make a purchase that might qualify for a tax credit, look for a manufacturer's certification sticker that indicates the energy-efficiency rating. Then go to *www.energystar. gov* to check if that rating will earn you a tax credit.

The purchase must be made and the item installed by December 31, 2011. The installation

costs, however, are not covered for insulation, doors, windows and roofs.

SMALL BUSINESSES
John W. Roth, JD, LLM

Provisions in the new law also help small businesses in various ways...

• **Tax-bracket stability.** If no new law had passed, all personal income tax rates would have gone up. The highest rate would have risen from 35% in 2010 to 39.6% in 2011.

Many smaller companies are structured as S corporations or as limited-liability companies (LLCs), so company profits are passed through to the business owner's tax returns. Therefore, the new tax law helps many business owners avoid higher taxes in 2011 and 2012.

• **Speedier depreciation.** Most purchases of new equipment for business can be deducted fully in 2011 rather than depreciated over several years. There are no limits on the amount that you can deduct.

This will make equipment purchases more attractive this year for many businesses. This speeded-up depreciation is set at 100% only for equipment placed in service from September 9, 2010, through December 31, 2011.

For equipment placed in service earlier in the year, you can use 50% bonus depreciation, and the new law calls for 50% bonus depreciation in 2012.

• **Research and development (R&D).** The research tax credit, which expired at the end of 2009, has been extended to 2011 and made retroactive to 2010. This tax credit helps companies offset the expenses involved in designing, developing and improving their products, processes, techniques, formulas and software. Typically, most of the tax credit's benefits are used to pay the salaries of people involved in research and development.

New IRS Rules on Reporting Profits And Losses

Mark Luscombe, CPA, JD, principal federal tax analyst for CCH, a global provider of tax, accounting and audit information, based in Riverwoods, Illinois. He is also developments chair of the partnership committee, American Bar Association tax section, and coauthor of a biweekly column about tax strategies for *Accounting Today*.

A recent ruling commands your investment broker to track and report more of your investment information to the IRS. Although that likely will mean higher taxes for many investors, the extra tracking could save money for some.

Until now, the IRS relied solely on investors to report how much profit (or loss) they made on the sale of stocks, bonds and mutual fund shares. You would report the dollar value of any sale on your income tax form and subtract your cost basis—how much you originally paid for the shares. But cost basis often has been tricky to figure out, especially if you have accumulated shares at different prices over many years...if you have to make adjustments for reinvested dividends and mutual fund capital gains distributions...or if a company had spin-offs or mergers since you bought the stock. The IRS estimates that inaccurate record-keeping by investors regarding investment profits and losses costs the federal government as much as $25 billion a year in tax revenue. In some cases, investors may have paid more than they had to because they didn't want to perform complex calculations for alternative versions of cost basis.

What's changing: The recent law requires your brokerage firm to track and automatically report directly to the IRS your cost basis on any sale.

Here are answers to some commonly asked questions...

•**Does the law affect all kinds of investments?** Brokerages must begin tracking and reporting profits and losses starting January 1, 2011, on stocks, including foreign stocks, real estate investment trusts (REITs) and exchange-traded funds (ETFs) that own foreign securities...January 1, 2012, on mutual funds, domestic ETFs and dividend-reinvestment plans (DRIPs)...and January 1, 2013, on individual bonds.

The calculations must include stock splits, reinvested dividends and company mergers. Brokerages do not have to report gains or losses for investments bought prior to these dates.

•**Do I need to do anything to be in compliance with the recent law?** As in the past, you must report profits and losses on the sale of any securities in a given year on IRS Form 1040 Schedule D when you file your tax return. Also, because the federal government allows you to calculate your cost basis—and your resulting profits and losses in several ways, you need to tell your brokerage firm which method you want it to use. *The options...*

•Specific-share identification allows you to designate the most expensive shares to sell first, resulting in a smaller capital gain.

•First-in, first-out method assumes that you are selling your oldest shares first.

•Average cost method averages the cost over all your shares.

If you don't specify a method, the broker will use the default method, which for stocks is first in, first out...for funds, the average-cost method.

•**What happens if my cost-basis calculations differ from what my brokerage firm provides me?** Contact the firm to resolve the discrepancy, which might reflect a mistaken calculation by the brokerage or by you or just two different methods of calculation. If necessary, have your firm file an amended 1099 Form with the IRS with the correct cost-basis amounts.

Home Assessment High? Challenge It!

If you think taxes on your home are too high, challenge the assessment. Home prices have fallen significantly, but many communities are resisting reductions in valuations because that would lower their tax collections.

What to do: Appeal within the amount of time stated on your tax bill or assessment notice—usually 30 to 90 days. Check the accuracy of the official property record at the tax assessor's office or online. File your appeal as quickly as possible, and plan to appear in person—most communities do not provide online appeals. For your hearing, provide a copy of your tax statement, data on at least five comparable homes assessed for less and any other supporting information. If you lose your appeal, consider asking for a review at the state level. Rules vary by state—consult a property-tax attorney.

Money, Time-Life Bldg., Rockefeller Center, New York City 10020, *http://money.cnn.com.*

Vehicle Credit Crackdown

The IRS is cracking down on vehicle tax credits. About 20% of credits claimed for alternative and plug-in electric vehicles bought during the first six months of 2010 were invalid, often because they were claimed for ineligible vehicles.

Time, Time-Life Bldg., Rockefeller Center, New York City 10020, *www.time.com.*

Debt Forgiveness Raises Your Taxes

The IRS considers forgiven or canceled debt to be a form of income. It requires creditors who agree to accept at least $600 less than the original balance to issue a Form 1099-C to the consumer, who then must pay tax on the phantom income. For example, if you have negotiated with a debt-settlement firm to pay off $6,000 of your $10,000 credit card balance, the $4,000 that was forgiven counts as income according to the IRS. Find out if you qualify for

an exception that will let you avoid tax—for example, some home owners who default on mortgage loans are excluded from owing tax on their foreclosure.

CreditCards.com.

IRS More Lenient About Liens

Under one recent policy, the IRS generally won't put a lien on a taxpayer's property until he/she owes more than $10,000 in back taxes. The previous threshold was $5,000 or more. In fiscal year 2010, the IRS filed nearly 1.1 million liens, up from roughly 684,000 in fiscal year 2007, the year before the recession began. A lien gives the IRS a legal claim to the property. The IRS also now is more likely to withdraw the lien for taxpayers who set up an installment plan to pay back taxes. And it has expanded a program to allow taxpayers with annual incomes up to $100,000 to negotiate a reduction in the amount of taxes owed—previously the income cutoff was $50,000.

USA Today, www.usatoday.com.

Are You Eligible for *Free* Tax Prep?

Free or low-cost tax preparation is available now from the IRS through a number of tax-preparation companies. The IRS offers *Free File* for taxpayers with adjusted gross incomes of $58,000 or less. You can use any of the 17 private companies and one nonprofit that are participating in the program. Each company has its own rules for who can use its services.

What to do: Go to *www.irs.gov* for more information, then visit individual company Web sites (listed on the IRS Web site) to find out each firm's requirements for participation.

Sandra Block, personal-finance columnist, *USA Today, www.usatoday.com.*

Turn Your Tax Refund Into Savings

Turn tax refund money *immediately* into savings by requesting US savings bonds. The Series I bonds are sold in increments of $50, and interest will accrue at an inflation-adjusted rate that resets every six months. To purchase the bonds, include Form 8888 with your tax return. They also can be delivered as a gift to whomever you designate.

AARP Bulletin, 601 E St. NW, Washington, DC 20049, *www.aarp.org/bulletin*.

There Are Twice as Many Tax Audits Now— What to Do If the IRS Comes for You

Mark S. Heroux, JD, a former senior trial attorney and special assistant US attorney with the IRS Chief Counsel's office. He is now partner in the tax services group at Baker Tilly Virchow Krause, LLP, in Chicago, one of the largest accounting firms in the US, *www. bakertilly.com*. He specializes in IRS procedures and dispute resolution.

IRS audits have more than doubled in the past decade. And, the number of taxpayers targeted is likely to continue to increase in the years ahead as the federal government tries to boost tax revenues to close its huge budget deficit.

High earners, small-business owners, self-employed people and those with offshore accounts face the greatest risks—but an audit can happen to anyone.

Most audits are just easy "correspondence exams"—the IRS computer identifies a math mix-up…mismatched data…a missing form… or some other straightforward mistake. Once you are contacted by the IRS, you mail in the additional payment or information requested and the matter often is resolved without any further fuss.

You face a much more significant audit if the IRS requests a meeting. Although many taxpayers choose to handle this on their own, it is best to hire an experienced tax attorney, certified public accountant (CPA) or enrolled agent (who is required to pass a test to represent taxpayers in dealing with the IRS). This could cost from a few hundred to a few thousand dollars, depending on the experience of the professional you hire, the complexity of the audit and where you live. The costs could climb even higher if there are appeals or the case goes to court.

Helpful: If you can't afford to hire representation, ask local law schools if they have a free or low-cost tax clinic that can provide representation.

Whether you work with a representative or go it alone, it pays to be aware of IRS agents' latest tactics…and the often-overlooked tools available to you.

THE TRICKIEST TECHNIQUES

•**The surprise phone call.** Prior to 2009, notifications of audits almost always were sent through the mail. Now IRS agents sometimes contact taxpayers by telephone out of the blue to tell them that they are being audited. The shock of this call may cause a taxpayer to say more than he/she should.

What to do: If you receive such a call, take down the IRS agent's contact information, say that you are represented by your tax preparer or tax lawyer (or that you may hire one) and that this representative will be in contact. Say nothing else—you have a legal right to consult a tax adviser before responding to IRS questions. And be aware that in certain cases, the person could be a scammer posing as an IRS agent in hopes of obtaining sensitive data, so don't supply personal information.

•**Inflexible deadline.** The IRS requires taxpayers to respond to most audit notices within just 15 or 30 days. Those deadlines have become increasingly inflexible in recent years.

Example: Fail to respond to a correspondence exam notice within 30 days, and the disputed amount becomes a final assessment to be handled by the collection department, making it very difficult and expensive to challenge the IRS's position—even when you can prove that the IRS is wrong.

What to do: Always contact the IRS by the deadline on the notice, and ask what in particular the IRS wants to cover. Do so by certified mail so that you have proof of when your reply was received. If you intend to hire a representative, do this as soon as possible so that your rep has time to respond.

• **Casual chitchat.** Anything you say to an IRS agent can be used against you, and agents increasingly are trained to get taxpayers to say things they shouldn't.

Example: An auditor swapped fishing anecdotes with the owner of a part-time boat charter business, and then asked whether the business ever was likely to make money. The owner jokingly replied that he loved fishing so much that he didn't really care if it did. The agent said this quip showed that the business was just a hobby, and the owner's tax losses were disallowed.

What to do: If you work with a representative, politely refer all questions from the IRS to your tax pro—even questions that appear innocuous. Let your representative meet with the IRS without you unless the representative specifically advises you to accompany him. If you do not hire a representative, politely avoid small talk. Respond to all financial queries by writing down the questions and promising to provide the requested information as soon as possible. Supply these answers in writing to reduce the possibility of misspeaking or saying too much, and keep a copy.

THE SHREWDEST STRATEGIES

It isn't easy to take on the IRS, but taxpayers and their representatives do have some tools at their disposal...

• **Ask to speak with a manager—twice.** If you can't see eye-to-eye with the agent handling your audit, you have the right to speak with the agent's "team manager." Unfortunately, team managers generally stand behind their agents' rulings. If this happens, ask to speak with the team manager's manager—the "territory manager." Territory managers tend to be more reasonable and flexible than lower-level

IRS employees and sometimes overrule low-level agents' decisions.

• **Turn the IRS's strict deadlines against the IRS.** Send in certified letters to the agent handling your audit. These letters might ask questions about your audit or provide information requested by the IRS auditor. If 30 days pass without any reply to your letter—as often happens—you have the right to request the free assistance of the IRS Taxpayer Advocate Service (877-777-4778, *www.irs.gov/advocate*). The Advocate Service can spur the IRS to action when it is dragging its feet or stand up for taxpayers when the IRS is not following its own rules. Most importantly, enlisting the Advocate Service's help encourages IRS agents to treat you kindly—agents typically tread with caution when this watchdog is standing over their shoulders.

• **Request a Fast-Track Settlement (FTS) if your audit involves a gray area of tax law.** The FTS option lets you enter the IRS appeals process even before the initial audit has ended. That could work in your favor if your audit involves a gray area of tax law. Why? An agent who handles an initial audit typically decides against the taxpayer if there is any chance that the taxpayer owes money...but an IRS appeals officer will take into account the odds that the IRS might lose if the case goes to court. Thus appeals officers are much more likely to back down or compromise when it's unclear which side the tax law favors.

Example: The agent questions whether you "actively participated" in a business. What constitutes active participation is a legal gray area.

You could wait until after the initial audit to appeal, but that likely would leave the audit hanging over your head for many months and inflate your representative's bill if you hire one. A tax pro should be able to advise you as to which issues fall into legal gray areas.

Warning: If an FTS makes sense in your case, request it as soon as the agent handling your audit indicates that he or she intends to pursue what seems like a gray-area tax issue. A new IRS policy makes this fast-track process unavailable once the agent handling the initial audit sends a 30-day notice officially ruling on an issue.

•**Request a face-to-face penalty-reduction meeting.** The IRS attempts to impose penalties almost every time it concludes that a taxpayer has underpaid his taxes. In most cases, those penalties are unjustified. IRS penalties generally are called for only when taxpayers knowingly fail to pay taxes, but not when they make honest mistakes.

The agents who specifically handle penalty abatements are much more likely to reduce or eliminate penalties when they have looked the taxpayer—or the taxpayer's representative—in the eye and heard in person an explanation of how the underpayment was accidental.

Scam Alert!

Scammers pretending to be from the IRS are sending out e-mails designed to frighten recipients into clicking on phony links that allow the scammers to steal data. A criminal group called Avalanche is sending messages warning that federal tax payments have been declined or that the number you entered on a tax form is incorrect. Clicking on the embedded links takes you to an innocent-seeming page that downloads a program to steal your user names, passwords, address book and other personal data.

What to do: Delete any e-mail claiming to come from the IRS. If you accidentally open such an e-mail, delete it before clicking on any links it contains. The IRS does not communicate with taxpayers by e-mail—only by postal letter.

Jane Bryant Quinn, personal-finance columnist, writing online at CBS MoneyWatch.com. Her Internet site is *http://janebryantquinn.com.*

What Does an Accountant Know About Life? Plenty! Hard-Won Lessons from a Very Shrewd Adviser

Edward Mendlowitz, CPA, partner with the CPA firm of WithumSmith+Brown in New Brunswick, New Jersey, *www.withum.com.* He has authored more than 400 professional articles and numerous books during four decades as a CPA, including *Power Bites: Short and to the Point Management, Leadership, and Lifestyle Advice I Give My Clients* (iUniverse). Mendlowitz has been a contributor to *Bottom Line/Personal* for three decades.

Top CPA and longtime *Bottom Line* contributor Edward Mendlowitz has worked closely with thousands of clients during his 40 years in the business. He has seen firsthand why some people and firms get ahead—and why others do not. *Among the hard-won wisdom he offers his clients…*

•**If you feel constantly under pressure, your planning needs to improve.** A certain amount of pressure is inevitable in business and life. There will be frenzied days and tight deadlines. Occasional pressure can prompt us to work harder. But frequent or never-ending pressure is not healthy and prevents us from doing thoughtful work.

What to do: If the pressure on you never seems to let up, don't blame your fast-paced career or your numerous responsibilities—examine your planning habits. *Ask yourself:* Am I starting my projects as soon as I could? Am I allocating enough time to projects to complete them without deadline pressure? Am I spending time on unimportant chores? Am I building enough time into my schedule to allow for any problems along the way, or am I assuming that everything will go perfectly? Am I delegating everything that can be delegated? Am I hiring additional staff or paying employees to work overtime when appropriate?

•**Managers solve problems…leaders anticipate them.** Putting out fires isn't enough to get you to the top. Middle managers who wish to make the leap to leadership must start thinking about what could go wrong before it does and what the smart response would be.

Example: A company is bidding on several large contracts that together would challenge its production capacity. A manager who wishes to show leadership abilities might quietly contact temp agencies to explore whether the company could add staff rapidly if all the bids are successful.

●**If you frequently fail to get what you want, you need to be clearer with others about precisely what you are looking for—** and that nothing less will be accepted. Most people can and will meet our high expectations, but it's up to us to ensure that they understand what those expectations are. It's also up to us to consistently and steadfastly refuse to accept anything less…and to hold ourselves to the same high standards we ask of them.

Example: If a supplier consistently misses important deadlines, you could send back all deliveries that miss deadlines or insist that future contracts include financial penalties for missed deadlines. Also, ask what you can do to help the supplier meet your deadlines. Perhaps you could submit your orders earlier in the day or in a particular format…or provide warnings when rush orders are imminent.

●**Trust in chemistry.** When relationships just do not feel right, projects often go wrong. Each of us has a particular style. When styles conflict, it is usually best to extricate yourself from the relationship. If the relationship is important, however, first take a stab at overcoming the lack of chemistry. Lay out the problem without blame, and ask the other person to work with you to solve it.

Example: "I feel a bit threatened when you start shouting. We need to find a solution to this if we're going to work together."

●**Don't apologize for who you are.** People will judge us based on the way we judge ourselves.

What to do: If we acknowledge our shortcomings, yet act with confidence because our strengths more than balance out our weaknesses, others will have confidence in us, as well.

●**Know your job, not just your title.** People often define themselves by their job *titles*…or define their businesses by the industries those businesses are in. This tends to constrict the opportunities they see for themselves.

Instead, think of yourself and your business in terms of the role that you play for your employers or customers. You might start to see opportunities to play a similar role in different sectors.

Example: A century ago, the owners of railroad companies defined themselves as being in the railroad business. Had they thought of themselves instead as simply providing shipping and transportation services, they may have expanded their businesses into trucking and airplane transport as those newer technologies developed.

●**Losing your temper mortgages your future.** It can feel good to blow up when people let us down, but venting anger at others forever damages our relationships with these people, and it costs us the respect of anyone else within earshot as well. I have seen it time and time again. When a manager blows up at someone who works for him, that person will never work as hard for that manager.

What to do: Always keep your cool in the workplace and with loved ones. When you feel like getting angry, try exercising for a while… or type up a letter venting at the person you are upset with, then file it.

●**Consider mistakes as part of the process of success.** Mistakes are not a sign of incompetence—they are a sign of having made an attempt. Without attempts there can be no successes, no learning and no growth. Bosses in particular should avoid routinely treating mistakes by underlings harshly. Otherwise, the employees will learn to stop taking chances.

●**Create excitement in those around you.** If you want to get the most from the people who work for you or with you, make those people look forward to coming to work every day.

Examples: Be free with compliments… share progress updates…give awards to your top performers.

10

Investing Insight

Billion-Dollar Mistakes: What We All Can Learn From Hotshots Who Lost Big

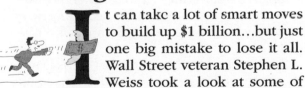

It can take a lot of smart moves to build up $1 billion…but just one big mistake to lose it all. Wall Street veteran Stephen L. Weiss took a look at some of the billion-dollar investment errors made by money masters over recent years to find out what went wrong—and what lessons we can learn from these expensive blunders…

1. Don't cut any corners. Just because you think you know a company and/or its management well doesn't mean that you can cut corners on your homework.

David Bonderman, a founding partner from the highly successful private equity firm TPG Capital, plunged $2 billion of his fund's money into troubled savings-and-loan giant Washing-ton Mutual (WaMu) in 2008 after little more than one week of studying the company. The fund's investment was wiped out when WaMu failed later that year.

There are two likely reasons why the usually cautious Bonderman felt he could move quickly on this gigantic investment. First, he probably believed that he already knew WaMu both inside and out because he had been on its board of directors six years earlier. Second, he likely trusted the optimistic opinion of his friend—Kerry Killinger, the CEO of WaMu. Unfortunately, his reasoning was flawed.

WaMu had issued huge numbers of high-risk mortgages to subprime borrowers during Bonderman's six-year absence, and he seemed not to realize the extent to which the WaMu

---

Stephen L. Weiss, a retired senior managing director and partner at Leerink Swann, LLC, a Boston-based investment bank. Weiss spent 24 years on Wall Street in senior management positions with companies such as Salomon Brothers, SAC Capital and Lehman Brothers. He is author of *The Billion Dollar Mistake: Learning the Art of Investing Through the Missteps of Legendary Investors* (Wiley, *www.thebilliondollarmistake.com*).

he was investing in differed from the one he knew. Bonderman isn't the first investor to fall victim to the familiarity pitfall. Investors who have made money with a stock tend to think that they can buy that stock again at a later date without doing much additional research. In reality, companies and markets can change substantially in just months.

Trusting the opinion of WaMu's CEO was a mistake as well. Killinger certainly knew his own company, and he probably would never intentionally mislead his friend—but Killinger was struggling to bail out WaMu, his job and his stock options. His opinion could hardly be considered objective.

No matter what you are told or think you know, do thorough research.

2. Don't break your own rules. If you occasionally violate your investment disciplines, you really have zero disciplines. Self-set rules can help investors remove emotion from their decisions and act objectively—but only if the rules are followed every time.

William Ackman, CEO of hedge fund operator Pershing Square Capital Management, had a policy of never making highly leveraged investments or putting his money in companies that were highly leveraged themselves due to all of the added risk imposed by the borrowed funds. Ackman consciously bent his own rule to make a major investment in the somewhat leveraged bookstore retailer Borders...then he broke his rule completely when he used leveraged options to make a significant investment in retailer Target. Both investments failed, costing his investors nearly $2 billion in early 2009. In the case of Target, relatively small losses by the stock were magnified by Ackman's use of highly leveraged options.

3. Passion is not an investment strategy. Kirk Kerkorian, president of the Beverly Hills–based holding company Tracinda Corporation, is one of the richest people in the world—but he is not the sort of billionaire who drives a Bentley. Kerkorian loves American autos. He has owned vehicles produced by each of the major American automakers and has made or attempted to make major investments in the companies as well.

Kerkorian earned money by investing in Chrysler (now managed and partly owned by Italy's Fiat) in the mid-1990s, and he came out about even when he invested in General Motors a decade later. He lost $800 million investing in Ford in 2008, however, and would have lost billions more had his 2007 bid for Chrysler been accepted. It should have been obvious to an experienced investor like Kerkorian that ever-increasing foreign competition and unfavorable union contracts indicated that US automakers were increasingly dangerous investments, but he was too in love with them to fully take their problems into account.

Similarly, Peter Lynch, former manager of the famed Fidelity Magellan Fund, encouraged all investors in his book *One Up on Wall Street* to buy the stocks of companies that make the products the investors love. But Lynch wrote that book more than 20 years prior, and the world has changed.

Thanks to the Internet and cable news networks, investment information now disseminates almost instantly. By the time you have developed a passion for a product, other investors have as well and this has been built into the company's price of shares. Your emotional connection to a company or its products could easily cloud your analysis of it as an investment.

4. Do not ignore warning signals. If any company's returns are significantly and consistently better than others in its sector, it might be doing something riskier than others in its sector.

It seemed perfectly natural that Chris Davis, chairman of Davis Selected Advisers, would invest heavily in insurance giant AIG between 2005 and 2008. Davis's family investment company had been pouring money into AIG and other leading insurers for generations, with great success. AIG's stock had easily outpaced the markets from 1990 through 2005. Trouble was, by 2005, AIG wasn't really an insurance company anymore. It had been moving quietly but deeply into other, riskier businesses since the late 1980s.

Most famously, the AIG Financial Products group, founded in 1987, was, by 2004, contributing billions to the company's annual revenues by trading complicated financial instruments. AIG's operations were so confusing that no outsider could really hope to figure out exactly how it made its money. But the fact that AIG consistently made more money than other insurers should have been the tip-off that there were hidden risks.

Smart management might be the reason for one company's financial model outperforming its competitors, but when the return on capital is much larger for long periods than that of its peers, investors should take it as a cause for an investigation, not celebration. The "Revenue and Expenses" section of a company's annual report might give you some idea of how that company actually makes its money. But in the case of AIG, how it achieved its performance was a mystery. When any company is an indecipherable black box—such as AIG or Enron before it—it's usually best to stay away.

"Big Picture" Trends From a Top Money Manager

Richard Bernstein, CEO of Richard Bernstein Advisors LLC in New York City, *www.rba-llc.com*, and manager of the Eaton Vance Richard Bernstein Multi-Market Equity Strategy Fund (ERBAX). From 1988 to 2009, he was at Merrill Lynch & Co. in several positions, including chief investment strategist, and he was selected for *Institutional Investor's* All-America Research Team many times. He is author of *Style Investing: Unique Insight into Equity Management* and *Navigate the Noise: Investing in the New Age of Media and Hype* (both from Wiley).

For Richard Bernstein, choosing specific stocks is not what is most important for successful investing. In his more than 25 years as a strategist on Wall Street with Merrill Lynch and other firms, he has spent most of his time looking at the big picture, figuring out what size companies were going to do best, which countries would shine and what industries would outperform each year. This approach to investing wound up making huge profits for his institutional and individual investors and helped keep them out of trouble when the market plunged.

We asked him how this approach can work now for our readers…

START WITH THE BIG PICTURE

Different areas of the stock market tend to do well at different times, depending on powerful trends in the US and global economies. For instance, during the previous decade if you owned shares of a variety of large-cap growth stocks—those issued by big companies with promising growth potential—you struggled no matter how talented a stock picker you were, while those investors who were positioned in commodity investments, such as gold, earned double-digit annual returns.

The secret is determining what the emerging economic environment is like and identifying overlooked and underestimated areas of the stock market that are best-suited for that new environment. That is where 90% of my mutual fund's returns are likely to come from.

Letting the big picture tell me where to invest helped me sidestep the bursting bubble of tech stocks in 2000 and the collapse of housing and financial stocks in 2008.

The problem with stock pickers who ignore economic trends is that they wind up chasing yesterday's story, investing in companies that have done well in the recent past, often just as the old trend that benefited them is on the wane.

Right now, there are five "Big Picture" trends that I think can lead us to the best areas of the stock market…

1. US STOCKS WILL SHINE

The market crash of 2008 has cast a long shadow, rattling many Americans so much that they still have little confidence in US companies, even though the stock market has posted two winning years in a row. With US unemployment still high, investors feel inclined to wait for signs of a stronger economic recovery before jumping in.

But by the time the US has regained its full economic strength and the unemployment rate is back to its historical average of 5% to 6%, the lion's share of the stock market rebound will have already passed.

Even though the US economic recovery is a weak one, it is no weaker than the recovery of 1991 or 2001. Many investors don't realize this and remain enamored with BRIC (Brazil, Russia, India and China) countries, even though the emerging-markets stock trend has now run its course, leaving little room for further gains over the next several years.

BRIC inflation rates are rising rapidly, and their stocks have become very expensive over the past dozen years. In a sign that the BRIC stocks are fading, the Standard & Poor's 500 stock index far outperformed BRIC stocks last year and early this year, on average.

What I am doing now: About 64% of my fund's assets are in US stocks now and just 1% in emerging markets. I'm also targeting sectors that are most likely to profit from the recovering economy. Financials and consumer discretionary stocks, such as retailers and media companies, make up about 35% of my fund's total holdings.

2. BET BIG ON SMALL-CAP

Small-cap stocks likely will do better than large-company stocks. I am most confident of this trend. Small-caps tend to perform best for several years coming out of a deep recession.

Improvements in economic activity lead to higher rates of growth in sales and earnings for smaller firms, relative to large companies. During 2010, small-cap stocks returned 27%, on average, compared to 15% for the S&P 500.

From the global perspective, US small-cap stocks have twice the average 2011 projected earnings growth of stocks from China and, by my calculations, are selling for about 50% less than Chinese stocks based on stock-price-to-sales ratios.

In addition, I fully expect mergers and acquisitions to heat up this year because so many large companies are flush with cash and looking to buy up small, growing firms. As deals are announced, investors tend to bid up shares of other small companies in the same sector.

What I am doing now: Small-cap stocks now make up about 25% of my total fund. My favorite sectors are those that do best when corporate balance sheets improve and credit becomes easier to get. I especially like stocks

of small-cap banks, which I think will be key in making more small-business loans and getting the economy going again, as well as consumer cyclical stocks (automobiles, retailing, media, travel and the like).

3. GOLD LOSES ITS LUSTER

Last year, gold had its 10th consecutive year of gains, driven by investor nervousness over the $14 trillion US national debt and fears of a depreciating dollar and hyperinflation. But the dollar actually bottomed out in 2008, and inflation expectations remain well under control.

What I am doing now: I'm avoiding gold and investing in asset classes and sectors that have stronger fundamental bases. Even if you think gold is in a long-term bull market, it is trading on pure emotion and momentum these days.

Momentum markets can fall very quickly, as evidenced by frequent sharp pullbacks in gold prices.

4. ENERGY IS POWERFUL

As we enter the middle of the US economic recovery, the historical trend is for energy stocks to take leadership positions. That's happening now as increased global demand for oil, natural gas and coal—along with a pickup in industrial production—will likely drive up the price of energy stocks this year.

What I am doing now: I'm currently putting 14% of my portfolio in US and foreign energy stocks, including oil and gas producers.

5. EUROPE RECOVERS

Heavy pessimism still hangs over European markets, which currently are the cheapest in the world. But the new trend here is that European corporations are doing better, even if the government balance sheets of many countries that use the euro still are a mess.

What I am doing now: I have about 34% of my portfolio in the developed world outside of the US, much of it in Europe. In particular, I think strong European banking franchises whose stocks are trading at bargain levels are attractive.

Three Time Bombs That Could Blow Up Your Portfolio

Gary Shilling, PhD, president of A. Gary Shilling & Co., Springfield, New Jersey, an economic consulting firm to leading corporations. He is also author of *The Age of Deleveraging: Investment Strategies for a Decade of Slow Growth and Deflation* (Wiley).

Marilyn Cohen, the CEO of Envision Capital Management, Los Angeles, which manages bond portfolios for wealthy investors. She is author of *Bonds Now! Making Money in the New Fixed Income Landscape* (Wiley). For more, go to *www.envisioncap.com*.

Pran Tiku, CFP, president of Peak Financial Management in Waltham, Massachusetts, which manages $350 million in assets. He is author of *Six Sizzling Markets: How to Profit from Investing in Brazil, Russia, India, China, South Korea, and Mexico* (Wiley).

After a decade-long string of financial calamities that shocked investors, shook institutions and left many retirement nest eggs in tatters, you might think that your investment portfolio could stand a little peace and quiet—and maybe even some growth. After all, the financial world is supposed to have learned its lessons from the bursting of the tech-stock bubble...scandals ranging from Enron to Madoff...the mortgage crisis...and what has been called the Great Recession.

Sadly, more financial time bombs are ticking, and although they might not all explode, it pays to be prepared. *We asked three top investment experts what they think are the biggest dangers ahead and what investors can do to protect themselves...*

DEFLATION AHEAD
Gary Shilling, PhD

Weakness in the economy, including unemployment of 9%,* plunging home sales and record foreclosure rates, could send home prices plummeting even further, as much as an additional 10% to 20% on top of a 30% pullback since 2006. The bleak outlook and sour mood among consumers who are reluctant to spend could push down other prices and wages as well.

Any sustained and widespread decline in prices may sound appealing, but it could create a vicious cycle that further depresses the

*Rates as of mid-August 2011.

economy—a cycle called deflation. Decreasing revenues for companies means lower salaries and more layoffs, which in turn means even weaker consumer demand. This deflationary spiral would be difficult to reverse and might last a decade or more.

What to do...

• **Invest in 30-year Treasury bonds.** They recently yielded 3.4%, which doesn't seem very impressive, but Treasuries are a smart buy for a few reasons. If deflation pushes down prices of goods and services by an average of just 2% each year for the next several years, you are in effect receiving a real return of more than 6% annually from your Treasuries. Also, bond yields typically drop in a deflationary environment. If the yield on new long-term Treasuries declines to 3% or lower, the Treasuries that you already own with higher rates become much more valuable. There is, of course, some danger that inflation will come roaring back and push up interest rates sharply, which means that the Treasuries you bought at lower rates would be worth less if you tried to sell them before maturity—but I don't expect that to happen anytime soon.

• **Focus on the stocks that provide stable dividends.** In a deflationary environment, you want to prune your portfolio as quickly as possible so that stocks represent only 20% to 40%. The overall market would stagnate or drift down, so you want to focus on cash-rich companies that are able to pay dividends and those that don't have to make price cuts, including drug, utility and telecommunications companies.

Avoid: Stocks of companies that offer big-ticket items whose sales would suffer—including upscale retailers and automakers—and the stocks of financial institutions, which would be hurt by lower demand for consumer credit and loans.

CALIFORNIA GOES BROKE
Marilyn Cohen

At least two dozen debt-burdened states are on the brink of insolvency, including California, with its $15 billion deficit, and Illinois, Michigan, Nevada and New York. State budgets have gotten squeezed by shrinking tax revenue, increasing public-employee pension costs and reluctance to make tough spending cuts. Over the next few years, any number of events could trigger a state's fiscal failure.

Among the possibilities: The federal government refuses to provide bailout money to a state on the brink of default...investors refuse to invest in new municipal (muni) bonds issued by certain states and municipalities that have run out of money.

Although states cannot declare bankruptcy, they could default on their obligations, as Arkansas did in the Great Depression, and postpone payment of their debts. A default by a state would mean many cash-strapped cities throughout the state no longer receive state aid, triggering an abundance of failures. The effect on muni bonds would be devastating as some states and cities declare a moratorium on payments of interest and/or return of principal for several years. Investors who wanted to sell munis before maturity would find their bonds had lost 50% or perhaps more of their value overnight.

What to do...

• **If you want to own individual bonds, contain your muni investments to Alaska, Georgia, Maryland, Tennessee and Texas.** These states have the strongest balance sheets and least debt. They will do just fine even if a large state, such as California, defaults. They even might benefit as scared muni investors look for safer, tax-exempt havens. Buy only AAA-rated general obligation (GO) bonds, the highest-quality bonds a state can issue.

Example: I recently purchased an Alaska State AAA GO bond yielding 2.23%, due to mature in 2018. That's the equivalent of a 3.43% taxable yield for someone in the highest tax bracket.

EUROPE GOES BUST
Pran Tiku, CFP

The trillion-dollar package put together to save Greece from defaulting on its debts has bought some time for the 26 other nations of the European Union (EU) to recover from the global recession. Troubled EU members such as Spain, however, are looking at an economic Catch-22. With unemployment at 20% and a severe housing bubble, Spain must make massive spending cuts to close up its deficit. Yet those austerity measures will inhibit growth. A default from Spain, the world's ninth-largest economy, would have gigantic consequences. Many major organizations throughout Europe and the US would suffer declines in revenue if Spanish consumers and the Spanish government slashed purchases. Moreover, the value of Spanish bonds and debt owned by international banks would plunge.

It isn't clear whether the EU and/or International Monetary Fund could—or would have the political will to—bail out Spain in a way that would quickly calm investors and world markets. Without such a rescue, you could expect the euro's value against the US dollar to plummet by another 20% or maybe more and the world economy to slip back into recession.

What to do...

• **Avoid mutual funds that track the MSCI EAFE stock index.** Of the nearly 1,000 stocks that this popular index tracks, nearly half are stocks of large companies in Europe. I've reduced my European exposure to less than 7% of my overall portfolio by using foreign funds that don't mimic the EAFE index. *My favorite fund now...*

• Ivy International Core Equity A (IVIAX), a large-cap fund ranked in the top 4% of its category over the past five years. It is worth its 5.75% load (sales fee). Although it keeps roughly one-half of its portfolio in Europe, the bulk of those investments are in multinational firms that produce much of their revenue from emerging markets with growing economies. *Performance:* 1.7%.** 800-777-6472, *www.ivyfunds.com*.

• **Plan on hiding out in cash and US Treasuries as much as possible if Spain or another EU nation defaults.** Then, after six to 12 months, start hunting for stock bargains. It will be too difficult to pick European stocks, which may suffer extreme volatility for years. Instead, focus on small-cap US stocks whose revenues are not dependent on exports. Currently, US stocks offer better value and lower risk than emerging markets. *My favorite small-cap fund...*

**Performance figures are annualized returns for the five years ending August 22, 2011.

•Paradigm Value Fund (PVFAX), a no-load fund that invests in small-cap US stocks with a value-oriented approach. This limits losses when overall markets plummet but allows the fund to outperform when the markets turn up. *Performance:* 3.0%. 800-239-0732, *www.paradigm-funds. com.*

What Would Warren Buffett Do Now? How to Pick Stocks That Are *True* Bargains

Prem C. Jain, PhD, CPA, professor of accounting and finance at McDonough School of Business at Georgetown University, Washington, DC. He previously taught at The Wharton School, University of Pennsylvania, and is the author of *Buffett Beyond Value: Why Warren Buffett Looks to Growth and Management When Investing* (Wiley).

Most investors would love to duplicate Warren Buffett's returns—increases of more than 20% per year, on average, since 1965 for shares of the billionaire's company Berkshire Hathaway. Including reinvested dividends, that means each $1,000 invested in the stock in 1965 is worth nearly $4 million today.

I have spent the past two decades studying every investment move that Buffett has made. In the MBA classes that I teach at Georgetown University, my students dissect his trades and deconstruct why they work. I find that Buffett's simple, homespun investment advice actually is much more appropriate for small investors than for professionals because it requires the ability to take a long-term perspective and the courage to go against the herd, attributes that most money managers lack.

Buffett's four favorite investment strategies, and how to apply them to your own portfolio today…

Buffett rule: **Remain within your circle of competence.** Buffett invests in companies only when he's able to confidently project how their businesses will fare for at least the next decade or two. He made his fortune with high-quality companies that offer easy-to-understand products and/or services like insurance, transportation, paint and carpeting.

How to use this advice: Invest 10% to 20% of the stock portion of your portfolio in a few stocks in one particular industry or subsector that you enjoy following and that you can get to know inside out. Put the other 80% to 90% in a diversified index fund, such as one that tracks the Standard & Poor's 500 stock index. Over time, you can add more stocks and reduce your holdings in the index fund.

Buffett rule: **Keep at least 20% of your money in cash.** Buffett has a war chest of money ready to snap up stock opportunities, and he waits for an opportune moment to deploy it.

How to use this advice: It's challenging for small investors to hold that much cash when interest rates on bank accounts and money-market funds are low. However, buying stocks at bargain prices can be so lucrative that it makes sense to always hold some cash so that you can take advantage of these opportunities.

Note that Buffett lets his cash percentage grow anytime he cannot find investments that will earn returns sufficiently above the risk-free interest rates offered by US Treasury bills. Risk-free rates are so low now—2.1%* for 10-year Treasuries—that you should be putting much, but not all, of your cash to work.

Example: Long-term investors can buy a conservative exchange-traded fund (ETF), such as SPDR S&P Dividend (SDY), which tracks companies that have increased their dividends annually for at least the past 25 years. You will earn a yield of around 3.3% even if the price of the ETF's shares remains flat for some time.

Buffett rule: **Be fearful when others are greedy…and greedy when others are fearful.** Some of Buffett's most astounding results come from his ability to remain rational in the face of market excesses. He famously avoided technology stocks back in 1999, just before the Nasdaq Composite Index lost 78% of its value. He started scooping up blue-chip stocks at the end of 2008, when the US was just coming out of the worst recession since 1929.

*Rates as of mid-August 2011.

How to use this advice: I expect the coming decade to be as volatile as the last one, but you can rely on simple mechanical measurements, such as price-to-earnings ratios (P/Es), to help you make rational, unemotional decisions in the face of mass optimism or pessimism. The P/E is the price of the stock divided by its earnings per share, a number that provides a snapshot of how the market expects the company to perform in the future.

Watching P/Es won't ensure that you will spot the bottom of a bear market or the top of a bull market, but they can save you from making big mistakes that take years for your portfolio to recover from.

When picking a specific stock, first check whether you are getting it at a bargain price by making sure that its current P/E is below its 10-year average. Second, determine whether the company is a good candidate to grow for many years by confirming that its earnings have grown faster than those of its industry and the broad market over the past 10 years.

Example: Throughout the 10 years prior to Buffett's purchase of Coca-Cola shares, the company's earnings per share grew at an average rate of 11.1% a year, compared with an average of 7.1% for the S&P 500 over the same period.

Helpful: You can find historical P/Es and growth-rate information on company Internet sites.

Buffett rule: **Look for outstanding, shareholder-friendly management.** Buffett places an enormous emphasis on meeting and evaluating CEOs before he buys stocks from their companies.

How to use this advice: Most of us can't sit down for lunch with CEOs, but we still can vet them carefully…

• **A CEO should have a history of earnings predictability,** increasing earnings for at least seven of the last 10 years.

• **Be suspicious if a CEO provides excuses or avoids responsibility for the company's weak performance** or pretends that there are only positives. Read the CEO's annual letters, and listen in on teleconferences held by executives to discuss quarterly earnings. (Check the company's online site for dates and phone numbers.) You can read transcripts of many of these teleconferences at *www.morningstar.com/earnings*.

• **Analyze a CEO's compensation package.** The CEO should own stock in the company worth several times his/her base salary…and his compensation should be based on company results so that he receives less in years in which the company underperforms.

All-Time High Predicted For US Stock Market

Expect the US stock market to top its all-time high in three to five years. Roughly 46% of the money managers surveyed by the financial weekly *Barron's* in its recent Big Money Poll predicted five years. Another 20% of these 110 experts were more optimistic, predicting three years. But 25% predicted 10 years, and 5% said 15 years. The Standard & Poor's 500 stock index, which last hit its all-time peak in October 2007, was up 78% from its March 2009 lows but still 23% below its peak. Those surveyed include asset managers for banks, mutual fund firms, pensions and other institutions.

Barron's, www.barrons.com.

Market Timing That Really Works!

Buy stocks when the public is selling, and sell when the public is buying. In the last 10 years, mutual fund investors consistently bought into the S&P 500 Index near its high and sold near its low.

Result: Individual investors paid 23% above the average price of the S&P 500 during the past decade. It can be very difficult to buck against common and/or accepted viewpoints, but that has consistently been a better way to make money—or limit losses—than following the crowd.

Vincent Deluard, CFA, executive vice president of research, TrimTabs Investment Research, New York City, which analyzed a decade of public buying and selling patterns, *www.trimtabs.com.*

Sector Serves Up Profits

Most "fast-casual" restaurant chains offer attractive stocks. Their menus are higher priced than menus from fast-food chains but cheaper than those of so-called casual-dining restaurants. This sector has been the shining star of the restaurant industry in recent years, with aggressive cost-saving measures and the strongest growth.

The attractive stocks now: BJ's Restaurants (BJRI)...Cheesecake Factory (CAKE)...Chipotle Mexican Grill (CMG)...Panera Bread (PNRA).

Robert M. Derrington, managing director and senior analyst at Morgan Keegan, one of the nation's largest regional investment firms, Nashville. Go to *www.morgan keegan.com* for more.

Euro Shock: How to Benefit from the Plunging European Currency

Christopher H. Arbuthnot, CFA, a portfolio manager at MFC Global Investment Management, Boston, and comanager of the John Hancock Global Opportunities Fund (JGPAX). It ranks in the top 1% of its category over the past five years, with an annualized return of 11.4%. Go to *www.jhfunds.com* for more.

The plunging value of the euro in recent months has sent many investors around the world fleeing from stock markets—while other investors bravely snap up bargains. I'm doing a little bit of both. *Here's why...*

THE FALLOUT IS UNCERTAIN

No one knows whether the meltdown of the European currency will play out like the 1994 collapse of the Mexican peso, which was contained within a few months by a $50 bil-

lion rescue package...or the 1997 Asian currency meltdown, which spread from Thailand to more than a dozen countries in Asia and lasted for some 18 months before a $40 billion International Monetary Fund plan stabilized currencies.

When the debt crisis in Greece caused the euro to dive against other currencies in May 2010, the global economies were in the midst of a vigorous recovery, strongly supported by emerging countries having modest debt loads and expanding economies. Now, it's not clear whether the 27-nation European Union (or EU) —which accounts for one-fifth of the global economy—will recover soon or fall back into recession.

Worst-case scenario: A large EU member, such as Portugal or Spain, defaults on its debt. Trillions of dollars of the country's government bonds owned by international banks and insurance companies become nearly worthless, and financial blight starts spreading around the globe.

Although such a cascade is only a remote possibility, it has made many investors nervous because if it did happen, it could throw the US back into a recession.

However, as bad as the rising deficits and debt of the US may be, the chances of a continued economic recovery here are good. Currently, the global mutual fund that I comanage, which can invest anywhere in the world, has 35% of its portfolio in US stocks, more than in any other part of the world.

Still, because this is not a time to take risks, most of the companies I am holding have lots of free cash flow, solid balance sheets and diversified business prospects that will enable them to do okay even if the recovery is slower and less robust than expected. These include various companies such as Google (GOOG), Intel (INTC) and Liberty Media (LINTA).

Europe, however, is a different story. Despite their $1 trillion rescue package for Greece, I have little conviction that leaders of the troubled EU nations can agree on a common path and successfully institute austerity measures, such as government layoffs and higher taxes, in those countries where debt levels are out of control.

I am now fully "hedging" my fund's exposure to the euro and the British pound, so currency fluctuations have little effect. In addition, I am especially focusing on companies that dominate their sectors, have high dividend yields and benefit from a weaker euro.

WINNERS AND LOSERS

While long-term fundamentals of any business should be the deciding factor when making stock decisions, major swings in the euro and shifts in global economic prospects can help you determine which stocks to favor and which to avoid. *Here, companies that have the most to gain or lose from the euro meltdown, including some that are available through foreign exchanges...*

Winner: **European multinationals.** Stock prices of these giant corporations are down more than those of most other European companies. But the cheap euro is a boon for them because they earn revenues in US dollars and other strong currencies outside of Europe and pay many of their expenses in euros.

My favorites now...

●**Vodafone Group PLC (VOD)** is now the second-largest wireless telecommunications organization in the world. Vodafone is based in Britain, whose pound has dropped nearly as much as the euro amid the European debt crisis. But Vodafone does business in more than 30 countries, including fast-growing emerging markets such as India, and its business tends not to fluctuate much based on economic swings. Its stock dividend yield was recently 5.3%.*

Recent share price: $26.73.

●**Deutsche Telekom AG (DTEGY)** is the largest telecommunications company in Germany. It generates more than half of its revenue in other countries, mostly in the US. Its dividend yield recently was 7.4%.

Recent share price: $12.95.

●**Electricité de France (*Paris exchange:* EDF),** the world's largest utility, operates in Europe, Latin America, Asia and Africa. Its dividend yield recently was 5.6%.

Recent share price: $20.64.

*Prices and rates as of mid-August 2011.

Winner: **Precious-metal companies.** Gold and silver typically have been used to preserve value in times of extreme stress, as we are seeing today. Many central banks and investors are spooked from the decline of the euro and have been accumulating gold and silver as a safety measure. That, in turn, is driving up the price of precious-metal stocks. I expect gold and silver prices to remain high and even set new records.

My favorite now...

●**Franco-Nevada Corporation (*Toronto exchange:* FNV),** based in Toronto, owns rights to precious-metal, oil-and-gas and base-metals (such as copper) properties, primarily in Canada, Mexico and the US. Buying the stock is less perilous than investing directly in gold-mining organizations. That is because Franco-Nevada, which has a strong balance sheet and no debt, benefits from successful exploration without incurring many of the operating risks associated with mining operations, such as escalating costs and environmental liabilities.

Recent share price: $44.26.

Loser: **European companies dependent on economic recoveries in EU countries.** Many large- and mid-cap stocks throughout Europe look cheap—they are down so far this year—but they're bargains only if European economies are able to demonstrate healthy growth. Currently there is too much risk to make them look attractive. Financial institutions such as banks and insurers are the most negatively impacted by deteriorating credit conditions and the risk for government defaults.

Loser: **US multinational corporations in sectors that depend on exports to Europe.** These include companies such as Alcoa and Dow Chemical that have severe limits on their ability to increase prices. Many of their stocks made impressive gains last year and have reported good earnings so far this year. But the rest of the year may be a disappointment.

Reason: A stronger dollar means that unless these corporations can raise prices, they will be earning less revenue on each sale. But many of their expenses will remain the same, thus lowering profitability. US multinationals also will lose business to their European competitors on exports to China, Japan and other Asian nations.

Exceptions: US multinationals that sell to more financially stable and growing areas of the world and don't depend on Europe.

Example of a multinational that is not hurt: Bunge Ltd. (BG), based in White Plains, New York. It is a leader in the markets for bottled vegetable oils, milling seed for the food-service industries and biofuel. It benefits from rising demand for protein-intensive diets in developing countries.

Recent share price: $59.59.

America's Best-Kept Investing Secret

Marc Johnson, CFA, editor of the Toronto-based *The Investment Reporter,* the leading financial newsletter in Canada. The newsletter, published since 1941, has one of the top five best-performance records over the past 25 years of any newsletter tracked by *The Hulbert Financial Digest.* See *www.investmentreporter.com.*

Many investors think that they need to put their money in exotic, fast-growing countries to get superior portfolio returns—but just across the northern US border you can find foreign stocks that are benefiting from a strong economy, a stable currency and regulations that protect investors.

Canada is perhaps the best-kept investment secret in the world right now. Foreign mutual funds and indexes tend to have minimal exposure to Canada because it's assumed that the country moves in sync with US markets. But that is not the case—in fact, the MSCI Canada stock index trounced the Standard & Poor's 500 stock index over the past 10 years, gaining 10.3% annually vs. 2.6% for the S&P 500 through July 31, 2011. Over the past decade, my own portfolio of blue-chip Canadian stocks gained a total of more than 200% even as the markets in many developed nations, including the US, went nowhere.

That trend is likely to continue, thanks to the resilient Canadian economy. Our northern neighbor is rich in natural resources—it has more untapped oil than any country except Saudi Arabia—and it has recovered faster from the worldwide recession than the US. Canada, whose unemployment rate is about 7.2%,* compared with 9.1% in the US, has restored most of the jobs lost since 2008. Its economy is expected to grow at a 3% annual rate in 2011, compared with about 2% for the US.

The best way to diversify your portfolio and improve your returns using Canadian stocks is to invest in the following...

FINANCIAL INDUSTRY STOCKS

For so many US investors, large financial institutions traditionally are the anchor of their portfolios because of their high dividends and stable cash flows. But this industry will remain wildly volatile in the US as long as mortgage defaults are rising and bank balance sheets are a mess.

Canada, on the other hand, had no banking or housing crisis, thanks to regulations restricting risky financial products, such as subprime loans. Not a single Canadian financial institution failed or needed a bailout. In fact, Canada's major banks have solid balance sheets and dominate their markets in underwriting residential mortgages, issuing credit cards, taking retail deposits and offering brokerage services. And all the restrictions on foreign ownership of Canadian banks help insulate them from competition. All of this adds up to high profits, low risk compared with US banks—and dividends that create nearly twice the average yield of the S&P 500 stocks. *My favorites now...*

●**Toronto-Dominion Bank (TD)** is the second-largest bank in Canada. It is well-capitalized and should grow steadily because of a highly profitable retail-banking operation with approximately 18 million customers worldwide. TD has a sterling reputation for first-rate customer service and convenience, with branches open seven days a week. That and its conservative balance sheet will help TD profit from turmoil in the US financial services industry. It is expanding aggressively in the US through its US-based subsidiary, TD Bank.

Recent yield: 3.8%.

Recent share price: $71.45.

*Rates and prices as of mid-August 2011.

• **Bank of Nova Scotia (BNS)** is one more aggressive alternative. The company is using its profitable operations from more than 1,000 branches in Canada to expand into emerging markets in the Caribbean, Central and South America, Mexico and Asia.

Recent yield: 4.2%.

Recent share price: $49.81.

BLUE-CHIPS DOMINATING THEIR MARKETS IN CANADA

One of the best reasons to invest internationally is that foreign businesses and sectors often focus on local markets that perform well regardless of whether the US is doing poorly. This kind of diversification can help prop up your returns as the US struggles with volatility and through many bear markets. Canada is expected to grow the quickest among the eight leading industrialized countries in the world (the G8) over the next two years. Many large Canadian companies don't depend on exports to the US but profit almost entirely from Canadian consumers. *My favorites now...*

• **BCE Inc. (BCE)** is the largest telecommunications company in Canada, with 20 million customers using its fixed-line phone, wireless, Internet and satellite-TV services. These types of services have less penetration among Canadians than in the US and therefore more room for growth. With more than $2 billion a year in free cash flow, the company also offers an attractive dividend that recently represented a 5.4% annual yield.

Recent share price: $39.22.

• **Shaw Communications Inc. (SJR).** This small but fast-growing communications firm provides more than three million subscribers in western Canada with high-quality cable-TV and phone services. Shaw's strength is in its state-of-the-art digital services, such as high-speed Internet and digital TV, which attracted more than 250,000 new customers last year. The customers who upgraded their service are spending almost 50% more per month than typical cable subscribers on services such as video-on-demand and pay-per-view.

Recent share price: $21.72.

• **Commodities.** As the global economy gets back on track, the emerging-market nations, such as China and India, will grow much faster than the developed nations and will need an increasing amount of natural resources to support that growth. Few countries will benefit from this long-term direction as much as Canada, one of the world's largest suppliers of commodities that range from aluminum and nickel to fertilizer and coal. *Favorites now...*

• **The Canadian National Railway Company (CNI)** spans Canada from coast to coast, hauling four million carloads a year. As Warren Buffett has pointed out in explaining his US railroad purchases in 2009, trains have a huge cost advantage over trucks during long hauls. Canadian National Railway runs more efficiently than any other railroad from North America and dominates the long-haul movement of every major commodity that Canada produces. After its trains unload their export cargo in British Columbia ports, they load up with Chinese goods for the trip back to Canada's more populous eastern regions. Over the past 10 years, the company's stock price has grown by an average of 20% a year, thanks to the rising demand and rising prices for commodities. It should continue to offer double-digit returns over the next decade.

Recent share price: $68.15.

• **Encana Corp. (ECA)** is the largest natural gas producer in North America, with nearly 13 trillion cubic feet of reserves. In addition to operations in Alberta, it has exploration operations in Australia, Azerbaijan and Greenland. Currently, the price for natural gas has dropped to near record lows, which explains why Encana's stock price is 65% below its five-year high. But I'm confident that the price of natural gas will rebound in the coming years because it is the most readily available clean-burning alternative-energy source to oil.

Recent share price: $23.68.

• **Potash Corp. of Saskatchewan Inc. (POT)** is one of the world's largest producers of crop fertilizers, such as phosphate, potash and nitrogen. The company is far below its highest earnings of two years ago because the global recession decreased demand for commodities, but patient investors will get rewarded. The increasing demand for grains to feed humans and animals means higher crop prices. Higher prices make it more profitable for farmers to use fertilizers to replace nutrients leached out of the soil and to raise crop yields per acre. Usage levels of potash in Brazil, China and India would have to double to match current rates in developed agricultural markets—an indication of the enormous potential for growth in demand.

Recent share price: $51.21.

•**Teck Resources Ltd. (TCK)** is one of the leading diversified mining companies in Canada, producing zinc, lead, copper and gold. It also leases out its lands for oil production. Back in 2008, the company took on a staggering $10 billion in short-term debt to acquire a company that mines coking coal, an ingredient necessary for steel production. When steel prices decreased during the recession, Teck's stock nose-dived. However, the company's proving to be remarkably resilient, paying down its debt through the sale of smaller assets and refinancing into longer-term debt. Shares are 25% below their January 2011 peak.

Recent share price: $37.88.

How to Boost Interest On Your Money Safely! Secrets to Earning a Much Higher Yield

Sheryl Garrett, CFP, founder of Garrett Planning Network in Shawnee Mission, Kansas, a network of more than 300 fee-only financial planners. She is also author of *Just Give Me the Answer$: Expert Advisors Address Your Most Pressing Financial Questions* (Kaplan Business). Garrett has been recognized by *Investment Advisor* as one of the 25 most influential people in financial planning. Her Internet site is *www.garrettplanning network.com.*

What is a cautious saver supposed to do right now? Many money-market and savings accounts (and Treasuries maturing in three years or sooner) provide annual yields of less than 0.5%,* while the best of them top off at 1.1%. One-year bank CDs do not do any better, offering up to 1.15%.

*Rates as of mid-August 2011.

There is a way to lift yourself out of today's yield basement and earn three times as much or even more on your money without turning to risky investments—*build a ladder for all of your fixed-income investments.* But you need to be more crafty than normal to make this work in today's environment. *Strategies...*

USE CDs AND BONDS

•**Spread your fixed-income investments over a big range of maturity dates instead of trying to time interest rate moves.** These investments can encompass certain CDs and Treasuries and possibly individual corporate and/or municipal (muni) bonds, although they can be much more risky than CDs and Treasuries, depending on how solid the company's or municipality's finances are. Every six months or a year between now and the time each investment matures is another rung of the ladder. As investments in each rung mature, you use the cash to create a new rung with the best yields that you can obtain within your comfort zone.

•**Structure your ladder to run no more than 10 years.** Currently, this is the sweet spot where you get the most attractive yields for the amount of time that you tie up your money.

Example: A 10-year US Treasury bond pays annual interest of about 2.1%, almost six times the rate of a three-year Treasury. But going from 10 years all the way out to 30 years offers you a little more than one percentage point additional annual interest. You can purchase Treasuries without paying commissions at *www.treasurydirect.gov.*

•**Keep the distance between the rungs of your ladder fairly tight.** Whether you use Treasuries, CDs or corporate or muni bonds, the length of time between rungs should be no more than 12 months. Any longer and you lose the flexibility to respond to a changing market. Spread out the total amount devoted to your rungs evenly because it's very hard to predict when interest rates will rise or fall.

Example: If you have $100,000 to build a ladder, you would put $10,000 in a fixed-income asset that matures at the end of year one…$10,000 in one that matures at the end of year two…and so on.

In the past, I typically have used US Treasury bonds to build rungs for the early years of my ladders because the bonds are backed by the US government—the closest you can get to a risk-free investment. However, I prefer using CDs insured by the FDIC for the early years now, because they are nearly as safe and currently pay much higher annual yields—as high as 2.35% for a five-year CD. To find the best available rates, go to *www.bankrate.com* or *www.money-rates.com*.

If you are willing to take on a little more risk, especially for years five through 10, consider corporate bonds. For that portion of your ladder, consult with the bond department at *www.etrade.com…www.fidelity.com…www.schwab.com…*or *www.vanguard.com*. All these brokerages have fixed-income specialists who help investors buy attractive bonds, and they charge reasonable markups. Ask for corporate bonds rated no lower than "A," maturing each year over the next five to 10 years.

Example: You could purchase a bond rated AA–, issued by Wells Fargo Bank, maturing in May 2016, recently yielding 3.1% annually.

Make sure that the bonds you buy are noncallable. A callable bond can be redeemed by the issuer prior to its maturity. That would be the equivalent of owning a ladder with collapsible rungs.

• **Consider using high-quality muni bonds instead of corporate bonds or perhaps Treasuries** for the longer portion of your ladder if you are in the 25% federal tax bracket or higher. Municipal bonds are issued mostly by state and local governments to produce money for public works projects and general revenue. The income that you get from them is exempt from federal taxes (as well as state and local taxes if you are a resident of the state in which they are issued). High-quality munis can yield more than Treasuries and CDs and are considered safer than comparable corporate bonds. If Congress raises tax rates in the next few years, which I expect it will, munis will look even more appealing.

Caution: A lot of states and municipalities have terrible budget shortfalls, so their bonds may be riskier than usual.

Best: Stick with the general obligation (GO) bonds, from states and municipalities, with ratings of AA or higher.

Example: An AA-rated GO bond from Englewood, New Jersey, maturing in August 2017, recently yielded 2.54%, which is equivalent to a yield of 3.4% on taxable bonds if you're in the 25% tax bracket and 3.9% if you're in the 35% tax bracket.

LADDERS FOR RETIREMENT

• **Use an income ladder to let your stock portfolio grow when you are nearing or in retirement.** This strategy often is referred to as "defined withdrawals," and it lets you stay invested in stocks long-term for potentially greater returns while making sure that you always maintain some guaranteed income.

Example: I know an investor in his 60s who retired with $1 million in investable assets. He keeps 60% of his portfolio in stocks and uses the remaining 40% to build a seven-year ladder of bonds, purchasing seven bonds with a face value of roughly $57,000 each. As each bond matures, he uses the principal to live on. He also sells enough stock to buy another seven-year bond to keep the ladder intact. This system gives him great flexibility. In years when there's a bull market and he can make a big profit on stocks, he may choose to sell more of them. In bear markets, when he would have meager profits or even a loss from selling stocks, he can put off selling. If the stock market does poorly for several years in a row, he will keep living off the proceeds of his maturing bonds but not buy new ones. His finances will remain in good shape even if his bond ladder shrinks to only two or three years before he can begin to replenish it. By then, stocks typically will have gone up again, and he can reestablish his ladder.

• **If you are considering fixed immediate annuities, use ladders for them, too.** Many investors who worry about running out of money in retirement are buying fixed immediate annuities issued by insurance companies. In exchange for a onetime, up-front payment, they receive a check each month for life. This can be a great strategy to cover the basic expenses that your Social Security check doesn't cover. The problem is that locking up a large amount of money in an annuity in today's low interest rate environment isn't smart.

Example: A 65-year-old has $300,000 and wants to buy an immediate annuity. A typical annuity policy purchased today would provide a monthly income of $1,899 for as long as he lives—more than twice the monthly payout of a 30-year Treasury—although all annuity payments would end upon his death and the insurer would not return the principal. If he waits one year or two to buy, however, interest rates (and monthly payments) might be higher.

Laddering provides a reasonable way to resolve this dilemma. He splits his money into equal parts and plans to obtain a $30,000 immediate annuity policy each year for the next 10 years. He'll never get the highest theoretical return in any given year that way, but by laddering his purchase over different interest rate environments, he can buy some annuity protection immediately without the threat of getting stuck with a low annual yield forever. For more information and free quotes on annuities, go to *www.freeannuityrates.com.*

Helpful tip: Calculate your income ladder returns for any potential mix of Treasuries, bonds and CDs at *www.incomeladders.com* (click "Income Ladder Calculator").

Gold Traps: You May Be Overpaying—or Not Even Getting the Real Thing

Allan S. Roth, CFP, CPA, president of Wealth Logic, LLC, a financial advisory company in Colorado Springs, with $400 million in assets. He is also author of *How a Second Grader Beats Wall Street: Golden Rules Any Investor Can Learn* (Wiley). He has owned gold coins in his own portfolio for the past three decades. His Web site is *www.daretobedull.com.*

The tripling of gold prices over the past five years has created a frenzy among many investors who are eager to join the gold rush—but it also has exposed many of them to gold-buying traps. *What you must know to avoid common and costly traps when buying gold as an investment...*

Trap 1: **Overpaying for gold.** You now can buy gold virtually anywhere in the world from hundreds of thousands of merchants, including banks, coin shops, department stores, Internet auction sites and mail-order companies. At the Emirates Palace Hotel in Abu Dhabi, you even can buy gold from an ATM that dispenses gold coins like a candy-bar vending machine. You would think all this retail competition would keep prices in a tight range, but sellers often charge large markups to unwary buyers. It's common on eBay to find gold coins minted by the US Treasury selling for 10% more than their value simply because buyers get caught up in the excitement of bidding.

What to do: Check the "spot" price for gold, the price at which investors are buying and selling gold per ounce at the leading commodity exchange in the US for metals, the COMEX in New York City. You can track the spot price at *www.kitco.com.* A reputable dealer should charge no more than a 5% markup.

Trap 2: **Buying counterfeit gold.** Because the sale of physical gold is not regulated, anyone can claim to be a gold dealer. As a result, thousands of ads flood TV, radio and the Internet. The consumer-protection agencies from Florida, Texas and New York are investigating millions of dollars in counterfeit gold scams in which sellers offer gold below the spot price and typically misrepresent the amount of gold and/or its possible resale value.

Most common counterfeits: Gold jewelry …and "rare" gold coins that are supposed to have historical or commemorative value. Because it is hard for buyers to determine the value of these gold items as investments, they rely on the sellers' expertise and honesty.

What to do: If you want to own physical gold, the safest, easiest-to-handle investment is gold coins minted over the past 20 years by the US Treasury. They ensure the highest accuracy regarding weight, gold content and purity. Stick with the one-ounce American Gold Eagle or American Gold Buffalo coins. There are millions of these coins in circulation, so they always will trade close to the current market price for gold. Order them directly from the US Mint (*www.usmint.gov*), which has a markup of about 5% above the spot price. Or you can buy from a reputable coin dealer who charges a similar markup. Make sure the dealer is a member of The Professional Numismatists Guild (951-587-8300, *www.pngdealers.com*) or of the Professional Coin Grading Service (800-447-8848, *www.pcgs.com)*. Their members agree to abide by strict standards.

Trap 3: **You allow a seller who sold you the gold to store it for you.** Some dealers offer services that function like an online bank. Your gold is deposited for you in an account. You can make withdrawals of gold and have it sent to you by mail. Other dealers use third-party vaulting firms that specialize in storing precious metals. While many of these storage options are legitimate, they expose you to a variety of risks. The gold you own could turn up missing or may never have existed. Or you could be charged exorbitant fees for storage, shipping and insurance.

What to do: Use a safe-deposit box at your bank. The chances of theft or damage are extremely small, and you can store tens of thousands of dollars' worth of gold coins for about $25 each year.* Although the contents of safe-deposit boxes are not covered by FDIC bank insurance, you can extend your homeowner's insurance to cover the contents of your box. If you would rather not store your own gold, consider investing in SPDR Gold Shares (GLD), the largest gold-owning exchange-traded fund (ETF). It's regulated by the Securities and Exchange Commission (SEC), and each share of GLD represents one-tenth of an ounce of gold. The gold backing the ETF shares (currently more than $60 billion), is kept in underground vaults and verified by third-party audits.

Recent share price: $184.59.

Trap 4: **You invest too much at once.** It is urgent to buy right away before the price rises higher. It is true that the price of gold has increased steadily since 2000, and it hit an all-time high above $1,900/ounce in mid-August 2011—but the price of gold is so volatile that it's impossible to predict whether it will sell a

*Prices and rates subject to change.

year from now for $2,400 per ounce or $600 per ounce. That's because prices are based primarily on investor sentiment about global political and unpredictable economic events.

What to do: If you want to invest in gold, start out "dollar cost averaging" (investing fixed amounts) every three months during the next few years so that you do not get stuck buying only at peak levels (and then get walloped by sharp pullbacks in price). Limit gold to a small portion of your portfolio—3% or under—and plan to hold it for 10 years or more. For most investors, buying gold should not be a tactical move aimed at making huge profits. Instead, hold it for the long term to diversify away from stocks and bonds, reduce the overall volatility of your portfolio and help guard against accelerating inflation and economic upheaval.

Trap 5: **You ignore the tax consequences.** It's hard to make money jumping in and out of gold investments because your profits get eaten up by high taxes. The IRS considers both physical gold and gold ETF shares to be "collectibles," so any capital gains when you sell are taxed at a 28% rate no matter what your income tax bracket, compared with a maximum of 15% on other investments in your portfolio, such as ordinary stocks.

What to do: Experienced and aggressive investors might want to gain exposure to gold through the stocks of gold-mining companies (or ETFs that track performance of those companies) instead of physical gold or ETFs that track gold prices. They add more risk to your portfolio than holding physical gold because they are exposed to the price of gold and the volatilities of the stock market. But any profits on such stocks are taxed at a 15% long-term capital gains rate if you hold them for more than one year. Also, you currently can locate bargains because share prices for the major gold miners have trailed rising gold prices for years. They are undervalued and are likely to catch up and rise faster than the price of gold.

My favorite way to invest in gold mining: Market Vectors Gold Miners (GDX), an ETF, holds roughly 30 of the world's largest gold-mining companies.

Recent share price: $61.30.

Tune Out the Financial Media

Marjory Abrams, president of Boardroom Inc., 281 Tresser Blvd., Stamford, Connecticut 06901.

Soon after my friend Myron Kandel, one of the founders of the cable-TV network CNN, launched his first show devoted to financial news, he received a complaint from his sister—"Last night, you put on a guy who says the stock market's going up…tonight, a guy who says the market's going down. It is so confusing. Why don't you just interview the guy who's right?"

Thirty years later, that's still the way many people feel about financial news. The truth is, there's little in the news that a small investor needs to pay attention to day-to-day. Tuning in and overreacting can muck up your portfolio and your retirement plans.

Among the financial experts who are able to think with a small investor's perspective, no one is more level-headed than Sheldon Jacobs, who served for a quarter century as editor and publisher of the top-rated *No-Load Fund Investor* newsletter and still is a contributing editor. *Here are his strategies for managing your financial news intake…*

• **Focus your financial news exposure on respected publications in print.** The printed word forces news outlets to be more thoughtful, less sensational. He turns to the trio of *The New York Times, The Wall Street Journal* and *Barron's.*

• **Think of investment picks as the beginning of the process, not the end.** The media's most helpful role is screening thousands of potential investments and presenting the most intriguing ones. Then do your own research. Don't just tell your broker to buy.

Helpful online resources: www.morning star.com and http://finance.yahoo.com.

• **Avoid listening to the experts who lack verifiable and successful long-term records.** Most of the media provide short-term recommendations based on current economic and market conditions. Such picks are entertaining, but these rapid-fire stock-picking entertainers would probably choose very differently if they knew that they were going to be held accountable five years from now.

While Jacobs believes we are now in a secular bear market (a long-term bear market that nonetheless might contain a number of short-term bull markets with potential for good investing) that could last for the next 10 years, he doesn't think that it's a reason to abandon a solid asset-allocation plan. "Just understand that you'll get lower returns from stocks over that period, closer to 6% to 7% annually," he says, "and plan appropriately."

Financial Planner Credentials

Financial advisers' credentials may not mean much—some require minimal or no training. There are nearly 100 professional designations for financial advisers now—twice as many as in 2005.

Most valuable: Established designations, such as certified financial planner (CFP) and chartered financial analyst (CFA), which each require extensive education and testing. But similar-seeming designations, such as certified retirement financial adviser (CRFA) and chartered senior financial planner (CSFP), require much less knowledge.

What to do: Before hiring an adviser, investigate and evaluate all of his/her credentials, training and expertise.

The Wall Street Journal, www.wsj.com.

Don't Overpay for Financial Planning

A fee-only planner gives you a price list upfront for work by the hour or task or for ongoing financial management. The fee-based planners may charge fees for some activities and earn commissions for others.

Brokerage house advisory accounts offer an investment plan and charge a percentage of assets. The broker also can earn commissions by selling you items not included in the plan.

What to do: Decide what sort of planning you need—onetime or ongoing—and talk to several advisers to find out what it will cost. For most investors, fee-only planning is best.

Jane Bryant Quinn, personal-finance columnist and author of *Making the Most of Your Money NOW* (Simon & Schuster). Her Web site is *http://janebryantquinn.com*.

for taxable accounts to avoid unnecessarily incurring big expenses from taxes and fees that may result when you rebalance. Not rebalancing at all saves on costs but means that over time your portfolio ends up heavily weighted in the investments that have gained the most and whose performance may be more likely to weaken.

Colleen Jaconetti, CFA, CFP, financial analyst, The Vanguard Group in Valley Forge, Pennsylvania, which studied the performance of a 60% stock/40% bond investment portfolio from 1926 through 2009 using various rebalancing strategies, *www.vanguard.com*.

Best Discount Brokerage Firms

Fidelity Investments was ranked the top discount broker, followed by TD Ameritrade and Scottrade, according to *SmartMoney*'s 2011 ranking of brokers based on costs and quality of customer services and financial products. In individual categories, ShareBuilder ranked best and OptionsXpress worst on commissions and fees...TradeKing best and ShareBuilder worst on customer service...Fidelity best and Share-Builder the worst for their selection of mutual funds and investment products...E*Trade best and ShareBuilder worst for research...and Fidelity best on banking services, with Vanguard worst in that category.

SmartMoney, www.smartmoney.com.

When to Rebalance

Avoid automatically rebalancing your portfolio too often. Based on research studies by Vanguard Investment Strategy Group, it's best to review your investments every 12 months or, at most, every six months. Rebalance only if the values of any of your investment categories, such as stocks or bonds, have wandered from your targeted allocations by a specified amount, such as five or 10 percentage points. That approach is especially useful

Investment Scams Even Smart People Fall For

Thomas R. Ajamie, JD, managing partner in the law firm Ajamie LLP, based in Houston. He recovered $429 million in the largest stock arbitration award in US history. He is coauthor of *Financial Serial Killers: Inside the World of Wall Street Money Hustlers, Swindlers, and Con Men* (Skyhorse). His Web site is *www.ajamie.com*.

Just because Bernard Madoff is behind bars doesn't mean that you are safe from thousands of other financial villains who could rob you of your nest egg. These swindlers will target everybody from the wealthy to regular folks with just a few hundred dollars to invest. They get even well-educated and very shrewd individuals to trust them. More than 7.3 million older Americans—one out of five over age 65—have been the victims of financial swindles, according to a survey conducted last year. To avoid falling prey, you have to know their tricks.

Thomas R. Ajamie, a lawyer who over the past two decades has recovered hundreds of millions of dollars for the victims of financial fraud, gives us important information below...

EVEN FBI AGENTS FELL FOR A BOND FUND THAT DOESN'T EXIST

If you were a federal law-enforcement official nearing retirement in the past decade, chances are that you got financial advice from Kenneth Wayne McLeod. He gave hundreds of seminars to employees from the FBI, the Drug Enforcement Administration, US Customs and Immigration Enforcement, explaining how to obtain the most out of government retirement benefits. He also did charity work dispensing financial advice to families of law-enforcement agents killed in the line of duty. McLeod made his money signing up more than 1,000 clients with his money-management firm. F&S Asset Management Group oversaw more than $30 million, much of this in a tax-free government bond fund that McLeod ran, with promises of annual returns of 10%. In June 2010, McLeod was confronted by investigators from the Securities and Exchange Commission (SEC) and admitted that there was never any bond fund. He was running a classic Ponzi scheme, using new investor money to pay off old investors.

Lesson: If it sounds too good to be true, it probably is not true. Be skeptical of all "high-reward/low-risk" investments, no matter how well-respected the investment manager is. In the low-interest-rate environment of the past few years, no bond investor could achieve a low-risk double-digit return. It is a major red flag whenever an investment manager guarantees high returns or gets them consistently year after year, no matter what the financial markets or the economy is doing.

Reason: High-return investments usually require substantial risk, which means that there will be lots of volatility—good years and bad years—if the investment is legitimate.

"RARE OPPORTUNITY" IS IRRESISTIBLE

A deaf woman from Maine became aware of what seemed like a sensational investment opportunity through an online chat site that is very popular with deaf people throughout the country. For a $50 or $100 investment, the Internet-based operation promised returns of about 1.2% a day. This company invested in "viatical settlements"—purchases of life insurance policies from their owners at discounted prices before the policies matured. In six months, a $50 investment could be worth $134,000, according to the company. Over 14,000 people—most of them deaf—invested $7 million plus.

The funds disappeared and were funneled into private accounts in New Zealand and Cyprus. The SEC does not have enough evidence to name any of the people behind the scheme but continues to investigate.

Lesson: Avoid investing in "rare opportunities" just because your friends or relatives have invested in them. Thieves know that the easiest way, by far, to create trust is through word of mouth from people with social, religious or cultural affiliations similar to your own.

AN EXPENSIVE FREE DINNER

Back in 1946, a Texas couple named Luke and Lillian Wentz had the good luck to invest $6,600 in Warren Buffett's fledgling company. When Luke Wentz passed away more than a half-century later in 1997, his spouse, a retired schoolteacher, found herself with Berkshire Hathaway stock worth $24 million.

Not knowing how to handle that amount of money, she turned to an insurance firm that promised elderly folks that they could save a fortune on estate taxes. People were invited to the local Steak & Ale for a free steak dinner and a complimentary seminar from Underhill & Best on how to pass on more of their life savings to their heirs rather than the government. These agency representatives convinced Wentz that she needed to liquidate all her Berkshire Hathaway stock and use the proceeds to purchase insurance and annuity products. Underhill & Best pocketed more than $2 million in fees and commissions for work that an estate-planning law practice could have accomplished for a fee of a few thousand dollars. Lillian died soon after, in 2002, and her grandsons had to sue Underhill & Best.

Lesson: There really is no free lunch. Underhill & Best's seminars were targeted at lonely seniors under the guise of educational and social events. The promoters promised free advice and door prizes to encourage attendance. A recent SEC investigation found that 60% of the firms offering similar free-meal seminars had behaved improperly in ways ranging from making unsuitable recommendations to misrepresenting how the adviser would profit.

Many financial dine-and-learn seminars are costly to you because the information you get may not be tailored to your specific situation, and you may hear only about investments that carry exorbitant fees.

Better: Many accredited financial planners offer free or low-cost one-on-one meetings. To find one, contact the National Association of Personal Financial Advisors at 847-483-5400 or *www.napfa.org.*

UNSAFE SAFEGUARDS

Thousands of financially intelligent investors who trusted Bernard L. Madoff Investment Securities LLC were fooled by what had appeared to be safeguards but actually were not. For example, Madoff's financial statements had been audited for nearly two decades by the small accounting firm Friehling & Horowitz, which filed audits every year with the SEC. David Friehling was even past president of a chapter of the New York State Society of CPAs.

But Friehling wound up being paid millions of dollars in fees by Madoff, who was a longtime friend of his, without actually examining the investment fund's bookkeeping. He ignored the fact that Madoff had full custody and control over the assets of his clients, which is how the crook was able to dip into their money so easily and keep his scheme undetected for so long. In 2009, Friehling pled guilty to nine criminal counts, including aiding and abetting investment-adviser fraud.

Lesson: Your investment manager always should be accountable to reputable third parties. When you invest, you're trusting your manager to make wise decisions with your money. But you can check that he reports his actions and results honestly and accurately to you.

My two most important rules for not getting burned by a financial scammer…

• **Your investment manager should retain a prominent independent auditor**—such as Deloitte & Touche, PricewaterhouseCoopers or Ernst & Young—to review the fund's financials annually, although even this is no guarantee.

• **Never let your investment manager take custody of your assets directly and pool them with assets of other investors.** Your assets should be kept in an independent custodial account with your name on it at a major, well-known institution, such as Chase Bank, Charles Schwab, Inc., Wells Fargo. The investment manager might have the ability to make investment decisions for you within your custodial account, but you should have 24-hour access to all your account information. Also, the

statements showing the value of your account each month should come from the institution, not from the investment manager.

Sure Sign of a Scam

High-yield investment programs (or HYIPs) promoted through social media sites almost always are scams. These unregistered investments, offered by unlicensed people and companies through YouTube, Twitter, Facebook and other such sites, claim to deliver returns as high as 20%, 30% or even 100% per day.

What to do: Avoid any investment whose returns seem too good to be true. Avoid any site that does not clearly explain how returns are generated…that involves offshore operations…or that offers incentives to recruit new investors. Many scams offer referral bonuses as high as 25% and pay bonuses from the new money, which is a hallmark of Ponzi schemes.

Financial Industry Regulatory Authority (FINRA) in Washington, DC, *www.finra.org.*

Whistle-Blower Rewards

Whistle-blowers are now eligible for up to 30% of the monetary sanctions collected in securities fraud cases. The new incentives are a part of the financial-regulation overhaul signed into law in July 2010 and come in reaction to multibillion-dollar fraud cases in recent years, including the Ponzi scheme carried out by Bernard Madoff. They apply in cases where a tipster provides information to the Securities and Exchange Commission (SEC) that leads to fraud sanctions of more than $1 million, including fines and ill-gotten profits. Previously, whistle-blowers were eligible for only 10% of any fine and only in those instances involving insider trading. For additional information, go to *www.sec.gov/complaint.shtml.*

John Nester, public affairs director, Securities and Exchange Commission, Washington, DC.

11

More for Your Money

Four New Negotiating Tricks That Can Save Anyone Big Money

We will usually make a counteroffer when given the price of a house or a car that we want to buy, yet most of us treat other prices and policies as if they were set in stone.

They're not.

Every professional and financial interaction is an opportunity for negotiation. People who fail to take advantage of this are leaving thousands of dollars or even more right on the table each year.

Negotiation does not mean offering lowball bids or making slick power plays. *There are practical strategies that offer greater odds of success without the risk of appearing cheap or confrontational...*

CITE THE COMPANY'S STANDARDS

Many organizations provide an official standard, mission statement, advertising slogan or motto that promises you excellent service and quality. Service providers, such as the telecom companies, financial firms and hotels, are particularly likely to have these.

Examples: Red Roof Inn promises on its Web site "freshly renovated, cozy rooms" and "luxuries like incredibly comfortable bedding." AT&T says on its site that its mission is to "connect people with their world, everywhere they live and work, and do it better than anyone else."

Prices, offers and rates ***throughout chapter*** subject to change.

Stuart Diamond, JD, a practice professor of legal studies and business ethics at The Wharton School of the University of Pennsylvania in Philadelphia. His negotiations course has been the most sought-after program by students for 13 years. Diamond has served as a consultant and adviser to numerous countries and Fortune 500 companies, as well as the United Nations and the World Bank. He won a Pulitzer Prize as a reporter for *The New York Times* and is the author of *Getting More: How to Negotiate* (Crown Business, *www.gettingmore.com*).

When a company lets you down, browse its Web site, ads and any other printed materials for written statements about its standards, mission or the high quality it delivers. Write them down, then calmly and politely quote them to the company representative. Next, describe the problems you've encountered, and ask the rep to gauge how your experience measures up to this promise or mission. If the employee agrees that your experience fell short, ask what he/she can do to make up for this.

If the employee will not admit that you deserve compensation, calmly ask how the CEO of the company might respond if he/she were brought into this conversation. Even if it is not realistic that the CEO of a big company would get personally involved in a minor disagreement, evoking the CEO forces the employee to consider the potential career fallout if a boss learned that he failed to live up to the company's standards. Most employees would rather give a customer a discount or perk than risk negative career consequences, particularly if a customer is friendly and polite.

Options if you cannot find relevant written standards or slogans…

• **Ask the company rep questions that establish their standards before describing your negative experience.**

Example: Ask, "Does your organization stand behind its services?" or "Does your company sell well-made products?" The answer will almost certainly be a yes. Now describe your poor experience, and ask what the company can do for you to match the standards that the rep just described.

• **Ask an employee to estimate the value of the subpar goods or services you received.**

Example: When the hot water in my expensive London hotel room did not work, I asked a front-desk clerk, "What is the value of my room without hot water?" He decided that it was half the normal room rate and reduced my bill.

BE AN ALLY TO SALESPEOPLE

Employees who sell big-ticket or big-margin items, such as furniture, appliances and jewelry, often earn much of their income through commissions or bonuses. The size of that com-

mission or bonus usually is not tied simply to how much customers pay for items. When you negotiate with these salespeople, start not by requesting a lower price, but by asking, "What can I do to help you earn a higher commission today?"

Examples: Perhaps one of two items that you are deciding between would result in a higher commission, even if it is not the more expensive item…or perhaps your salesperson would receive a larger bonus if you purchased multiple things at the same time rather than spreading out purchases. Even if there is not anything you can do to boost the commission, asking this question casts you as the salesperson's ally in reaching his income goals. That is likely to make the salesperson more willing to help you reach your goal—a lower purchase price or other perks. Most customers instead start negotiations by asking for a lower price, creating an adversarial relationship with the salesperson.

Helpful: If you are not certain whether a salesperson receives commissions, it's OK to politely ask.

TAP INTO BIG-BUYER DISCOUNTS

The big spenders often qualify for big discounts. *Even if you're an ordinary customer, you might be able to negotiate for these volume discounts if…*

• **You buy two big-ticket items.** If most of a merchant's customers buy just one big item at a time, buying two should entitle you to extra savings.

Example: At some of the appliance and electronics stores, buying just two televisions qualifies for a volume discount—but few customers know to ask. If you do not need two, perhaps you could team up with a friend who is shopping for something similar. Ask the salesperson what he could do for you if you buy more than one pricey item. If the answer is, "I can't give you a discount," ask him, "Who can?" The store's manager or owner might be more flexible.

• **You buy the most expensive of two or more comparable products.** The expensive unit likely provides a much larger profit to the merchant—and perhaps a larger commission to the salesperson—than the cheaper one. It's in the salesperson's financial interests for you to choose it, so you may get a much bigger discount. Explain that you're trying to decide between some comparable items, and ask the salesperson or store manager what he can do to encourage you to buy the expensive one. Don't do this unless there's a valid reason to buy the pricier item, such as superior workmanship.

• **You belong to a local organization with many members who also could turn into customers with your influence.** Inform the business owner or manager that you work for a big local employer…have a position of leadership in a large local association…or live in a major condo complex or retirement community. Point out that you might be able to steer other members of the group toward the business, then ask what the business can do for its most loyal customers.

UNITE WITH MERCHANTS

The Internet often offers lower prices than area stores, but buying locally has its advantages, too. The local seller might provide better product support, and buying local might mean that there's no wait for delivery.

You can use low online prices as negotiating tools even if you prefer to buy locally—merchants sometimes will lower their prices or throw in other perks, such as service plans, to compete with Internet sellers.

Unfortunately, customers who attempt to use Internet prices as negotiation tools generally do so by saying that they have found a low price online, then asking the local merchant to match it. This direct approach tends to remind merchants and salespeople that the Internet poses a major threat to their businesses and jobs, which often triggers feelings of fear and anger. Those feelings greatly reduce the odds of successful negotiations.

Instead, say, "I'd rather buy this from a local business such as yours than on the Internet, but the Internet price is lower. Is there anything you can do to help me buy from you?" This casts you as an ally working with the seller against the looming threat of the Internet, increasing the odds that the merchant will do what he can to help you.

How to Get *Up to 90% Off* on Restaurant Meals, Movie Tickets, Haircuts, More

Gregory Karp, who writes the syndicated "Spending Smart" column that appears in *Chicago Tribune*, *The Baltimore Sun* and many other newspapers. Based in Chicago, he is a three-time winner of the Best Column Award from the Society of American Business Editors and Writers and is the author of *The 1-2-3 Money Plan: The Three Most Important Steps for Saving and Spending Smart* (FT Press). His Web site is *www.gregorykarp.com*.

Bargain hunters already know that the Internet is a great place to obtain low prices on merchandise. Now a rapidly growing array of Web sites is offering savings from 50% to 90% on services and experiences, such as restaurant meals, spa services, carpet cleaning, dry cleaning, movie and theater tickets, haircuts, gym memberships, yoga classes and dance lessons.

These "local deal" or "deal-of-the-day" sites, including Groupon.com and Restaurant.com, negotiate special group rates with area eateries and service providers, then sell vouchers to the public that work much like gift certificates—except that you buy them at steep discounts to their face value. Local businesses agree to offer these deep discounts to attract large numbers of new customers who, they hope, will come back and pay full price in the future.

Examples: A $25 voucher to a local restaurant might cost $10 or even $2…a voucher good for a series of yoga classes that normally would cost $250 might cost as little as $25.

Consumers use a credit card to pay online for the voucher, print their voucher at home, then bring it to the local business to redeem it. With many of these sites, each deal is available for just one day. The vouchers need not be used that same day, however—most don't expire for months. On some sites, deals take effect only if a certain number of users purchase the voucher. If not, the deal is voided and no one is charged.

The widest variety of offers is available to people who live in or near major cities, but

191

some of these Web sites serve smaller cities and suburban regions, too, and others plan to soon expand into them.

Helpful: You also might want to sign up for discounts in a city that you plan to visit.

Here's a look at the sites worth trying, how they work and how to sidestep the traps that can turn seemingly great deals into money losers…

WHERE TO FIND DISCOUNTS

Among the Web sites that offer the most attractive deals and cover the largest number of regions…

• **Groupon.com** is the largest of these sites, available in more than 500 local areas worldwide. Sign up to get their daily deal e-mails. Most Groupon.com deals offer 50% to 90% off at a restaurant or spa or for some leisure activity. Each deal is available for just one day, and the offers take effect only if a predetermined minimum number of users sign up. If not enough people sign up, your credit card is not charged.

Recent example: $22 for two pottery classes that usually cost $45.

• **LivingSocial.com** is in 309 regions worldwide and it works in much the same way as Groupon.com. The discounts typically are 50% up to 90%…restaurants, spas and theaters are among the businesses most often featured… and every deal is available for purchase for just one day. Unlike with Groupon, however, there's no sign-up tipping point—if you want to purchase a voucher, you can, regardless of how many other LivingSocial users sign up. Plus LivingSocial provides an added savings twist. If you can convince three other people to purchase the same deal, you will receive your voucher for free.

Recent example: $9 for two movie tickets that usually cost $20 or more.

• **BuyWithMe.com** is not yet in as many regions as Groupon or LivingSocial, but each of its deals is available for seven days, not just one—so there is far less pressure for you to make a quick decision.

Recent example: $35 for hair styling at a salon that normally charges $75.

• **Restaurant.com** offers discounted vouchers for more than 18,000 restaurants nationwide. Enter your zip code, and Restaurant.com will locate any offers in your area. Unlike the previously covered sites, Restaurant.com offers typically are available for an extended period, not just for a single day or week. Many Restaurant.com vouchers impose restrictions on how and which days of the week they can be used, so read the fine print. The site often e-mails offers of extra discounts off its usual discounts to people who register.

Recent examples: Many local restaurants provide $25 vouchers for $10 or less…or $100 vouchers for $40 or less through Restaurant.com. Those fees may be discounted by an extra 80% from time to time, so you actually can pay just $2 for a $25 meal.

AGGREGATOR SITES HELP

There are other, smaller sites that offer attractive deals in certain areas, and new local deals sites come out all the time. Rather than trying to monitor all of them, consider using a "deals aggregator" site, which monitors the individual sites and consolidates their current offers into a single list or map.

Examples of aggregator sites: DealNews.com (click the "Local" tab)…DealRadar.com… 8Coupons.com…and YipIt.com.

Not all aggregator sites service every geographic area or every deal site, and each reports local deals in a different fashion. Check several before deciding on the one that does the best job helping you find deals that you really want. Aggregator sites typically feature only short-term deals, not those available for extended periods, such as the ones offered by Restaurant.com.

BEWARE DRAWBACKS

A big discount does not necessarily mean that something is a great deal. If you're not familiar with the business that's offering the discount, look for reviews from other customers on sites such as Yelp.com or CitySearch.com —or Chowhound.com just for restaurants—or ask friends their opinions.

Other issues that can make a seemingly great deal a bad money move…

●**Small businesses can get overwhelmed when a large group of customers signs up for these discounts,** causing a temporary decline in quality. It makes some sense to wait a week or two for the crowds to diminish before redeeming a voucher offered by a smaller business.

●**Unused vouchers are money wasted.** Keep your vouchers well-organized, and note their expiration dates on your calendar. Do not buy a voucher just because it seems like too good of a deal to pass up—buy it only if you are certain that you will use it.

Helpful: You might be able to resell your voucher—if you realize that you'll never use it—on Lifesta.com, a daily deals marketplace site. A voucher generally is transferable unless it specifically says otherwise. There is no cost to post a voucher for sale, but Lifesta takes 99 cents plus 8% of the sale price if you find a buyer. It also is a good place to buy daily deals that you missed when they initially were offered.

You often cannot redeem vouchers the same day. Most sites won't let you print out your voucher until a certain number of people sign up for it or until the day after it is purchased.

Exception: Restaurant.com vouchers generally can be printed and used the same day.

There could be an important caveat hidden in the small print. Some vouchers cannot be used on the most popular days of the week. Others have high minimum-purchase requirements or other rules.

Example: A restaurant voucher might be valid only Monday through Thursday.

Helpful: If there is a problem with any of the discounts, contact the specific Web site by e-mail or toll-free number.

How to Find the *Real Deals* at Outlet Malls

Linda Arroz, lifestyle analyst for Makeover Media, a Los Angeles–based consulting firm covering fashion and related sectors. She has served as marketing director and spokesperson for fashion designer Carole Little and editor in chief of *Big Beautiful Woman Magazine.* Arroz has twice been named one of the 25 Most Powerful Players in the fashion industry by *California Apparel News.* Her Web site is *www.lindaarroz.com.*

Outlet malls are popular destinations for bargain hunters, but buyers need to beware—many outlet goods are not great deals these days.

Factory outlets are no longer packed to the rafters with the good bargains that they used to feature, including the previous season's unsold brand-name clothing, samples and miscut factory seconds with minor defects.

Although outlet malls provide nonclothing items ranging from housewares to furniture—categories that still provide good bargains in many cases—most shoppers are there for the clothes, and clothing designers have increasingly cut clothes in smaller lots or cut only to order, resulting in much less overstock.

When overstock and factory seconds do exist, they now are likely to be sold to discount chains, such as Loehmann's…Marshalls…Ross Dress for Less…TJ Maxx…and Tuesday Morning, not allocated to factory outlets.

Reason: Clothing company execs consider it safer to unload unsold goods in large lots to discounters, rather than gamble that they will sell well in outlets. Publicly traded clothing companies are particularly anxious to get unsold goods off their books quickly to keep their balance sheets tidy.

To make up for this lack of inventory, many apparel and accessory companies stock their outlet stores with merchandise made specifically for those outlets. Yes, these straight-to-outlet products are cheaper than the makers' retail store goods—but they also are of lower quality. That is fine for shoppers whose primary goal is to own garments bearing prestigious logos and labels, but not for those who want top quality.

Example: The straight-to-outlet sweater might lack double stitching…or be made from a blend of fibers rather than 100% cashmere.

Overstock apparel that does make its way into outlet malls these days usually is not as much of a bargain as it seems. These clothes typically are priced at about 20% below "suggested retail," but many of these items were offered for well below suggested retail during sales at retail stores.

HOW TO FIND QUALITY MERCHANDISE

It is still possible to get bargains at outlet malls, but only if you shop very carefully.

Note: If you're not sure where outlet malls are, the Web site OutletBound.com can help you track down names and Web sites of outlet stores and malls.

Here's how to find quality merchandise…

•**Focus on nonclothing items.** Clothes get most of the attention at outlet malls, but these days, the big outlet savings typically are on nonclothing merchandise, including furniture, housewares and luggage. Nonclothing outlet stores are much less likely to be stocked with lower-quality, straight-to-outlet merchandise. And the items often are marked down by 30% or more—occasionally much more—because of nicks, chips, dents and scratches.

In many cases, this damage is minor and easily repaired or hidden. Sometimes it is no different from the normal wear the item would develop after a few uses anyway.

Examples of luggage and cookware outlet stores with the best deals: Samsonite outlets for luggage…Le Creuset outlets for cookware.

The discounts on mildly damaged furniture can be particularly sharp because outlets don't want these bulky items taking up floor space for long.

Examples of furniture outlet stores with the best deals: Crate & Barrel…Pottery Barn… Ralph Lauren Home.

•**Shop for shoes.** Shoes are less likely to be straight-to-outlet, lower-quality goods, and they often are there because of small scuffs that are hardly noticeable.

Examples of shoe outlet stores with the best deals: Puma and Adidas outlets for sneakers…Kenneth Cole and Cole Haan outlets for shoes and boots.

•**Be aware that the biggest names can yield the best savings.** Elite brands, such as Chanel, Dolce & Gabbana and Gucci, generally do not put out lower-quality outlet-only product lines for fear that these lesser products could sully their gold-plated images. Thus the outlet stores of the highest-end designers tend to be stocked with actual top-quality discounted overstock.

Exception: Handbag maker Coach does feature lower-priced but lower-quality, straight-to-outlet handbags, among other merchandise.

•**Ask the way to the discount rack.** Most outlet stores still have an area filled with major markdowns of 40% or more, but it might be hidden away in a distant corner of the store. This merchandise often includes damaged or miscut products, so examine these goods particularly carefully.

•**Determine why items are in the outlet before buying.** Is this something made specifically for the outlet? Is there hard-to-spot damage? Some outlets do note this clearly on merchandise, but not all.

Example: Ann Taylor's straight-to-outlet garments are clearly marked "Ann Taylor Factory" on the label, but Brooks Brothers' straight-to-outlet products are identified less clearly as belonging to the company's "346" product line.

Employees at outlets generally will disclose why products are there. If the reason is damage, ask the salesperson if the discount can be increased. The size of the discount on damaged goods typically depends on the degree of damage, which is subjective and thus potentially negotiable.

•**Try on outlet clothes before buying.** Garments sometimes wind up in outlets because they've been miscut or mislabeled as the wrong size. Don't wait until you're home to find out that your purchases don't fit. Even if the outlet allows returns—not all do—the outlet mall might be too far away for a second visit.

HOW TO GET THE BEST DEALS

•**Hunt down outlet mall and store coupons.** Visit the Web site and Facebook page of the outlet mall you plan to go to and the Web sites of the designers whose stores you are likely to visit there. You might find coupons providing savings of as much as 15% to 20% off regular outlet prices.

Example: Join Chelsea Premium Outlets' VIP Club online to receive a free coupon book (*www.premiumoutlets.com*).

• **Visit welcome centers at outlet malls as soon as you arrive.** Valuable coupon books often are available there, either for free or for a small fee, typically less than $5. Ask if there are special discounts for members of groups you belong to, such as AAA or AARP.

Example: Members of AARP qualify for free coupon books featuring savings of up to 20% off from Tanger outlet malls (*www.tangeroutlet.com*, more than 30 malls across the US). Tanger also offers special savings booklets to AAA members, plus free $5 gift cards to AAA members who visit multiple Tanger malls during a single calendar year.

• **Check the retail price before paying the outlet price.** Perhaps you could find a better price on the same item at a discount retailer or even at a regular retail store when it's having a big sale. Or perhaps you could purchase a version of the same garment made from better fabric in a retail store or online for only a few dollars more—and have a wider choice of sizes and colors.

If you or one of your outlet shopping partners has a smartphone, visit a shopping Web site, such as PriceGrabber.com, Shopzilla.com or ComparisonShopping.com, to compare the prices on your selections before going to the register.

If you don't have access to a smartphone, do some price research shortly prior to your outlet mall trip. Visit retail stores or Web sites of those stores and of favorite designers that sell directly to consumers.

Jot down the prices of the products that you are most likely to buy, then bring these notes with you when you go to the outlet mall.

• **Shop at outlet malls when retail stores have sales.** Factory outlets typically have their biggest sales at the same times of year that retail stores do—on the weekends of Memorial Day, Labor Day, President's Day, Columbus Day, around Thanksgiving and the week after Christmas.

Save Extra at Major Retail Stores

Kmart, Sears, Lands' End and The Great Indoors share *Shop Your Way* rewards—you can earn points that can be used to purchase items from any one of the four participating stores. Dillard's offers a credit card with which you can earn shopping passes for every 1,500 points earned in a calendar year—the passes are good for 10% off all purchases made in a single day. Costco and Sam's Club offer $100/year higher-level memberships giving special benefits—Costco offers 2% back on most purchases (up to a maximum rebate of $500) and automatic discounts on selected products and services.

Tod Marks, shopping-trend columnist, *Consumer Reports Money Adviser*, 101 Truman Ave., Yonkers, New York 10703, *www.consumerreports.org*.

Get Cash for a Gift Card You Don't Want

You can buy or sell gift cards online at Web sites such as *www.cardpool.com* and *www.plasticjungle.com*. Other sites, including *www.swapagift.com*, let you trade cards. Card values vary by site. So do the rules for purchases or trades. Some sites offer a limited guarantee in case a card you buy turns out to be invalid.

What to do: Check each retailer's site for its rules on reselling its cards. Check each reselling site for available cards and the site's rules governing their sale and purchase. Compare deals from several sites, and buy only from sites that offer a guarantee.

Consumer Reports Money Adviser, 101 Truman Ave., Yonkers, New York 10703, *www.consumerreports.org*.

Got Lots of Change? What to Do with It...

Receive full value from Coinstar coin-counting machines by putting the value of your change on a retail gift card good at Amazon, iTunes, Lowe's, Old Navy, Starbucks or other stores. You also get full value if you donate your coins to major charities. Coinstar coin-counting machines charge 9.8 cents per dollar if you ask for cash. To find a machine, go online to *http://locator.coinstar.com*.

Better Homes and Gardens, 1716 Locust St., Des Moines 50309, *www.bhg.com*.

Make an Extra $2,500 A Year...Tax-Free! Secret Below...

Susan Samtur, editor of *Refundle Bundle*, a bimonthly magazine that lists coupon and rebate opportunities. She is also author of *Supershop Like the Coupon Queen: How to Save 50% or More Every Time You Shop* (Berkley). Her Web site is *www.couponqueen.com*.

Shoppers who dismiss rebate and refund offers as more trouble than they're worth should think again. Each year, I receive roughly $2,500 in rebate checks for buying products—primarily in supermarkets—that I would have purchased anyway. I have gotten rebates for buying cereal, detergents, dog food and frozen pizza. Many of these rebates are $5 or beyond, which is a very respectable return on the few minutes required to clip out a few proofs of purchase and complete a short rebate form, even after subtracting the cost of a stamp and an envelope.

Bonus: The IRS considers rebate checks a reduction in purchase price, not income, so this money is tax-free.

LOCATING GREAT REBATES

Rebates often are not widely publicized. *To turn rebates into a steady stream of income, you need to know how to find them...*

•**Look for altered product labels.** Specially marked packages sometimes signal rebate offers. Before you put an item in your cart, scan the shelf to see if other boxes, other sizes or competing products feature unfamiliar wording or graphics. Also, keep an eye out for shelf displays featuring small peel-off pads of rebate forms.

Be particularly vigilant when shopping for items in categories with a lot of competition, such as cereal and coffee...household cleaners and detergents...beer...and paper goods. Rebates are particularly common in these categories. These also tend to be products that don't go bad quickly, if at all, making it safe to stock up if multiple items must be purchased to earn the rebate.

Example: Receive a $10 rebate by purchasing $20 worth of 3M Permanent labels or Post-it Notes by the close of 2011 (log on to *www.3mproductivity.com*, then click "Special Offers").

•**Sign up for the e-letters of companies that produce the products you buy.** These newsletters often feature rebate offers as well as other savings. Find a company's Web site by typing its name into Google.com, then look for a link on the site labeled "Sign up" or "Special offers."

Recommended: Create a special e-mail account to use for these newsletters so that your main e-mail account is not flooded with product offers and updates.

•**Skim newspaper and magazine ads for rebate offers.** Sunday sales circulars usually are prime sources.

•**Sign up for the pharmaceutical chain rebate programs.** CVS (*www.cvs.com*), Rite-Aid (*www.riteaid.com*) and Walgreens (*www.walgreens.com*) provide extensive rebate programs on many kinds of products, including over-the-counter medications, baby food and household cleaners. These programs are now Internet-based, so you don't even have to mail in rebate forms.

•**Examine the packaging of any product marked "new" or "new and improved."** New and updated products are particularly likely to feature rebates because companies know that they must provide special inducements to convince consumers to try something different.

•**Web sites of office-supply retailers,** such as Staples (*www.staples.com*) and Office Depot (*www.officedepot.com*) typically feature a wide range of rebates on everything from paper to computers. Click on "Rebate Center" for Staples and "Mail-in Savings Center" for Office Depot.

Ritz Camera's Internet site is another good place to find valuable discounts on consumer electronics (*www.ritzcamera.com*, then click "Rebates & Coupons").

•**When you shop at Bed, Bath & Beyond,** stop by the customer service department and request the sheet of current manufacturers' rebate offers.

Examples: Recent Bed, Bath & Beyond rebates have included $10 off an Oneida 18-inch nonstick roaster pan and $10 off a Cuisinart coffeemaker.

Rebates can be used in conjunction with the widely distributed Bed, Bath & Beyond coupons, which often provide 20% off any single item or $5 off purchases greater than $15. If you do not get these coupons already, sign up to receive them at *www.bedbathandbeyond. com* (click on "Email Signup").

•**Before buying oil, antifreeze, air filters and other automotive items that require frequent replacement,** check product packaging and shelf displays for rebate offers. The companies that make these products know that people who work on their own cars tend to be very brand loyal and that a big rebate might be the only way to lure them away from the competition.

Example: Buy one Prestone Bug Wash, get one free before December 31, 2011 (*www. prestone.com*, click "Special Offers Available").

•**Visit the refund discussion board at my Web site, CouponQueen.com.** Select "Forum/Blog," followed by "Discussions," then "Manufacturers Refunds" to read about recent rebate offers.

GET THE MOST FROM REBATE OFFERS
Strategies to maximize rebates…

•**Create a label supply network.** Tell your friends and relatives that you are collecting proofs of purchase and receipts from particular products, or post this on your Facebook page. People who don't bother with rebates might be pleased to hand over their labels. Those who do use rebates might be willing to swap with you if you are pursuing different offers.

•**Save promising labels and receipts even if there is no rebate.** Some companies—such as those listed below—provide rebates so frequently that it's worth saving proofs of purchase even when a rebate is not offered. You might be able to use them if a new rebate offer appears soon. Save all your grocery store register receipts, as well—many rebates do require these.

Helpful: I save proofs of purchase in shoe boxes…refund forms in an envelope…and receipts in another envelope.

•**Seek out free samples.** Receiving a free sample in the mail might not be quite as appealing as receiving a rebate check, but samples have one big advantage over cash-back rebates—you don't have to purchase anything to earn them. You might not even have to use a stamp—many free samples now can be obtained by completing a quick online form.

Example: The Web site *www.allyou.com* offers a new free sample each day. Just click the listing in the "Daily Free Sample" box. You also can request the freebies offered on previous days by clicking "See full calendar," then choosing earlier dates.

More from Susan Samtur…

Top 10 Companies for Supermarket Rebates

The following companies offer rebates far more often than most…

•**Colgate-Palmolive.** *www.colgate.com*.

•**Crest/Oral-B.** *www.crest.com* and *www. oralb.com/coupons*.

•**General Mills.** The brands include Betty Crocker, Bisquick and Pillsbury. *www.general mills.com*.

•**Kellogg's.** *www.kelloggs.com*.

• **Kraft Foods.** The brands include Maxwell House, Miracle Whip, Oreo, Oscar Mayer, Planters and Ritz. *www.kraftfoodscompany.com.*

• **Nestlé.** The brands include Carnation, DiGiorno, Dreyer's, Häagen-Dazs, Hot Pockets, Stouffer's and more. *www.nestleusa.com.*

• **Nabisco.** *www.nabiscoworld.com.*

Example: Join Nabisco's Facebook page, and qualify for discounts on Nabisco cookies each month.

• **Ragú.** *www.ragu.com.*

• **S.C. Johnson.** The brands include Drano, Glade, Off, Pledge, Raid, Shout, Windex and Ziploc. *www.rightathome.com.*

• **3M.** Rebates on Scotch Tape, Post-it Notes and other home and office products are common. *www.3m.com.*

Buy Organic for Less

Steve and Annette Economides, nicknamed "America's Cheapest Family" by *Good Morning America*. See *www.americascheapestfamily.com*. Based in Scottsdale, Arizona, they are the coauthors of *Cut Your Grocery Bill in Half with America's Cheapest Family* (Thomas Nelson).

Organic foods could cost 50% to 100% more than similar nonorganic items. *Here's how to eat organic at a reasonable price...*

• **Shop around.** Prices vary from store to store and from week to week. Do not assume that upscale stores that carry a lot of organic foods, such as the national chain Whole Foods, always will be more expensive than the traditional supermarkets. They often have weekly specials that are as cheap as or cheaper than mainstream supermarkets.

The smaller specialty markets, such as the chains Trader Joe's (*www.traderjoes.com*) and Sprouts Farmers Markets (*www.sprouts.com*), also have reasonable prices on organic foods.

Helpful: Organic meat often can be purchased at supermarkets or specialty markets for half its usual price or less when it is approaching its sell-by date. You then can freeze it until needed. (If you see that the meat is near

or at its sell-by date and it's not yet marked down, ask the manager whether you can get it for less.)

In general, prices tend to be lowest in regions where multiple stores sell organic foods. If you live in a town that has no such competition, it could be worth driving to a larger community that does.

• **Try a food co-op.** Co-ops are formal or informal nonprofit organizations that purchase food at wholesale prices and then make this available to members at a low cost. Many specialize in organic foods. Type in "Food co-op" and the name of your city or state into Google to find co-ops in your area, or try the Coop Directory Service online site (*www.coopdirectory.org*).

• **Visit local organic farms.** Many organic farmers will sell directly to the public, which lowers prices by cutting out the middleman. Sometimes this is done by subscription, with consumers receiving a bag of organic fruits and/or vegetables each week for a very reasonable flat fee. Occasionally an organic farm will lower prices even more for those customers willing to do a little farmwork.

• **Obtain a cow or pig.** If you live in a rural location, you could purchase an organically raised cow and pig from a local rancher or a farmer. The rancher or farmer may butcher it for you or you can have it butchered by students in the butchery program of an area tech school. The total cost could be around half what you would pay for the same amount of organic meat in a store. If you buy a whole cow, it would be helpful to split the purchase with one or two other families.

Coupons That Help Military Families

Certain military bases overseas will accept expired manufacturers' coupons for food and nonfood items, including detergent and paper products, that help members of the US armed forces save money. Some bases accept coupons that are up to two months past their expiration dates. Go to the online site of the Overseas Coupon Program (*www.ocpnet.org*) to find out about specific bases that accept particular coupons.

Mary Hunt, editor, DebtProofLiving.com, based in Paramount, California.

Discounts for People With Disabilities

David Squar, founder of DisabledDiscounts.com, an online resource guide owned and operated by people who have disabilities and their caregivers, *www.disabled discounts.com*. Squar has researched disability-related issues for more than two decades, ever since his wife was diagnosed with multiple sclerosis.

Living with any type of disability, including chronic illness, can present many physical challenges. And the ever-increasing financial burdens can make daily living even more complicated.

Good news: There are discounts available to help people with disabilities bridge the financial gap—discounts that can save hundreds, maybe even thousands, of dollars per year.

Unfortunately, very few of these discounts are publicized. *Here's how to find discounts in your area...*

•**Contact local Community Action programs and Area Agencies on Aging.** These nonprofit organizations are not specifically designed to help the disabled. The Community Action programs will primarily assist low-income individuals, while the Area Agencies on Aging assist seniors. However, a significant percentage of low-income individuals and seniors are disabled, so the employees and the volunteers who work for these organizations often know about savings opportunities for the disabled, too. *To help you locate the organizations that serve your area, contact...*

•Community Action Partnership, 202-265-7546, *www.communityactionpartnership.com*.

•National Association of Area Agencies on Aging, 202-872-0888, *www.n4a.org*.

•**Find nonprofit foundations associated with your disability or disease.** These associations—and their regional chapters—often know where to locate discounts on the medical supplies, mobility equipment and support services that those suffering from the condition require. Some of these organizations have negotiated special discounted rates with suppliers, and a few will even provide subsidized equipment directly.

Associations that do a particularly good job with this include...

•American Liver Foundation, 212-668-1000, *www.liverfoundation.org*.

•ALS Association, 800-782-4747, *www.alsa. org*.

•Hemophilia Foundation, 800-424-2634, *www. hemophilia.org*.

•Muscular Dystrophy Association, 800-572-1717, *www.mdausa.org*.

•National Kidney Foundation, 800-622-9010, *www.kidney.org*.

•National Multiple Sclerosis Society, 800-344-4867, *www.nationalmssociety.org*.

Example: The Muscular Dystrophy Association's Equipment Assistance Program helps MD sufferers who are registered with that organization obtain free secondhand wheelchairs, hospital beds, patient lifts and other equipment if they lack the financial means and insurance to obtain these things on their own.

If there is no large organization for your disability, contact local chapters of the organizations listed earlier and ask if they can provide guidance on locating discounts for someone with your specific condition.

•**Visit the Web site E-Bility.com to download accessibility software.** The software can render personal computers easier for disabled people to use. Some software is free. (On *www. e-bility.com*, click on "Resources," then "Links," then "Software" for a list of programs.)

Example: Camera Mouse, a free download, lets those with limited use of their hands control the mouse pointer on their computer screens simply by moving their heads. A Webcam is required (*www.cameramouse.com*).

•**Sign up for a pair of federal government discounts for the disabled.** *The two excellent programs...*

•"That all may read" program from the Library of Congress mails audiobooks to people whose vision or physical impairments make it impossible for them to read printed books. The program is free—you even can borrow an audiobook player for free and return the audiobooks that you've borrowed postage-free when you're done with them. More than 60,000 audiobooks are available (*www.loc.gov/nls*).

•The National Park System's Access Pass offers those who are permanently disabled free admission for life to national parks and other federal recreational lands. The pass also provides gratis admission for up to three accompanying adults. (Admission is always free for children.) Expanded amenities, such as camping and boat launching, are not free but often are discounted by 50% (*www.nps.gov/fees_passes.htm*).

•**Contact all your utility providers.** Power companies and communications companies sometimes offer special discounts to customers who have special needs. If the customer service representative you're speaking to does not know of any such discounts, ask to speak with a manager—disabled customer discounts often are unknown even to the company's experienced reps. *Examples of discounts...*

•Pacific Gas & Electric customers who rely on life-support equipment or whose health conditions make them especially dependent on heating or air-conditioning can purchase power at the lowest available household rate through PGs Medical Baseline Allowance program (800-743-5000, *http://pge.com*).

•Customers of AT&T and Verizon Wireless whose disabilities make it difficult for them to use a telephone directory often qualify for free directory-assistance calls. Contact AT&T (at 800-464-7928, or 800-772-3140 in California, *www.att.com* and type "Customers with Disabilities" in the search box) or Verizon Wireless (800-922-0204, *http://aboutus.vzw.com/accessibility*) for details.

•**Ask your veterinarian if he/she knows of any discounts or financial assistance programs** for service animals or pets belonging to the disabled. If he does not, ask regional animal-focused nonprofits the same question. Veterinarian professional associations, animal lovers' groups, even state governments sometimes discount or subsidize the cost of animal care for disabled owners with limited financial means. *Examples...*

•The Feline Veterinary Emergency Assistance Program will provide financial assistance when cats belonging to disabled people require surgery that their owners cannot afford (*http://fveap.org*).

•The Pet Project offers low-cost pet food, veterinary services and animal care to pets belonging to residents of Broward County, Florida, who suffer from severely disabling conditions or terminal illnesses (954-568-5678, *www.petprojectforpets.org*).

•The state of California's Assistance Dog Special Allowance provides $50 each month to the disabled owners of service animals if certain conditions are met (916-657-2628, *www.cdss.ca.gov* and type "Assistance Dog Allowance" in the search box).

Don't Get Ripped Off on Craigslist: Scams Even Smart People Fall For

Skip Press, longtime Craigslist enthusiast as well as author of *The Complete Idiot's Guide to Making Money with Craigslist* (Alpha). He is a Hollywood screenwriter, former editor of *Entertainment Monthly* and author of more than 30 books. His Web site is *www.skippress.com*.

I'm one of more than 50 million US users of Craigslist, the top source of free classified ads on the Internet. Since the online marketplace started up in the 1990s, I have used it to buy and sell all sorts of merchandise—ranging from computers to cars. I've used it so much that I've written a book about it.

Here, common mistakes on Craigslist and how to get the very best deals...

SCAMS SELLERS FALL FOR

People who post merchandise for sale on Craigslist may get more fraudulent responses than genuine replies. Often they contain Web links. If you click on such a link, your computer may become infected with a virus, or a "cyber-robot" may harvest your e-mail address. (The crooks then sell the addresses to spammers.) Sometimes the link comes only in a second follow-up message after you have responded to an innocent-looking question, such as, "Is the product still available?" Never click on links in e-mail from people you do not know.

Other common scams for sellers to watch out for...

• **Buyers who pay more than the asking price.** They will e-mail you a complicated story giving their reasons (they received a check from an estate, or they made a mistake and sent too much). They then ask you to refund the extra. You send them a check for the difference between the amount they sent and the price of your item and then discover that their check has bounced.

• **Buyers who want you to send the item before they have paid for it.** They come up with an excuse (a birthday, a vacation trip) so that you will deliver the item right away. Some buyers will claim that they have sent payment through Western Union or another wire service. Since it can take days for money to go through with these services, you may find out too late that payment was never sent. Accepting payment through PayPal usually is better.

• **Buyers who pay by certified or cashier's check.** These sound official but can be faked. If you deposit a fraudulent check, you'll take the loss. Again—stick with payment through PayPal.

SCAMS BUYERS FALL FOR

If you are a buyer, be aware that the more expensive the item is, the more prevalent the scams...

• **"Vehicle for sale" requires an especially suspicious eye.** Craigslist says that offers to ship cars after purchase are 100% fraudulent.

How it works: You notice a vehicle listed at a very low price. When you communicate with the seller, you learn that the car is overseas and must be shipped. You will receive a complicated message detailing a complicated method of payment (through an escrow service, Western Union, etc.). Don't bite. Do stop all communication with the "seller." If the listing is still online, flag it (all ads have a special area in the upper-right-hand corner to do this). If enough people flag a listing, Craigslist will pull it—and you will help prevent other people from being burned.

• **Stolen merchandise.** Another reason that a price may seem much too good to be true—the merchandise may be stolen. Before buying a computer, bicycle, jewelry or other valuable item, ask the seller to send you the original purchase receipt, owner's manual, installation disk or other proof of ownership. Trust your instincts if the seller is vague about proof.

• **Fraudulent housing.** Beware of all listings for rentals and lease-to-own housing that require a deposit. Once you send in your deposit (often via Western Union to an overseas address because the "home owner" had to leave the country unexpectedly), you are mailed the keys. When you go to the house, you find out that the keys don't fit and the house is really for sale, not rent—and your money has disappeared. The listing was probably cribbed from a house-for-sale posting.

SELLERS' MISTAKES

You are more likely to sell any item for a higher price if you avoid common mistakes...

• **Creating unclear headlines.** Instead of simply browsing through local listings, many prospective buyers use the search feature on Craigslist or Google to locate, say, a used cell phone with certain features. To help them pull up your listing, create a headline that is specific and succinct. Headlines can contain up to 70 characters. Use your allotment smartly. Always include important information such as size, brand/model and condition (for example, "New"). Avoid all unnecessary words ("Look!") and abbreviations that people may not know ("EUC" for "Excellent Used Condition").

Real headlines that need help: "Brand-New Mattress" lacks manufacturer and size. "Simmons King-Size Beautyrest Mattress" lacks the item's condition.

• **Not including photos.** Many people won't click on a listing unless search results show that it includes photos. (You can post up to four.) But don't rely solely on photos to communicate what your merchandise looks like. Colors may not show up well on buyers' computers. Patterns may not be clear. Make sure that descriptions are clear and complete.

A bad ad I recently found: The headline reads, "Large Chinese Vase." No photos are included. The description says, "Large, very pretty ornamental hand-painted authentic Chinese vase/planter—acquired it many years ago—not our taste—maybe it is yours."

What is the size of the vase? The color? Pattern? Shape? Condition? Age? Questions can be e-mailed to sellers, but many folks won't take the time.

●**Not protecting your privacy.** When you create a listing, you can have your e-mail address automatically "anonymized"—Craigslist will assign the listing a made-up e-mail address so that your real one is not seen by people who send you an e-mail response. But if you answer the e-mail, your e-mail address is no longer anonymized, and the person who received the response may use it to send you junk messages.

Solution: Set up an e-mail account to use only with your Craigslist postings. Use Yahoo (*www.yahoo.com*), Gmail (*www.gmail.com*) or another free service.

I often include my phone number in my listings so that prospective buyers can call me. If you don't want to give out your number, consider signing up for Google Voice (*http://voice.google.com*). The service assigns you a free phone number that bounces incoming calls to a number you already have.

How to Avoid Bad Online Merchants

Google now positions companies that are the subject of negative articles lower down in search results. Before, the search engine did not differentiate between positive and negative mentions of a company, so *any* press that a company received resulted in a higher rank-

ing. But a high ranking on Google still does not guarantee a positively ranked company. If your product search brings up a merchant that you are not familiar with, do a search on the merchant before making your purchase to find out whether the merchant has been criticized.

The New York Times, www.nytimes.com.

The Best Online Deals

According to a yearlong survey that analyzed more than a million sale items on the Internet, certain items tend to cost less on specific days of the week. *Take a look...*

Mondays: Men's and women's dress pants and sunglasses.

Tuesdays: Men's apparel.

Wednesdays: Shoes and kids' clothing.

Thursdays: Women's handbags.

Fridays: Accessories, such as jewelry, belts and scarves.

Saturdays: Intimates, jackets, outerwear.

Sundays: Swimsuits.

Study by ShopItToMe.com, which monitors sales at more than 200 online retailers, reported at CBS Money-Watch.com.

PayPal Pointers

To stay safe when using PayPal, do not link your PayPal account to your bank account or debit card—if you do and a thief gets access to your PayPal account, he/she could wipe out your bank account.

Better: Link your PayPal account to a credit card so that you can dispute a charge through PayPal and your card issuer if a problem arises. Avoid clicking on links in PayPal e-mails—the messages could be phony, and the links may steal data.

CreditCards.com.

Beat the High Cost of Online Shipping

Attention shoppers who hate online shipping charges. A new program that's called ShopRunner (go to *http://shoprunner.com*) has started providing unlimited two-day shipping and returns at the online stores of about 40 retailers and brands for a single fee of $79 per year. Participants include AutoZone, Barnes & Noble, Calvin Klein, Drugstore.com, GNC, Petsmart, RadioShack, Rockport, Shoes.com, Speedo, Sports Authority and Toys "R" Us. Several already offer unlimited free shipping but not within two days...others offer free shipping if you buy a minimum amount. The ShopRunner program resembles a similar two-day shipping program offered by Amazon.com called Amazon Prime, also for $79/year.

Howard Davidowitz, chairman of Davidowitz & Associates, consulting firm for the retail industry in New York City, http://davidowitzassociates.com.

What *Never* to Buy Used

Used cribs, children's furniture, car seats and children's bicycle helmets may not meet today's standards of safety and/or may have been recalled, so buy them *new*. Used tires can be unstable and unreliable. And, old mattresses could be infested with bugs, mold, mites and bacteria, as could swimsuits, undergarments, shoes, hats and makeup. Used pet supplies are likely to have stains and odors.

US News and World Report, 1050 Thomas Jefferson St. NW, Washington, DC 20007, www.usnews.com.

Secondhand Savvy

Do not buy the following products used... Laptop computers, digital cameras and video cameras often are dropped or banged around—buy a used one only if it is a refurbished unit with a warranty from a reputable store. Plasma and high-definition TVs can cost hundreds of dollars or more to fix and still can be trouble-prone, so buy a new one with an extended warranty. DVD players use costly lasers that can wear out anytime, and the price for new players has been coming down for years. Vacuum cleaners easily can cost more to fix than to buy new—good, basic upright vacuums sell for less than $100.

Liz Pulliam Weston, personal-finance writer and author of Your Credit Score: Your Money & What's at Stake (FT Press). Her Web site is www.asklizweston.com.

Best Thrift Shop Deals

To find the best deals at secondhand stores, go to thrift shops in wealthier neighborhoods—donations typically come from local residents. Shop early in the week—donations often come in on weekends. Look for category bargains—for example, all shirts may be priced at $3 regardless of brand. Find thrift shops at *www.thethriftshopper.com*, and look for consignment shops—which often are more upscale—at *www.consignmentshops.com*.

AARP Bulletin, 601 E St. NW, Washington, DC 20049, www.aarp.org/bulletin.

Cut Computer Printer Costs

To keep printer costs as low as possible, use black ink whenever you can—it costs lots less than color ink. Ignore low-ink warnings—you can print up to 20% more after the warning appears. Look for a "Draft" or "Fast" mode after you hit print or under the "Properties" button on a PC...or an image-quality setting under "Print" on a Mac—printing in draft mode uses about half as much ink and is fine for many jobs.

What else to do (Windows only): Use a free utility such as GreenPrint (*www.printgreener. com*) to avoid printing online pages that are blank, contain only a URL or have unwanted images.

Consumer Reports Money Adviser, 101 Truman Ave., Yonkers, New York 10703, *www.consumerreports.org.*

When to Leave the Lights On

Turning compact fluorescent lightbulbs (or CFLs) on and off causes them to burn out more quickly.

Guideline: If you expect to return to the room within 15 minutes, don't turn off a light with a CFL. A CFL usually costs at least $2.50 more than an incandescent bulb, but it will save you nearly $5.41 in the cost of electricity per year.

United States Department of Energy, Washington, DC, *www.energysavers.gov.*

Simple Secret to Saving On Cable TV

Pay less for your cable TV simply by asking. Research all the plans that your cable-TV company and its competitors are selling. Then call your company and get through to a person, not a recording. Explain that your bill is higher than you wish, and ask the company to match one of the bargains you have located. Some customer-service reps, but not all, will agree—but you can call again if the first one refuses. Of course, you also may cut costs by checking your service contract carefully and dropping items you do not need…or buying a package that includes phone and Internet service as well as cable.

The Motley Fool, a multimedia financial-services company, *www.fool.com.*

Good Deals on Refurbished Cell Phones

Refurbished cell phones can be good buys when you want to upgrade or need a new phone. Carriers inspect and certify their refurbished phones—and even new models may be available just a few months after introduction. Refurbished phones are sold by the carriers themselves and by authorized retailers, such as Best Buy. Also check out Web sites, such as Amazon.com and Overstock.com—you could get a good deal if you can find a phone that is compatible with your carrier or has been unlocked so that it works with multiple service providers.

Kiplinger's Personal Finance, 1729 H St. NW, Washington, DC 20006, *www.kiplinger.com.*

Is a Prepaid Cell Phone For You?

Prepaid cell-phone plans cost as little as $10 a month and require no contract. They are best for people who talk 200 minutes or less a month.

Drawbacks: Per-minute rates and roaming charges may be higher, and nights and weekends and mobile-to-mobile calls are not unlimited.

Joe Pawlikowski, senior editor, Prepaid-Reviews.com, based in Guelph, Ontario, Canada.

Robocall Restrictions

Prerecorded phone sales are banned unless a consumer gives written permission to the company making them. Firms that violate the ban may be fined as much as $16,000 per call.

What to do: If you get an unauthorized robocall, report the name of the company and the phone number to the Federal Trade Commission (877-FTC-HELP, *www.ftc.gov*).

Robocalls still are allowed from debt collectors, political and charitable organizations, and firms doing surveys and providing information, such as flight cancellations and delivery notices.

Jon Leibowitz, chairman, Federal Trade Commission, Washington, DC.

Put on Hold Again? What to Do...

To avoid waiting on hold when contacting customer service, go to LucyPhone (*www.lucyphone.com*), and search for the company you are trying to contact. Once you find the company, enter your telephone number and click "Start." LucyPhone will contact the company and then call you with your options for contacting the company representative. Once you have decided upon an option, LucyPhone will call you back once it has reached a person. Similar services include GetHuman.com and DialAHuman.com, which offer company phone numbers and the buttons to press in order to be connected to a person. All of these services are free.

Now Is the Time to Go Medical Bargain-Hunting

Charles B. Inlander, health-care consultant and founding president of the People's Medical Society, a consumer advocacy organization active in the 1980s and 1990s. He is the author of 20 books, including *Take This Book to the Hospital with You: A Consumer Guide to Surviving Your Hospital Stay* (St. Martin's).

With the economy still in the doldrums, this may be a great time to get some deep discounts on medical services and equipment. For example, an optometrist I recently spoke with told me that his business is still off, so now he is discounting all of the eyeglasses he sells by at least 30%. A psychologist told me that she has started offering up to three sessions of counseling at 50% off to anyone who has lost his/her job within the last year.

In general, recent reports show that doctor visits are down by as much as 7%. Add to that a decline in elective surgeries, including knee replacements, cataract removal and cosmetic surgery, and what we have is a wonderful opportunity for consumers to do some medical bargain-hunting.

Here are the best ways to find good deals on high-quality services in your community...

• **Ask the right question.** Many times, getting a discount is as simple as asking for one. Do not be afraid to ask a surgeon (if you are contemplating surgery) or any type of health provider if he could "do better" after discussing the cost of a medical procedure or service. This is especially helpful if a big out-of-pocket cash outlay is involved because you have no insurance or your insurance does not cover a particular service, such as dental care or cosmetic surgery.

Insider secret: Don't worry about getting lower-quality care if you pay the discounted price. Research shows that price does not affect quality when it comes to medical care.

• **Get the ammunition you need to negotiate.** When my wife recently needed a dental implant, our dentist and the surgeon he recommended quoted her a price of more than $3,000. But we shopped around and located two other highly recommended surgeons and dentists who were offering the very same procedure at a price of $2,000. When we told that to our dentist, he and the surgeon agreed to match the price.

Insider secret: When negotiating for a discount, you will have the best luck if you comparison shop and are able to quote a lower price from a competitor.

• **Don't forget about discounts on equipment.** You've probably seen those TV commercials for motorized scooters and wheelchairs. If you're insured, the deal may look good. But if you are not covered, you may be able to match the price or do even better at a local medical equipment shop that is looking for customers. And even if you are insured, many local stores will throw in a maintenance contract at no additional charge just to get your business. Hearing aids also are being sold at the steepest discounts in years. With several phone calls, you often can find deals at 20% to 50% off retail price.

Remember: Hard times mean good deals for those who look for them. So don't put off what you thought you couldn't afford. Like all other businesses these days, medical and health providers badly need your patronage and very often will reduce their prices to get it.

More from Charles Inlander...

Mail Order or Drugstore? How to Choose...

Not long ago, I asked one of my favorite friends, who is a retired pharmacist, what he thought of mail-order pharmacies. Are they as reliable as a neighborhood pharmacy? And what about price?

Here is what he said: "I get most of my prescriptions via mail order. But you must do your homework so you'll know how to best use a mail-order or local pharmacy."

Important pros and cons follow to help you determine when to use a mail-order or local pharmacy...

• **Neighborhood pharmacies.** If you are filling a onetime prescription, such as an antibiotic for an infection or a painkiller after recent surgery, your local pharmacy is the way to go.

Pros: Your prescription can often be filled while you wait, and you can speak face-to-face with a pharmacist when you pick up the prescription. Some pharmacies will deliver your medication to your home the day the prescription is filled, which is handy when you are ill or housebound.

Cons: Some pharmacies, especially small, "mom-and-pop"–type stores, will not accept your employer's or health plan's prescription medicine insurance. Since many smaller pharmacies may not have the drugs your doctor ordered on their shelves, it may take one day or two to get them. Drugs at local pharmacies also are usually more costly than those

bought via mail order, and many chain drugstores will not dispense a greater-than-30-day supply even if your doctor writes the prescription for 90 days. (This allows the pharmacy to collect a copay or dispensing fee each time you refill.)

• **Mail-order pharmacies.** They are ideal for medications you take on a regular basis.

Pros: Mail-order prices are generally lower than those charged by local and chain pharmacies because mail-order overhead is lower. The mail-order pharmacies routinely fill up to 90-day prescriptions with your onetime copay, saving you more money. All the major online pharmacies, including Medco Health Solutions (at *www.medco.com*)...CVS's Caremark (*www.caremark.com*)...and the AARP prescription discount program, Walgreen Health Initiatives (*www.walgreenshealth.com*), offer a pharmacist on duty 24 hours a day to answer questions, so there's no waiting for information.

Cons: Mail-order pharmacies are not practical for drugs you need quickly, although some do have overnight delivery options at a steep price. You need to plan your refill orders well in advance (typically 15 days before your prescription runs out). Also, if you need to speak to a pharmacist often, you'll likely get a different person each time you call.

Caution: Some Internet mail-order companies are bogus. And, for this reason, the FDA recommends buying only from US mail-order pharmacies that are licensed to sell in your state. Find your state board at the National Association of Boards of Pharmacy, *www.nabp.net*, and check out the mail-order company you want to use.

You Better Shop Around For Generics

The price of a generic drug can vary dramatically from store to store.

Example: In a California town, a 30-day supply of the statin *simvastatin*, a generic version of Zocor, sold for $7.71 at Costco...$19.87

at one independent drugstore…$24.36 at Wal-mart…$63.59 at CVS…and $89.99 at Walgreens.

Self-defense: Check the prices from several stores—you usually don't need to be a member of wholesale clubs to get prescriptions from them.

Devon Herrick, PhD, a health economist at National Center for Policy Analysis, Dallas.

Free Antibiotics for Everyone

Free antibiotics are available at the in-store pharmacies of Giant Food, Stop&Shop and Publix. These supermarkets allow anyone to take prescriptions to their in-store pharmacies and receive a two-week supply of common generic antibiotics at no cost. Among the medicines given away are *amoxicillin, cephalexin, ciprofloxacin, erythromycin* and *penicillin.* The program is ongoing for an indefinite time at all stores, and you can get the antibiotics more than once.

Real Simple, Time-Life Bldg., Rockefeller Center, New York City 10020, *www.realsimple.com.*

Why You Shouldn't Store Vitamins in the Bathroom or Kitchen

Vitamins and supplements can lose potency when stored in kitchens or bathrooms.

Reason: Humidity in these rooms can cause slight chemical changes in vitamins and dietary supplements, making them less effective.

Self-defense: Store bottles away from humid areas.

Lisa Mauer, PhD, associate professor of food science, Purdue University, West Lafayette, Indiana, and leader of a study published in *Journal of Agricultural and Food Chemistry.*

Dental Discount Programs

A dental discount program can be worth-while if you suddenly face a costly procedure. The plans usually give you 10% to 60% off within a few days of your signing up.

Cost: Generally $80 to $160/year for individuals, $130 to $200/year for families.

What to do: Call your dentist's office to find out which plans it accepts and which ones give the best benefits for the type of procedure you need. Do not join a plan based on its advertising.

Alternative: Ask your dentist if he/she will give you a discount if you pay in advance by check rather than with a credit card—some dentists may give you 10% off.

Money, Time-Life Bldg., Rockefeller Center, New York City 10020, *http://money.cnn.com.*

Pricier Pet Food Not Always Better

Expensive pet food isn't necessarily better. When experts on pet nutrition from seven top veterinary schools were asked, most said that they fed common-brand pet food found in grocery stores to their own pets. It's much better to read the label on pet food to know its nutritional content than to pay a high price and assume that you are getting high-quality food. Look for the words "complete and balanced" on the label. Learn how to read and understand pet-food labeling (and much more) at the PetEducation.com Web site. In the "search articles" box, enter "AAFCO" (for the American Association of Feed Control Officials) for articles on AAFCO food standards and label information for dogs, cats and other pets.

Survey conducted by *Consumer Reports,* reported by ConsumerAffairs.com.

Have the Best Groomed Dog on the Block— For a Lot Less

Groom your dog at home for a fraction of the cost of professional grooming.

Supplies: Dog shampoo, a dog detangling spray, dog brush, towel, bucket or hose and electric pet clippers.

To start: First wet the animal's coat. Lather your dog's coat with plenty of suds, working your way back from the head. Then rinse and towel-dry. Stand the dog on a towel. Apply detangling spray to the animal's coat, and brush from head to tail. Trim coat with clippers using the appropriate blade—high-number blades for a closer shave around the face and backside... lower-numbered blades on longer-haired areas, such as the ears and legs. Check the Internet for clipping instructions for particular breeds. Clean ears—gently pull fur away, and wipe off visible wax with a cotton ball.

Caution: Have a professional groomer clip the dog's nails.

Real Simple, Time-Life Bldg., Rockefeller Center, New York City 10020, *www.realsimple.com.*

Cheaper Medical Care For Your Pet

If you can't afford medical treatment for your pet, contact the American Animal Hospital at *www.aahahelpingpets.org.* It has a fund that works with selected veterinarians to provide financial help for emergency and nonelective treatments.

An alternative: Check with animal organizations and breed clubs for veterinary care assistance.

Your Dog, Box 8571, Big Sandy, Texas 75755, *www.tufts.edu/vet/publications.*

Hiring a Contractor?

Before hiring a general contractor, get multiple estimates for your planned project. Also, read customer reviews and complaints.

Free Web sites to check: ConsumerAffairs.com, Checkbook.org, PissedConsumer.com, Yelp.com and PlanetFeedback.com. Also, check out AngiesList.com ($3.50/month or $29/year).

Confirm that your contractor's liability coverage is adequate and current with your state licensing board. Also, negotiate the maximum hourly rate—you may save money if the job is completed sooner than expected. Demand a lien release so if there's a dispute, he/she can't make financial claim against your property.

AARP Magazine, 601 E. St. NW, Washington, DC 20049, *www.aarp.org/magazine.*

Honey Storage

Honey keeps for decades, even centuries, when properly packaged and stored. If honey crystallizes, place the honey jar in warm water and stir until the crystals dissolve.

The National Honey Board, *www.honey.com.*

When Buying Butter, Make It Organic

Organic butter is worth the higher price. It is made from the milk of cows that are fed organic feed and doesn't contain pesticides, antibiotics or any added growth hormones, all of which may be found in conventional butter. Nonorganic butter has been ranked by the Pesticide Action Network North America as one of the 10 foods most contaminated with toxic chemicals linked to breast cancer, immune system suppression and other conditions.

Andrew L. Rubman, ND, director, Southbury Clinic for Traditional Medicine, Southbury, Connecticut.

12

Richer Retirement

Money for Life! Six-Step Plan Helps Your Nest Egg Thrive Even If the Market Dives

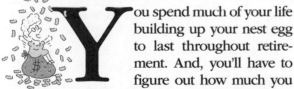

Y ou spend much of your life building up your nest egg to last throughout retirement. And, you'll have to figure out how much you can take out each year without draining it too quickly.

Then just when you think that you have a good plan, the stock and bond markets go on a roller-coaster ride that throws you off track, as they have in recent years. There must be a better way.

Philip G. Lubinski, CFP, knows a better way, and he has been proving that it is effective for nearly three decades. *We asked him to explain how his plan works and why it's especially valuable today…*

THE SIX SEGMENTS

The traditional investment strategy that most people follow is to divide your retirement savings between stocks and bonds. In the first year of retirement, you withdraw a predetermined percentage of the total amount, typically 4%, to pay for your living expenses. Every year after that, you increase your withdrawal rate slightly to adjust for inflation.

But the market crash of 2008 forced many people to alter their savings and spending plans drastically to avoid running out of money.

Better way: Divide retirement savings into six distinct segments, a strategy that I call the "income for life" retirement-planning model.

Each of the first five of these segments finances a specific five-year period of your retirement. A sixth segment will provide additional

---

Philip G. Lubinski, CFP, founder, First Financial Strategies, LLC, in Denver. About 25 years ago, he pioneered the income-for-life model, which has since become very popular among financial planners, 3,000 of whom he has trained. To get more, log on to *www.plubinski.retirement time.com.*

funds in case you (and/or your partner) live for longer than 25 years in retirement. If not, this sixth segment serves as an inheritance for your heirs.

This strategy has been proven in a study to allow retirees to maintain their initial principal and weather bad markets even if their initial withdrawal rate is as high as 5.66% rather than the traditional 4%. *Here's a closer look...*

SEGMENT 1:
PAYS FOR THE FIRST FIVE YEARS

Allocation: 28% of your initial retirement nest egg.

Investment strategy: Invest Segment 1 assets initially in a type of guaranteed annuity that will reach maturity when you retire and typically pays higher rates than certificates of deposit (CDs). The best time to purchase it is around five years prior to retirement.

At the start of your retirement, this annuity can be exchanged for a five-year immediate-income annuity, which provides you a monthly check for five years...or the proceeds can be invested in "laddered" CDs that mature over the first five years of retirement. If you buy an annuity, make sure it is from a company rated A or better by A.M. Best (*www.ambest.com*).

These guaranteed investments ensure that market fluctuations have no effect on the early years of your retirement.

Investment goal: 2% annual return.

Result: Over the five years in this segment, you can withdraw $490 per month for each $100,000 in your overall retirement portfolio.

When to invest for Segments 2 through 6: You make these investments at the beginning of your retirement. Then when you enter each segment, you transition from the recommended strategy to a mixture of ultrasafe investments, such as immediate-income annuities and laddered CDs.

SEGMENT 2:
PAYS FOR YEARS SIX THROUGH 10

Allocation: 26% of your initial retirement nest egg.

Investment strategy: Invest this money either in a laddered portfolio of investment-grade bonds that will mature in five years or less...

in five-year CDs...or in a deferred fixed-annuity contract that will not provide income until you enter year six of your retirement.

Investment goal: A 4% annual return from the date that the income-for-life model is established until the dawn of Segment 2, which is five years into retirement.

Result: You can withdraw $554 per month for each $100,000 in your portfolio.

SEGMENT 3:
PAYS FOR YEARS 11 THROUGH 15

Allocation: 20% of your initial retirement nest egg.

Investment strategy: Invest 40% of these assets in a diversified portfolio of stocks and "alternative" asset classes through either low-expense index mutual funds or, my own pick, exchange-traded funds (ETFs). Include funds that track US large-, mid- and small-cap stocks ...foreign stocks...emerging markets...commodities...real estate investment trusts (REITs).

The same fund categories apply to Segments 4 though 6 but with a greater tilt toward small-cap value and emerging-market stocks.

The remaining 60% of these assets should be invested (and reinvested upon maturity) in bonds maturing in five years or under, which also are the types of bonds to use for Segments 4 and 5. (There is not enough extra reward in long-term bonds to justify their risks.) A 50/50 stock/bond allocation is acceptable if you have a high risk tolerance and need to be aggressive to reach your desired retirement income.

Investment goal: A 6% annual return from the date that the model is established until the dawn of Segment 3, 10 years into retirement.

Result: You can withdraw $627 per month for each $100,000.

SEGMENT 4:
PAYS FOR YEARS 16 THROUGH 20

Allocation: 13% of the nest egg.

Investment strategy: Much like the Segment 3 strategy, but this time invest 60% into stocks and 40% in bonds.

Investment goal: 8% annual return.

Result: You can withdraw $722 per month for each $100,000.

SEGMENT 5:
PAYS FOR YEARS 21 THROUGH 25

Allocation: 7% of the nest egg.

Investment strategy: Similar to Segments 3 and 4, but 80% is invested in stocks and 20% in bonds.

Investment goal: 10% annual return.

Result: You can withdraw $824 per month for each $100,000.

SEGMENT 6:
PAYS FOR REMAINING YEARS

Allocation: 6% of your starting retirement nest egg. This amount can be increased if allocating the prescribed amounts to Segments 1 and 2 would result in more income than required early in retirement.

Investment strategy: At the start of retirement, invest Segment 6 assets entirely in the non-bond fund categories used for Segment 3. This money isn't touched for at least 25 years, long enough that even the most volatile investment classes are not that risky.

Investment goal: A 12% annual return, not counting any money used to purchase longevity insurance, which typically provides guaranteed annual income starting at age 85.

Result: If your Segment 6 investments earn a 12% annualized return, you should have just as much money in this segment after 25 years as you had in your entire retirement portfolio when your retirement began.

A Fresh Look at Annuities

Robert Carlson, CPA, JD, editor of *Retirement Watch*, a personal-finance newsletter in Oxon Hill, Maryland, *www.retirementwatch.com*. Carlson is chairman of the board of trustees of the Fairfax County Employees' Retirement System and author of *Invest Like a Fox...Not Like a Hedgehog* (Wiley).

Annuities have long been considered an investment that insurance salespeople push on an unsophisticated client, not something that smart investors seek out. While annuities may offer tax-deferred earnings and, often, a relatively secure stream of retirement income, many of them also feature steep fees and commissions, inflexible distribution rules and impenetrable complexity.

Example: Many investors who purchased "variable" annuities in the 1990s thought they were obtaining an ultrasafe investment...until they endured steep losses from 2000 through 2003, when the stock market plunged.

Yet some annuities could have a place in a wise investor's portfolio. They can serve as a welcome safe haven in a time of stock market and real estate volatility. They can reduce the odds of outliving retirement savings in a time of shrunken nest eggs. They can offer an opportunity to defer taxes. And in recent years, several of the more reliable insurance companies have instituted a few changes that tackle some of the drawbacks.

Instead of simply relying on the advice of a commissioned insurance or investment professional, start by reviewing the various types of annuities listed below. If any seem like they might help you to reach your financial goals, shop for the best terms using the buying strategies provided here or hire a fee-only financial planner to help.

Annuities often are talked about as if they were a single type of investment. *In fact, there are several different types of annuities; each is appropriate for different investors and investment goals...*

VARIABLE ANNUITIES

What these are: Variable annuities essentially are a way to invest in mutual funds except that the funds' earnings are tax-deferred and withdrawals can be scheduled as monthly payments that are guaranteed to continue for as long as you (or your spouse...or someone else designated) live. Many of the variable annuities sold these days also feature a component that caps the potential capital losses. This feature is an attempt by insurance companies to attract investors who were scared off by the losses suffered in variable annuities a decade ago. Unlike some annuities, variable annuities do not offer a guarantee about the amount that you will receive during retirement when you purchase the product. The size of the distributions depends largely on the performance of the mutual funds you select within your annuity.

Problem: Very high fees. The typical variable annuity charges annual fees in the neighborhood of 2%, and some charge 3% to 4%.* One-time commissions of 5% or more are common, too, as are surrender fees of 5% to 6% or more if you attempt to withdraw money in the years immediately after investing. Also, investment gains within the variable annuity are taxed as income when the money is withdrawn, not as capital gains, and withdrawals made prior to age 59½ are subject to a 10% penalty.

Appropriate for: High-tax-bracket investors younger than age 55 who have maxed out 401(k)s and IRAs for the year, who desire to do even more tax-deferred investing and who will not need this money for at least 15 to 20 years. It takes decades of tax-deferred growth for the advantages of variable annuities to outweigh their additional fees.

Buying strategy: If you decide to purchase a variable annuity, do so through a large, low-fee mutual fund company or discount broker, such as Fidelity Investments, Charles Schwab or Vanguard. All of these tend to charge lower fees and commissions than do commissioned agents. Choose aggressive investments within the variable annuity, and do not withdraw this money for at least a decade, preferably two decades or longer.

IMMEDIATE ANNUITIES

What these are: The immediate annuities operate much like traditional pensions. In exchange for your lump-sum payment, you will receive a fixed amount each month, quarter or year for the rest of your life…or the rest of your spouse's life…or for some predetermined number of years, depending on the distribution option you select.

Problem: Low returns. The fixed payment that you receive from an immediate annuity is based in part on prevailing interest rates at the time the annuity was purchased—and interest rates are extremely low right now. A 60-year-old man who puts $50,000 into an immediate

*Rates subject to change.

212

annuity, for instance, currently could receive a monthly income of just $280 for the rest of his life.

Immediate annuities also are likely to reduce the size of the estate you leave to your heirs, particularly if you die relatively young. Some immediate annuities make payments to heirs when the annuity purchaser dies within a predetermined time frame, but adding this type of provision further decreases the size of the distributions that the annuity owner receives during his/her life.

Appropriate for: Retirees who desire an ultrastable source of income with no market risk and/or retirees who fear that they might outlive all their savings, perhaps because they come from families whose members tend to live long.

Buying strategy: If the security of an immediate annuity appeals to you, wait to buy. Interest rates are likely to rise in the coming years, increasing the distributions offered by immediate annuities. The distributions you receive also will increase the older you are when you purchase your annuity.

If you don't want to wait, at least "ladder" your way into presumably rising rates, putting only 20% of the total amount you intend to invest into an immediate annuity this year, then adding an additional 20% in each of the coming four years. One good place to obtain annuity quotes is *www.immediateannuities.com*.

Alternative: Longevity annuities, a relatively new product that has become available in recent years, are similar to immediate annuities. Rather than make payments immediately upon the purchase of the annuity, however, longevity annuities will do so only when the annuity buyer reaches some advanced age—often 75, 80 or 85. Buyers who die before this age receive nothing, but those who live long enough receive much, much more per month than from an immediate annuity. A longevity annuity is a viable option if you fear that you will outlive your money but your financial situation seems secure for the first 15 or 20 years of retirement.

Example: A 65-year-old woman currently would receive a monthly income of about $140 from a $25,000 investment in an immediate annuity—but she could receive $1,169 starting at age 85 from a longevity annuity.

EQUITY-INDEXED ANNUITIES

What these are: Equity-indexed annuities (EIAs) are deferred annuities, so their distributions do not start up immediately but rather at some predetermined future date. The size of their distributions is determined in part by the performance of an underlying stock market index—very often it's the Standard & Poor's 500 stock index or the Russell 2000 Index. But unlike index funds, EIAs come with safeguards against losses—there is typically a guarantee that the principal won't decline much or at all in value, plus a guaranteed minimum annual return of 2% to 3%, so your investment could make money even in years when the underlying index falls. There is often a death benefit, as well—a designated heir receives a check if the annuity owner dies before receiving some predetermined amount.

Problem: Complexity. Insurance companies that provide EIAs use extremely complicated formulas to calculate these annuities' returns. Doing so makes it very difficult for investors to compare EIAs or to predict how much they can expect to earn from one. Investors should not expect to receive the full returns of the underlying index—EIA returns generally are capped at about 6% per year. On top of this, high EIA annual fees, surrender fees and commissions eat into profits.

Appropriate for: Conservative investors who seek stock gains but who do not want to risk losses.

Buying strategy: Ask the financial experts you speak with for data on the past 10 years of annual returns on the EIAs that they recommend. Compare those past returns to get some notion as to which EIAs truly offer the best returns and/or lowest risks. Also, compare commissions and annual fees.

CHECK RATINGS

Do not buy annuities issued by an insurer rated lower than A by A.M. Best (*www.ambest.com*) or Moody's (*www.moodys.com*). A low-rated insurer is more likely to fail.

Don't Depend on An Inheritance

Baby boomers will inherit $8.4 trillion—but that won't solve their retirement savings concerns. The median inheritance will be $64,000. The top 10% of heirs will receive a median inheritance of $335,000...the bottom 10%, only $8,000.

Best: Work with a financial adviser to determine how much you need to save from your earnings to be able to retire comfortably.

Steve Vernon, FSA, an executive faculty member and research fellow, California Institute for Finance at California Lutheran University, Thousand Oaks, and the author of *Live Long & Prosper! Invest in Your Happiness, Health and Wealth for Retirement and Beyond* (Wiley). His Web site is *www.restoflife.com*.

What's Ahead for Social Security? Strategies to Maximize Your Benefits

Theodore Sarenski, CPA, CFP, president and CEO of Blue Ocean Strategic Capital, LLC, a financial-planning organization based in Syracuse, New York, *www.boscllc.com*. He is a member of the American Institute of Certified Public Accountants' Social Security Task Force and was one of the authors of that organization's white paper on Social Security reform.

Social Security is supposed to be a security blanket for most Americans, but lately it hasn't felt all that comforting.

Because of the cost-of-living formula used by the Social Security Administration, its benefits recipients are not receiving an increase in 2011 for the second year in a row. And under current rules, the entire Social Security system is in danger of becoming insolvent. To avoid that, the cochairs of a bipartisan commission on the federal deficit recently proposed raising the normal retirement age, increasing the annual limit on income that is subject to the Social Security payroll tax and other controversial changes.

Here, Social Security expert Theodore Sarenski addresses some of the questions and concerns that many people have…

•**Why are benefits not rising when it feels like living expenses are going up and up?** The Social Security cost-of-living formula has not been particularly fair to retirees lately. The formula's inflation index has not climbed for two years largely because home values have plummeted and car prices have stagnated. But retirees typically don't buy a lot of homes and new cars. Many of the things that they spend on—health care, heating fuel and utilities, for example—have in fact increased in price.

Cost-of-living increases are likely to resume once values of real estate stabilize. Meanwhile, remember that there was a large 5.8% cost-of-living increase in benefits three years before. The system wouldn't seem quite so unfair if that increase had been spread evenly over the past three years.

However, under the proposal from the deficit commission's cochairs, cost-of-living adjustments would become less generous starting in 2012 under a new formula.

•**Are benefits going to end if the Social Security system starts to run out of money?** No. It is true that the system began to run at a deficit by 2010, and its reserves are indeed on course to be depleted—but not until 2036. Most likely, the government will make changes in the tax and/or benefits rules in time to prevent that.

Even in the very unlikely occurrence that the reserves are completely exhausted, the system would still be able to pay around 75% of its obligations through 2085 by distributing the taxes paid into the system each year by people still in the workforce.

•**How likely is it that the government actually will make changes to Social Security?** My prediction is that politicians will continue feeding us Social Security scare stories every election year, but they will not substantially alter the system for many years, perhaps even decades. Over the 75-year history of the Social Security system, lawmakers have generally waited until disaster was imminent before making changes. That said, America's financial problems are very pressing, and politicians might conclude they cannot solve these problems without slashing the cost of the Social Security system.

•**What are the possible changes?** In addition to changing the cost-of-living formula, the commission cochairs made the following five proposals. (The commission's entire list of budget reduction recommendations failed to receive enough votes for approval, but some aspects of the plan could surface in the future.)

1. Slowly raise the normal retirement age to 68 by 2050 and to 69 by 2075…increase the early retirement age from 62 to 64…and at the same time provide a "hardship exemption" for people physically not able to work past the age of 62. The normal retirement age increase would affect only people born after 1960. Currently, the normal retirement age for people born in 1960 or later is 67.

2. Gradually raise the annual limit on income subject to the Social Security payroll tax from the current $106,800 until it's near $190,000.

3. Give retirees an option to collect half their benefits early and the other half at a later age. This would allow the early retirees to draw some income from the Social Security system, perhaps to supplement income from a part-time job, while also allowing some of their benefits to continue to grow by delaying them until age 70.

4. Establish a new special minimum benefit to keep most low-wage workers above the poverty line.

5. Provide a "benefit bump-up" for older retirees equal to 5% of the average benefit. The bump-up would get phased in over five years, starting 20 years after a retiree first becomes eligible for benefits.

The federal cochairs also proposed several alternative changes, which include increasing the benefits for low-income widows or widowers… capping the spousal benefit at one-half the average worker's benefit, rather than one-half of the partner's benefit…and reinstating college benefits for child survivors—benefits that were eliminated in 1981.

•**How can I maximize my benefits?** Unless health problems or family history suggests that you are likely to pass away prior to age 77, you'll get more money from the system by waiting until your late 60s or age 70 to start receiving your benefits. Delaying the start of your benefits until at least age 66 is attractive if you are married because it increases your partner's spousal and survivor benefits, too, by up to 8% per year.

Two strategies to maximize benefits...

1. "62/70 strategy." Married people should consider this. The lower-earning spouse, usually but not always the wife, claims benefits based on her own earnings at age 62, with her husband claiming spousal benefits on her earnings as soon as he reaches his full retirement age—66 if he was born between 1943 and 1954. Then the husband switches to his own benefits when he turns 70, with his wife switching to spousal benefits based on his earnings. This couple receives the largest possible benefit checks after the husband turns 70 but still gets benefits before then.

2. "File-and-suspend" strategy. If one spouse has no significant earnings history, this strategy is a second option. Here, the wage-earning spouse files for benefits when he reaches the normal retirement age, then immediately asks that those benefits be suspended. Then his partner can claim spousal benefits based on his suspended account, while the amount that will be stated on the wage earner's eventual monthly checks continues to increase until he ends the suspension in his late 60s or at age 70, the age at which the benefits rate stops rising.

•**For someone who would like to work a few more years, is there a risk that taking a low-paying job at the end of a career will drive down the earnings history on which his/her future Social Security checks will be based?** Continuing to work is far more likely to increase someone's eventual Social Security benefits than it is to reduce them even if the late-career job does not pay well. Benefits are established based on the 35 highest-earning years among your final 40 working years, not on the final salary, as they are with some pension plans.

If someone has worked for fewer than 35 years, even a small paycheck will boost benefits because it will replace $0 earning years in the calculations.

If the person already has 35 working years, the small paychecks might not boost the earnings history but will make it easier to delay the start of Social Security benefits beyond age 62, thereby increasing eventual monthly checks by up to 8% per year, simply based on age, until age 70. Just try to avoid starting benefits while you're still working—that would increase the odds that your benefits will be taxed.

Working additional years is likely to reduce Social Security benefits only if someone already has worked 40 years and had high earnings in the early years relative to the rest of his career. Continuing to work in this situation could bump those long-ago high-earning years out of the most recent 40 working years, removing those years from the benefits equation.

•**For someone in debt who is worried that creditors and debt collectors are going to grab his Social Security benefits, is there anything that can be done to protect those benefits?** Creditors and debt collectors usually cannot legally garnish Social Security benefits. Unfortunately, when banks receive court orders directing them to freeze accounts, they often do so, even when the accounts contain Social Security assets. Most account holders do not fight this because they do not realize it is illegal.

If this happens to you, be sure to contact the bank and point out that Social Security income is in the account and cannot legally be frozen. Then insist that the assets be released. Be aware, however, that Social Security benefits can be legally frozen or garnished if the debt involves unpaid federal income taxes or child support.

Fast-Track Social Security

Quicker Social Security payments are now available to thousands of people with disabilities and to even more in future years. The fast-track system, called *Compassionate Allowances*, sends payments quickly to people with serious diseases who clearly qualify for both Social Security and Supplemental Security Income benefits.

Some examples: Early-onset Alzheimer's disease, cancers and rare genetic diseases.

People with covered diseases will be automatically approved for their disability payments —bypassing a standard five-step process that can take months or even years for a decision. For details on the program and the listing of 88 conditions to which it applies, access the Social Security Administration at *www.socialsecurity.gov/compassionateallowances*.

Michael Astrue, Commissioner of Social Security in Washington, DC.

Why the Month You Retire Matters...

The month you retire can affect your benefits and taxes. If you are working when you start to collect your Social Security—and are younger than the full retirement age—your benefits could be reduced if you make more than $14,160 for the year. So retirement earlier in the year may be better. But higher-income workers might want to retire later in the year to push the start of benefits to the next year and get closer to full retirement age. Accrued vacation pay may affect benefits because it is considered earned income.

What to do: Do the calculations to determine what is best for you. If it becomes too complicated, consult a knowledgeable financial adviser.

Chicago Tribune, www.chicagotribune.com.

For Widows and Widowers...

Widows and widowers need to claim a Social Security survivor benefit carefully to maximize the amount they receive. A widow or widower is entitled to a benefit equal to 100% of the deceased spouse's benefit if the survivor waits until full retirement age. Claims prior to retirement age are reduced. But in some cases, earlier claims result in more total benefits.

Example: For some people, it is better to start collecting survivor's benefits at age 60 or 62—and then, at age 66 or later, switch to benefits based on your own full earnings record if those benefits are worth more than the survivor benefit.

What to do: Seek out a knowledgeable financial adviser—calculations are complex.

William Reichenstein, PhD, CFA, professor of investment management, Baylor University, Waco, Texas, and leader of a study of several different approaches to survivor benefits, published in *Journal of Financial Planning*.

Divorced? You Could Be Entitled to Much More Social Security

Barbara Shapiro, CFP, a certified divorce financial analyst (CDFA) and vice president of HMS Financial Group, a financial-planning, wealth-management and investment practice located in Dedham, Massachusetts. For 19 years, Shapiro has counseled clients on financial planning during and following divorce. She is regional director of the Institute for Divorce Financial Analysts, a certification and education organization located in Southfield, Michigan. For more, go to *www.bshapiro-cdfa.com*.

Breaking up is hard to do—but on the bright side, it may provide some extra retirement benefits.

The Social Security system has special rules and options for people who have divorced—rules that allow some to claim significantly larger benefits than they otherwise would receive.

But do not expect the Social Security Administration (SSA) to inform you that you are eligible for those higher benefits. It is up to a divorced person to inform the SSA of a prior marriage and to request benefits founded on his/her former spouse's earnings history (800-772-1213, *www.ssa.gov*). Otherwise, you may be leaving thousands of dollars on the table, particularly if your former spouse earned significantly more than you did.

Here's what you need to know about Social Security benefits if you have already divorced…are going through a divorce right now…or are considering divorce…

IF YOU WERE THE LOWER EARNER

If your marriage lasted at least 10 years and you have not remarried, you likely will be eligible to declare Social Security benefits based on your previous spouse's earnings history—assuming that those benefits exceed the benefits that you would receive based on your own earnings. Unlike the current spouse, who must wait for the wage earner to file for benefits before claiming the spousal benefits, an ex need not wait unless the marriage ended within the past two years. Inform the SSA that you wish to file as an "independently entitled divorced spouse." There is no downside to doing this—it will have no effect on your ex's benefits, and if it turns out that your own benefits exceed those available to you through your ex's earnings, you will simply receive your own benefits instead.

Your benefits as a divorced spouse likely will be very similar to those that would have been available to you had you remained married, and like a married person, you must opt for either benefits based on your own earnings or benefits based on the earnings of the current or former spouse. You can't claim both at the same time.

What you will be eligible for…

While your ex is alive, you will be eligible for a monthly "spousal benefit" equal to 50% of this previous spouse's full retirement benefit, starting at your full retirement age. You could begin these benefits as early as age 62, but doing so would permanently reduce your monthly checks by as much as one-third. For larger monthly payments, wait until full retirement age.

The cochairmen of a bipartisan deficit commission suggested capping spousal benefits at just 50% of the average wage earner's benefit, which would decrease the monthly benefits of some spouses and ex-spouses of high earners. Even if such a rule is ever adopted, however, it likely would exempt those already in or near retirement.

After your ex passes away, you will be eligible for monthly "survivors benefits" equal to 100% of the monthly amount that your former partner was entitled to receive, instead of the 50% spousal benefit. Benefits for survivors can be started as early as age 60—age 50 if you are disabled—but your checks will be permanently reduced if you start receiving them before your full retirement age. Divorced former spouses are not eligible for the special lump-sum death benefit paid to surviving spouses.

Even though you cannot simultaneously receive Social Security benefits based on your own earnings history and benefits based on your ex's earnings, you can switch between these if future Social Security reforms or life events affect the amount that you would receive.

Example: One divorced woman declares benefits founded on her own earnings, which are greater than the 50% spousal benefits she would receive based on her ex-husband's earnings. When her ex passes away, she switches because the 100% survivors benefits she'd receive based on his earnings exceed her own benefits.

IF YOU REMARRY

You likely will lose your right to benefits based on your ex's earnings history if you remarry. *Two exceptions…*

If this new marriage also ends—whether it is due to divorce, annulment or your new spouse's death—you once again will become eligible to get benefits under your first ex's earnings history, regardless of how long the second marriage lasted. If you also are eligible for benefits based on the second partner's earnings—you are likely to be eligible if this marriage lasted for at least 10 years, or if it ended because of the death of this second partner—you will be allowed to choose whichever partner's earnings history is more beneficial to you.

A new marriage will not prevent you from claiming survivors benefits founded on your ex's earnings if the new marriage occurs after your 60th birthday—after your 50th birthday if you are legally disabled. This is true whether your ex dies before or after you turn 60 and remarry. If you are nearing 60 and considering remarriage, it could be worth delaying the wedding.

IF THERE ARE MINOR CHILDREN

If you're caring for your ex-spouse's natural or legally adopted child…this child is younger than 16 and/or legally disabled…and your ex passes away, you might be eligible to get benefits of up to 75% of your ex's total retirement benefit as a surviving divorced parent. These parental benefits are different from the 100% survivors benefits mentioned above that could be available to you when you reach retirement age and are available even if you have not yet reached retirement age and even if your marriage did not last for 10 years. They end when the child turns 16 unless the child is disabled. The child also is entitled to benefits based on the deceased parent's earnings, typically up to age 18, or 19 if he/she is attending high school full-time.

Note: All of the minor children and caregiving parents combined cannot receive over 150% to 180% of the deceased wage earner's benefit. If there are numerous claimants and this cap is reached, each claimant will receive a reduced benefit.

Example: When a husband passes away, his ex-wife is caring for their 14-year-old son while his new wife is caring for his four-year-old daughter. Because there are four total claimants—two wives and two children—each will probably receive between 37.5% and 45% of the husband's full benefit amount, rather than the 75% each would have received had the ex-wife and oldest child not filed for these benefits.

IF YOU ARE THE HIGHER EARNER

If you earned more than your former spouse during your career, filing as an "independently entitled divorced spouse" will not increase your benefits. On the bright side, as discussed above, your ex's ability to claim spousal and survivors benefits based on your earnings will not reduce your Social Security benefits or the benefits available to your current spouse except, perhaps, if you pass away while your ex is caring for your minor or disabled children, as described earlier.

Your ex's Social Security benefits could become an issue for you if your ex requests a modification to your alimony agreement after age 62, however. You and your attorney or a financial professional should take a close look at the ex's use of the Social Security system. An alimony increase is less likely to be granted if you can establish that your ex could boost his/her income by maximizing Social Security benefits instead.

Example: A 66-year-old woman took her ex to court to request an increase in alimony until age 70, stating that she wished to delay the start of her Social Security spousal benefits until then. Her ex-husband's advisers successfully countered that there was no practical reason for this woman not to start her Social Security spousal benefits immediately. Unlike the benefits available to wage earners, spousal benefits do not increase by waiting beyond full retirement age.

IF YOU ARE CURRENTLY DIVORCING

The right of one former spouse to claim Social Security benefits based on the other's earnings does not need to be negotiated during divorce proceedings. These benefits are legal entitlements, but not a negotiable component of the marital assets. Do consider the precise length of the marriage before the divorce is finalized, however. If it ends even one day short of 10 years, you will not be entitled to potentially valuable Social Security benefits based on your previous partner's earnings. Reaching the 10-year mark is particularly important for the spouses who have limited earnings histories of their own. If the marriage appears on course to end just shy of the 10-year mark, ask your divorce lawyer if the process could be dragged out slightly, or ask your spouse to agree to a brief postponement. The date the divorce is finalized is what matters, not the date of legal separation.

Retirement Tax Break Helps Low-Income Earners

The Retirement Savings Contributions Credit can reimburse up to 50% of the first $2,000 of retirement-plan contributions by decreasing tax owed. It is separate from the usual IRA or 401(k) tax breaks. It cannot be used by people who are not subject to income tax for the year… and is graduated according to income. Singles earning less than $28,250 in 2011…joint filers earning $56,500…and heads of household earning $42,375 may be eligible if they contribute to a qualified retirement plan. See IRS Form 8880 (800-TAX-FORM or *www.irs.gov*) to determine how much of the credit you can claim.

Catherine Collinson, president, Transamerica Center for Retirement Studies in Los Angeles, *www.trans americacenter.org.*

What You Need to Know Before Making a Roth Conversion

State taxes on Roth conversions vary widely. A recent rule allows people to convert an individual IRA to a Roth IRA regardless of income, which means that not only would they have to pay federal income tax on the converted assets but also state tax for some but not all conversions. Nine states have no income tax or do not tax IRA distributions—Alaska, Florida, Nevada, New Hampshire, South Dakota, Tennessee, Texas, Washington and Wyoming. Some other states that do have income taxes give exemptions for retirement income—exact terms vary. Other states tax all income without regard to its source.

What to do: Check with your financial adviser and state tax department before doing a conversion.

Kiplinger's Retirement Report, 1729 H St. NW, Washington, DC 20006, *www.kiplinger.com.*

How to Avoid High IRA Fees

Fees may consume half your annual IRA investment. According to a recent study, the average contributor puts $4,000 per year into an IRA. Mutual funds, financial advisers and brokers charge fees on the total account value every year. The average fee paid by investors is about 2%, which works out to $2,180 a year based on the average total size of an existing IRA. That is more than half a year's $4,000 investment.

What to do: Replace high-cost mutual funds with exchange-traded funds (ETFs) or with index mutual funds, instead of actively managed funds, which tend to have much higher expenses. Look into fund fees before investing.

Mitch Tuchman, chief executive for MarketRiders, a self-help portfolio-management Web site that analyzes fees paid by IRA investors, *www.marketriders.com.*

New Rules for Roth 401(k) Conversions

Ed Slott, CPA, president, Ed Slott and Company, LLC, Rockville Centre, New York, and editor of *Ed Slott's IRA Advisor* (*www.irahelp.com*). He is author of the *Secrets to Financial Freedom* program, which is available at *www. keepyoursavings.com.*

Many questions have arisen about the recent federal rules that allow a traditional 401(k) to be converted into a Roth 401(k).

I'll explain the rules, but first it is important to point out that even when you are eligible to convert to a Roth 401(k), you often are better off rolling the funds into a Roth IRA. That's because the Roth IRA allows you to undo the transaction at a later date—a Roth 401(k) does not. If the account's value drops or you realize that the conversion to a Roth IRA pushes you into a higher tax bracket, you can undo it, get your taxes back and then have the option of reconverting under more favorable circumstances, such as when it triggers less in taxes.

If, despite this, you do prefer a Roth 401(k), which offers better protection against seizure by creditors than an IRA, you can convert only if the employer sponsoring the 401(k) plan offers Roth 401(k)s and chooses to allow these conversions.

In addition, converting any 401(k) that you built up with your current employer generally is allowed only if you are eligible for a distribution—that is, you are at least 59½ years old or separated from the company.

However, there is a provision under which employers can allow employees younger than age 59½ to convert the 401(k) assets that were contributed as matches by the employer—but not your own contributions. Also, if you have rolled over a 401(k) from a previous employer, you may be eligible to convert those assets, even if you are younger than 59½.

If you do qualify, you must pay income tax on any pretax 401(k) money that you convert to a Roth. Generally, you should pay the tax with money from outside the 401(k) so that you don't diminish your tax-advantaged investment.

Beware: If you do choose to pay the tax bill using money from the 401(k), you'll also pay the early-withdrawal penalty unless you're at least 59½ years old.

More from Ed Slott, CPA...

For the Best Advice on Roth Conversions...

The advice on Roth IRA conversions is frequently *incorrect*. Traditional IRAs can be converted to Roths without any income limitation—but financial advisers don't always understand the complications.

Examples: Some say that people age 70½ or older can convert and not take the required minimum distribution from the traditional IRA for 2011—but that is wrong. Some say money converted to a Roth must stay there for at least five years—but that isn't always correct.

Best: Check with a financial adviser knowledgeable about the complexities of IRAs. To find one, go to *www.irahelp.com*.

Take 401(k) Fees Into Account

More disclosure of 401(k) charges is required under federal rules that went into practice on July 16, 2011. Direct and indirect fees must be disclosed, such as fees for legal services, record keeping and maintaining toll-free phone numbers. Hidden fees of just 1% per year can reduce retirement returns by 15% over 30 years. And fees often are higher than that. Plans with fewer than 100 participants now pay an average of 2.03% per year.

What to do: When fees are disclosed, take them into account when planning your retirement expenses.

The Pittsburgh Post-Gazette, www.post-gazette.com.

Take Help When You Can Get It

Few employees use the 401(k) guidance that their employers offer. Seventy percent of 401(k) account holders said that their 401(k)s are their only or primary source of retirement savings—but only 47% said that they are very confident when making investment decisions …and fewer than 10% who have access to advice actively use it.

What to do: Find out what advice your employer makes available—more and more companies are providing advisory services as part of their retirement-planning offerings.

Study of 401(k) plan participants sponsored by The Charles Schwab Corporation.

401(k) Alert

Several employers are now taking retirement savings. A few cash-strapped companies—typically small, private firms—have redirected employee contributions illegally to cover bills. Check your account statements to make sure that there are no shortfalls or gaps in contributions. If you suspect your employer, contact the US Department of Labor.

David Wray, president of the Profit Sharing/401k Council of America, based in Chicago, an association of 1,200 companies that sponsor defined-contribution plans, *www.psca.org.*

The Best Place to Live In the World!

France is the world's best place to live. Based on health care, culture and leisure, France offers the best quality of life. Australia is second, followed by Switzerland and Germany. To get the entire list, go to *http://international living.com* (click "Quality of Life Index").

Jackie Flynn, publisher, *International Living*, which has conducted a Quality of Life Index for 30 years.

10 Worst States For Retirees

The 10 worst states for retirees, based on taxes, climate and the states' fiscal health are Illinois, California, New York, Rhode Island, New Jersey, Ohio, Wisconsin, Massachusetts, Connecticut and Nevada.

Examples of problems these states face: Illinois has the worst financial health of any state...California and Rhode Island's finances are in disarray...New Jersey has the highest property taxes and highest total tax burden, followed by New York and Connecticut...Wisconsin has high property taxes, an overall high tax burden and cold weather...Nevada is the "foreclosure capital of the world."

John Brady, president, TopRetirements.com.

Retirement Home Tip

Do not buy a retirement home until after you stop working. Even though real estate might seem like a bargain today, realize that your life may change in unexpected ways, so wait at least one year after retirement while you figure out what you want and need. Medical facilities and/or convenient shopping could outweigh recreation once you're older, so realize that today's vacation home may not make a good year-round retirement home.

Appealing destinations for retirement: Charlotte, North Carolina, and Sacramento, California, because of their relatively low prices and varied lifestyle amenities.

Robert Irwin, licensed real estate broker in Westlake Village, California, and author of more than 60 books, including *The Armchair Real Estate Investor* (Kaplan) and *Tips & Traps When Negotiating Real Estate* (McGraw-Hill). His Web site is *www.robertirwin.com.*

Try Before You Buy

Before buying a home in a retirement community, ask if you can stay over one or two nights. A short stay will give you a better notion of how it would be to live in the community and whether the facilities meet all your needs. Many adult communities now are letting potential home buyers stay over two or three nights for as little as $99 per night.*

AARP Bulletin, 601 E St. NW, Washington, DC 20049, *www.aarp.org/bulletin.*

*Price subject to change.

Spend Time with Animals Without the Work of Owning a Pet

You don't need to own a pet to spend time with animals. Volunteer to walk dogs and help clean cages at your local animal shelter.

Also, spend a few hours a week at the shelter providing these animals with human interaction—grooming and playing with the animals so that they are better socialized and more likely to be adopted. Volunteer your home as a foster home for dogs or cats.

Consensus of veterinarians and shelter managers, reported in *Catnip*, Box 8517, Big Sandy, Texas 75755.

A Senior's Best Friend

Seniors who go on walks with shelter dogs get more health benefits than seniors who walk with a friend or spouse. Walking speed, balance and confidence improve more when older adults take regular walks with dogs kept at local shelters.

Possible reason: Awareness that the dogs need the seniors' time and attention. Check in with your local shelter to see if volunteers are needed.

Rebecca Johnson, PhD, an associate professor and Millsap Professor of gerontological nursing and public policy, University of Missouri, and director, Research Center for Human-Animal Interaction, both in Columbia, Missouri.

Simple Longevity Secret

Independent observers were shown photos of 230 professional baseball players from a 1952 baseball registry and were asked to rate each player's facial expression. When these ratings were then compared with the ballplayers' mortality data in 2009, players who had smiled broadly were found to have lived five years longer, on average, than those who had not smiled.

Theory: A positive emotional state of mind promotes longevity.

Self-defense: Do your best to cultivate positive emotions so that you'll have more occasions to smile broadly.

Ernest Abel, PhD, professor of obstetrics-gynecology, Wayne State University School of Medicine, Detroit.

Supermarket Discounts For Seniors

David Smidt, the founder and president of Senior-Discounts.com, a Web site based in Albuquerque, New Mexico, that tracks discounts available to those age 50 and up.

An increasing number of supermarket chains now offer senior discounts, in part to lure older shoppers away from low-priced chains such as Walmart. Many local food co-ops offer senior discounts as well. *Among the chains with discounts…*

•**Earth Fare organic supermarkets** typically provide a 5% discount on "select days" to those either age 55 and older or 60 and older. *www.earthfare.com.*

•**Fred Meyer stores** offer those age 55 and older 10% off select goods on the first Tuesday of each month and on all Tuesdays in November and December. *www.fredmeyer.com.*

•**Fry's Food Stores Senior Rewards Program** offers customers age 55 and older a 10% discount on most purchases on the first Wednesday of each month. *www.frysfood.com.*

•**Harris Teeter's program** offers those age 60 and older a 5% discount every Thursday. *www.harristeeter.com.*

•**Kroger supermarkets** often provide customers who are either at least 55 years old or at least 60, depending on each store's version of the policy, either 5% or 10% off most purchases on one day each week or month. *www.kroger.com.*

•**Shop 'n Save supermarkets** often offer a 10% discount one day each week to shoppers age 55 and older. *www.shopnsave.com.*

*Offers and rates subject to change.

13

Lasting Legacy

Make Your Heirs Millionaires: Your Most Important Estate Planning Document Is *Not* Your Will...

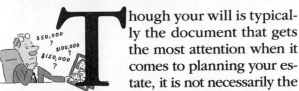

Though your will is typically the document that gets the most attention when it comes to planning your estate, it is not necessarily the most important document. If you have well-funded IRAs, it is likely that the piece of paper that matters most to your heirs' financial future is the form that designates which beneficiary or beneficiaries you choose to inherit the IRAs.

Why? For one thing, it takes legal precedence over your will. And it could play a major role in determining how much your IRAs are worth to each of your heirs...how much they are required to withdraw each year under IRS

required minimum distribution (RMD) rules... and how much money goes to the government in the form of taxes. Because federal income tax rates are expected to climb in the coming years, the beneficiary designation form will become even more important.

Unfortunately, most people don't realize that improperly completed forms deprive heirs of thousands of dollars or more.

Here, common and costly traps...

Trap 1: **You name your estate rather than a person as the beneficiary.** If you name a person as beneficiary, tax laws generally allow that person to "stretch" the required withdrawals over his or her projected lifetime—so the assets can continue to grow tax-deferred

Ed Slott, CPA, president of Ed Slott and Company, LLC, an IRA advisory firm based in Rockville Centre, New York (*www.irahelp.com*). He is host of the PBS special *Stay Rich Forever & Ever* with Ed Slott and editor of the IRA Planning section of *The CPA Journal*. He is author of *Stay Rich for Life! Growing & Protecting Your Money in Turbulent Times* (Ballantine) and the *Secrets to Financial Freedom* program, available at *www.keepyoursavings.com*.

(or tax-exempt for a Roth IRA). This can mean decades of additional tax benefits.

Example: If you name your son beneficiary of your IRA and he is 40 when you die, he can stretch withdrawals out over his projected remaining life span of about 43 years. If there is $500,000 in your IRA at the time of your death…the account earns 6% annually… and your son takes full advantage of stretch rules, that $500,000 will turn into $2.4 million in total distributions before taxes.

If you name your estate as beneficiary, however, this stretch option disappears. Your heirs will have to withdraw the money from your IRA either by the end of the fifth year following your year of death…or if you have a traditional IRA and you die after age 70½, within a time period based on how much longer someone your age is expected to live.

What to do: Keep your IRA out of your estate by naming a real person or several real people as beneficiaries.

Trap 2: **You do not inform your heirs where the beneficiary designation form is.** If it can't be located, your estate likely will be named the beneficiary, and the stretch option will be lost.

What to do: Keep one copy of the form in your own records and a second with your financial adviser or attorney. Inform your heirs where both copies can be accessed, and put a written explanation somewhere in your home of where these and additional important documents are located. Review your designations annually, in case circumstances change, and remember to update all copies of the form if you make changes.

Trap 3: **You neglect to name contingent beneficiaries.** Often, an IRA owner believes that there is no need to indicate a "contingent beneficiary" if he/she is certain that he wants the assets to pass to the primary beneficiary. But if the primary beneficiary dies before the IRA owner does and the owner neglects to update the form, the money reverts to the estate.

What to do: Always be sure to name a contingent beneficiary.

Trap 4: **You "mix" co-beneficiaries of different ages or types in one account.** If you name multiple beneficiaries, every one of them will be required to take their minimum distributions based on the expected life span of the oldest one. That is not a major issue if all your beneficiaries are of similar ages—but if there is a significant difference in age, the younger ones could lose much of their ability to stretch out withdrawals.

Example: If you name your 40-year-old daughter and 75-year-old spouse as co-beneficiaries, your daughter will have to withdraw her share of the money within 13 years (based on your spouse's expected span of life) rather than slowly over your daughter's expected remaining life span of about 43 years.

Naming your spouse and anyone else co-beneficiaries also could deprive your spouse of the right to do a rollover into the spouse's own IRA, then treat the account as his or her own. Doing a rollover lets spouses delay making any withdrawals until they get to 70½— but only if the spouse is the sole beneficiary of the deceased partner's IRA.

If you name a nonperson, such as a charity or your estate, as a co-beneficiary, all beneficiaries will have to withdraw all of the money from the account either within five years following the year in which you die…or if you have a traditional IRA and die after age 70½, within a period based on tables that estimate how much longer someone of your age is expected to live.

What to do: If you want to divide IRA assets between heirs of substantially different ages… between your spouse and anyone else…or between human heirs and other types of legal entities…divide up your IRA into separate accounts prior to your death, then name a different beneficiary for each of those accounts.

If you don't do this, after your death your beneficiaries could divide your IRA into separate accounts based on the portions that you specified for each of them and gain the same advantages—by law, they have until the end of the year following the year of your death to do this. But heirs often fail to understand the advantages of this or they just fail to get around to it, so it's better to do it yourself.

Trap 5: **You select beneficiaries who will cash in the IRA quickly.** An heir who has major debts or who tends to spend money as soon as he receives it is not an ideal IRA beneficiary, because he won't gain the advantage of deferring taxes for years.

What to do: If you have more than one heir and have assets in tax-deferred retirement accounts and non-tax-deferred accounts, consider leaving the IRA to the heir who is likely to let the money continue to grow tax-deferred. Leave other assets to the beneficiary who is likely to tap the account quickly.

More help: If you have a Roth IRA as well as non-Roth savings, consider leaving the Roth to your heirs who are in the highest tax bracket, assuming that these high-bracket heirs are likely to take advantage of the stretch option. Money can be withdrawn from Roth accounts without triggering income taxes, which makes these assets especially valuable to the heirs in high tax brackets.

Ask your financial planner or accountant to help you understand the amounts that your heirs will receive on an after-tax basis so that you can balance the gifts in a way that you consider fair.

Trap 6: You neglect to inform beneficiaries that you already paid taxes on a portion of the IRA contributions. If you have made "nondeductible" contributions into your traditional IRA, your beneficiaries do not need to pay taxes on that part of your savings when they withdraw it. Trouble is, many people do not tell their heirs about their nondeductible contributions. Most heirs end up paying taxes that already have been paid.

What to do: Tell your beneficiaries verbally about your nondeductible contributions, and also attach written reminders to your beneficiary designation form and your estate plan. Attach a copy of your most recent IRS Form 8606 (*Nondeductible IRAs*) to the beneficiary designation as well.

Trap 7: You fail to specify how the IRA should be divided up. People tend to assume that if they list multiple beneficiaries, the money automatically will be divided equally among all those listed. This is not always the case.

What to do: If you want the money to be divided equally, you must write the word "equal-

ly" after the beneficiaries' names or include a fraction or a percentage after each name. Otherwise it is up to the institution managing the account to infer your intent.

Warning: 55% Estate Tax Ahead! Update Your Will Now

Herbert E. Nass, Esq., founding partner of Herbert E. Nass & Associates, a law firm specializing in wills, estates, probate and trusts. The practice offers locations in New York City…Harrison, New York…and Norwalk, Connecticut. Nass also is author of *The 101 Biggest Estate Planning Mistakes* (Wiley). His online site is *http://nasslaw.net.*

Congressional dysfunction has made estate planning even more confusing and complex than ever. The federal estate tax expired at the end of 2009. It is back in 2011, but just for two years. The new tax rate is 35%, and the exemption has jumped to $5 million ($10 million for married couples) but only until December 31, 2012. After that, the tax rate rises to 55% and the exemption drops to $1 million, unless Congress changes this in the meantime.

Many estate plans are poorly equipped to deal with these major estate tax law changes.

Consider reviewing and updating—or creating—your estate plan. When you are doing so, be careful to avoid or eliminate the common mistakes that could cost your heirs extra time, money and/or aggravation. *Here are 10 of the most common mistakes…*

Mistake 1: Your plan assumed the $3.5 million exemption that prevailed in 2009 was forever. There often are legal ways to reduce or avoid estate taxes—but if your estate was drafted more than two years ago and was worth significantly less than $3.5 million, your attorney might not have bothered with these.

What to do: If your estate is worth between $1 million and $5 million, ask your attorney to confirm that your estate plan is adaptable enough to minimize taxes whatever the eventual size of the estate tax exemption. If you are married, confirm that under your estate plan, your combined estate tax exemption does not diminish when the first spouse dies and his/her assets pass to the other spouse.

Mistake 2: **You used the incorrect procedure for signing your will.** Each state has its own detailed rules about the proper procedure for signing, or "executing," a will. If any of these rules are violated, a court might not accept the will as valid.

Execution mistakes are most common when people draft their own wills, but they also occur when attorneys who do not specialize in estate planning draft wills...when attorneys mail wills to homebound clients to be signed... and when people make changes to wills without their attorneys' knowledge to avoid extra attorney fees. In many states, witnesses need to hear the signer of the will state that this is his/her will, not just view the signing.

What to do: Sign or modify your will in the presence of an experienced attorney who specializes in estate planning...or make sure that you have extensive knowledge of the rules.

Mistake 3: **You provide excessive detail about personal property.** Going into exhaustive detail in your will about who gets what might seem like the best way to avoid confusion or arguments among your heirs, but the truth is, it's likely to make things worse.

Unless you update your will every time you acquire or dispose of a possession, your will's list of items will differ from what you actually own. Such disparities tend to create confusion and trigger arguments among heirs. Extreme detail in a will also can attract unwelcome attention from the IRS.

Example: A wealthy man's will included a boat that he had sold years before. An IRS agent refused to believe this boat had been sold until the heirs produced an affidavit from the buyer attesting to the transaction.

What to do: Rather than list your possessions in detail, simply write down "my tangible personal property" and provide an outline for how heirs should divvy it all up. For instance, your children can take turns choosing from your personal possessions. Make note of par-

ticular possessions only when you feel it is important to make a specific bequest.

Mistake 4: **You fail to put tangible personal property into revocable living trusts.** Revocable living trusts let estates avoid the costs and delays of the court process called probate—but they work only if the title to the property actually is transferred to the trust. Attorneys typically help clients transfer titles to financial assets and real estate when these trusts are developed, but personal possessions, such as vehicles, jewelry, art and furniture, often are overlooked.

What to do: If you have a revocable living trust, ask your attorney whether your tangible personal property is listed in it. If not, ask the attorney for instructions on how to put it in.

Mistake 5: **You fail to confirm how real estate is titled.** Your careful estate planning could be completely derailed if your attorney misunderstands how your real estate is titled.

Example: A woman's estate plan included a credit shelter trust intended to shield her valuable New York City real estate from estate taxes. But her attorney didn't realize that her husband was listed as the joint owner on the title. Joint ownership meant that the property passed directly to the husband upon the woman's death, rendering the trust irrelevant—and eventually saddling the family with a fortune in taxes that could have been avoided.

What to do: Make absolutely sure that all of your real estate is titled correctly.

Mistake 6: **You fail to arrange for someone to take care of your home(s) after you pass away.** Vacant houses can result in very expensive problems. Vandals might break in... storms might shatter windows...pipes might freeze and burst.

What to do: If no one will be living in your home immediately after your death, specifically ask one of your heirs or a trusted neighbor to look after the property. Identify this caretaker in your will so that the executor does not block this person's access to the home. If no one is available, instruct the executor of your estate to hire a caretaker.

Mistake 7: **You neglect to take the steps necessary to allow a dependent or friend to**

continue living in your home. The executor of the will generally has a legal duty to sell the deceased's home as quickly as possible after its owner's death, assuming that there's no surviving joint owner. Anyone residing in the home probably will get evicted—even if it is someone the deceased would not have wanted kicked out. That's particularly problematic these days, since many adult children have lost their jobs in this economy and have been forced to move back in with their parents.

What to do: Include a clause in your will specifying who is permitted to live in your home following your passing, the amount of time that this person is permitted to live there and the amount of rent, if any, that should be charged.

Mistake 8: **You accidentally disinherit the stepchildren.** Many wills simply divide assets evenly among descendants. Stepchildren are not considered descendants by the law, however, unless they have been legally adopted.

What to do: If you have stepchildren and want them to share in your estate, make sure that your attorney knows about your stepchildren. If you draft your will yourself, list each child and stepchild by name, rather than simply indicating "my descendants" or "my children."

Mistake 9: **You make a minor change to a will by adding in a codicil.** Codicils (supplements to a will that do not require rewriting the will) are vestiges of the precomputer days when it was time-consuming and expensive to make minor changes to the will itself. Today, making minor adjustments to any will usually is much cheaper and easier than adding a codicil.

Adjusting the will itself also provides added privacy. If you have a falling-out with a friend or a relative and use a codicil to remove this person as a beneficiary or executor, both the original will and the codicil will be in the public record, available for anyone to see.

Example: Rock Hudson removed a friend named Tom Clark from his will prior to Hudson's death in 1985 and presumably did not want that change to be publicly known. Yet the breakdown of that intimate relationship is well-known today because Hudson used a codicil to make this change.

What to do: Before agreeing to add a codicil, ask your attorney whether it would cost you less to make a change by updating the will itself. Also, lean toward the update if privacy is an issue.

Mistake 10: **You remove the staple from a will.** The seemingly harmless act of pulling out the staple that binds the pages of your will, perhaps to make a photocopy, could produce big-time headaches for your heirs. If someone contests your will, he/she could argue that the extra staple holes are evidence that an important page was removed or replaced.

What to do: If you make a copy of your will, do so by folding pages back, not separating the pages.

Important Estate Tax Update

Martin Shenkman, CPA, JD, estate and tax-planning attorney with offices in both New York City and Paramus, New Jersey. He is also author of numerous books about estate planning, including Estate Planning for People with a Chronic Condition or Disability *(Demos Health). His Web site is* www.laweasy.com.

The major recent federal tax package signed into law in late 2010 means that the estates of the vast majority of Americans who die in 2011 or 2012 will not be subject to federal estate tax. But it does not mean that we can stop worrying about estate taxes entirely. Though it's often overlooked, many states impose their own estate taxes and/or inheritance taxes (which are imposed on beneficiaries rather than estates).

Under the new federal law, up to $5 million ($10 million for married couples) is exempt from the federal estate tax in 2011 and 2012. Above these amounts, the tax rate is 35%. Fewer than 1% of taxpayers will face any federal estate tax. Before the tax deal was reached, the top estate tax was slated to be 55% this year, with an exemption of just $1 million.

Unfortunately, many states have estate tax rates of 16% or higher and exemptions of $1 million or lower. Some of those states likely will make some type of adjustment to their estate taxes in 2011 in response to the federal changes, but don't expect state estate taxes to disappear. That means estate-planning strategies featuring bypass trusts and marital trusts still can save many families hundreds of thousands of dollars.

Also included in the new tax law: Extensions of the 2010 income and capital gains tax rates and unemployment benefits...a patch for the alternative minimum tax (AMT) in 2010 and 2011 that prevents it from applying to millions of additional taxpayers...and, for 2011 only, a reduction from 6.2% to 4.2% in the Social Security payroll taxes paid by employees on up to $106,800 in annual wages.

THE STATES WITH ESTATE TAXES IN 2011

	Top Rate	Exemption
Connecticut	12%	$2 million
Delaware	16%	$3.5 million
Hawaii	16%	$3.6 million
Illinois	16%	$2 million
Maine	16%	$1 million
Maryland	16%	$1 million
Massachusetts	16%	$1 million
Minnesota	41%	$1 million
New Jersey	16%	$675,000
New York	16%	$1 million
North Carolina	16%	$5 million
Ohio	7%	$338,333
Oregon	16%	$1 million
Rhode Island	16%	$859,350
Tennessee	9.5%	$1 million
Vermont	16%	$2.75 million
Washington, DC	16%	$1 million
Washington State	19%	$2 million

More from Martin Shenkman, CPA, JD...

Plan Ahead

Planning your funeral should be an integral part of estate planning. State what type of service you want and where you want it held... whether you prefer burial or cremation...and whether you want to donate your organs or leave your body to science. Address religious issues—this can be a sensitive area that can cause family conflict if you don't specify what you desire to have done in terms of customs and observances.

Here's an Estate Plan That Works...Even When the Tax Rules Change *Again*

Robert Carlson, CPA, JD, editor of *Retirement Watch,* a personal-finance newsletter in Oxon Hill, Maryland. He is chairman of the board of trustees of the Fairfax County Employees' Retirement System and author of *Invest Like a Fox...Not Like a Hedgehog* (Wiley). Go to *www.retirementwatch.com* for more.

Even though taxes are said to be one of the two certain things in life, there is much about them that is uncertain. Estate planning is especially tricky now because of tremendous uncertainty over the new rules that determine how much tax your estate and your heirs should pay in 2010, 2011, 2012 and beyond.

Solution: Build flexibility into your will and other elements of your estate plan so that you don't have to redo them over and over to adjust for changes in the law...the size and makeup of your estate...the size and makeup of your family...and your family's financial needs.

Without this flexibility, the wrong strategies or even the wrong wording could cost your heirs many thousands—or possibly even millions—of dollars. Also, paying an attorney to make frequent adjustments to an estate plan can get expensive. And people often neglect to make intended changes.

NEW CHANGES IN RULES

The uncertainty centers on rules that eliminated the estate tax in 2010, then restored it in 2011 and 2012 with a tax rate of 35% and a $5 million exemption ($10 million for married couples). In 2013, the tax rate climbs to 55% and the exemption falls to $1 million ($2 million for couples), though it is quite possible Congress could change the rules again before then. There was an additional twist in 2010. When assets inherited in that year were sold, heirs had to pay capital gains tax on the entire amount that these assets gained in value over the years.

Beginning in 2011, gains from the sale of inherited assets will once again be computed using the value of those assets at the time that they are inherited as the "stepped-up" tax basis, which could save heirs from paying a great deal of tax. (Heirs of those who died in 2010 can choose between 2010 and 2011 rules.)

Your estate plan may lack flexibility if it was last updated more than two years ago or was drafted by someone, even your attorney, who does not specialize in estate tax planning…or if you created your own estate plan utilizing a software program or kit.

THREE STRATEGIES

To increase the odds of your estate plan being flexible…

• **Use a flexible formula to protect assets from the estate tax.** Credit shelter trusts, also known as bypass trusts, maximize the amount that couples can pass to their heirs free of estate taxes by preserving the estate tax exemption of the first spouse to die.

The problem is, the wording used in wills to transfer assets into these trusts often is so inflexible that changes in estate tax law can have unintended consequences.

Example: Wills often say that whatever amount is exempt from the federal estate tax should be put in a credit shelter trust or pass directly to a descendant, with the remainder of the estate passing to the surviving spouse.

But if any future Congress should do away with federal estate tax once again, the amount exempt from estate tax would be unlimited. Such a will would transfer all your assets over to your trust, and accidentally disinherit your spouse (although your spouse might be able to legally challenge such a will). Don't assume that this problem is solved if the estate tax is reinstated with a high exemption. The new estate tax exemption could be large enough to absorb all but the biggest estates entirely. This, too, would leave your spouse disinherited.

If your estate plan includes a credit shelter trust, ask your attorney to confirm that the formula used to fund this trust in your will is flexible enough to account for a wide array of possible future changes to the estate tax exemption. A flexible formula might state that your credit shelter trust will receive the lesser of the federal estate tax exemption amount or some predetermined amount (expressed either as a dollar amount or as a percentage of your estate).

• **Tell your heir to just say no to part of the inheritance.** Heirs can legally "disclaim" part or all of an inheritance. If you totally trust one of your heirs, ask your estate-planning attorney to set up a "disclaimer trust"—a trust that receives any assets disclaimed by this primary heir. Leave most or all of your estate to this heir, and ask the heir to sit down with an attorney and a financial planner after your death to decide what portion of the estate to disclaim based on prevailing tax laws and the financial needs of your other heirs. The disclaimer trust then acts as a credit shelter trust, shielding any disclaimed assets from unnecessary estate taxes.

• **Avoid large, specific bequests.** Wills that specify which valuable possessions or sizable investments go to particular beneficiaries often lack the flexibility to adapt to changes in how much particular properties, items and/or investments are worth. These wills also lack the flexibility to deal with changes in tax law, such as 2010's elimination of stepped-up cost basis, which could have resulted in big capital gains bills for many heirs. Specific bequests are most common with charitable donations and with real estate and small-business holdings, which often are left to just one heir because they can be difficult to divide or comanage.

Example 1: A woman's will bequeaths $200,000 to her favorite charity, with the "remainder" of her estate divided among her children. The will was last updated five years ago, before investment losses reduced the overall value of her estate from $500,000 to $200,000. If she dies before her portfolio can rebound, the charity receives her entire estate and her children get nothing, though that was not what she intended.

Example 2: A man wishes to divide his estate evenly between two children but wants to leave his home entirely to his daughter. The home is worth $400,000 when his estate plan is drafted, so his will gives $400,000 in cash to his son and the home to his daughter, then evenly divides the remainder of the estate. If the value of the man's home fell dramatically in the recent real estate downturn, his daughter will receive much less than her brother, although this was not her father's intention.

Ask your attorney to remove particular bequests of items of significant value from your will (bequests of items that mainly have sentimental value are not a problem)…or to rewrite these bequests with the caveat that they are not to exceed a predetermined percentage of your overall estate value, with a contingency plan if they do. *Example:* "I hereby bequeath to Harvard University the lesser of $100,000 or 5% of the total value of my estate."

Strategy That Prevents Challenges to Wills

*P*remortem wills and trusts, which are filed while someone is living, help avoid challenges to estate plans after death. Once beneficiaries and disinherited individuals are notified of the existence of the will or trust, they have a set period—often 30 to 120 days—to review and challenge the validity of the document in court. Once the court declares that it is valid, they then cannot challenge the will or trust after the person dies. In some states, including Delaware, you do not have to be a resident to set up a premortem trust there. Other states accepting premortem wills or trusts or both are Alaska, Arkansas, Nevada, North Dakota and Ohio.

Michael M. Gordon, JD, a director at Gordon, Fournaris & Mammarella, PA, Wilmington, Delaware, *www.gfmlaw.com.*

Don't Forget Your Pets…

*T*ake steps now to ensure your pet is taken care of if you are in an accident. First, choose a caregiver—someone your dog or cat is familiar with who can get into your house and knows how to take care of the animal. Always keep the caregiver's contact number in your wallet so that you can give it to emergency personnel if you are ever involved in an accident. Also, draft up instructions for the caregiver. Provide information that includes your pet's feeding and walking schedule, your vet's phone number and the location of the animal's medical records, food, leash and other items. Approve treatment in advance. Sign a statement for your vet that allows him/her to treat your pet if needed. Finally, post a rescue alert sticker on your window—this tells firefighters and other emergency personnel that a dog or cat is in the house.

Your Dog, Box 8517, Big Sandy, Texas 75755, *www.tuftsyourdog.com.*

Debts of the Deceased

*T*here are restrictions put on lenders when someone dies. All debts remaining are settled from the estate before heirs receive their inheritances. While the estate is being settled, credit card companies must stop adding fees and penalties to accounts. Outside of the estate, surviving family members usually are not obligated to pay the debts of the deceased.

An exception: Property acquired by couples throughout marriage in the community-property states of Alaska, Arizona, California, Idaho, Louisiana, Nevada, New Mexico, Texas, Washington and Wisconsin. In those states, when a spouse dies, creditors may be able to use the property to satisfy debts of that spouse.

What to do: If debt collectors phone, refer them to the estate executor or administrator.

Jonathan Pond, financial adviser in Newton, Massachusetts, *www.jonathanpond.com,* and author of *Safe Money in Tough Times* (McGraw-Hill).

Bank Accounts Frozen At Death

Bank accounts are frozen at death unless they are held in a living trust, by joint tenants with right of survivorship or in a payable-on-death account. All other accounts may not be used until the estate is settled in probate court, although a judge may let an estate's executor or administrator use an account to pay funeral expenses.

What to do: Set up accounts in a living trust, a joint account with right of survivorship or a payable-on-death account so that heirs can use them as needed. This also avoids the lengthy and costly probate process.

Michael Halloran, wealth-management adviser, Jacksonville, Florida, quoted at *www.cnbc.com.*

How to Get an Obituary Into a Top Newspaper— A Touching Tribute to a Departed Loved One

Alana Baranick, who wrote obituaries for the *Cleveland Plain Dealer* for more than 16 years. Located in Cleveland, she currently is director of the Society of Professional Obituary Writers (*www.obitwriters.org*) and is chief author of *Life on the Death Beat: A Handbook for Obituary Writers* (Marion Street).

An obituary in a widely read newspaper is a touching final tribute to a departed loved one. Major papers' obituary pages generally focus on the deaths of the famous, but they also run obits for those who are not widely known—if the deceased is noteworthy in some way.

Among the major papers most likely to run obits of those not famous…

• **Atlanta Journal-Constitution** (at *www.ajc. com/news/atlanta-obituaries-2500.html*).

• **Chicago Tribune** (see *www.chicagotribune. com/news/obituaries*).

• **Cleveland Plain Dealer** (*www.cleveland. com/obituaries*).

• **Philadelphia Inquirer** (*www.philly.com/ inquirer/obituaries*).

• **The Oregonian** (*http://blog.oregonlive.com/ lifestories/index.html*).

• **Washington Post** (*www.washingtonpost. com*, search "Obituaries").

Note: *The New York Times*'s obituary section tends to focus on the deaths of prominent or famous people, which leaves less room for the obituaries of those who are merely notable—but even *The New York Times* features some of these.

To significantly improve your odds of placing a prominent obituary…

CHOOSE A HEADLINE

Consider what a newspaper reporter might view as interesting and distinctive about your loved one's life. "Beloved Parent" is not very distinctive—but "Raised 18 Children" is…"War Veteran" is not distinctive—but "Won the Distinguished Service Cross" is…"Longtime Local Resident" is not distinctive—but "Lived in the Region for 102 Years" is.

Do not wait until your beloved one dies to think all this through. You will have too much on your mind that day to give this your full attention, and it cannot be delayed—if an obituary doesn't run within a day or two after the death, it may not run at all.

Questions to consider…

• **Did this relative ever hold a position of professional prominence?** This might be president or CEO of an area company…attorney in a well-publicized court case…principal of a local school…or coach of a local athletic team of note.

• **Was this relative a community leader?** Did he/she ever run a local civic or charitable group…or coordinate any annual community event?

• **Was your loved one ever the focus of a newspaper article during his/her life?** If newspapers considered your loved one worth writing about then, they might consider the death noteworthy now.

Example: *The New York Times* ran an obituary of Mel Cuba in January 2010. Cuba's claim to fame was that he helped rescue four children from drowning in 1933, a story that ran in New York papers at the time.

• **Is there a compelling story?** Newspapers love a good story.

Example: If your loved one was an inventor with 200 patents, he/she might make a good article, even if none of the patents ever became a profitable product.

DO THE LEGWORK

• **Compose an e-mail to obituary writers prior to your loved one's death.** For now, save this message in the "Drafts" file of your e-mail program or as a document on your computer. If you would like to increase the chances that your own obituary will make the papers, you can compose the e-mail about yourself. If you're writing your own e-mail, send a copy to a relative, explaining why you're sending it and what needs to be done when you die.

In the subject line of this e-mail, write "Possible Obit," followed by the person's name and a brief summary of what's most newsworthy.

Examples: "Possible Obit—Jonathan Doe, Coached Washington High to 1967 State Championship"…or "Possible Obit—Maryann Jones, Founded Statewide Plant-a-Tree Program."

In the body of this e-mail…

• Summarize the most notable accomplishments. Mention only the things that make this person distinctive and interesting. Including uninteresting details reduces the odds that a busy reporter will read the message.

• Explain any connection the deceased has to the newspaper's region. *Example:* "He lived in Chicago from 1952 to 1977."

• If articles about this person ran in newspapers, cite these publications, dates and pages on which they appeared. Better yet, scan copies of the articles into your computer and attach the scans to your e-mail (with date and name of publication).

• Include photos. Send in head shots as well as appropriate photos, such as one showing the deceased building a model ship, packing meals at a hunger center, shaking hands with someone famous. Contact the newspaper for the best e-mail address for sending photos. Be sure to let the obit writer and/or editor know where these photos have been sent.

• List phone numbers and cell-phone numbers of yourself and other family members. Reporters might need to reach a relative fast for additional details.

• **When your loved one passes away, add the date of death to this e-mail and send it to newspapers** large and small in every region where the deceased had any connection.

Some newspapers have specific directions on their Web sites for submitting obituary candidates. If not, send your e-mail to every obituary writer at the newspaper. Click on each of the obituaries on the newspaper's Web site to find these writers' names and e-mail addresses. If you send your e-mail to just one obituary writer at a newspaper, that person might be out that day or busy with other assignments.

14

Travel Talk

Surprising Secrets to a Great Vacation

Was your recent vacation everything you hoped it would be? Studies indicate that people often are disappointed by their vacations because their getaways just do not feel very memorable or special enough. And what enjoyment they do get fades as soon as they return to everyday life. In my field of behavioral economics, I study the happiness and satisfaction people derive from choices they make about how to use their money, time and energy. When it comes to vacations, I have learned that what people believe will make them happy often doesn't. *And I've learned some simple strategies for enjoying vacations much more...*

•**Do lots of research and planning ahead of time.** It sounds counterintuitive, but people get the biggest boost in happiness from the anticipation in the weeks before their vacations. All of the planning, dreaming, reading guidebooks and surfing the Internet for recommendations doesn't just serve to enhance the actual vacation—it can be one of the best parts of the vacation. The more extensive your preparation is—even going so far as to take a scuba-diving course before going to an exotic beach locale or a foreign language course before going to Europe—the more elation you will feel overall.

•**Consider taking multiple shorter vacations rather than one longer trip.** Duration counts for very little when you recall your vacation experience and how it makes you feel. Enjoying several three- or four-day weekends

Dan Ariely, PhD, the James B. Duke Professor of Psychology and Behavioral Economics at Duke University, Durham, North Carolina. He is a regular commentator on National Public Radio's *Marketplace* and author of *The New York Times* best seller *Predictably Irrational: The Hidden Forces That Shape Our Decisions* and *The Upside of Irrationality: The Unexpected Benefits of Defying Logic at Work and at Home* (both from Harper). His Web site is *www.danariely.com.*

throughout the year has the same energizing and stress-reducing effects as hoarding your vacation days for a two-week grand tour. It's also easier to do—and less guilt-producing if you have a demanding job—plus you get the pleasure of anticipating several trips.

Another disadvantage of long trips is that vacationers adapt very quickly to their vacation and get less and less pleasure as the trip goes along.

Example: The first night at a five-star hotel is magnificent. After a few nights, you are annoyed that the room service is not prompt enough...or that the pool does not stay open late enough.

Of course, you can't travel very far if you're just going for a few days, so if you do decide to take a longer vacation, you may get more satisfaction out of it if you break it into two or three distinct periods, changing locations and activities for each segment.

• **Plan at least one high point during the vacation.** People tend to believe it's the overall average of the various vacation experiences (easy travel, delicious food, good weather) that determines your happiness. But studies reveal that what actually matters is doing something memorable. That might be attending a special musical concert or hiking through the ancient ruins. Even if everything else is just so-so, the memory of that peak moment and the sense of vitality it gives can leave you feeling great about your vacation.

In fact, peak moments are a far more important factor than how much money you spend or whether you do everything on your itinerary. So if you come across a museum that you absolutely adore, your best bet is to go ahead and spend the rest of the day there and skip the sights you may have felt obligated to visit.

If you prefer the familiar to the new on your vacations—such as relaxing at the same beach house each year—you still can improve your satisfaction level over previous years. Try injecting some variety into your stay, even if it's just cooking a meal that you've never tried before and inviting acquaintances you just met to share it with you.

• **Save the highest point for near the very end of your trip.** People often are anxious to get to their favorite restaurant or activity right away on their trip, but that actually can work against maximizing your enjoyment. Memories of a great first day will have faded by the end of the trip, but not before making everything else that follows seem a little less special. Our research suggests that how you feel on the final day of your vacation colors your impression of the overall experience almost as much as peak moments, so make that day a fulfilling one. Avoid hanging around the hotel on your final day because you're tired or have postcards to write.

Don't sweat the low points during a vacation. Getting your passport stolen in Italy or the airline losing your luggage may seem ruinous to your trip. But if you don't view them as disasters, such events really don't deter from your enjoyment of a vacation. In fact, if a vacation headache is memorable enough, you might even recall it fondly.

Examples: While dealing with your stolen passport, you met some delightful Hungarians ...your adventures with your missing luggage become a funny story that you tell for years to come.

• **Take photos, but not too many.** Avoid documenting your entire trip with hundreds of shots. Taking and keeping many photos dulls positive memories because when you see all of them, you're reminded of all the relatively tedious moments. You need just a few photos of spectacular moments to bring on powerful and pleasing memories.

• **Keep all the memories of your vacation alive once you return home.** Studies indicate that the pleasurable feelings you have from a vacation fade very fast. The boost to your happiness is gone within a few weeks unless you make a conscious effort to shape and enhance the memories and feelings.

To help do this, display a few select photos from the vacation where you can see them every day (on your computer screen saver or on your night table). Also, relive the trip with friends and/or family. The more you can use your vacation in social situations to provide conversational fodder, the longer-lasting your enjoyment.

Cheaper and Better Off-Season: Have a Great Time in Paris, Rome, Hawaii, More... For Lots Less

Pauline Frommer, developer of the Pauline Frommer Guidebooks (Wiley) and a cohost of *The Travel Show*, a nationally syndicated radio show. She is a two-time winner of the North American Travel Journalists Association's "Best Guidebook of the Year" award. The daughter of Arthur Frommer (founder of the famous Frommer's travel guides), she has been traveling extensively since she was four months old. For more details, go to *www.frommers. com/pauline.*

We might dream of seeing Paris in the spring or escaping to Hawaii in the dead of winter, but visiting popular destinations during their peak seasons means paying top dollar and contending with massive throngs of fellow tourists. Some popular vacation spots are as much as 50% cheaper* in the off-season, yet still thoroughly enjoyable.

Off-season travel destinations must be selected with care, however—in some locations, the weather is unpleasant in the off-season or many of the tourist attractions and amenities are shut down.

Here, the best off-season bets...

• **Hawaii.** Hawaii's peak seasons are winter, summer and when schools are out for spring and Thanksgiving breaks. Instead, plan your visit for October or in early November, before Thanksgiving week.

The state's off-season weather is virtually indistinguishable from the peak-season weather, and lodging rates can be 40% lower during autumn. There could be substantial off-season savings on vehicle rentals and airfare as well, though this varies. The only downside is that October and November are poor months for whale watching in Hawaiian waters.

Savings strategy: Rent a condo rather than a hotel room. Thousands of Hawaii property owners rent out their homes and condos, often at very attractive rates during the off-season. I located a two-bedroom condo right on the

*Rates and offers subject to change.

beach in Maui for $59 per night. Condos have kitchens, so you can eat in and reduce dining bills. Get listings on HomeAway.com...FlipKey. com...Rentalo.com...and VRBO.com.

• **Orlando's theme parks.** If you visit the theme parks during the peak summer season and major holidays, you'll spend most of your vacation standing in lines. In Orlando, those lines virtually disappear in January and February (except during President's week, when some school children have a vacation). That means much more fun per hour. Meanwhile, Orlando hotel rooms that cost $69 to $89 per night in summer can be had for as little $29 a night in winter.

Orlando's winter weather can have ups and downs, but there are plenty of beautiful days when temperatures climb into the 60s. Theme parks do close some rides for refurbishment in the winter but usually only a few at a time.

Savings strategy: The Web site MouseSavers.com tracks Disney-related deals, including discounts on golf and spa treatments.

Warning: There's much less upside to visiting southern California's theme parks in the off-season. Hotel prices do not fall sharply in the winter, and California theme park lines do not disappear in the off-season.

• **Las Vegas.** In Las Vegas, there are 12,000 more hotel rooms than there were a year ago, thanks to new hotels and expansions of hotels. The troubled economy and the huge number of rooms have combined to provide attractive lodging rates. Those already low prices plummet by an additional 50% or more in the off-season—in January, February and the summer. I've found weekday rates as low as $29 for appealing rooms on the Strip, and as low as $12 off the Strip (add $20 on weekends). It's much easier to get tickets for popular shows in the off-season as well.

To get the best off-season rates in Las Vegas, avoid visiting when the city hosts major events and conferences...on any holiday...and during major sporting events, when gamblers flock to the city to place their bets. During the winter, this means avoiding Super Bowl week, Valentine's week, Christmas week, the NCAA basketball tournament in late March and the largest of the conferences and trade shows, such as early January's Consumer Electronics Show. The Las Vegas Convention & Visitors Authority's Web site provides a list of the city's conventions, including the number of visitors expected (*www. lvcva.com*, select "Meeting Planners," then "Convention Calendar"). Avoid the opening week of the World Series of Poker.

Savings strategy: Hotels on the Strip offering off-season deals include Circus Circus (800-634-3450, *www.circuscircus.com*), Stratosphere (800-998-6937, *www.stratospherehotel.com*), Excalibur (877-750-5464, *www.excalibur.com*) and the Imperial Palace (866-523-5658, *www. imperialpalace.com*). Off of the Strip, consider Station Casinos (800-678-2846, *www.stationcasinos.com*) or Sam's Town (800-897-8696, *www. samstownlv.com*).

Helpful: To make sure you are getting the best deals at hotels, try discounter sites, such as HotelsCombined.com and TravelWorm.com.

● **Rome, Paris and London.** Most travelers tour the famous European capitals in summer when prices are steep and streets, restaurants and museums are crowded with tourists. And temperatures in Rome, in particular, can turn sweltering. In winter, lodging prices decrease by as much as 40% and airfares by as much as 50%...crowds all but disappear...and Roman temperatures turn more pleasant. Of course, Paris and London can be both cold and rainy in winter, but those cities often are rainy even during the peak season.

Savings strategy: In London, Travelodge (*www.travelodge.co.uk*) often has the best hotel bargains. Most of the hotel chain's rooms feature couches that pull out, perfect for the family of four. The chain is not affiliated with America's Travelodge hotels.

In Rome and Paris, the best off-season lodging deals often are condos rented from their owners. Locate properties through the rental Web sites mentioned earlier, in the section on Hawaii.

Warning: Stick mostly with Europe's major cities in the off-season. Touring the European countryside is far less enjoyable in the winter weather, and many rural inns and tourist attractions close down entirely in the off-season.

● **Cruises.** September and October tend to be the cheapest times to go on a cruise almost anywhere. Also, the "repositioning cruises" that move the ships from one region to the next offer bargains. A cabin that would ordinarily cost $70 or $80 per person per day might cost less than $40 per day on a repositioning cruise.

Repositioning cruises typically occur in late April and late September. They generally last 10 to 14 days, a little longer than the average cruise...they spend a lower percentage of their time in port...and the ports that they do visit often are not the most popular cruise destinations. Repositioning cruises thus are ideal for those who enjoy relaxing on a ship at sea, not port hopping.

Savings strategy: Book all cruises through large travel agencies that specialize in cruising. These agencies often receive attractive perks from cruise lines, including special shipboard credits, which they pass along to their customers. Top cruise agents include CruisesOnly.com (800-278-4737)...VacationsToGo.com (800-338-4962)...CruiseBrothers.com (800-827-7779)...and CruiseStar.com (800-662-5450).

More from Pauline Frommer...

Travel Bargains Now

The tough economy has resulted in some great travel bargains here and abroad...

● **Las Vegas.** Thousands of new hotel rooms mean cut-rate prices on accommodations.

● **Cancun and the Mayan Riviera.** Bargain-priced travel packages abound because of the publicity about violence elsewhere in Mexico, far from Cancun.

Also: The US dollar is very strong now in Mexico.

● **Caribbean cruise.** Competition among the many new cruise ships has lowered the prices significantly.

● **Guatemala.** A family of four can eat out for $12, and airfares from the US are low. Costa Rica and Panama are good deals as well.

● **Iceland.** The exchange rate is favorable to US visitors. Icelandair also offers great deals on air/hotel packages.

•**Ireland.** Hit hard by the financial crisis, Ireland is the greatest travel value in western Europe now.

•**Number of the taxi, limousine, shuttle or car service** that is supposed to meet you at the airport.

Nancy Dunnan, editor, *TravelSmart, www.travelsmart newsletter.com.*

Fastest Way to Get a Passport

Need a passport ASAP? Use the State Department's Expedited Service program at a post office or via mail. It costs $60* above the usual $110 passport charge—plus the cost of overnight delivery—but it cuts waiting time to two to three weeks instead of a month or more.

Helpful: Provide the State Department your travel dates by indicating them on the form or visiting your regional office—you may get even faster service. If you are leaving within two weeks, go to a State Department regional office and bring proof of your departure date.

To find an office and make an appointment: Call 877-487-2778 or go to *http://travel. state.gov/passport.*

*Prices subject to change.

Don't Leave Home Without These Key Phone Numbers

Six phone numbers to carry on paper when traveling so that you'll have them even if your cell-phone battery is dead…

•**Airline's toll-free reservation number.**

•**Your travel agent's number.**

•**If traveling on business, the direct number of the person who handles your company's travel.**

•**Help line of your credit card issuer.**

•**Toll-free phone number of your connecting airline.**

Keep Cell-Phone Charges Down When Abroad

Using your cell phone abroad can lead to a huge bill. If you are planning to travel abroad, call your carrier to have international roaming turned on, but turn off your cell phone's data service when you're not using it to avoid charges for automatically downloading e-mails and other data. If your cell phone is from Verizon or Sprint, it is on the CDMA wireless network and can be used in about 40 countries. Phones from AT&T and T-Mobile are on the GSM network and work in about 220 countries. Ask your carrier whether it offers an international discount program.

Examples: AT&T and Sprint both provide plans for about $5 a month* that reduce international call prices. If you are going to a country where your regular phone does not work, you may be able to rent a phone.

USA Today, www.usatoday.com.

*Price subject to change.

Get More for Your Dollar Overseas

Before leaving on a trip, phone your credit card company and find out about foreign conversion fees—which can be up to 3% on purchases.* Also, consider using a credit card whose issuer does not charge such fees, such as Capital One. Avoid ATM charges by using a bank that has a partnership with a bank at your destination—this can save you out-of-network

*Rate subject to change.

ATM fees—call your bank for details. And be sure to ask about cash discounts.

Example: A hotel that requires a credit card when you arrive may offer a discount if you pay with cash when you are leaving.

Watch exchange-rate news while traveling—a rate change that helps the dollar may make it better to pay your hotel bill on one day than on another. Consider buying traveler's checks in local currency before you leave.

Consensus of travelers, reported online at Bankrate.com.

Airfares Are Soaring But You Can Still Find Amazing Bargains

George Hobica, founder of Airfarewatchdog, which reports on airfare bargains, including unannounced and unadvertised rates in New York City. He previously was a travel writer for *Travel + Leisure, National Geographic Traveler, Real Simple* and other magazines. Go to *www. airfarewatchdog.com* for more information.

Increased demand, reduced capacity and higher fuel prices have all pushed airfares skyward this year. Airlines have increased fares by an average of 30% compared with a year ago for peak travel months and in some cases, by as much as 50%.* Many big airlines are imposing new surcharges from $10 to $30 per one-way domestic flight on nearly all days throughout vacation season, calling them "peak travel days."

Bargains still exist, but only for travelers who know how to find them…

●**Check as many of the fare-comparison Web sites as your time and patience permit.** Many travelers assume that all of these sites produce the same results, and so they use just one. In fact, the lowest fares often turn up on just one or two sites, particularly with overseas flights. Sites to try include CheapAir.com, CheapTickets.com, Expedia.com, Hotwire.com, Kayak.com, Orbitz.com and Travelocity.com. Travelocity.com and Expedia.com do well at

*Rates and prices subject to change.

combining one-way fares on different airlines into a cheap round-trip.

Helpful: If you can be flexible with your travel dates, favor Travelocity.com, Orbitz.com and CheapTickets.com. They make it easy to search a wide range of departure and return dates.

●**Check the airlines' own Web sites.** Airlines increasingly save their very best fares for their own sites to build customer loyalty and avoid paying commissions to third-party travel sites. If you're not sure which carriers fly your desired route, note which appear when you enter the route into third-party fare-search sites.

Helpful: Definitely search for airfares on Southwest.com, depending on where you are traveling, and sign up for Southwest's "DING" special discounts. Also visit Allegiant.com if flying to or from such cities as Los Angeles, Las Vegas, Orlando and Phoenix. Southwest and Allegiant don't work with third-party online sites.

●**Divide your flight into segments.** Sometimes it's cheaper to break a single flight into two different flights, perhaps on different airlines, than to obtain a single round-trip ticket. This is most likely to save money when flying internationally or to or from a small city with limited direct flights outside of the region. You will have to find these segment savings yourself—or locate a helpful travel agent—because airfare-search sites typically do not pick them up. One way to find these savings is to make note of where you would transfer if you made the journey on a single ticket, then check rates to that transfer airport and from that airport to your destination.

Examples: When traveling from the US to Asia, you can cut costs and visit a second city by buying one ticket, for example, to Singapore and a second ticket from Singapore to your final destination on discount airline Air Asia (*www.airasia.com*). When traveling to Europe, it could cost much less to buy one ticket to Dublin and a second ticket from Dublin to the final destination on discount airline Ryan Air (*www.ryanair.com*), as long as you're traveling light, because Ryan Air imposes steep baggage fees.

A warning: Allow several hours to make connections between such flights, as airlines are not very sympathetic about missed flights when a different airline's mistake created the problem. Consider skipping this strategy entirely to places where winter weather often causes delays.

•**Sign up for airline frequent-flier programs.** Program members often receive e-mails about special fares and discounts. The airlines' sites provide instructions on how to enroll.

•**Purchase a combined hotel-and-airfare package.** These packages sometimes cost little more than the cost of airfare alone. Hotel-and-airfare packages are particularly attractive to Europe this summer. Many of the travel companies that put these packages together bought blocks of seats on summer flights to Europe a year ago, when airfares were very low.

These packages are available through most of the major travel search sites. Also try United Vacations (*www.unitedvacations.com*) and Virgin Vacations (*www.virginvacations.com*), which sometimes offer attractive package bargains. Priceline.com and LastMinute.com typically offer the best package rates when trips are booked within three or four days of the departure date.

•**When you find a standout fare, pounce.** Great fares tend to disappear quickly online. If you spot a fare substantially lower than any you've previously found, grab it.

If you locate an even better fare within 24 hours, you should be able to cancel your earlier purchase for a full refund. Refund restrictions sometimes apply, however, so read the cancellation policy on the Web site before buying.

Airfares Not Fair

Airfares can go up by 50% or more by the time all supplementary fees are added in. Checked-baggage fees, fees for seats with extra legroom and other airline fees significantly raise base fares.

Study by Consumer Travel Alliance, a nonprofit consumer organization in Springfield, Virginia, reported in the *Los Angeles Times.*

Best Time to Get a Deal On Airline Tickets

The best time to buy low-cost airline tickets is Tuesday at 3 pm eastern time.

Reason: Major airlines announce sales on Monday night, and competitors match these sales on Tuesday. It takes a few hours for sale prices to work their way through the system.

Least expensive times of day to travel: First flight of the day…noon…dinnertime.

Least costly days to fly: Tuesday, Wednesday and Saturday.

Rick Seaney, CEO and cofounder, FareCompare.com.

Airlines Most Likely to Provide Frequent-Flier Tickets

Your best chance to get a free frequent-flier award ticket may be at a certain airline. One recent study polling 22 airline Web sites for availability of frequent-flier award seating found huge discrepancies in availability, with some airlines making it almost impossible to use frequent-flier miles for a free ticket. The results of the Web poll reported that Southwest was able to fill 99% of requests…Air Canada, 94%…Lufthansa, 86%…Alaska, 75%…Qantas, 73%…Continental, 71%…United, 69%…British Airways, 65%…American, 58%…Air France, 56%…Delta, 13%…US Airways, 11%. If you try to book a flight with miles and no seats are available, try again later. Airlines sometimes open up more award seats if the flight is not selling.

The Wall Street Journal, www.wsj.com.

Can't Find the Airline Seat You Want? Try These Helpful Sites...

To get a frequent-flier seat or an upgrade, consider using an online service that alerts you when a seat opens up on the flight you want. ExpertFlyer (*www.expertflyer.com*) is tied into more than 40 airlines worldwide. More than half of its customers who search for an award seat do find one that works for them. MileageManager's AwardPlanner (*www.mileage manager.com*) works with nine airlines and lets you enter up to five different itineraries. Both services have free trial periods. After that, ExpertFlyer starts at $4.99 per month*...Mileage Manager costs $14.95 per year.

What to do: First try finding seats through the airlines' own sites. If this takes too much time or doesn't work for you, try out the alert sites to see if one of them is worth the price for you.

The Wall Street Journal, www.wsj.com.

*Prices subject to change.

How to Get the Best Seat On the Plane

For a better chance of having an empty seat next to you when flying, choose an aisle seat near the back of the plane—and ask if the middle seat is free when making your reservation or check online.

Useful tip: Most airlines release premium seats that they hold for frequent fliers exactly 24 hours before flight time.

To get the best possible seat in coach: Fly at off-peak times, when the chance is higher that you can get a good seat or change seats after everyone is aboard. If you have elite status in a frequent-flier plan, you may be able to get a better seat at no extra cost.

Travel + Leisure, 1120 Avenue of the Americas, New York City 10036, *www.travelandleisure.com.*

First Class Being Phased Out

First-class airline seats are slowly disappearing. Airlines are shrinking or even eliminating first-class seating as consumers increasingly search for less expensive tickets. AirTran could drop all first class when its merger with Southwest is completed. Qantas is eliminating first class on most routes. United is decreasing the size of its first-class sections and might, after completing its merger with Continental, move toward eliminating them on certain routes, if not altogether.

Bryan Saltzburg, general manager, new initiatives, TripAdvisor in Newton, Massachusetts, *www.tripadvisor. com.*

Airline Perks for a Price

Pay for faster airline check-in and quicker boarding if you are traveling on American, United or Southwest. They are providing convenience features for extra cost to travelers who are frustrated by longer lines, battles for overhead storage space and penalties for changing reservations. American will let you board ahead of other coach passengers for $9 to $19 each way* and offers a discounted fee to change flights...United gives access to priority check-in and security lines for $19 to $49 each way...Southwest offers boarding ahead of other customers for $10 each way (Southwest has open seating). Each of these airlines also offers perks for other services at varying prices. Check airline Web sites for more information.

The Wall Street Journal, www.wsj.com.

*Prices subject to change.

Sail Through Airport Security

To save time going through airport security, carry *solid* toiletries—these items do not have to be placed in a separate plastic bag like liquids.

Examples: A bar shampoo, such as J.R. Liggett's A Natural Traveler, $14 for 3.5 ounces* (*www.jrliggett.com*)…shaving soap with bowl, such as eShave Avocado Oil & Linden, $28 for 3.5 ounces (800-947-4283, *www.eshave.com*)… skin-moistening Serenity Soapworks lotion bar, $5 for two ounces (*www.etsy.com/shop/serenity soapworkstx*)…Uncle Harry's All Natural Tooth Powder, $3 for one ounce (*www.uncleharrys. com*), or ReadyBrush individually sealed pre-pasted toothbrushes, seven for $5 (Walgreens. com and Amazon.com).

Money, Time-Life Bldg., Rockefeller Center, New York City 10020, *http://money.cnn.com*.

*Prices subject to change.

Privacy at the Airport

You do not have to disclose your medications to an airport security screener—and you can conceal their names on bottles by putting tape over them. The Transportation Security Administration (TSA) considers medication use a matter of medical privacy—but screeners have the right to test medication bottles to be sure that they do not contain explosives or anything that is not allowed on aircraft.

Wired, 520 Third St., San Francisco, California 94107, *www.wired.com*.

Are You in the TSA's Database?

Airport screeners keep track of troublemakers. The Transportation Security Adminis-tration (TSA) maintains a database of travelers who threaten screeners or display excessive anger. Database information could be shared with various government agencies, airlines and rail and bus systems.

Transportation Security Administration, US Department of Homeland Security, Washington, DC, *www.tsa. gov*, reported in *USA Today*.

How Safe Are Full-Body Airport Scanners?

Mahadevappa Mahesh, PhD, associate professor of radiology and medicine, Johns Hopkins University School of Medicine, and chief physicist, Johns Hopkins Hospital, both in Baltimore. His analyses of airport scanners have been published in *Journal of the American College of Radiology* and *British Medical Journal (BMJ)*.

The full-body scanners now in airports are safe for everyone, including children and pregnant women. *Different airports use different scanner types…*

• **Millimeter radio wave scanners,** which look like glass booths, bombard travelers with radio waves and collect the reflected waves to generate images. The radio energy projected is tens of thousands of times lower than the energy of radio waves generated by most cell phones.

• **Backscatter scanners** (they look a lot like two refrigerators) are the source of most people's concern. They do use X-rays, but of a type that does not penetrate the body—the X-rays bounce off the body and are captured by detectors. These are fundamentally different from transmission X-rays, which are used in medical diagnosis. The radiation from the backscatter systems is very low—a single scan is equal to roughly just four to five minutes of air travel. The annual limit set by the Nuclear Regulatory Commission would be reached if a person undergoes 2,500 to 5,000 scans per year, which is highly improbable.

Bottom line: Both of these new scanning systems are safe for everyone, but passengers who remain worried are entitled to refuse a scan and have a thorough pat-down instead.

Finally...Passenger Rights!

The recent *Airline Passengers' Bill of Rights* states that domestic carriers must permit passengers to disembark if a plane has been sitting on the tarmac for three hours. US airlines operating domestic flights must provide food and water within two hours of the delay, as well as working toilets. The *Bill of Rights* went into effect on April 29, 2010. Airlines that do not adhere to it face fines of $27,500 per passenger.

Nancy Dunnan, editor, *TravelSmart, www.travelsmart newsletter.com.*

More Flight Cancellations Ahead

More flights are likely to be canceled because airlines face fines for stranding passengers on tarmacs. The government can levy a fine of $27,500 per passenger for tarmac delays longer than three hours. Outright cancellation doesn't bring penalties—so airlines facing bad weather are likely to cancel flights.

Robert Herbst, founder, AirlineFinancials.com, an airline information site, St. Louis.

Stranded at the Airport?

In case you have to sleep at the airport, check SleepingInAirports.net for practical information about securing safe, sanitary overnight or hourly accommodations. The site reviews more than 7,500 US and international airports as places to spend the night if your flight is delayed or canceled. It gives information on the comfort of the chairs and other seating, overnight lighting, availability of 24-hour food and more. Organized by continent and country.

Caution: Airport facilities change often.

How *Not* to Get Bumped

Reduce your chances of getting bumped by checking an airline's bump information before booking your flight. Go to *http://aircon sumer.ost.dot.gov* (click on "Travel Tips & Publications," then "Air Travel Consumer Report." In these reports, look for the "Oversales" section). In 2010, US airlines had a bump rate of 1.09 for every 10,000 passengers, down from 1.23 in 2009.

Also: Join frequent-flier programs—members are less likely to be bumped. Choose your seat when you make your reservation—people who must wait for seats until check-in are more likely to be bumped. Check in early or online—later arrivals are much more likely to be bumped.

Tom Parsons, CEO and founder of BestFares.com, which tracks travel costs and discounts.

More from Tom Parsons...

Baggage Fees Waived If You Have These Credit Cards

Baggage fees are waived for Delta and Continental credit card holders. Delta waives its fee of up to $50* for the first checked bag on a round-trip ticket for anyone who holds a Delta American Express credit card. Continental is waiving its $50 round-trip fee on the first checked bag for anyone holding a Continental Airlines Chase credit or debit card. Delta and Continental also will waive the fees for anyone traveling with the cardholder (up to nine people on a reservation). Other airlines have adopted similar policies. Both the Delta and Continental Chase cards have annual fees.

*Price subject to change.

FDA Warns: Airline Meals May Be Unsafe

FDA inspectors visited airline caterers LSG Sky Chefs, Gate Gourmet and Flying Food

Group, which combined operate 91 kitchens and prepare more than 100 million meals a year for Delta, American, United, US Airways, Continental and other large airlines.

Among the infractions: Foods stored at improper temperatures...meals prepared with unsanitary equipment...employees who practiced poor hygiene...and inadequate pest control. Meals prepared under these conditions may result in food-poisoning outbreaks.

Self-defense: Consider bringing your own food or eating before you board a plane.

Roy Costa, RS, MS, MBA, consultant and public health sanitarian, Environ Health Associates, Deland, Florida, *www.safefoods.tv.*

Hand-Washing on the Airplane

Tap water on airplanes typically is contaminated with bacteria, so how do you wash your hands safely?

Simply use the soap and water when in the airplane's lavatory. Bacteria can grow anytime water is stored, as it needs to be for airplane use—but these bacteria usually are not harmful. The benefits of hand-washing far outweigh any concerns about bacteria in the water.

David O. Carpenter, MD, director, Institute for Health and the Environment, University at Albany, State University of New York.

Airplane Myth Dispelled

The risk of getting sick from being on an airplane is actually low. Airplane air is refreshed 20 times per hour, versus 12 times per hour in an office building. Most plane air is circulated through hospital-grade filters that remove 99.97% of bacteria.

Mark Gendreau, MD, aviation and emergency-medicine expert and vice-chair, emergency medicine, Lahey Clinic, Burlington, Massachusetts.

Car Rental Firms Now Charging No-Show Fees

No-show penalties for car rentals may be charged to people who reserve cars and do not pick them up. As many as 30% of renters make reservations but do not show up at the rental counter. Rental firms are implementing technology to process credit card numbers at the time of reservation—and might charge customers fees if they do not claim a vehicle or cancel with at least 24 hours' notice. If you need to cancel due to extreme circumstances, such as a death in the family or flight cancellation, call the rental company's customer service department and request a waiver of the no-show fee.

Neil Abrams, auto-rental consultant at Abrams Consulting Group, Inc., Purchase, New York, quoted in *Kiplinger's Personal Finance.*

Luxury Hotels for Less

Discounts on luxury hotel rooms are more available now. Facing lower demand, top hotels are offering rooms at up to nearly half off—by listing anonymously through Priceline. com, Hotwire.com and Travelocity.com.

Example: With Travelocity.com's new "Top Secret Hotels" option, after a user types in a destination and travel dates, he/she gets a list of unnamed hotels with star ratings, prices and general locations.

Tom Botts, managing partner at the advisory firm Hudson Crossing, LLC, in New York City, *www.hudson crossing.com.*

Hotels That Pay Your Baggage Fees!

Some hotels pay airlines' checked-baggage fees for their guests. In a plan to increase weekend and leisure traveling, Holiday Inn, Kimpton Hotels and other chains are paying checked-bag fees that airlines charge. Some chains require travelers to fill out forms for refunds...others ask for bag-fee receipts and then offer a credit on the hotel bill. Some restrictions apply.

Example: Some hotels require you to pay with Visa.

Peter Yesawich, PhD, chairman and CEO, Ypartnership, a marketing services company for travel, leisure and entertainment clients in Orlando, Florida, *www.ypartnership.com.*

Hackers Hit Hotel Industry Hard

Credit card information at hotels often is not secure. Hackers hit the hotel industry more frequently than many other industries. Card information is easy to steal, and hackers quickly use it to run up charges, often while card holders still are traveling and may not notice what is going on.

What to do: Check credit card bills carefully after any travel, and immediately report unrecognized charges to your card issuer.

The New York Times, www.nytimes.com.

Bedbug Registry

Before you travel, go to *http://bedbugregistry.com* to see if a bedbug infestation has been reported at your travel destination. You can search by the name of your hotel or by city and state...or click your location on a map. Optional e-mails tell you where bedbugs are reported nearby.

Bedbugs Begone

Bedbugs have been discovered in clothing stores, movie theaters and additional public places, and there is no guaranteed way to prevent them from hitching a ride home with you. If you develop itching or bites after being in a public place, all you can do is change your clothes as soon as you return home—in the bathroom, not around upholstered furniture—and then put the clothes in a hot dryer to kill the bugs.

Hotels and other overnight accommodations merit special precautions. In a hotel, put suitcases in the bathroom or on the TV stand or other hard surface upon check-in. Check the bed, box spring and headboard for insects and small black specks. If you find any, ask for a room change and inspect the new room, too.

When you return home, open suitcases outside. Wash and dry clothes with hot settings. Then put empty luggage in the car for a few hours on a very hot or very cold day—extreme heat or cold kills bedbugs.

Jerome Goddard, PhD, associate professor of medical and veterinary entomology, Mississippi State University, Starkville, and coauthor of a study of bedbugs that was published in *The Journal of the American Medical Association.*

Hotels That Cater to Guests with Allergies

In addition to cleaning rooms with hypoallergenic products and washing linens with fragrance-free detergents, Hyatt, Marriott and Hilton hotels now offer guest rooms that have medical-grade air purifiers and chemical- and fragrance-free bath products. These rooms cost $20 to $30 more per night.* To see a list of all hotel locations that offer these types of rooms, go to *www.pureroom.com.*

The New York Times, www.nytimes.com.

*Prices subject to change.

Hospital Alert for Travelers

Hospitals close to various popular tourist locations may not provide adequate care to vacationers. Almost two dozen US hospitals with worse-than-average ratings for fatalities from heart attack, heart failure or pneumonia are in or near top tourist destinations, such as the Florida coasts and Las Vegas. One-quarter of low-rated hospitals are near a state park—most of which do not have any other hospitals nearby.

Self-defense: Vacationers, especially those with chronic medical conditions, should check in advance on quality hospitals in areas they are visiting at *www.hospitalcompare.hhs.gov.*

USA Today analysis of data from the US government site Hospital Compare.

Top Death Risk for Americans Overseas

Road accidents are the biggest death risk for Americans overseas. More than 1,800 US travelers died in road accidents from January 2003 through June 2010—that's one-third of the Americans who died outside the US of non-natural causes.

Analysis of State Department data by *USA Today.*

An Airline for Pets

An airline for pets permits animals to freely board planes, provides carriers on board and escorts the animals to the Pet Lounge at the end of a flight. PetAirways carries animals between selected cities for fees as low as $99 one way.* Most airlines charge $100 or above one way for a pet in the main cabin, and pets

*Prices subject to change.

in cargo can cost more. It serves New York City, Chicago, Denver, Los Angeles and Washington, DC. Planes carry up to 50 animals, along with a trained attendant to monitor their safety.

Information: 888-PET-AIRWAYS, *http://pet airways.com.*

Nancy Dunnan, editor, *Travel Smart, www.travelsmart newsletter.com.*

Where Your Pets Are Welcome

Learn where your pet will be welcome while traveling. DogFriendly.com publishes free listings of all kinds of dog-friendly resorts and travel destinations nationwide…a list of top 10 dog-friendly vacation resort areas…dog travel books…and dog-friendly guides for highway travel. PetsWelcome.com gives you thousands of hotels, B&Bs, ski resorts, campgrounds and beaches that are pet-friendly…provides advice on how to take your pet anywhere…and has a discussion board where pet-owning travelers can exchange various information and answer each other's questions.

DogFriendly.com and PetsWelcome.com.

Going on a Cruise? Be Sure to Pack This…

When going on any cruise, pack a power strip. Many cruise ship cabins have only one power outlet. You are likely to need more for all the electronics that you bring along—laptop computer, cell phone, iPod, etc.

Erik Torkells, author of *The Smart Traveler's Passport: 399 Tips from Seasoned Travelers* (Quirk).

Outsmart Thieves When Traveling

George Hobica, founder, Airfarewatchdog.com, New York City.

Keep your valuables safe when traveling. *See below for helpful tips when at airports and hotels…*

At airports: Air travelers should wait until they are just about to walk through the scanner before putting anything valuable into the mouth of the X-ray equipment, such as a laptop or purse. That way their valuables will not be sitting unattended on the other end where anyone can get to them. All travelers should buy small locks for carry-on bags, especially if taking overseas flights—someone could go through the bag while you sleep. Get to the baggage claim area as quickly as possible so that no one can take your checked luggage.

At hotels: Keep a television on when leaving your room, and keep the bathroom door slightly open with the light on inside—then put the "Do Not Disturb" sign on your door. Hide anything valuable that you must leave in the room—for example, put a laptop computer inside a bag of dirty laundry.

What else to do: Put cash and loyalty cards in one wallet and credit cards and identification in another—if you are ever held up, give the thief the wallet with the cash and loyalty cards.

Pickpocket Protection

Your pocket is most likely to be picked in Barcelona, Rome, Paris, Madrid and Athens when you are traveling in Europe.

To avoid being pickpocketed: Strap your purse across your chest, or wear your back-pack under your arm rather than on your back…put the strap of your backpack or purse under your chair leg when sitting in public places…keep valuables such as airline tickets, passports and jewelry in the hotel safe while you are sightseeing.

TripAdvisor.com, online travel booking and information Web site based in Newton, Massachusetts.

Family Vacations

Multigenerational vacations are increasingly common as parents take along their adult children who cannot find jobs and have little discretionary income. Many cruise lines, hotels and resorts are offering discounts for additional bookings like "Grandparents Stay for Free" packages.

A caution: Traveling together can increase bonding with some families, but it also can create more tension among family members. Decide before the trip how much togetherness is enough—not all members of your family will want to do things together all the time.

SmartMoney, 1755 Broadway, New York City 10019, www.smartmoney.com.

Into Space…

Space travel could be available to tourists by 2015. Under an Obama administration proposition, capsules holding four crew members and three tourists would go from Cape Canaveral to the International Space Station. Boeing has won an $18 million contract for preliminary development of a seven-passenger capsule.

The New York Times, www.nytimes.com.

15

Fun Finds

Video Calls to Friends And Family: It's Easy— And *Free*!

hen AT&T demonstrated their "picture phone" at the 1964 World's Fair, the device was hailed with oohs and aahs. Almost half a century later, video calling is finally easy enough that it can play a big role in your communications.

Picture and sound quality tend to be quite good. Computer-to-computer video calls usually are free—even internationally. *How to get it going...*

CALLING WITH A COMPUTER

The best way to place video calls is through your computer, although that means both parties must have the same video-calling service setup. The software required is free and easy to use. You'll need a high-speed Internet con-

nection and a Webcam that is either built-in or installed.

If your computer does not have a Webcam, consider buying a Logitech Webcam Pro 9000 ($67.99* list, *www.logitech.com*). It offers good picture quality and works well with the major video-calling programs.

There are currently three major video-calling services...

• **Skype is the most popular,** in part because it's very easy to install and use. Once it's set up, you just select the person you want to reach off a list you create and click "Video Call." (On a Mac, select the person, click the green phone button, then the blue video button.) If the person you are calling has Skype turned on, his/her computer will ring like a

*Prices subject to change.

Tom Merritt, host of This Week in Tech's "Tech News Today." He previously was executive editor of the technology news online site CNET, a division of CBS, wrote CNET's "The Real Deal" consumer technology how-to column and was executive producer of TechTV's Web site. Go to *http://twit.tv/tnt* for more.

phone, but you might want to send an e-mail or call in advance so that the person knows to expect your video call.

To install Skype, visit *www.skype.com*, click "Get Skype" and follow the directions. Skype's software will help you add names to your contact list. Unlike the other video-calling services, Skype also lets users place ultra-low-cost voice-only calls from their computers to any traditional phone.

● **Apple iChat.** Apple's video-calling program is very much like Skype, but it's available only on Apple computers. You could use an Apple MobileMe, AOL AIM or Google Talk account. Some newer Apple computers allow you to add special effects, such as fish floating across the screen or the Eiffel Tower in the background, and up to four callers can take part in a video conversation at once. If your Apple computer does not have iChat, you can add it by downloading the free version available from CNET (*http://download.cnet.com/mac*).

● **Google Video Chat.** Sign up for your free Gmail e-mail account (*http://mail.google.com*). Then log on to *www.google.com/chat/video* and click on "Install voice and video chat." To place video calls, just click on the name of anyone in your Gmail account contact list and then click the video camera icon next to his name.

Which of the three services should you use? You might want to set up two or all three of them and then, at any given time, use whichever one that a particular contact tends to use.

VIDEO CALLS WITHOUT A COMPUTER

It is increasingly possible to place a video call without a computer...

● **Call from your phone.** Apple's new iPhone 4 has a feature called FaceTime that allows you to video-chat with someone on another iPhone 4 (but only over WiFi networks) by touching a button on the screen (*www.apple.com*). The Ojo Personal Video Phone, which connects to a home Internet router (*www.ojophone.com*), and the Saygus VPhone smartphone (*www.saygus.com*) have the ability to place video calls. Skype now offers cell-phone–based video-calling software for smartphones. And the new HTC EVO 4G phone from Sprint (*www.sprint.*

com) allows you to install an application that lets you make video calls.

● **Call from your TV.** Some LG (*www.lg.com*), Panasonic (*www.panasonic.com*) and Samsung (*www.samsung.com*) high-end model HDTVs come with ability to place Skype video calls if you purchase a Webcam designed for the TV. An Internet connection is required. Some Panasonic Viera models feature WiFi wireless Internet capabilities, while others must be connected via cable.

Why You Shouldn't Store Photos on Facebook

Don't use Facebook to store photos. When you upload a photo to Facebook, it gets stored at a decreased resolution. Photos printed from Facebook often make blurry prints. Also, if you then delete the photo from your camera, you've lost the original. Always keep a backup copy of the full-resolution photo.

The Washington Post, www.washingtonpost.com.

Watch TV on Your Computer...and Maybe Cancel Cable!

Harry McCracken, founder/editor of Technologizer.com, a Web site offering news and reviews of high-tech products, Internet sites and related topics, based in Daly City, California, *www.technologizer.com*.

Watching TV shows via computer has become as simple as browsing the Web.

Advantages: Shows can be viewed whenever you want. They typically include fewer commercials than on TV or no commercials at all. You might even be able to cancel or just cut back on your cable subscription and save hundreds of dollars per year. Available shows range from recent episodes of *60 Minutes* and

House to decades-old episodes of *The Donna Reed Show* and *Father Knows Best* to highlights from sporting events.

BEST OPTIONS

•**Clicker.com.** The best way to access TV shows is through the Web site Clicker.com. Just enter the name of a program, and hit "Find" to link up to any episodes available online. Or browse Clicker.com's more than 12,000 show listings, which include a total of more than one million episodes. Expect to access recent episodes of most current network and basic cable programs online at no cost. Older episodes of current shows and episodes of pay cable shows often are available, too, but there might be a charge. Access to older programs no longer on the air is spotty but improving rapidly.

Warning: Some Clicker.com listings that appear to be complete episodes are brief video clips. These often display run times of just a minute or two.

You also can go directly to sites that carry many old and/or new shows...

•**Hulu** (*www.hulu.com*) offers, for free, recent episodes of most programs on ABC, Fox and NBC (but not CBS), such as *The Simpsons* and *Modern Family*, and classic shows, including *The Mary Tyler Moore Show* and *The Bob Newhart Show*. Hulu is rolling out Hulu Plus, with access to additional episodes of current shows, not just those that aired recently, for $7.99 per month.*

•**CBS** (*www.cbs.com*). Free TV episodes of many of the network's current shows are available with a reduced number of commercials. Some classic CBS shows are there, too, including *Perry Mason* and *The Twilight Zone*.

•**TV Land** (*www.tvland.com*) provides episodes of classic TV shows for free.

Examples: Gunsmoke...The Andy Griffith Show.

•**Netflix** (*www.netflix.com*). Sign up for one of the cheapest Netflix services—their $7.99-per-month one-DVD-at-a-time plan—and you also receive unlimited access to Netflix Watch Instantly, through which you can view a wide range of movies and television shows online with no additional fees.

*Prices subject to change.

Examples: 30 Rock...The Dick Van Dyke Show...and The George Burns and Gracie Allen Show.

•**Apple iTunes** (*www.apple.com/itunes*) and Amazon Video on Demand (*www.amazon.com/videoondemand*) offer a wide variety of TV shows, including HBO and Showtime programs, but at a price—typically 99 cents or $1.99 per episode. These pay services often feature additional episodes that no longer are available for free online.

FROM COMPUTER TO TV

If you would like to tap the rich archive of programs available online but would rather see them on your TV screen, devices such as Roku (*www.roku.com*, starting at $59.99) and Apple TV (*www.apple.com*, $99, works only with HDTVs) allow video content from some of the video Web sites to be viewed on a TV screen through either a wireless connection or an Ethernet cable. Most modern video game consoles, such as Wii and PlayStation 3, will play Netflix online video content on a TV.

Health Danger at The Movies

Reusable 3-D movie theater glasses could be covered in bacteria. It does not matter whether the glasses are wrapped or unwrapped. Reusable glasses are supposed to be cleaned after being worn, but all the pairs tested had bacteria on them. Most bacteria were harmless, but one pair harbored *Staphylococcus aureus*, which can cause staph infections.

Self-defense: Clean the glasses with an alcohol wipe before wearing them...or wash them with soap and water in the theater bathroom. Wiping with a tissue is less effective.

Study of 3-D movie glasses by Good Housekeeping Research Institute.

Paddle Tennis: Easy and Fun!

Patrick Netter, known as The Gear Guru, is a sports, health and fitness expert. Based in Los Angeles, Netter founded the fitness equipment store High-Tech Fitness and created a guide to fitness equipment of the same name. His Web site is *www.gearguru.com*.

If you haven't played paddle tennis, you might want to give it a try. It's great for individuals of all ages and skill levels. Most find it simple to learn, and it is less physically demanding than other racquet sports, such as squash and regular tennis, with fewer chances of sustaining an injury, particularly to the rotator cuff (shoulder).

HOW IT DIFFERS FROM TENNIS

Paddle tennis is similar to traditional tennis but varies in some significant ways...

• **The court is smaller**—20 feet by 50 feet versus 36 feet by 78 feet. That means less running around, making it easier for out-of-shape or less agile players.

• **Paddle.** Unlike strung tennis racquets, the paddles have solid heads, with small, aerodynamically drilled holes. The paddles also are smaller than tennis racquets—9.5 inches wide by 18 inches long. Once 100% wood, paddles now are made of high-tech composite materials that are lighter and give more power.

• **Ball.** One standard tennis ball, which you puncture to decrease the bounce, is used for each set.

• **Serve.** Unlike with tennis, there is one underhanded serve per point, and players cannot begin the serve higher than 33 inches or lower than 31 inches from the ground. The server can strike the ball directly or let it bounce first before striking it, but he/she cannot change methods of serving during a set.

• **Scoring.** The same as tennis (four points to win a game), but matches generally tend to be shorter, with sets often played in only 15 to 20 minutes.

PLATFORM TENNIS

There is a variation of paddle tennis, called *platform tennis*, which is played on a court that is about one-quarter the size of a tennis court and enclosed by a tensioned fence that looks like chicken wire. The ball remains in play even when it is hit off the fence on a bounce.

Platform tennis offers the benefit of yearlong play. The court is built on a raised foundation—which makes it easier to have a heated floor to melt snow and ice in the winter. Platform tennis is particularly popular in the Northeast for tennis players who want to play outside during winter months.

MORE INFO

There are a growing number of public and private paddle and platform tennis courts in the US. For information on paddle tennis, go to *www.theuspta.com*. For information on platform tennis, go to *www.platformtennis.org*.

Why You Need Butterflies and Bees in Your Garden...and How To Attract Them

Doug Tallamy, PhD, professor and chair of the department of entomology and wildlife ecology at University of Delaware, Newark. He is also author of *Bringing Nature Home: How You Can Sustain Wildlife with Native Plants* (Timber Press) and was awarded the Silver Medal by the Garden Writers Association of America in 2008. For more, go to *http://bringingnaturehome.net*.

Your garden can be more than a haven for you and your family to appreciate. It also can be a refuge for endangered bees and butterflies.

Three-quarters of all flowering plants—and more than one-third of food crops—depend on bees, butterflies and other pollinators for fertilization. Yet in just the past few years, the population of honeybees bred for use in commercial agriculture has dropped dramatically. Wild bees, butterflies and various pollinating bird species also are in decline.

Possible causes for the decline include parasites, disease and pesticides, but there is no doubt that one major cause is loss of habitat—the plants that pollinators use for food, mating and nesting.

By landscaping with pollinators in mind, you can attract them to your garden, adding to your pleasure and helping to protect threatened species. *How to plant for pollinators…*

• **Choose native plants.** Many of the plants that we are used to enjoying in North American yards are originally from China and Europe, including the traditional lawn. They are not part of the local region's food web—the complex network of plants and wildlife that depend on one another for survival. Some insects and birds have very successfully adapted to nonnative plant species, but most cannot adapt and may die out.

Also, many modern hybrid plants have been bred for appearance and extra bloom time but have lost the fragrance, nectar and pollen that once sustained butterflies and bees.

Rather than depend on hybrids for bloom time, choose different native plants that bloom at different times of year. By doing this, you can offer pollinators a succession of plants in flower from early spring to late fall.

To learn about native plants in your region, visit the Web site of the Pollinator Partnership (*www.pollinator.org*). Or contact your regional native plant society—the North American Native Plant Society lists state and regional groups at *www.nanps.org* (click on "Resources," then on "Native Plant Societies"). Your nearby cooperative extension office, which may offer free agricultural education and information (*www.csrees.usda.gov/extension*), also could help. Or talk to docents at your local arboretum.

• **Plant in groups.** Grow plants close together to provide overlapping canopies of different heights. This pattern is inviting to pollinators and gives them protection from predators.

• **Plant for larvae as well as adult pollinators.** Butterflies need more than flowers and nectar to survive. They also require plants for their larvae to feed on. A few species of plants, such as black-eyed Susan and milkweed, provide both. But in most cases, host plants that can feed larvae are different from flowering plants that provide nectar. Even the so-called butterfly bush provides nectar but no food for larvae. Good host plants are woody, such as viburnum, black cherry and oak.

• **Avoid pesticides.** Even natural pesticides can be deadly for bees. Also, wiping out insects starves the birds that feed on them. Plant diversity is a better solution to the pest problem than pesticides. A variety of native plants will support insects' natural enemies, including birds, keeping the different populations in balance—and making for a beautiful and life-sustaining environment around your home.

How to Get Rid of Pesky Gophers

Do you have gopher holes all over your lawn? One of the most effective ways to get rid of a gopher is by flooding its main tunnel—to find the tunnel, look for a fresh hole.

Run a garden hose into the gopher's tunnel, turn on the faucet and let the water run until the hole fills. Often the flooding will collapse parts of the tunnel, making it less habitable.

There also are many traps available in garden centers and in hardware stores. Of these, box traps, which are catch-and-release traps, are the easiest to set up.

Best: Safeguard catch-and-release trap.

Cost: Generally $40 to $60.*

Make sure to release the gopher five to 10 miles away from your property—otherwise it might find its way back.

Michael Bohdan, pest control professional, Texas.
*Prices subject to change.

Chemical-Free Weed Removal

David R. Mellor, master groundskeeper at Fenway Park, Boston, and author of *The Lawn Bible* (Hyperion) and *Picture Perfect* (Wiley).

One way to get rid of weeds without any toxic chemicals is simply to pull them out. Many lawn tools, such as Grandpa's Weeder ($26*) and The Weed Bully ($30), can be used for this.

*Prices subject to change.

Two alternatives: Pour boiling water mixed with white vinegar on the weeds. Or buy a lawn torch, such as Weed Dragon ($70) or Hot Spotter ($100), which attaches to a propane tank and can be used to burn weeds—but use it only when the lawn is wet to avoid fire.

To prevent weeds from growing: Use corn gluten in early spring—it is an effective pre-emergent (a natural nontoxic herbicide) and is available at garden stores.

The best defense against weeds: An active, healthy, growing lawn. It chokes the weeds, which grab hold when the lawn is sparse. To keep your lawn healthy, feed it with Scotts Organic or Scotts Fenway Park Lawn Fertilizer, and water with one inch of water (for approximately 60 minutes) per week.

Best time to water: Between 2:00 am and 7:00 am.

Quick Trick Keeps Mold Off Berries

Rinsing berries in hot water prevents mold. Heat water to 125°F. Swish berries in the water for about 30 seconds. This significantly reduces development of mold on strawberries, raspberries and blackberries, so these berries will keep longer. For blueberries, which have thicker skins, use 140°F water for 30 seconds.

The New York Times, www.nytimes.com.

How to Make Your Grill Shine—and Food Taste Better

Gary Wiviott, a Chicago-based "barbecue life coach" who provides grilling tutorials and demonstrations. He founded the culinary Web site LTHForum.com, won the *Chicago Tribune's* 2007 Good Eating Award for contributions to the city's culinary scene and is author with Colleen Rush of *Low & Slow: Master the Art of Barbecue in 5 Easy Lessons* (Running Press, *www.lowslowbbq.com*).

Grill cleaning often is neglected. That's so unfortunate, because conscientious grill care improves the taste of grilled foods—grills coated with baked-on grease and grime can impart unpleasant flavors—and dirty grills tend to break down faster as parts clog and corrode.

They even can be safety risks. Accumulated grease suddenly can ignite, burning anyone standing nearby.

EACH TIME YOU GRILL

Just before you place food on your grill, use a pair of long metal kitchen tongs to dip a balled-up paper towel into cooking oil, then wipe the oil across the hot bars of the grate. The oil coating makes food and grease less likely to stick to the bars, which makes cleanup easier later. Any type of cooking oil is fine, but grape seed, peanut and canola oil all have relatively high flash points, which reduce the odds that they will ignite.

After you remove food from the grill, close the lid and—if you have a gas grill—turn the temperature all the way to high. The intense heat will cook off much of the food residue. After five minutes, turn off the heat, and while the grill is still warm but not hot, scrape the grate using a wire-bristled brush. If you use a charcoal grill, you cannot quickly crank up the heat, but you can close the lid for five minutes, then scrape the grate as best you can.

When the grate has somewhat but not completely cooled, put on heat-resistant gloves, flip the grate over and scrape the underside with the wire brush. If the grit on your grate proves stubborn, the next time you are done grilling, lay a sheet of aluminum foil over the grate and cook off the residue. The foil concentrates the heat onto the grate.

Helpful: For all charcoal grills, use natural lump charcoal, such as Royal Oak or Wicked Good. This burns cleaner than other coals, leaving less residue.

Warning: If your grill has a drip pan, empty it after every use to avoid grease fires.

16

Car Care

How to Find an *Honest* Auto Mechanic

An auto mechanic informs you that the loud clunking sound you hear means that your car needs thousands of dollars' worth of repairs. But how can you really tell whether a mechanic has diagnosed the problem correctly? And how do you know whether he/she would charge a fair price?

"Auto mechanic" is among the least-trusted professions in the US, according to a 2010 survey by sales and management training company Sandler Training. Many mechanics are honest and skilled, while others have earned that mistrust—and it is not always easy to tell the good from the bad.

Here are ways to improve your odds of selecting a competent, honest mechanic or auto-repair shop, even if you know next to nothing about cars…

•**Choose a Bosch Authorized Service Center** and/or an ASE Blue Seal of Excellence repair facility. Bosch, a producer of consumer goods and automotive and industrial technology, is extremely selective about which independent repair shops it allows into its network of more than 1,000 US facilities. Membership is a virtual guarantee that the garage is well-equipped and customer friendly and that its mechanics are well-trained and highly skilled (*www.boschservice.com/findsvccenter*).

Certification from the National Institute for Automotive Service Excellence (ASE) is a strong indication of competence as well. Any mechanic who carries this designation has passed, within the past five years, at least one of the challenging exams administered by the institute.

David Sturtz, cofounder and CEO of RepairPal.com, an auto-repair information Web site with more than one million visitors each month. RepairPal has a team of 26 expert ASE-certified technician advisers with a combined 500 years of professional experience. The site provides parts-and-labor-cost estimates for repair work, customer reviews of repair shops and other auto information.

Note: The presence of one ASE mechanic does not guarantee that he is the mechanic who will work on your car or that the shop's ASE-certified technician passed an ASE exam related to the specific repairs that your car requires.

Example: Possessing an ASE certification for brakes does not ensure that the mechanic is skilled with engine or transmission repairs.

What to do: Ask specifically whether the facility has earned the ASE Blue Seal of Excellence. This means that at least 75% of the shop's car technicians are ASE-certified and that every area of service offered by the shop is covered by at least one ASE-certified technician (*http://locator.ase.com/blue*). Ask for an ASE-certified technician to work on your vehicle.

AAA certification is a less reliable indication of a repair shop's quality. Each AAA regional office sets its own standards, and some do a better job vetting repair shops than others.

•**Look for longevity.** It's a good sign if a repair shop has been around for at least five years and an excellent sign if it has been in business for 20 years or longer. Low-quality and dishonest shops rarely manage to last that long, particularly now that consumers can share complaints on the Internet. If the garage does not say when it was established on its Web site, ask when you call or ask longtime area residents which shops have been around the longest.

Possible exception: Bad repair facilities located near highway exits sometimes can survive by taking advantage of drivers from out of town who are unaware of the shop's poor reputation.

•**Search for the opinions of other consumers on the Internet.** Web sites CitySearch.com and Yelp.com provide consumer reviews of local businesses, including auto-repair facilities. My Web site, RepairPal.com, also offers consumer reviews of repair shops.

Not all Internet opinions should be given equal weight, however. Some business owners post glowing reviews of their own companies under bogus names to mislead consumers. And some consumer complaints about auto-repair facilities are unfairly negative—sometimes car problems are legitimately difficult to diagnose or expensive to fix.

Give significant weight to online opinions only if you uncover more than a few reviews and they have a strong positive or negative trend. *Take complaints seriously if they report that...*

•The shop billed customers for significantly more than the initial estimate, particularly if the shop did not contact these customers for approval as costs climbed.

•Vehicles' problems recurred after the shop claimed that they were fixed.

•**Call a shop that doesn't handle cars like yours to ask for a repair facility recommendation.** A facility that specializes in Japanese vehicles might not be equipped to repair your European or American car—but it might know a local shop or mechanic who is.

•**Pick a shop that makes you wait.** If a repair shop cannot quickly fit your car into its schedule, it typically means that the shop is good. Shops that cheat their customers usually do not do so by overbilling for parts or labor—that would be too easy for a savvy consumer to spot. Instead, dishonest facilities tend to inflate bills by recommending expensive, time-consuming repairs that cars really don't need. Very busy shops have little to gain by doing this because they have enough legitimate business to fill their mechanics' work hours.

Helpful: If you need your car fixed fast and a busy shop can't get to it immediately, politely ask this busy shop to recommend another shop in the area. Quality shops usually know which other local shops can be trusted.

•**Have routine maintenance performed by a full-service repair facility,** not a specialized lube or brake shop. A full-service repair facility might charge a few dollars more for an oil change or a brake pad replacement than a specialty shop would, but this is an effective and inexpensive way to get a sense of whether you like and trust the repair shop before you have a serious car problem.

Patronizing a repair shop for routine maintenance also makes you a regular customer, increasing the odds that the shop will treat you fairly and find a way to fit you in when it's busy.

• **Stay away from repair facilities that push unnecessary add-on procedures.** If any shop recommends an "engine flush" or a "transmission flush," head for the door. Engine oil and transmission fluid should be changed according to the vehicle manufacturer's maintenance schedule, but flushing these systems is expensive and almost certainly unnecessary. It even could damage the vehicle.

Also, be wary of shops that insist that an alignment is automatically required whenever brake work is done. Sometimes an alignment is needed, but not always. If a shop pressures you to agree to an alignment beforehand, it is probably just looking to boost your bill.

• **Stay away from repair facilities that fail to recommend sensible add-on procedures.** Sometimes tackling several auto-maintenance jobs at the same time is a money saver. If the mechanic fails to recommend additional work that could reduce the odds that a problem will recur—or that might as well be done because a difficult-to-access section of the vehicle will be opened up anyway—it could indicate that the shop hopes to create another big repair or maintenance bill in the future (or that the mechanic is incompetent).

To determine if additional procedures are appropriate, go to *http://repairpal.com/estimator*, enter all the requested details about your vehicle and work that it currently requires, then click the "Get Estimate" button. Scan down to the section labeled "Best Practices." Any additional work that should probably be done will be listed here, along with other useful details.

Examples: If you ask any mechanic to change the timing belt, he should recommend replacing your water pump as well with most vehicles. A water pump is unlikely to last for the life of a vehicle, and having it replaced at the same time as the timing belt should reduce the cost of replacement by more than 50%, so its replacement generally is seen as a shrewd money move even if the pump is still working. If your vehicle's cooling system must be opened up, such as when your radiator needs to be replaced, the mechanic likely should recommend replacing the thermostat as well. It's unlikely that your current thermostat will last for the life of your vehicle, and having a new

one installed when the cooling system is open anyway should decrease the cost of replacement by at least 50%. If your car's heater core fails, the mechanic likely should recommend replacing your engine mounts, too, assuming that these are worn. Worn engine mounts may allow your engine to move around more than it should, damaging the heater core. If the shop does not replace these mounts, the replacement core might become damaged as well.

Does Your Car Smell Funny? An Odd Odor Often Signals Trouble...

Eric Peters, a Washington, DC–based automotive columnist and author of *Automotive Atrocities! The Cars We Love to Hate* (MBI). A member of the International Motor Press Association and the Washington Auto Press Association, he has been writing about cars for 17 years. His latest book is *Road Hogs* (MBI). His Web site is *http://eric petersautos.com.*

Lots of smells can invade an automobile, some that are benign and others that signal trouble.

Here, common car smells, what they are trying to tell you and how you or your mechanic can get rid of them...

ROTTEN EGG/SULFUR SMELL

Especially if it is very strong and constant, this could be a signal that your car's catalytic converter isn't properly processing the by-products of combustion. There could be a problem with the converter itself or with the engine.

What to do: Have a constant sulfur smell checked out quickly to avoid ruining the catalytic converter.

Cost: A car manufacturer's factory replacement unit can cost $300 or more.*

Helpful: Avoid buying gas from lightly trafficked gas stations. The fuel might be old and possibly contaminated, which can trigger problems with your car's emissions control system and possibly damage the catalytic converter.

*Prices subject to change.

GASOLINE SMELL

All vehicles built since the early 1980s have vapor-recovery systems designed to prevent gasoline vapors from leaching out into the surrounding air. So if you do smell gasoline, other than when you are filling the tank, it's quite possible that your system for vapor-recovery is not working properly—or worse, that there's an actual gas leak somewhere. The latter is an obvious fire hazard.

What to do: If the gas smell is strong, it is best not to drive the car at all and instead call for a tow to your dealership or repair shop. The possible repairs could involve problems that range from simply replacing a leaky fuel rail (which connects fuel lines and injectors) to repairing or replacing a gas tank.

Helpful: Be sure that you fully tighten your gas cap after filling up. It is an integral part of the modern car's emissions control system. If you leave it loose, vapors will escape and, in addition to the gas smell, your car's "check engine" light probably will come on, requiring a visit to a repair shop or auto-parts store to clear the code from the computer that triggers the light (some shops will do it for free).

SICKLY SWEET/OILY SMELL

Engine coolant has a very distinctive sweet/oily smell. If you notice this smell outside the car, check underneath for puddles and drips to see if there is a leak somewhere in the cooling system.

If you notice this smell inside your car, check for dampness around the passenger side foot well. If you find wetness, you probably have a leaking heater core. A related symptom is a sticky film coming out of the defroster ducts that settles on the windshield.

What to do: This is one of those problems that starts out small and gets worse over time, so the sooner you can get it fixed the better. Repairs could range from replacing leaking hoses (a replacement hose costs about $25) to replacing a heater core, which can cost several hundred dollars.

MUSTY/MOLDY SMELL

Condensation may be collecting in the vehicle's air-conditioning system instead of draining out as it should.

What to do: Look underneath the car in the area near the passenger-side floor pan, usually toward the front, where it meets up with the firewall that separates what's under the hood from the passenger compartment.

If there is mud or caked-on debris, try to wash it away with your garden hose. The air-conditioning system's drainage holes could be blocked, causing the moisture buildup. If you can't find anything obvious, it's a good idea to take the car in for a professional diagnosis. Mold can be unhealthy as well as unpleasant.

If the air-conditioning system needs major work or the ducts need to be taken out, it can be a big job costing several hundred dollars. But if it can be cleaned out without disassembly (shops have chemicals and tools for this), then it will cost less. Moldy smells also can be caused by water getting into the carpets from leaky windows or doors.

Helpful: Many late-model cars have cabin-filtration systems, but drivers often neglect to periodically clean or replace the filters. Check your owner's manual to see whether your car has a cabin-filtration system, and adhere to the recommended service schedule for its cleaning and replacement.

ACRID/BURNING HAIR SMELL

The friction material that lines clutch discs and brake pads can produce this smell, especially during hard use or abuse, such as riding the clutch or brakes excessively.

What to do: Try to correlate the smell with the situation. For example, if it's present when you are descending a long, steep grade, it is probably coming from your brakes. If it happens when you're accelerating and you have a manual transmission, it's more likely to be the clutch.

If the brake pads and/or shoes are worn out, they will need to be replaced. Replacing front brake pads typically costs less than $100. If the clutch is failing, replacing it can cost $500 to $800.

Helpful: Downshift the transmission into a lower gear when driving sharply downhill (in automatics, just go down one gear from the "drive" position) to prevent overusing the brakes, which could lead to decreased brake performance as well as excessive wear and tear. If you have a manual transmission, avoid riding the clutch for very long when starting out and when stopping. Smooth, progressive engagement will help extend clutch life.

BURNING OIL SMELL

This often is the result of a failing gasket or seal that lets engine oil seep onto hot engine parts, where it cooks off. The good news is that if the leak is minor (just some light wetness or, at most, a few drops), it's usually more of an unpleasant annoyance than an urgent problem. The bad news is that small leaks often become bigger leaks. If the oil smell is coming from the tailpipe (look for smoke with a bluish haze), it is a symptom of a worn-out engine in which oil is seeping into the combustion chamber and being burned up along with the air and fuel.

What to do: Mention the leak the next time your car is in for service. A repair shop will perform tests to evaluate the engine.

THAT "NEW-CAR SMELL"

This smell is the result of the evaporation of *volatile organic compounds* (VOCs) from plastic and rubber—the materials that are used to make most of the interior parts of the vehicle, such as dashboards, seat materials, carpets. It typically goes away as the car ages.

What to do: Keep the windows open to allow better airflow.

For a Better Deal on a New Car...

For the best deal on a new car now, look at higher-end models, which are not selling well. Consider autos made by manufacturers that are trying to repair their reputations or grow market share, such as Toyota and Hyundai. Investigate rebates and other incentives on luxury sedans, such as BMW 335d, and SUVs, such as Land Rover's midsize Range Rover.

Jesse Toprak, vice president of industry trends and insights, TrueCar.com.

Nice Cars for Seniors

The best cars for senior drivers have easy access, good visibility, comfortable seats and a roomy driving position.

Consider: Subaru Forester XT Limited small SUV ($27,720*)...Hyundai Azera sedan ($26,270) ...Honda Accord family sedan ($22,730)...Honda Odyssey minivan ($28,580).

Consumer Reports, 101 Truman Ave., Yonkers, New York 10703, *www.consumerreports.org*.

*Prices subject to change.

Auto Leasing Making A Comeback

When used-car values fell after gasoline prices hit $4/gallon, the companies that finance leases lost billions of dollars because vehicles were worth less at lease-end than they had anticipated. Chrysler Financial stopped all its leasing, and GMAC came close to stopping. But leasing is on the rise again as consumers return to the desire for luxury cars, such as BMW and Mercedes-Benz. Leases of these cars usually require lower monthly payments than taking out a loan to buy them.

Bankrate.com.

When to Consider Refinancing Your Car

Many consumers finance through dealers—and often do not obtain the best rates available. If you have a credit score of 720 or higher, you may do better by refinancing.

What to do: Go to *www.moneyaisle.com* to compare rates from banks and credit unions. Try *http://autos.yahoo.com* and *www.bankrate.com* for tools to help you calculate what rates you may qualify for. Contact lenders directly to find out if they offer auto refinancing.

The Wall Street Journal, www.wsj.com.

How to Get the Best Resale Value

To get the best resale value for a vehicle, buy a type that retains more of its value for longer—you can do the research online. Choose a body style that holds value in your geographic region, such as pickup trucks in Michigan. Expect four-wheel- and all-wheel-drives to hold their value better in colder areas. Buy standard colors, not trendy ones that may be out of date in a few years. Avoid upgrades that don't add to a car's value, such as high-end stereos.

Also: Consider trading a car in for another made by the same manufacturer—you usually will get a higher value that way.

Philip Reed, senior consumer advice editor, Edmunds. com, which analyzes car-pricing trends and reviews vehicles. He was quoted online at *www.bankrate.com.*

Top Resale Values For 2011 Cars

The 2011 nonluxury class vehicles with the best future resale values are the Honda Fit, Mini Cooper, Subaru Outback, Toyota Tacoma and Ford F-Series Super Duty.

Kelley Blue Book, *www.kbb.com,* and *Automotive Lease Guide, www.alg.com.*

Not Using Your Car Much? Put It to Work

Rent out your car when you don't need it to make extra money. Online peer-to-peer rental networks let you list your car, choose hours of availability and set a price. The sites handle insurance, fuel and credit card processing, but they are available only in certain metropolitan areas, including Boston and San Francisco.

What to do: Access the sites of RelayRides (*http://relayrides.com*) and SprideShare (*http://spride.com*) to find out how their procedures work and whether you want to participate.

Bloomberg Businessweek, 1221 Avenue of the Americas, New York City 10020, *www.businessweek.com.*

How to Save Big At the Pump

Rick Doble, founder of Savvy-Discounts.com, based in Smyrna, North Carolina. He is coauthor of *Cheaper: Insiders' Tips for Saving on Everything* (Ballantine). His Web site is *www.savvy-discounts.com.*

Little tricks that can save you big bucks when you fill up your vehicle at the gas pump...*

•**Get that "Check Engine" light checked promptly.** When this dashboard warning light comes on, this often means that the vehicle's oxygen sensor has failed—and that could reduce the engine's fuel efficiency by as much as 40%.

Annual savings: Up to $928.

•**Replace your car air filter regularly.** A clogged air filter can reduce fuel efficiency by up to 10%. Filters typically last about 12 months or 12,000 miles, but inspect yours every three months. If you notice significant amounts of grime on the filter, replace it. Check your air filter every one to two months if you do a lot of driving on dirt roads. Replacing an air filter is a simple job—the vehicle's owner's manual explains how. Replacement air filters typically cost less than $15.

Annual savings: $232, not including the cost of replacement air filters.

•**Check your tire pressure at least once every three months.** Keeping tires inflated to the recommended tire pressure could boost your fuel efficiency by 10%. It also could extend the life of your tires and reduce the odds of a dangerous blowout. The proper tire pressure should

*All savings estimates are based on a gas price of $4.00 per gallon and typical vehicle use of 12,500 miles per year at 21.5 miles per gallon.

be printed in the owner's manual, inside the driver's door of the vehicle or inside the glove compartment on a sticker.

Annual savings: $232.

• **Use cruise control when traveling on an open road.** Cruise control keeps the vehicle's speed much steadier than you could on your own. Even slight surges in speed result in noticeably lower fuel efficiency.

An exception: Turn off the cruise control when driving on mountainous terrain. Trying to hold to a specific speed on steep inclines and declines tends to use more gasoline, not less gas.

Annual savings: $160 to $320.

• **Stick to the speed limit.** One recent study found that driving 65 miles per hour (mph) instead of 75 mph resulted in an average fuel savings of 12%. All vehicles with poor aerodynamics, such as vans, RVs and SUVs, are likely to save even more by slowing down.

Annual savings: Perhaps $145 to $290, depending on how much and how quickly you drive.

• **Avoid sudden starts and stops.** Coast gently to stoplights and stop signs. Accelerate conservatively. Braking hard and accelerating rapidly decrease fuel efficiency by anywhere from 5% to more than 30%. If there is more than one way to reach a destination, select the shortest route that has the fewest stop signs and stoplights.

Annual savings: Anywhere from $116 to more than $700, depending on how aggressively you drive.

• **Go easy on your air conditioner (A/C).** Modern cars have efficient A/C systems, so running the A/C won't decrease your fuel efficiency by much, but you still can save as much as 5%.

Best: Try to use the A/C when driving on highways—the drag created by open windows decreases fuel efficiency at high speeds—but open the windows when driving slowly.

Annual savings: About $60 if you use the vehicle's A/C half the time.

• **Lighten up.** Take stuff out of the trunk, and remove rarely used roof racks.

Annual savings: Around $44 for each 100 pounds removed.

Harmful Disease Lurking In Your Car?

Using water instead of windshield wiper fluid increases Legionnaire's disease risk.

Recent finding: Drivers who did not add windshield wiper fluid to the water in their car reservoirs had an increased risk for Legionnaire's disease, a rare disease that can result in severe pneumonia.

Theory: When the water in the reservoir is sprayed on the windshield, the bacteria can come through the car vents and get into the lungs of the driver and passengers, producing infection. Adding windshield wiper fluid kills infection-causing bacteria and decreases risk.

Anders Wallensten, MD, PhD, epidemiologist, Swedish Institute for Infectious Disease Control, Stockholm, Sweden, and coauthor of a study of 142 people, published in *European Journal of Epidemiology*.

Hybrid Health Danger

Hybrid cars may put off radiation similar to that from cell phones. The radiation comes from the electromagnetic field made by the current flowing from the batteries in the back to the motor that's in the front. An Israeli government agency is studying radiation emissions. The effects of hybrid radiation on health have not yet been determined, but a research committee in Israel has recommended against replacing diesel-powered police cars with hybrids because of medical hazards to officers exposed to radiation for long periods.

Study by a research committee funded by Israel's Ministry of Environmental Protection.

Deadly Car Dangers— *Off* the Road

Marjory Abrams, president of Boardroom Inc., 281 Tresser Blvd., Stamford, Connecticut 06901.

A coworker's friend was killed when she pulled into her driveway and jumped out of her car to speak with the real estate agent showing her house…and the car rolled onto her. Cars require 100% of your attention even when they are not on the road.

•**Rolling-vehicle danger.** People who have automatic-transmission cars should always put them in "park" when they park. Those with manual-transmission cars should leave them in gear. Parking brakes need to be checked regularly by a mechanic.

Also: Check recalls for your specific vehicle at *www.recalls.gov/nhtsa.html*.

•**Service station danger.** Static electricity can ignite gasoline vapors. According to Robert Renkes of the Petroleum Equipment Institute (PEI), such fires typically occur when people start the pump, get back into their vehicles to talk or stay warm, then go back out and touch the nozzle. (You can view a video of a refueling fire at *www.pei.org/static*.) *Dos and don'ts from the PEI and the National Fire Protection Association (NFPA)*…

•Do not get into your car while refueling. Sliding against a fabric or leather seat can create static electricity. If you do get into the car, discharge any electricity by first touching metal on the outside of the car—away from the gas tank—before removing the nozzle.

•After refueling, leave the nozzle in place for a few seconds to avoid drips.

•If a fire starts during refueling, don't remove the nozzle or try to stop the flow. Leave the area, and call for help.

•**Carbon monoxide (CO) danger.** If you need to warm up a vehicle, pull out of the garage immediately after starting it. A study published in *American Journal of Public Health* shows that most CO garage deaths occur despite open doors or windows.

•**Trunk-entrapment danger.** Most trunk-entrapment deaths occur in summer. In one two-month period, at least 11 US children died that way. Cars should be locked when adults are not nearby so that kids can't pop the trunk or get into it through fold-down seats.

Cars manufactured beyond 2001 have emergency trunk releases, which offer glow-in-the-dark handles, inside of the trunk. Older cars can be retrofitted using the $18 kit,* available from AAble Locksmiths (203-882-0600, *www. aable locksmiths.com*).

*Price subject to change.

A Smart Brake System

There are now brake systems that prevent unintended acceleration. The brake-override system—known as smart pedals—senses when brakes are pressed while the gas pedal is engaged. The smart brake system interrupts the electronic signal that keeps the car moving forward, and the vehicle slows down to a safe idle speed. The system, which costs only $1 to $3 per vehicle* to produce in at the factory, is already in use on all Mercedes, BMW, Volkswagen, Audi, Nissan and Infiniti models. Toyota recently started installing these systems as standard on Toyota and Lexus models and will add it to some older vehicles during recall-related repairs.

USA Today, www.usatoday.com.

*Prices subject to change.

What Teen Drivers Need To Know Right *Now*

Half of teenagers talk on cell phones while driving…and one-third of teens of driving age send text messages while driving. This is in spite of mounting evidence showing the dangers of inattention and distraction when driving. Talk to your teen about the dangers.

Amanda Lenhart, senior research specialist, Pew Research Center's Internet and American Life Project, University of Michigan, Ann Arbor, and author of a study of 800 teens, published at *www.pewinternet.org*.

More Towns Charging Accident Fees

Some car accident victims are being asked to pay for emergency municipal services, such as police and ambulances. To raise money, some local governments are charging accident-response fees, also known as crash taxes. In most places, only nonresidents get a bill. In a few places, only those found to be at fault are billed.

Mary Bonelli, senior vice president, Ohio Insurance Institute, Columbus, *www.ohioinsurance.org.*

Hybrid Hazard

Hybrid cars injure more pedestrians than traditional-engine vehicles. The chance of hitting a pedestrian is 50% higher for hybrids in regions with speed limits of 35 miles per hour or less. At low speeds, hybrids operate on electric power, so it is harder for them to be heard.

Refaat Hanna, MD, statistician, National Highway Traffic Safety Administration, Washington, DC, *www.nhtsa.gov,* and leader of a study of collisions in 12 states.

Car That Racks Up The Most Tickets

Mercedes SL drivers tend to get the most traffic tickets. Drivers of this sports car collect four times as many tickets for moving violations as drivers of other cars, on average. The second-most-ticketed car is the now-discontinued Toyota Camry Solara convertible.

Robert U'Ren, senior vice president, Quality Planning, Jersey City, which reviewed data on about two million cars, *www.qualityplanning.com.*

Stricter Speeding Fines

You could be fined for driving just barely beyond the posted speed limit. Police and state troopers have traditionally given drivers a five- to 10-mile-per-hour (mph) "cushion" before enforcing the speed restriction, so if you were driving 60 mph in a 55-mph zone, it almost always would be overlooked by law enforcement. But now cities and states are trying to increase revenues, so police are giving out fewer warnings and writing more tickets for small speeding violations. Enforcement varies by location. Of course, always drive carefully.

James Baxter, president of National Motorists Association, Waunakee, Wisconsin, *www.motorists.org.*

How to Be Sure Your Car Is Safe for Winter

Paul Brand, motoring columnist for the *Star Tribune* in Minneapolis for the past 23 years, *www.startribune. com.* He is author of *How to Repair Your Car* and *How to Repair Your Pickup or SUV* (both from Motorbooks). He also is a driving instructor with the Skip Barber Racing School and teaches law-enforcement pursuit driving. He is based in Lake Placid, Florida.

Winter weather brings slippery roads and reduced visibility. Is your car up to the challenge? *Simple things to do to keep your car running safely next winter…*

TIRES

•**Check tire condition—but not the old-fashioned way.** Car owners often are advised to use a quarter to gauge tire tread. According to this advice, if the top of Washington's head disappears into a groove between the treads, the tire still has at least $\frac{5}{32}$ of an inch of tread and remains viable. That is fine for summer, but when you drive in snow or ice, anything less than $\frac{5}{32}$ of an inch of tread increases the risk for skids.

Put away the quarter, and buy a tire-tread gauge, available in auto-parts stores for around

261

$5.* If the reading is less than ⁵⁄₃₂ of an inch, replace your tires with a new set of all-weather tires or, even better, set them aside until spring in favor of a set of winter/snow tires.

Helpful: Make sure that any tire you use carries the rating "M+S" (sometimes written as MS, M/S or M&S) on its sidewall. This means the tire meets the Rubber Manufacturer Association's standards for use in mud and snow.

• **Increase tire pressure to the upper limit of the vehicle's acceptable tire pressure range.** Tires lose around one pound of pressure for every 10°F that the outside temperature drops. If you fail to add air in late autumn, your tires are likely to be badly underinflated by the dead of winter. Driving on underinflated tires not only reduces gas mileage and tire life, it reduces traction.

Maintain the tire pressure that is recommended on the sticker inside your car's driver-side doorpost, gas cap or glove compartment door—*not* the one on the sidewall of the tires. The inflation figures on sidewalls are the recommended air pressure for a maximum load, not the recommended pressure for your car.

WINDOWS

• **Top off the windshield washer reservoir,** and store an extra bottle of washer fluid in the trunk. Drivers use up washer fluid very quickly during winter storms.

• **Replace wiper blades with special winter blades.** Your current blades still might be up to the job of clearing away rain, but fresh blades will be stronger, sharper-edged and better able to cope with ice and snow.

Select a "winter blade" that has a rubber covering around the blade's structural elements. This covering prevents the parts of the blade that need to flex from freezing, increasing the odds that the blade will work in the cold.

Don't pay extra for winter blades that claim to be made from special high-tech materials or that are heated. These features are just marketing gimmicks that do nothing.

Helpful: When you use a gas station squeegee to clean the exterior of car windows, also run the squeegee's sponge along the surface

*Prices subject to change.

of your wiper blades that comes in contact with your windshield.

• **Give your windows and windshield a thorough cleaning on the *inside*.** Even drivers who diligently clean the exteriors of their cars' windows and windshield often neglect interior glass surfaces. These interior surfaces can collect fingerprints and dog-nose prints, which are not very visible in warmer weather. When temperatures drop during the winter, however, moisture adheres to the prints, increasing window fogging and decreasing visibility.

Use a "foaming" automotive glass cleaner to remove smudges from interior glass. Foaming cleaners won't run down the glass and into defrosters or doors. Use a wadded newspaper to wipe the glass cleaner away, as newspaper doesn't leave lint and cleans well.

WINTER-PROOFING MAINTENANCE

• **If you change your own oil, do it before it gets cold.** It's no fun to crawl under a car in a frozen garage or driveway. Check the levels of coolant, brake fluid and power steering fluid before the cold arrives as well.

If it's too late, do not put off a required oil change until the next warm period. Pay $20 or $30 to have a pro do it.

• **Replace the cabin air filter.** If you live in a cold location, you likely drive with your windows rolled up all winter long. The quality of the air in your vehicle until spring depends on the condition of the cabin air filter. An old, clogged cabin air filter also can reduce the effectiveness of your windshield defroster.

Replacing these filters is an easy do-it-yourself job in some vehicles but requires removing several parts in others. If your vehicle's manual doesn't provide the directions, ask an auto-parts store employee if this is an easy do-it-yourself task with your vehicle. A replacement air filter costs about $10 to $15.

Note: Some cars more than 20 years old do not have cabin air filters at all.

• **Apply a silicon spray to the car's rubber door gaskets.** This reduces the odds that the gaskets will freeze to the frame and prevent entry or exit. Spray a small amount of aerosol lubricant into your car's door locks, so the locks don't freeze shut.

17

Happy Home Life

Five-Minute Marriage Makeover: Little Ways to Fall in Love Again

The heart-pounding physical attraction of new love can bring a couple together, but it can't keep them together. This intense physical attraction usually fades within six months to two years into a marriage.

Long-term love may not have the same passion, but its depth and tenderness can be even more satisfying. That type of satisfaction does not come automatically. For committed couples, keeping romance alive takes attention.

Yet even busy couples can reignite the spark by spending just a few minutes a day giving each other the right kind of attentiveness...

CLASSIC CONNECTION BUILDERS

• **Greet each other with a 10-second hug.** A peck on the lips and a quick squeeze does not give you time to bond after you have been apart all day. Ten seconds is enough to get the attachment hormone oxytocin flowing in your system.

• **Touch when you pass.** Make contact any time you pass each other in the house, whether with a sensual stroke along the small of the back or a quick high five.

• **Go to bed at the same time.** Even if one of you is a lark and the other an owl, don't miss out on a special connection during bedtime. Snuggle together in bed until the lark falls asleep—then the owl can get up and continue with the evening.

• **Leave each other love notes**—on the refrigerator, on the bathroom mirror or in your partner's jacket pocket.

• **Meet for lunch.** Getting together during the middle of the workday offers a different

Barton Goldsmith, PhD, a psychotherapist located in Westlake Village, California. He is a syndicated columnist and radio host. His books include *Emotional Fitness for Intimacy: Sweeten & Deepen Your Love in Only 10 Minutes a Day* (New Harbinger). His Web site is *www.bartongoldsmith.com.*

dimension to both your lives. Pack a picnic basket, brown-bag it or meet at a restaurant.

• **Make dinner together.** Food is sensual, and preparing it together can be powerfully bonding. Then eat by candlelight.

• **Write your companion a thank-you note every time he/she gives you a gift or does something special for you,** no matter how small. As you are writing it, allow yourself to feel deserving of admiration, and allow your heart to fill with gratitude for your lover.

FAST AND SIMPLE ADVENTURES

• **Schedule an "unplan" day.** Agree to get up on a weekend morning, and go somewhere neither of you has previously chosen. Get in the car, flip a coin, let it land on the local map and start driving in that direction. When you see something that looks interesting, stop and check it out. Have lunch, and decide whether to keep going or drive back. Take a different route home.

• **Create an adoration list.** Ask your partner to write down seven nonmaterial things that would make him/her feel cherished and loved by you, and make a similar list yourself.

Examples: Getting served breakfast in bed…going sailing together…celebrating the anniversary of your first date…getting a back rub without asking for one.

Exchange lists and start planning these special treats for each other.

• **Give each other a makeover.** Go to the mall—or a high-end boutique—and pick out some items that you would like to see each other wear. Have fun trying on new clothes for each other.

• **Play tourist.** Whenever you read in the paper or online about an unusual local place that welcomes visitors—a wildflower farm, a brewery, a historic landmark—save the information and schedule an excursion.

CREATIVE INTIMACY ENHANCERS

Each of these exercises takes only a few minutes and lets you experience your partner in an unexpected way.

You might try one of these before you go on a "date." Your time together will have new excitement.

• **Picture the future.** Sit facing each other, with knees touching. Shut your eyes, and use three minutes to silently visualize the future that you would like to have with your partner. Open your eyes, and take turns sharing with each other what you saw. Now close your eyes again, but this time, each of you should visualize the future that the other person just described. Open your eyes, and tell each other what you experienced.

• **Play the alien game.** Pretend your partner is from another planet and knows nothing about love on Earth. Your job is to teach your new guest about love, but without speaking— only gestures and looks are allowed.

• **Touch hearts.** Put your hand over your partner's heart while your partner puts his/her hand over your heart. Feel each other's heartbeats for a minute.

• **Hug backward.** Stand back-to-back, with your backs touching, and hold hands. Spend a few minutes becoming aware of each other from this new point of view. Talk about any sensations you are noticing and any emotions that come up. Giggling is fine, too.

• **Play a game of 20 questions.** What's your partner's favorite movie? Favorite song? Think of 20 (or 10 or five) things you don't know about each other, and take turns asking questions.

Risk Factor for Marital Discord

Living together before getting engaged is a risk factor for marital trouble.

Recent finding: Partners who lived together before they were engaged had lower levels of satisfaction after getting married and more negative communication than those who waited until they were engaged to live together.

Galena K. Rhoades, PhD, senior researcher, department of psychology, University of Denver, and leader of a study of 1,050 people, published in *Journal of Family Psychology.* Her Web site is *www.rhoadesconsulting. com.*

The Surprising Reason Men and Women Cheat (It's Not Sex)

M. Gary Neuman, a licensed psychotherapist in Miami Beach, Florida, who is the creator of the Reconnect to Love Intensive Program, an all-day counseling program for couples. He is an ordained rabbi and author of *The New York Times* best seller *The Truth About Cheating.* His most recent book is *Connect to Love: The Keys to Transforming Your Relationship* (both from Wiley). His Web site is *www.mgaryneuman.com.*

Why do men and women have affairs? That is what I wanted to find out when I surveyed more than 700 married men and women.

Of all the men I studied, half had cheated on their wives and half had remained faithful. When I asked these unfaithful men about the reasons they were dissatisfied with their marriages at the time of their affairs, I expected sexual dissatisfaction to either top the list or be way up there. But merely 8% reported that factor to have been the problem. Almost half (48%) stated emotional dissatisfaction to have been the primary issue. I was dumbfounded. Clearly, men have more emotional needs than most people assume.

Here, more truths about why husbands and wives cheat and what we all can do to boost the odds that our partners will stay faithful...

HUSBANDS WHO CHEAT

Approximately half of all married men will cheat on their wives at some point during the marriage. *What wives can do to keep their husbands faithful...*

•**Show more appreciation for what he does and less disappointment for what he doesn't do.** Saying "thank you" is a start, but actually *showing* appreciation is even better—most men value deeds over words.

Examples: Give him back rubs...cook his favorite meals...buy his favorite magazine.

•**Show appreciation even if he's only doing those things that you expect him to do** and even if he never verbalizes his desire for appreciation. Express your thankfulness for his hard work earning money for the family, even if you work just as hard or earn more money. Men are under tremendous societal pressure to provide for their families and often feel underappreciated when their efforts in this area go unacknowledged.

Some wives fear that if they show appreciation, their husbands will conclude that they must be doing enough and stop trying to do more. In reality, it is the unappreciated husbands who are not likely to try harder—and more likely to seek out the appreciation that they need from other women.

•**Keep an eye on his friends.** Wives typically worry when their husbands form friendships with other women. But sometimes it is the husband's relationships with other men that increase the odds of an affair. When married men have male friends who cheat and brag about it, it greatly increases the odds that they will cheat, too.

Wives often have a sense of which of their husbands' friends are unfaithful. The question is what to do about it? Husbands tend to ignore wives' requests to avoid particular friends.

Instead, encourage your husband to invite his friend over to your home rather than see him elsewhere. The closer you are when your husband is with this man, the less likely the conversation is to turn to extramarital affairs.

Meanwhile, arrange for you and your husband to spend as much time as possible with friends who are happily married. The more time couples spend together with couples who seem happy and faithful, the greater the odds that they will be happy and faithful, too.

Helpful: If infidelity comes up in conversation, tell your husband, "If one of my friends ever cheated, I'd understand if you wouldn't want me to spend time with her. I'm just asking you to bring him to our house more and spend less time with him." This gets the point across without making your husband feel as if you're ordering him not to spend time with his friend.

•**Ask him about his father.** Studies have shown that if a husband knows that his father cheated, it greatly increases the odds that he will cheat.

To find out more about his father, ask him some questions like, "What was your parents' marriage like when you were a kid?" and "Did your dad ever do anything inappropriate that you knew about?" If your father-in-law was unfaithful, this helps to heighten your husband's day-to-day awareness of it, reducing the odds that the same behavior pattern will sneak up on him.

Warning: Do not criticize your father-in-law—that might make your husband feel the need to defend his father. Also, do not warn your husband outright that his father's cheating increases the odds that he will cheat—he might take this as an accusation.

WIVES WHO CHEAT

Wives do cheat nearly as often as husbands. Unfaithful wives often cannot pinpoint a single cause for their affairs. *In spite of this, there are some specific things that husbands can do to reduce the odds of infidelity...*

• **Find time to talk.** Wives who say that they are happy and faithful also tend to say that they spend at least 30 uninterrupted minutes every day talking with their husbands. Wives who report that they are unhappy and/or unfaithful tend to say that they speak with their husbands for less than 30 minutes per day.

Unfortunately, many husbands strive for efficiency in conversation, discussing important matters as quickly as possible and avoiding all chitchat entirely. More men need to understand what most women already understand—that time spent just hanging out and relaxing and chitchatting with each other is crucial to relationships.

What to do: Every day, find at least a half-hour to talk to your spouse without interruption from the TV, cell phones or kids. Make a mental note of interesting newspaper articles and personal experiences throughout the day. When couples talk daily, they begin to think of each other throughout the day when things come up and they mark these things in their minds to share later.

• **Say "I understand" when she discusses her problems.** Unfaithful wives often report that one reason for the affair was their husbands' inability to understand them.

The simplest way to convince your wife that you understand her is to reply, "I understand," when she shares her problems. Also ask lots of follow-up questions, such as, "What happened next?" and "How did that make you feel?" Provide your opinion or potential solutions to her problems only if she specifically requests this.

Helpful: Husbands sometimes avoid telling their wives "I understand" out of fear that this understanding will be misconstrued as assent to the wife's opinion. However, women tend to be better than men at grasping the difference between the responses "I understand" and "I agree."

• **Show appreciation for what she does.** Husbands aren't the only ones who appreciate appreciation. Showing that you care and are grateful for what they do keeps wives faithful, too.

The good news for husbands is that women are far better than men at sharing what makes them feel appreciated, so it takes all the guesswork out of it. And even small gestures such as thank-yous, hugs, kisses or unexpected token gifts such as flowers go a long way toward making wives feel wanted.

One Little Word That Can Change Your Marriage

Couples who use the pronoun *we* behave in more beneficial ways during disagreements. Couples who regularly talk about their conflicts by saying *we*, *our* and *us* show more affection and less anger during an argument. Couples who regularly use pronouns that express separateness—such as *I*, *you* and *me*—have lower levels of marital satisfaction. Using the word *we* during arguments may help couples align themselves on the same team.

Benjamin Seider, a graduate student in psychology at University of California, Berkeley, and lead author of a laboratory study of 154 couples, published in *Psychology and Aging*.

Don't Let Boredom Creep In

Couples who are bored with their marriage after seven years are likely to be dissatisfied with their marriage at year 16—even if there had not been obvious tensions or conflicts in the seventh year.

Self-defense: Share unique and challenging experiences to prevent boredom from developing in your relationship.

Irene Tsapelas, PhD candidate, Stony Brook University, Stony Brook, New York, and author of a survey of 123 married couples, published in *Psychological Science*.

How Being *Too Supportive* Can Harm Your Marriage

Giving too much support—usually as unwanted advice—is a bigger risk factor for marital unhappiness than not giving enough support.

Reason: Someone who does not get enough support from a spouse can get more from family and friends, but someone who is given too much support cannot escape it.

Erika Lawrence, PhD, an associate professor, department of psychology, University of Iowa, Iowa City, and leader of a study of 103 husbands and wives, published in *Journal of Family Psychology*.

Most Marriages Survive Infidelity

When the man admits to an affair, 70% to 80% of marriages survive...and when the woman admits to an affair, 60% to 70% survive. A woman's affair usually fulfills her emotional and sexual needs better than the marriage does. Male affairs are usually "high-opportunity/low-involvement affairs," very often one-night encounters.

Barry McCarthy, PhD, sex therapist and psychology professor, American University, Washington, DC.

Facebook Fosters Divorce

Facebook is a growing cause of divorce. At some law firms, as many as 20% of divorce petitions name the social-networking site Facebook as a contributor to the divorce. The most frequent reason Facebook was mentioned was because of inappropriate sexual chats and flirtatious behavior with people met online.

Mark Keenan, the founder and managing director of Divorce-Online, divorce information and resource firm, Swindon, UK, *www.divorce-online.co.uk*.

Want a Divorce but Can't Afford It? How To Live Together— *Peacefully*

Joel D. Block, PhD, an assistant clinical professor of psychiatry at Albert Einstein College of Medicine in the Bronx and senior psychologist at North Shore–Long Island Jewish Medical Center, Glen Oaks, New York. He is author of *Naked Intimacy: How to Increase True Openness in Your Relationship* and *Broken Promises, Mended Hearts: Maintaining Trust in Love Relationships* (both McGraw-Hill). His Web site is *www.drblock.com*.

You would like a divorce, but the legal fees and cost of two residences are beyond your means. For now, you have to continue living together. *How to make this work...*

IF THERE ARE CHILDREN AT HOME

•**Explain to the children that you have decided to sleep apart and live apart (together) in the house.** The essence of your statement goes something like this, "We have given our best effort to making this marriage work, and we have not been successful. We have decided to stay together but to live as independently of each other as possible. Nothing we do will change our love and caring for you..." Children need certainty and are better off knowing what's happening than wondering about it and drawing their own (perhaps frightening) conclusions.

● **Establish a code of behavior.** Arguing in front of the children is always harmful and so is speaking negatively about the other parent. An agreement defining acceptable behavior should be drawn up in writing and signed by both partners.

Example: "Rather than airing grievances in front of the children, they will be aired privately every Tuesday evening."

Also, if either or both of you decide to date while you still live together, people you're dating should not come to the home.

● **Divide up care of children.** Who is in charge of whom, and when, must be carefully defined. And block out times for separate vacations. If they are to be without the children, plan for coverage.

MONEY AND SPACE

● **Divide up the expenses if both partners work.** Whatever you decide should not be viewed as "forever" but renegotiated each year.

● **Write a list of household chores, and split them equitably.**

● **Decide who sleeps where.** If there are separate bathrooms, it's better if each has his/her own. (As a courtesy, notify the other partner if you plan to have guests sleep over.)

● **Get separate phone lines.** Separate phone lines with password-protected voice mail are worth the expense to maintain your privacy. Password protected e-mail accounts also are suggested.

● **Reassess the situation periodically.** The financial hardship of a divorce should be periodically weighed against a living arrangement that may slowly eat away at integrity and well-being. Living together but estranged is not recommended for the long term.

New Fathers Suffer from Postpartum Depression, Too

About 10.4% of American men become depressed either during their mate's pregnancy or in the year following the baby's birth.

Reason: Pregnancy and new parenthood are times of immense change and anxiety for both parents—including an overall rethinking of life roles, from being independent adults to parents who are responsible for an infant. Symptoms include persistent sadness and/or irritability... low energy...changes in sleep and appetite... persistent negative thinking...feelings of hopelessness...and loss of interest in hobbies.

Self-defense: Learn about the symptoms at the Web site of the National Institute of Mental Health (*www.nimh.nih.gov*) and/or by speaking with your primary care physician or a specialty mental health professional.

James Paulson, PhD, an associate professor of pediatrics at Eastern Virginia Medical School, Norfolk, and the leader of a study of 28,004 men, published in *The Journal of the American Medical Association*.

SIDS Alert

Sudden infant death is linked to low levels of *serotonin* in the brain. The brain chemical serotonin helps babies wake up and move their heads to take in more air when there are high levels of carbon dioxide around them. Babies with low levels of serotonin may not sense the high carbon-dioxide levels—and fail to wake up, resulting in *sudden infant death syndrome* (SIDS).

Best: Always put infants to sleep on their backs, never on their stomachs, on a firm surface with *no* toys, loose bedding, pillows or blankets.

Hannah Kinney, MD, associate professor of pathology, Harvard Medical School and Children's Hospital, both in Boston, and leader of an autopsy study published in *The Journal of the American Medical Association*.

Vaccine Combo Can Cause Seizures

Combining vaccinations increases risk for fever-related seizures in toddlers. The measles, mumps and rubella (MMR) and chicken pox vaccines often are administered in a four-in-one combination shot that's known as the *ProQuad*.

Recent finding: Children ages one to two who receive the ProQuad shot are twice as likely to suffer seizures within seven to 10 days after the injection than children who receive separate MMR and chicken pox vaccines.

Nicola Klein, MD, PhD, codirector, Kaiser Permanente Vaccine Study Center, Oakland, California, and author of a study of 459,461 children, published in *Pediatrics*.

Leading Choking Hazard For Kids

Over 10,000 kids are treated for choking each year in US emergency rooms. Hot dogs cause roughly 17% of choking incidents among kids under age 10. The American Academy of Pediatrics wants hot dogs "redesigned" so that they are less likely to cause choking.

USA Today, www.usatoday.com.

A Better Test for Food Allergies in Kids

Kids diagnosed with food allergies might not have them at all, as blood and skin tests do not necessarily indicate a *true* allergic response. These tests measure the level of the antibody *immunoglobulin E* (IgE), which the body may produce in response to a food. But having IgE antibodies does not necessarily mean that a person will develop allergic symptoms from eating the food.

More accurate: An oral food challenge test, in which doctors give a child tiny amounts of various foods to ingest and closely watch for signs of a reaction. But food challenge testing is time-consuming and expensive, so parents generally prefer the quicker and easier blood and skin tests.

Hugh Sampson, MD, professor of pediatrics, division of allergy and immunology, Mount Sinai School of Medicine, New York City.

How Family Meals Help Kids with Asthma

Family mealtimes help asthmatic children by decreasing their anxiety—so their lung function improves. Children with asthma frequently have separation anxiety—they worry about being away from their parents in case of a breathing emergency. Positive interaction at family meals reduces asthmatic children's worries and can help them breathe more easily.

Barbara H. Fiese, PhD, professor of human development and family studies, University of Illinois, Chicago, director of the university's Family Resiliency Center and leader of a study published in *Journal of Child Psychology and Psychiatry*.

Beach Sand Alert

Digging in beach sand can make children sick.

Recent finding: Children under the age of 11 who dig in beach sand have a 44% greater risk for diarrhea than those who do not dig in the sand.

Reason: Beach sand can contain dangerous bacteria, including *E.coli* and *enterococcus* from sewage outfalls, storm-water runoff and domestic and wild animals.

Chris Heaney, PhD, epidemiologist, researcher, University of North Carolina at Chapel Hill, and leader of a study of 27,365 people who had visited seven US beaches, published in *American Journal of Epidemiology*.

Playground Danger

Going down a playground slide with your child on your lap can lead to injuries.

Recent finding: 13.8% of *tibia* (shin) fractures in children were the result of the child going down a slide on an adult's lap. Injuries occur when the child's leg gets stuck in one place while the adult and child continue moving down the slide.

John T. Gaffney, MD, American Academy of Orthopaedic Surgeons fellow, Winthrop University Hospital, Mineola, New York, and author of an 11-month study on child injuries, published in the *Journal of Pediatric Orthopaedics*.

Bounce House Health Hazard

Inflatable bounce houses have high levels of lead. In lab tests by a California advocacy group, the vinyl used to make the houses, commonly used at children's parties, was found to contain more than 70 times the federal limit for lead in children's products.

Self-defense: Be sure that children wash their hands and faces with soap and water after using bounce houses to avoid getting lead in their mouths. Just using sanitizer won't get rid of the lead. Once you get home, have children change clothes and then put the clothes right into the washer.

Study by Center for Environmental Health, Oakland, California, *www.ceh.org*.

How to Deal with a Cranky Child

Remain calm when dealing with an irritable child. Often, the child is upset when he or she feels as if the world is demanding more than he is capable of. His behavior is not directed at you personally. Don't attempt a quick fix. Authoritative directives, such as "Sit down and be quiet," don't teach the child any helpful coping skills. Empathize with the child—saying that you do understand will help to soothe him. Encourage the child to communicate with you. Ask questions to understand what is bothering him. Teaching a child how to identify and express his feelings helps him learn to cope when he is upset.

Psychology Today, 115 E. 23 St., New York City 10010, *www.psychologytoday.com*.

Is It Really ADHD?

Attention-deficit/hyperactivity disorder (ADHD) may have been misdiagnosed in more than one million children. Children who are the youngest in their grades are 60% more likely to be diagnosed with ADHD than older children in the same grade. ADHD symptoms are synonymous with immaturity—the inability to stay on task, being "squirmy," etc.

Todd Elder, PhD, assistant professor of economics, Michigan State University, East Lansing, and leader of a study of nearly 12,000 children, published in *Journal of Health Economics*.

What You Need to Know Now If Your Child Has ADHD

Children diagnosed with *attention-deficit/ hyperactivity disorder* (ADHD) are at higher risk for depression and suicide.

Recent finding: 12% of children diagnosed with ADHD between ages four and six had a plan for suicide at least once between the ages of nine and 18, compared with 1.6% of children who weren't diagnosed with ADHD.

Best: Seek help from a clinical psychologist or child psychiatrist to avoid this outcome.

Benjamin B. Lahey, PhD, professor in the department of epidemiology, University of Chicago, and leader of a study of 248 children, published in *Archives of General Psychiatry*.

Are Kids Getting Their Drugs from YOU? The Appalling Truth About Teen Substance Abuse

Robert Stutman, a 25-year veteran of the Drug Enforcement Administration (DEA). He served as special agent in charge of several DEA field divisions, including the New York field division, the country's largest. In 1990, Stutman founded The Stutman Group, a consulting company that designs and implements substance-abuse prevention programs in Boca Raton, Florida. He is special consultant on substance abuse for CBS News and speaks to more than 100 groups a year. *www.thestutmangroup.com.*

America's drug problem is staggering. Illegal use of drugs has now climbed to 20 million Americans.

Even more shocking: Many addicts began abusing drugs or alcohol as kids under the watchful eye of well-intentioned parents.

Parents fail to take steps that might direct their kids away from addiction because they don't fully understand how much drug use has changed since they were young. Today there are different drugs, different dangers and a different demographic of young people who are at risk. *Here's what parents need to know now...*

• **Drug abuse begins early.** A generation ago, the average age of first drug use among eventual users was 15. Currently the average starting age is alarmingly low—12 or 13. This is a huge problem because the younger people are when they first try drugs, the greater the odds that they will become addicted.

Important: Begin speaking with your kids about the dangers of drugs before they even set foot in junior high school (see the article on the following page). By high school, it may be too late.

• **The drugs that teens abuse today are not the ones your generation used.** Today young people are much more likely to abuse prescription medications than marijuana and LSD. In fact, one in five high school students have taken a prescription drug that they didn't get from a physician. Teens almost always get their pharmaceutical drugs from their parents'

medicine cabinets or the cabinets of friends' parents.

Dozens of different pharmaceuticals can be abused. As a rule of thumb, if there's a sticker on a pill bottle warning against driving after use, it's likely that teens take the drug to get high. Even over-the-counter medications such as cough suppressants are abused.

If anyone in your house is prescribed a medication that has a warning sticker about driving after use, buy a lockbox or a safe and lock up these pills. Do this even if you trust your kids completely—you don't want your kids' friends or your babysitter to be tempted.

• **Abusing prescription medicine often is more risky than abusing illegal drugs.** Many teens—and even parents—incorrectly assume that anything prescribed by a doctor can't be all that dangerous. In truth, many prescription medicines are extremely dangerous when not used as intended.

Example: OxyContin is a time-release pill that is designed to suppress pain over six to eight hours. Drug abusers crush up these pills into powder so that the full dose is absorbed at once.

Fact: Very soon, fatalities from misuse of prescription medications are likely to surpass auto accidents as the single leading cause of accidental death in the US.

• **Drug abuse is not just a problem for cities, minorities, the poor and kids who underachieve in school.** Rural and suburban kids are just as likely as city kids to abuse drugs or alcohol—perhaps even slightly more likely.

White kids are as likely as African-American kids to do so. Private school kids are as likely as kids at public school. Teens on sports teams are just as likely to abuse drugs as any other teen. Teens who do well in school are somewhat less likely to misuse drugs and alcohol than those who do poorly, but good grades are not the ironclad evidence of nonuse that many parents imagine them to be. Even smart kids can be drug users, and some of them are smart enough to maintain their grades after they start using.

• **Those who start drinking as teens are almost twice as likely to become alcoholics.** Alcohol is the most socially acceptable drug in our culture, but that doesn't mean it's not dangerous. Drinking just one or two alcoholic drinks is not a problem for most adults, but when teens drink, they almost never stop at just one or two—they consume until they are intoxicated.

The teenage brain is especially prone to addiction, including alcohol addiction, because it is still developing. Those who start drinking as teens or preteens are approximately twice as likely to become alcoholics as those who wait until their 20s.

• **Do not drink to get drunk in front of your child**—even if your child is still too young to fully understand what drinking means. As early as age two, children begin forming life-long beliefs and behaviors based on what they see their parents doing.

And, certainly never allow your teens to get drunk in your presence. Some parents permit their teens to drink at home because they think this is safer than the teens drinking elsewhere and then driving home. I am somewhat sympathetic to this thinking, though studies suggest that teens who drink with their parents are slightly more likely to become alcoholics than those who do not. I am not sympathetic when parents allow kids to drink to the point of drunkenness at home. That only increases the odds of future drinking problems.

More from Robert Stutman…

What Every Parent Must Do

Many parents believe that nothing they do or say about drugs gets through to their teens. While it's true that parents cannot control their teens completely, all kids learn important life lessons from their parents—even when neither parent nor child realizes that learning is taking place.

• **Have dinner as a family as often as possible.** Families that eat together are much less likely to have kids who become addicts. Children who have dinner with their parents at least three times a week are less likely to develop drug or alcohol problems.

• **Tell your children regularly and emphatically that you want them to stay away from drugs,** including alcohol and prescription medications. Your teens might roll their eyes, but at some level, your words are likely to have an effect—studies now show that kids who realize their parents care whether they use drugs are less likely to use them.

Helpful: For information about talking with children about drugs, see *How to Raise a Drug-Free Kid* by Joseph Califano, Jr. (Fireside)…and explore the links section on my Web site (*www. thestutmangroup.com*, then click "Links").

• **Confront your teen if you smell cigarette smoke on his/her clothes or discover other evidence of tobacco use.** Teens who use tobacco are at greater risk than nontobacco users of becoming drug addicts. If you smoke, quit.

• **Inform your teens that if one of their friends ever passes out from drinking or drug abuse in their presence,** they should immediately roll this person onto his/her side (to prevent suffocation if the person vomits), then phone 911. Thousands of lives would be saved if every teen knew this.

Social Networking Identity Theft Threat

Prevent a child's identity theft on Facebook by making sure that he/she does not post his complete birth date or address and uses the "friends only" privacy setting.

Also: Explain to him what sorts of postings might make a bad impression on colleges and potential employers. And if he wants to make purchases on Facebook, be sure that he does not store the PayPal password on his Internet browser and doesn't bill anything to you without your permission.

Money, Time-Life Bldg., Rockefeller Center, New York City 10020, *http://money.cnn.com*.

Are Your Teens Addicted To Facebook?

Facebook can become an addiction. Some teenagers do recognize this and voluntarily cut back on using the social-networking site, for example, by deactivating their accounts or having someone change their passwords and keep control of the passwords until the user is ready to have them back. Facebook has 350 million members of all ages who collectively spend 10 billion minutes at the site every day. An average user spends more than 55 minutes per day on Facebook.

Kimberly Young, PsyD, psychologist and director, Center for Internet Addiction Recovery, Bradford, Pennsylvania, www.netaddiction.com.

Teach Teens About Money

Most parents consider their teens "quick spenders" and believe that their teens do not have enough guidance about the financial realities of adult life. But only one-third of parents have taught teens how to balance a checkbook…only 29% have explained how credit card interest and fees work…and just 20% involve teenagers to a significant extent in family budgeting and spending decisions—with 25% saying that they do not involve their teenagers at all.

What to do: When possible, include teens in discussions about household finances. Give teens an allowance, and stick to it. Encourage teens to get part-time or summer jobs. Teach them about credit cards and checkbooks. Help teens to make automatic savings part of their lives, perhaps by partially matching what they save—for example, 25 cents on the dollar.

Parents & Money survey of 1,000 American parents with teens ages 13 to 18, conducted by Kelton Research on behalf of Charles Schwab Foundation.

How to Get Along Better With Your Kids, Grand-Kids, Young Coworkers

Lynne C. Lancaster, cofounder and partner of Bridge-Works, LLC, a consulting, research and training company that specializes in bridging the generation gap, located in Sonoma, California. She is coauthor of The M-Factor: How the Millennial Generation Is Rocking the Workplace *(Harper Business). Her Web site is http://generations.com.*

Many of the "Echo Boomers"—people born between 1982 and 2000—are our children or grandchildren. Some even may be our employees, colleagues and service providers.

The better we understand this generation—sometimes called the "Millennial Generation" or "Generation Y"—the better we will be able to get along with its members and even learn from them.

This generation exhibits significantly different priorities, expectations, attitudes and work styles than those who came before, even when compared with their immediate predecessors, Generation X.

Example: While Gen Xers tend to be independent and entrepreneurial, most Millennials prefer to work in collaborative teams.

Seven things that are worth knowing about Millennials…

1. They're very close to their parents. Past generations often rebelled against their parents as they reached adulthood. Not this one. Many Millennials consider their parents to be their most valued advisers. That is generally a positive trait, but this can lead to some very uncomfortable situations, particularly in your workplace—more than 10% of adult Millennials think it's OK to have a parent contact their manager when they have a problem. Yes, the times have changed.

Response: If a Millennial in your life leans so heavily on his or her parents that he is not developing life skills, try to give this person responsibilities that provide these skills.

Example: A grandmother asks her teenage grandson to figure out how and where to get her broken lawn mower fixed and to coordinate the repairs with the repairman.

2. They expect to start at the top. Millennials' parents and teachers continually showered them with praise to build up their self-esteem. This might have worked a bit too well—many members of this generation seem to expect to start at the top and climb rapidly from there. Even the recent recessionary job market has not taught them humility. Employers often are shocked when Millennials boldly ask for raises and promotions after just months on the job.

Response: If a Millennial asks for more than he has earned, remind yourself that what appears to be a sense of entitlement sometimes is just poorly expressed ambition. There is nothing wrong with being ambitious. Explain to the Millennial that others have worked long and hard to earn what the Millennial is asking for, so the request could be seen as disrespectful. Then offer to provide opportunities for learning or growth that will help the Millennial move in the direction that he wishes to go.

Example: A Millennial desires to be put in the lead of an important project with her neighborhood association. But the association president instead offers to make her the special assistant to the more experienced project manager so that she can learn the ropes before taking a leadership role.

3. They expect their careers to have meaning. More than 50% of adult Millennials say they would accept a reduced salary or a less prestigious job to do work that is meaningful. More than 90% say that it is important to them to give back to the community via their companies.

Response: When you recruit or market to the Millennials, emphasize how your company improves the world or the region. Connect Millennials' contributions back to the company's or group's central goals if this connection is not obvious.

Example: A Millennial receptionist is dissatisfied with her job, which she sees as meaningless. The CEO of the company explains to her that providing superior customer service is crucial for client retention in the company's competitive sector and that the receptionist's

efforts are a crucial part of that customer service. He shows the receptionist a note he received from an important client praising the friendly greetings he receives when he calls.

4. They have great expectations but little experience to caution them when those expectations are not so reasonable. Millennials frequently underestimate how difficult it is to build a successful career, business or family. They often fail to consider the hidden costs involved in owning a home, investment property, boat or other major purchase.

Response: If a Millennial you know is about to make a major decision without a clear grasp of the costs or challenges, do not simply tell him what you think—such unsolicited advice often is neglected. Instead, offer to help this young person compile a list of questions that should be asked before taking the leap. Recommend that the Millennial pose these questions to someone he respects who has taken a similar leap. Help the Millennial find someone to ask if necessary.

Examples: An employer encourages Millennial job candidates to speak with other staff members about the job's day-to-day responsibilities, hours and career trajectory prior to signing on. A grandfather very concerned that his grandson is rushing into home ownership helps the young man compile a list of potential costs beyond the mortgage, such as maintenance, utilities, landscaping, homeowners insurance and taxes. The grandfather suggests that the grandson speak with an experienced home owner he trusts for a realistic estimate of these costs.

5. They move fast. Millennials grew up with high-speed Internet and superfast computer processors, and they expect the real world to move at the same accelerated speed. Sometimes this need for speed translates into productivity—but not always. The challenge for older generations is to convince Millennials that sometimes the fastest solution is not the best one.

Response: Do not just tell Millennials to do things your way. Instead, explain all the advantages of your approach. Members of this generation generally are willing to adapt to slower approaches if they understand the benefit of doing so. Meanwhile, be open to learning new, fast techniques from members of this generation. Some of their strategies have merit—particularly when dealing with other Millennials.

Example: A sales manager tells his Millennial salesman to meet with clients face-to-face, while the salesman thinks that communicating via text messages is better because it's quicker. The sales manager can explain that in-person meetings tend to create stronger, more lasting bonds—but he also should listen to what the salesman has to teach him about how members of the Millennial generation communicate. If some of this salesman's clients are Millennials, they might respond favorably to text messages. Perhaps the salesman could give texting a try with a few carefully selected clients, then both could objectively evaluate the result.

6. Social networks are their natural habitat. Members of older generations often see social network Web sites, such as Facebook, as little more than a waste of time. To many Millennials, however, these Web sites are the primary way that they prefer to communicate with other people.

Response: When you show something to or discuss something with a Millennial that you consider private, specifically tell the Millennial that the information is not to be mentioned on the Internet.

Examples: Your organization's not-yet-announced new product...an embarrassing fact about a family member...or a less-than-flattering photo of you should be identified as off-limits online.

7. They love to collaborate—and expect to be heard. This generation grew up playing interactive Internet games with teammates sometimes a half a world away, working on school projects in groups and having unprecedented input on family decisions. They are not used to working alone.

They also quickly become frustrated when they are not included in the decision-making process.

Response: Solicit Millennials' opinions before making important decisions. They will appreciate being asked, even if you do not follow their suggestions in the end. Allow them

to collaborate with other Millennials on projects. If you attempt to have a Millennial work alone, he might collaborate informally anyway, by discussing the matter with friends. Better to keep work teams official and in-house so that you know who is involved and that confidential information remains secure.

Example: A young employee, asked to prepare a report on her own, solicits advice from her former college classmates and accidentally reveals corporate secrets in the process.

One Big Happy Family— Secrets to Staying Close To Married Kids

Susan Forward, PhD, therapist in private practice in Westlake Village, California. She has worked as therapist, instructor and consultant for many southern California psychiatric and medical facilities. She is author of several best-selling books, including *Toxic In-Laws* (Harper). Her Web site is *www.susanforward.com*.

A very wise person once said, "Parenting is the only love where the goal is separation." When a child grows older and gets married, the transition can be difficult for parents. Well-meaning parents may not realize that some of their actions may be undermining the new marriage as well as their relationships with their children. *What to do...*

• **Focus on the positive.** It is normal to feel a sense of loss that you are no longer number one in your child's life. While acknowledging this feeling of loss, be willing to shift your attention to the benefits. To do so, ask yourself all love-based questions rather than fear-based questions.

Fear-based questions focus on what you are giving up. They develop out of the assumption that there is not enough love to go around.

Examples: Will we still have family holidays together? Is my child's partner a threat to me? Will I never see my son?

The love-based questions focus on what you have to give and gain. They grow out of the assumption that love is unlimited.

Examples: What do these children and their new partners bring to my life? How does what I say or do affect them? How can I make the new person in the family feel welcomed and at ease?

• **Don't give unsolicited advice.** Even your best-intentioned suggestions are likely to be perceived as criticism. Instead, ask the couple, "Would you like some help with this?" or "I have some ideas about this situation—would you like to hear them?" Respect the answer. If they do ask for advice, do not expect or pressure them to follow it.

Helpful: Whenever you catch yourself saying or thinking the word *should*, stop. You are likely to be imposing your values on the couple. Even if you are certain that you are right, your input will not be welcome and may create a chasm between you.

Better: Pause before you speak. Take a deep breath…count silently to three…and ask yourself, *What are the potential effects of what I am about to say?*

Keeping silent can be particularly difficult where grandchildren are concerned. You may worry or disapprove when your children make child-rearing choices that you disagree with. Unless a child's safety is at risk, it is better to keep your opinions to yourself.

• **Be willing to apologize.** An apology is one of the greatest gifts parents can give their children. When you apologize, you change the balance of power. The parent becomes not as formidable, more accessible. Whether you said or did something thoughtless or you innocently pushed someone's hot button, take responsibility for doing so. If you are not sure what you did wrong, use a calm, friendly tone and the phrase "Can you help me understand…?"

Example: "I am so sorry that I upset you. Can you help me understand what about it bothered you?"

• **Maintain a healthy distance.** The line between inclusiveness and smothering can be hard to discern. Some families enjoy a great deal of contact, such as a tradition of having Sunday dinner together each week. Others are more hands-off.

No matter what your custom has been, do not assume that these traditions will continue unchanged. The young couple may want to create their own traditions.

Better: Invite, but don't pressure. Have an open discussion about what the couple would prefer.

Example: "We would love to have you at our family dinners, but we want to respect your needs, too. How much extended-family time feels comfortable to you?" Do not be surprised if their needs continue to change over time.

And never drop by for a visit unannounced, even if you used to do so before your child got married.

• **Work on yourself and develop interests apart from your children.** Take classes, join clubs and expand your circle of friends. Having a support system outside your immediate family keeps you from relying on your children to make you happy.

Despite all your best efforts, misunderstandings can arise because you or your child or your child's partner still has unresolved family conflicts that are triggered by others' behavior. Self-development is a lifelong process. Rather than assuming that you have everything under control, be willing to talk to a counselor or clergy person about issues that you could learn to handle better.

• **Do not get caught in the middle.** Never talk about your child's spouse behind his/her back. And if your child comes to you to complain about his/her spouse, avoid taking sides. The situation may only escalate, and you could be blamed.

Better: Say, "Honey, I support you and I'm here for you, but I'm not a professional and I'm not going to give you advice about what to do. If the two of you can't sort this out, I encourage you to talk it over with a counselor."

• **Keep expectations realistic.** While some sons- and daughters-in-law become beloved friends and confidants, many do not. You lack a shared history, and your preferences and tastes may be very different.

If you feel that there's a distance between yourself and your child's companion, make it a point to share some of your own experiences. Encourage the partner to tell you more about himself. You may never be best buddies, but the more he finds out about your life and you about his, the closer you two are likely to be.

If you feel that your child's spouse is not nice to you, put it out on the table. Say, "I will always try to treat you with courtesy, and I really would appreciate the same."

Make Older Relatives More Comfortable at Family Gatherings

There are several things you can do to make the oldest members of your extended family more comfortable at family get-togethers. First, offer to drive them to your home if they need assistance. Grandchildren who recently obtained their driver's licenses may be willing to help—which can lead to intergenerational bonding. Also, seat older people with physical challenges appropriately—for instance, place someone with hearing loss close to a person who can repeat parts of conversations to him/her. And, ask older adults about their life experiences so that they feel included in conversations. Consider bringing out old photograph albums for everyone to review and discuss together—another bonding experience.

Rheta Rosen, PhD, professor emerita, Ryerson University, Toronto.

Rabies Self-Defense

Most US cases of rabies are caused by bats. If a bat is found indoors, everyone exposed to it should get rabies shots, even if there is no evidence of a bite. Also, anyone who is bitten by a raccoon, skunk or fox—or by a cat or dog whose vaccine history is unknown—should be immunized against the fatal disease.

Current immunization guidelines: One immune globulin shot as soon as possible after exposure and four doses of rabies vaccine over a 14-day period. Shots are required unless the animal is captured and tests negative for the disease within 10 days.

Caution: Do not capture any animal yourself. Call the police or local animal control.

Richard O'Brien, MD, spokesperson, American College of Emergency Physicians (www.acep.org). He is also attending emergency physician at Moses Taylor Hospital, and associate professor of emergency medicine, The Commonwealth Medical College of Pennsylvania, both in Scranton.

Flowers Toxic to Cats

Tiger, Easter, stargazer and other types of lilies can cause irreversible kidney failure in cats—and are so potent that just a few nibbles can kill a small kitten, although adult cats can sometimes be saved through swift veterinary care. Other common houseplants also can be dangerous for cats and dogs—ask your veterinarian for a list, or go to *www.aspca.org*.

Sharon L. Peters, pet columnist, USA Today, www.usatoday.com.

Cat Bite? Why You Need To Get to the Doctor

A cat bite should be seen by a doctor within 12 hours if it is deep or if the area around the bite gets red or swells. You may need oral antibiotics and possibly a tetanus shot. Feline bites are more likely than dog bites to become infected because cats' long, sharp teeth often drive bacteria deep into tissue. After any animal bite, immediately wash the area well with warm water and soap, apply antibiotic ointment and cover with a bandage.

University of California, Berkeley, Wellness Letter, 500 Fifth Avenue, New York City 10110, www.wellnessletter.com.

Why Your Pet's Food May Be a Risk to You

Casey Barton Behravesh, DVM, PhD, researcher at Centers for Disease Control and Prevention in Atlanta, and lead author of a study of salmonella in pet food, published in *Pediatrics*.

Dry pet foods can carry *salmonella* and cause infection in humans. According to the FDA, there have been at least 13 recall announcements involving about 135 pet products since 2006 because of salmonella contamination. Between 2006 and 2008, one salmonella outbreak linked with pet food sickened 79 people in 21 states. Almost half of these victims were children age two and younger.

Most became infected by touching affected animals or pet food dishes and then placing their hands in their mouths. Symptoms of salmonella infection include bloody diarrhea, abdominal cramps and fever. There have been no reported problems with wet pet food according to the FDA.

Self-defense: Wash your hands after contact with pets, pet food and pet bowls, and keep young children away from areas that have pet food.

Worry No More About Losing Your Pet!

Microchips do help reunite pets and owners. Lost cats that have microchip identification are 20 times more likely to be reunited with their owners than cats not having chips. And, dogs with microchips are about two-and-a-half times more likely to be reunited.

Linda Lord, DVM, PhD, assistant professor of veterinary preventive medicine, The Ohio State University, Columbus, and leader of a study of 7,704 animals, published in *Journal of the American Veterinary Medical Association*.

Design on a Dime: Low-Cost Tricks for Big-Time Style

Kelly Edwards, design coordinator for HGTV's *Design on a Dime* and cohost and design coordinator for the makeover program *Tacky House* on the STYLE Network. She lives in Santa Monica, California. Her Web site is *www.kellyedwardsinc.com*.

You don't have to have a big decorating budget to spruce up your home. *Here, ways to give your place a welcoming, stylish look without spending a lot of money...*

• **Layer one rug over another.** Large area rugs with a lot of detail can be expensive. If you have a small, patterned carpet in an area that could use a larger one, place a larger, inexpensive jute rug (TheCompanyStore.com has several styles) underneath it to give the feeling of a large, elegant area rug.

• **Frame black-and-white pictures,** as they make a sophisticated wall display. At a thrift store or used-book store, buy books illustrated using black-and-white photographs/drawings. Cut out the pictures that appeal to you, place them in simple inexpensive frames—Ikea has nice ones—and group them on one wall. For bigger prints, I like to do three on a wall...for smaller prints, five or six.

• **Visit hotel liquidator outlets.** These stores buy furniture from hotels that are redecorating, and the pieces often are in great condition and surprisingly stylish and affordable.

Example: I paid $25 each for two marble end tables and $40 for a marble console from a high-end hotel in Los Angeles. New, these would have cost hundreds of dollars.

Search the Internet under hotel liquidators and the name of your city. I also shop at salvage yards (for architectural artifacts from old buildings), estate sales and CraigsList.org.

• **Declutter your bookcases.** Instead of covering every inch of space with books, give the eye places to rest—leave some shelves empty except for a single, treasured object. You also can group books by size or color.

To create the look of custom built-ins, stand two freestanding bookcases side by side and attach molding between them and around the edges.

• **Wallpaper the powder room.** Wallpapering a small room gives you a lot of impact for little money. Prepasted wallpaper can make the job easy. Bold, graphic prints are trendy now. If you prefer a classic look that won't go out of style, grass cloth is a sophisticated choice. Even if you want to have a professional put up the wallpaper for you, it shouldn't cost more than $30 to $60* for the labor per roll of wallpaper.

• **Add glass to kitchen cabinet doors.** You can change the look of your kitchen without going to the trouble of replacing the cabinets. Remove just two or three cabinet fronts, and have a handyman use a jigsaw to cut a large rectangle in each one. (You can do this yourself if you are skilled with a jigsaw.) Smooth the edge of the cutout…stain or paint it if necessary…and have a glass cutter cut a piece of glass to fit each door. The glass costs about $4 to $8 per square foot. Behind the glass doors, display your collection of vases, a stack of colorful dishes or your good china.

• **Spray paint older appliances.** All white kitchen appliances look dated now. To get the look of an expensive new refrigerator, I painted my old fridge using Rust-Oleum Universal Spray Paint in glossy black. Unplug the empty fridge, remove the doors and roll it outside. Sand it lightly, give it two coats of paint and let dry overnight.

Important: Protect the inside of the fridge by sealing it off with plastic and painter's tape.

• **Add a mirror to any room.** Mirrors add ambient light, and their frames draw the eye. Place a mirror behind a lamp or underneath a sconce to reflect light.

• **Freshen up bedroom furniture.** Change the knobs on a dresser or a nightstand—my favorite now is brushed bronze ring pulls. For an updated look, combine stain and paint. I like to stain the outside of the piece dark walnut and paint the drawer fronts white.

• **Display collections on old silver trays.** Sterling silver trays are easy to find in thrift stores. I clean them up with half a lemon. Use them to organize shells, jewelry, old bottles

*Prices subject to change.

or demitasse cups. A tray makes any group of objects look intentional and artistic.

• **Make your entryway welcoming.** If your entryway is small, use a table or dresser that fits comfortably to one side without limiting your walkway. Top it with fresh flowers in a vase. Have a brightly painted chair or bench for guests to sit on as they remove or put on their boots and wraps.

Save $2,000 and Improve Your Home's Value with Easy DIY Projects

Katie and Gene Hamilton are creators of *www.diy ornot.com*, which was featured in the March 2010 issue of *Money* as one of "The 20 Best Money Web Sites." Located in St. Michaels, Maryland, they are the authors of 20 home-improvement books, including *Home Improvement for Dummies* (Wiley) and *Fix It and Flip It* (McGraw-Hill). They are founders of Move.com, which they sold to R.R. Donnelley & Sons.

I f you're a home owner who likes working outside, consider doing these home-improvement projects yourself. You'll save at least 50% of what retaining a professional would cost.* These projects require more grunt work than talent and only a small investment in materials and tools. Each of them will improve the value of your property.

• **Power washing.** To keep your house at its best, consider giving it an annual cleanup with a power washer. You can hire a building cleaning service for $377 to power wash a typical 1,200-square-foot house. Or you can rent a gas-powered washer rated at least at 1,200 psi (which means that it delivers 1,200 pounds per square inch of water) with detergent for $160 and pocket a nice savings of 58%. Figure that you'll spend a solid two days on the job.

Savings: $217.

*In this article, the costs to retain a professional are based on several of the estimating publications that contractors use to bid on their jobs. The material costs are based on information from major national retailers and manufacturers. All costs are subject to change.

•**Gutter cleaning.** An important seasonal maintenance chore for every home owner is cleaning and repairing gutters. A handyman will charge $102 to clean and make minor repairs to 200 linear feet of gutters on a one-story house. If you have a sturdy ladder, garden hose, bucket and rubber gloves, you can do the job in two hours for $40 (the cost of some caulk and roofing cement) and save 61%.

Warning: If you have a very high home or uneven terrain, it may be safer to hire a pro.

Savings: $62.

•**Painting the garage.** You'll pay a painting contractor $307 to spray paint the exterior of a typical one story, two-car garage. You can do the job in a weekend for $100, for the cost of the paint and renting an airless sprayer for a day. That's a 67% savings. Figure that you'll spend the better part of the first day prepping the area before you paint.

Savings: $207.

•**Pruning.** A landscape service will prune and groom a small tree and some bushes for $80, but for an investment of $36 (for pruning shears and a lopper), you can do it and save 55% in three hours. You'll save the full $80 the next time you prune.

Initial savings: $44.

•**Mulching.** You could pay a yard service $324 to lay a four-inch-deep spread of organic mulch in a 300-foot area or buy mulch (30 to 35 bags) yourself for $75. In a day, you can complete the job and save 77%. If you have a vehicle that can haul it, you won't have to pay extra to have the mulch delivered.

Savings: $249.

•**Laying a gravel path.** Consider installing a gravel path as a walkway or winding footpath through your garden. The project involves digging and hauling material, but you'll save 57% by doing it yourself. For a three-foot-wide, 100-foot-long gravel path, the landscape contractor will charge $349 including gravel. It'll cost you a long day's work and $150 for the material.

Savings: $199.

•**Building a patio.** This is strenuous labor and time-consuming—it takes about a week to do—but every time you use your new patio, you'll appreciate your sweat equity. A contrac-

tor will charge $2,275 to build a 15-foot-by-20-foot brick patio. You can do it for about half that ($1,100 for the material).

Savings: $1,175.

You'll find step-by-step directions for the projects in this article at *www.diyornot.com*, along with cost analyses of many more home-improvement projects.

When *Not* to Clean Your Oven…and Other Tricks To Keep Appliances Running Longer

Vernon Schmidt, who provides more than 35 years of experience in appliance repair. Currently he trains new appliance technicians in Indianapolis. Schmidt also answers appliance questions through his RefrigDoc.com online site and is the author of *The Appliance Handbook for Women: Simple Enough Even Men Can Understand* (AuthorHouse), available through Amazon.com and *http://refrigdoc.com*.

How long your appliances last isn't just a matter of how well they are built. How you treat them matters as well. *Here are some simple tricks to keep your major appliances running as long as possible and avoid expensive repairs…*

•**Dishwashers and clothes washers.** Use less detergent. People tend to fill dishwasher soap cups to the brim and use the amount of clothes detergent recommended on the bottle or box. That is way too much. Modern dishwashers and washing machines use less water than those of decades past, so less detergent is needed. Also, more powerful and concentrated detergents are available today. Using excessive amounts of detergent creates a soapy residue inside of the machine that results in a buildup of mold and mildew, which smells and eats away at the rubber parts, shortening the appliance's life.

In a dishwasher, try using just one-half to one full teaspoon of liquid or powder detergent. If that does not clean your dishes—perhaps because you have hard water—gradually increase the amount up to one tablespoon.

If you have used too much detergent in the past, also use a dishwasher cleaner, available in most supermarkets, to remove soap residue. Leading brands include Glisten and Finish.

Alternative: Use solid tablets that include premeasured detergent. If you have soft water, split the tablets in half. Do not use liquid gel packs—too much detergent and too sudsy.

In a clothes washer, use just two tablespoons of regular detergent, or one tablespoon of concentrated detergent if you have soft water and your washer is a modern front-load or high-efficiency top-load machine.

If you have hard water and/or your clothes washer is not a modern front-load or high-efficiency top-load machine, use one-quarter of the amount of detergent recommended.

Only when you are washing extremely dirty clothes should you use the amount of detergent recommended on the label.

• **Clothes dryers.** Clean out your dryer's exhaust line at least once each year. If the plastic or flexible-metal ductwork that your electric dryer uses to vent hot air is clogged with lint, the dryer's heating element will overheat and might fail. Clogged lines can cause serious mechanical problems for gas dryers, too. And with either electric or gas, a clogged vent can double or triple the amount of energy required to dry a load of clothing. On a gas dryer, the lint that builds up also can cause carbon monoxide to vent into the home and possibly start a fire.

If your dryer's exhaust line is too long to clear out by hand, purchase a dryer-vent cleaning kit with a flexible extension rod long enough to reach the whole length of your dryer's exhaust line. These are available at home-improvement stores for under $50.* Remember to clean both the exhaust line that leads from the dryer to the wall and the part inside the wall.

• **Refrigerators.** If your older refrigerator's rubber-door seal gaskets are becoming brittle, apply a layer of Vaseline to keep them supple. Reapply whenever the gasket feels dry.

It is probably time to replace the gasket if it has cracked or split. Replacing door gaskets

*Prices subject to change.

on older machines is a labor-intensive job that usually costs $200 to $300 per door.

Also: On most refrigerators, you'll need to clean the coil—the metal piping typically located behind a removable panel at the base of or behind the refrigerator—at least once a year. Clean it at least twice a year if a dog or cat that sheds lives in the home. A refrigerator's compressor is forced to work much harder when the coil is covered with dust or pet hair. That can cause overheating and compressor failure. Having a new compressor installed is likely to cost more than $400 in parts and labor.

Your refrigerator's manual should include directions for cleaning off its coil. Even if the owner's manual says that the coil is self-cleaning, it still needs to be cleaned at least once a year. I have never seen a clean "self-clean" coil on a refrigerator after two years of use.

• **Ovens.** There isn't much you can do to extend the life of an oven, but there is something you can do to reduce the odds that it will fail at a particularly inconvenient moment.

Best: Wait until after the November/December holidays to run the self-cleaning cycle.

People tend to run oven self-cleaning cycles immediately before big cooking days, such as Christmas, Thanksgiving and important dinner parties. Unfortunately, ovens are the most likely to break during or very soon after these self-cleaning cycles because of the high temperatures involved. It isn't easy to get a broken oven fixed around the holidays either.

Would Your Kitchen Pass A Health Inspection?

One in seven home kitchens would fail the health code inspection done at restaurants. When research participants were asked about food-handling practices in their own kitchens, including refrigerator temperature and whether produce was washed before being eaten, 14% of home kitchens received a grade lower than C.

For safe food-handling practices, log on to *www. fsis.usda.gov* (search for "Safe Food Handling").

Jonathan Fielding, MD, MPH, director, Los Angeles County Department of Health, which analyzed an Internet quiz taken by 13,000 adults.

Laundry Lessons

To dry laundry more quickly, put towels and heavier clothes through a second spin cycle in a top-loading washer…or do a second drain-and-spin cycle in a front-loader. When a dryer load is done, add the next load of clothes quickly—while the dryer is already hot—so that the machine does not have to warm up again. Also, add one clean, dry towel to a wet load to absorb dampness and help everything dry faster.

Good Housekeeping, 300 W. 57 St., New York City 10019, *www.goodhousekeeping.com*.

Skip the Scented Cleaning Products

Avoid using scented cleaning and laundry products. Even products that claim to be "green," organic or natural may emit hazardous chemicals.

Recent finding: Nearly one-quarter of the chemicals emitted by scented household products, such as air fresheners, detergents, fabric softeners and disinfectants, are categorized as toxic or hazardous…and more than one-third of products tested emitted at least one chemical identified as a probable carcinogen.

To avoid potentially dangerous chemicals: Clean with baking soda and/or vinegar… open windows for ventilation instead of using air fresheners…and buy products without any fragrance.

Anne Steinemann, PhD, professor of civil and environmental engineering and public affairs, University of Washington, Seattle, and lead author of a study of 25 fragranced consumer products, published in *Environmental Impact Assessment Review*.

Ants Away!

Place uncooked Cream of Wheat or cornmeal on ant nests, and sprinkle it where ants travel. The ants eat it, then it expands in their stomachs and kills them. This method is much less expensive than calling an exterminator or using chemicals, and it is safer than using poison.

Mary Hunt, editor, DebtProofLiving.com, based in Paramount, California.

A Dishwasher and More!

Surprising items to clean in the dishwasher…Baseball caps—put them on the top shelf, but do not wash them with dishes, because food can get trapped in the cloth…tools having metal or plastic handles…hairbrushes and combs made of plastic—not ones made of wood or with natural boar bristles…fan grilles, switch plates and vent covers if they are plastic, aluminum or steel and are not painted or plated…light-fixture covers that aren't antique, enameled or painted…potatoes—use a rinse-only cycle with no detergent. Always put plastic items on the top shelf of the dishwasher.

Real Simple, Time-Life Bldg., Rockefeller Center, New York City 10020, *www.realsimple.com*.

The Trick to Perfect Rice

For fluffier rice, rinse off raw grains before cooking to get rid of surface starches and allow water to adhere to cooked grains. After the rice has cooked, pull the pot off the heat and drape a clean, dry kitchen towel over the top of the pot and place the pot lid on top of the towel. Let it sit for 10 minutes. The towel will absorb the steam and help prevent rice grains from sticking together.

Cook's Illustrated, 17 Station St., Brookline, Massachusetts 02445, *www.cooksillustrated.com*.

18

Success Secrets

Make Your Dreams Come True—One Simple Thing Could Be the Key

We all have many excuses for why we've not yet achieved our goals...and why it is not worth making all the changes required to pursue our goals now. "It's too hard"..."too frightening"...or "just not the right time."

We take the safer, easier way out, whether that means staying in our current job rather than trying something different that we would rather do...keeping quiet rather than standing up for ourselves...or continuing to indulge in bad habits rather than disciplining ourselves to change behaviors, such as overeating or not exercising.

According to principles taught by the executive-coaching firm The Handel Group, these excuses come from our "inner chicken," that voice in our head that prevents us from taking a challenging path. We accept our inner chicken's excuses as valid, even when they are clearly flawed, because believing that the easy course is the proper course is less painful than admitting that we are deeply and perhaps irrationally afraid of the alternative.

TO OVERCOME YOUR INNER CHICKEN

• **Think about what you would like your life to be like.** What are your desires in your professional life...family life...social life...and financial life?

Thinking about your goals lures your inner chicken from its pen to offer up excuses. Write down your chicken's excuses. Become familiar with them. This familiarity will make it easier to see through them later.

Beth Weissenberger, cofounder and vice chairman of The Handel Group, a corporate, private and educational coaching company based in New York City. The Handel Group's corporate clients include Sony BMG and New York University School of Medicine. For more information, go to *www.handelgroup.com*.

Example: When a middle manager who attended one of our seminars thought about all his professional desires, his inner chicken warned him that his family life was too busy for him to devote more time to his career…and the economy was too iffy to take professional chances. When his boss asked if he would like to lead an important presentation, the manager's first thoughts were that he was too busy and that failing at this assignment could cost him his work at a time when new jobs were scarce. But because he learned that it was his inner chicken speaking, he identified his excuses as fear responses. He figured out how he could schedule his time so that he could make the project a priority without neglecting his family. He also reminded himself that, in a tough job market, not taking a chance could be as risky as taking one.

• **Ask an expert or friend to evaluate your inner chicken's excuses.** Obtaining an outside perspective often is the best way to separate valid excuses from those rooted in fear.

If an excuse is medical in nature, ask your doctor whether it is valid…if it is professional, ask a career coach, business consultant or mentor…if it is regarding relationships, speak with a marriage counselor or a pastoral counselor. If this expert agrees that your excuse is valid, that does not free you from pursuing the goal—it simply means that you should pursue it via a different route.

Example: Your goal is to lose 50 pounds, but your inner chicken warns you that jogging could damage your knees. If a doctor agrees, give up jogging—but replace it with biking or swimming.

If you lack the time or money to consult an expert, ask a friend or family member to evaluate the excuse—but choose this evaluator carefully. Family and friends tend to let us get away with our excuses because they want to tell us what we want to hear…or because their own inner chickens make similar excuses. Your evaluator must be both savvy enough to see through flawed excuses and plainspoken enough to tell you difficult truths.

If you find an effective evaluator, ask this person to serve this role for you on an ongoing basis. Send him/her a weekly e-mail sum-

marizing your goals, the steps you have taken to pursue them and your excuses for not doing more. Request an honest critique.

• **When your inner chicken starts clucking, remind yourself of the high costs of remaining in your box.** We all prefer the safety of our comfort zones, and the chicken helps us stay there. But we pay a huge price for this safety.

A life without risk is a life without any excitement and adventure…without feelings of accomplishment and without any hope of fulfilling our dreams. Reflect upon all these costs whenever you're tempted to choose the comfortable path. Our greatest happiness usually is found on the other side of fear.

Also, consider that facing fears is good practice. Like it or not, events outside of our control force us out of our comfort zone eventually. We will be better able to cope with these situations if we previously have taken ourselves out of this comfort zone.

Example: Those who have remained in one job their whole career for fear of change are likely to have more trouble rebounding from a job layoff than those who have been through the job-hunting process several times before.

• **Confront your inner chicken about being nonconfrontational.** Our inner chickens often are afraid of standing up to others. They feed us reasons why it's better to just live with the annoying behavior of people around us. They convince us that confrontations are unpleasant…and that voicing a lot of displeasure only makes bad situations worse.

The secret to overcoming an inner chicken's nonconfrontational nature is to learn how to stage successful confrontations. *Five keys…*

• Consider the situation from the opposite side before speaking up. Does this person have a good reason for doing whatever is annoying you? Are you doing anything that annoys this person?

• Wait until this individual is alone before raising the subject. People tend to become embarrassed and defensive when confronted in a group.

• Ask for "permission" to raise a difficult concern before voicing your complaint. "I have something difficult to say. Is it okay with you if I say it?"

- Present your complaint as something that could be done differently, and not as a matter of right and wrong.

- Assume that this person does not realize that he/she is causing offense. Avoid any hint of righteousness or blame. Remember that this is all your opinion and from your point of view.

- **Do one thing each day that scares you.** Tell someone what you really think, even if it is not what he wants to hear. Schedule an appointment that you have been putting off. Try a new food. Ask for a discount at a store. Spend time with a teen who has been angry and distant.

It's best to face fears that bring you closer to your goals, but facing any fear at least teaches you that you can stand up to your inner chicken. Facing one fear each day eliminates the paralysis of trying to face all of your fears at once. After you become good at addressing small fears, you can work up to larger issues.

Helpful: Keep a list of fears and the actions you could take to confront them all. That will make it harder for your inner chicken to convince you to take a day off from facing fears.

- **Call yourself names.** Whenever you hear excuses in your head, call yourself a chicken. Silly as it sounds, this self-teasing can balance out your inclination to listen to your chicken— and drive you toward braver choices.

Bouncing Back from a Bad Mood *Fast*

Karen Salmansohn, host of the show "Be Happy Dammit" on Sirius satellite radio. Located in New York City, she is author of *The Bounce Back Book: How to Thrive in the Face of Adversity, Setbacks, and Losses* (Workman). Her research into bouncing back from problems began after she was the victim of an assault. Her online site is *www.notsalmon.com.*

Bad breaks and difficult days often darken our disposition—but we don't have to let those low spirits linger. We actu-ally have more control over our moods than we realize.

How to quickly bounce back from having the blues…

"TRAVEL" TO A HAPPIER TIME

Make a list of five of the happiest moments out of your past. Then close your eyes, and imagine one of those moments in as much detail as possible. Visualizing your happy times encourages your brain to release *endorphins*. This helps lower blood pressure and makes us feel happy, almost as if the pleasant experience were occurring at this very moment.

Helpful: The more sensory details you include in your visualization, the greater the odds that you will experience this mood-boosting endorphin release. Where are you standing in your vision? Can you feel the breeze on your face? Do you have something in your hands? What do you hear, see and smell?

IMAGINE THAT OTHERS ARE CONSPIRING TO HELP YOU

Bad moods often feed paranoia—the sense that others are working against you. To feel better, imagine that other people are plotting to your benefit instead.

If you have trouble imagining such things, that might be a sign that you should be spending more time with helpful, positive-minded people. Then positive thoughts on your behalf won't be so hard to imagine.

COUNT YOUR COMPLAINTS

When you air any particular complaint for the third time (to yourself or others), imagine it turning to vapor and floating away. Voicing our problems or writing about them in a journal can help us get them out of our system. But when we vent about the same problems over and over, the retellings don't help us move on—they keep us in a rut.

After the third time, mention the problem again only if the additional mention is part of a genuine effort to fix the problem…reposition your goals and plans in response to the problem…make light of the problem…or cast the problem in a new and more positive light.

Example: It is OK to mention a health problem again to say that it was a wake-up call to start a healthy diet.

285

ASSIGN YOURSELF A TASK

Achieving a task helps you feel more in control. Researchers at the University of Michigan found that nothing matters more to people's sense of well-being than whether they have a strong feeling of control over their lives. To exercise your sense of control—and boost your mood—assign yourself an achievable task related to a personal goal, large or modest. Set a deadline so that you can measure the accomplishment.

Examples: Clean one room...get 30 minutes of exercise...or speak with one professional contact about a career transition that you might like to make.

RETELL THE INCIDENT

Retell the incident that is making you feel awful in a less painful way. Martin Seligman, PhD, the director of the University of Pennsylvania's Positive Psychology Center, has discovered that the way we tell ourselves the stories of our setbacks can mean more to our moods than the severity of those setbacks.

If you tell yourself a problem or misstep is temporary, limited to a single occurrence or mainly someone else's fault, you are likely to rebound quickly...but if your "self-talk" claims that the error is permanent or a reflection of who you are, your ill mood is likely to linger.

Example: If you've been laid off, replace the thought *I wasn't good enough to keep my job* with *This economy is costing a lot of good people their jobs, but it will turn around.*

MORE MOOD BOOSTERS

• **Repeat the word "forward."** Saying "forward" silently to ourselves when we feel bad reminds us that our bad mood likely is related to a past event—but the past is far less important than where our lives are headed in the future.

• **Cuddle a loved one.** Experiencing tender, caring physical contact can improve your mood and even lower your blood pressure. If there's no one you can turn to for a hug, visit a pet store and hold a few puppies. Some animal shelters even will let you take a dog home for a week without a long-term commitment.

• **Let yourself feel bad—later.** If you cannot reverse your bad mood, postpone it. Select a time later in your day or week to feel bad. Pencil it in on your calendar. Your mind might be willing to go along with this because you're not denying the right to feel bad—only delaying when this happens. Better yet, you might not feel like feeling bad anymore once the bad-mood time arrives.

Former FBI Agent Tells How to Get Your Way Without Saying *Anything*

Joe Navarro, retired FBI counterintelligence and counterterrorism special agent and supervisor who has studied nonverbal communications extensively, Tampa, Florida. He now consults with the FBI, the State Department and corporations. Navarro is author of *Louder Than Words: Take Your Career from Average to Exceptional with the Hidden Power of Nonverbal Intelligence* (HarperBusiness). His Web site is *www.jnforensics.com.*

We are all being watched—our body language, our actions and our facial expressions send signals that others receive and evaluate. I learned as an FBI agent to quickly and assuredly assess the meaning of these signals so that appropriate action—at times, lifesaving action—could be taken.

Psychologists have estimated that from 60% to 80% of all communication is nonverbal—yet most people put no thought into the messages their bodies are sending. *Here, five vital nonverbal messages and how to send them...*

"I'M IN CHARGE HERE"

You don't necessarily have to be smarter or more experienced than the rest of a group to be accepted as the leader. *Some leaders send nonverbal signals that encourage others to follow them...*

• **Claim territory.** When standing up, hold your arms slightly away from your sides, feet slightly apart. When you sit at a shared space, such as a conference table, spread your materials out slightly farther than the width of your shoulders, claiming that space as your own. Organized, polite people tend to arrange their papers in a neat pile, then fold their hands on top. Unfortunately, this sends the message to others that you can be dominated.

Many young men instinctively claim territory in these ways, but most women and older men must remind themselves to do so.

To let people know that you are standing your ground and that your decision is final, stand behind a table or a desk, lean forward slightly, spread your arms a little away from your body, spread all your fingers apart and plant your fingertips securely on the surface. This stance sends an unmistakable message of authority and should be used by men and women only as a last resort.

• **Hold your fingers wide when you make hand gestures.** Spreading your fingers sends a powerful signal of confidence, control and domination.

• **Put on a performance of "cool and collected" even when you don't feel it.** People gravitate toward those who remain serene in difficult situations and avoid those who seem overemotional and prone to panic. At the start of any potentially difficult day, silently say to yourself, *I might face problems today, but even if there is yelling and screaming, I am going to transcend it.* When difficult moments arrive, silently tell yourself, *I have a responsibility to stay calm to help maintain the calm.* Sending yourself these messages increases the chance that you will send the nonverbal message *I'm cool, collected and worth following...*

"I'M CONFIDENT. YOU CAN TRUST WHAT I SAY"

Our signals help determine whether others trust our words...

• **Steeple your outspread fingers.** Steepling —touching the fingertips together with hands pointed up and the fingers spread wide—is an extremely powerful nonverbal signal of confidence. Jurors are more likely to believe testimony when the witness steeples, for example. Women, in particular, tend to underuse these steepling signals.

Warning: Hand wringing or rubbing interlaced fingers together sends the opposite signal—that you lack confidence or feel stress.

• **Enter rooms without hesitation.** Striding into a room with confidence creates a crucial first impression that you believe in yourself, so others should believe in you, too. If you pause or slow down when entering—even for just a moment to get your bearings or locate your assigned seat—your hesitation could be taken as a sign of uncertainty.

• **Keep your chin up.** Holding your chin high shows that you have the confidence to expose your neck, something primates don't do when they feel threatened.

• **Remove your thumbs from your pockets.** Hooking your thumbs in your pockets when standing will make you appear insecure. (Hands in the pockets are okay, but preferably just one, not both.)

"YOU SHOULD HIRE ME"

There are so many qualified applicants for practically every job opening these days. *The nonverbal messages applicants send to interviewers often help determine whether or not they get the job...*

• **Use hand steepling to indicate confidence,** as previously discussed.

• **Sit forward on your chair with both feet on the floor.** Sit back and cross your legs only after the interviewer does so.

• **Remain focused in on the interviewer's face.** Your gaze can move around his/her face, but not around the room, even when the interviewer allows his gaze to wander. A wandering gaze can send a message of disrespect and is acceptable only for the higher-status individual in a conversation.

• **Review where your résumé and other documents are inside of your briefcase before the interview.** This should help you retrieve them quickly and smoothly during the interview, if necessary. People are less likely to trust people who seem disorganized.

"LET'S CALM DOWN"

Saying "calm down" tends to make people more upset, not calmer. *Better to send nonverbal calming signals, including the following...*

• **Position yourself at an angle to the upset individual.** You are likely to make tense situations even worse if you position yourself directly face-to-face. Like all primates, humans tend to feel threatened when "squared off."

Alternative: Take a walk with this person.

• **Tilt your head slightly to one side.** Tilting the head exposes the throat, one of the most vulnerable regions of the human body. When you do this, you send a strong subconscious message that you feel comfortable and safe, so everyone else should, too. Tilting your head also communicates that you are listening intently.

• **Step back or lean back in your chair.** Creating a few inches of extra space during a tense moment can lower everyone's blood pressure.

• **Uncross your arms and remove your hands from your hips.** These arm positions seem aggressive and angry, aggravating tense situations.

If you are most comfortable standing with your hands on your hips, turn your hands so that your thumbs are forward. This makes you seem inquisitive, not angry.

• **Cross your legs at the ankles when standing.** The primitive part of the human brain avoids crossing the legs when it senses danger, in case we need to flee quickly. When you cross your legs, it says that you are neither anxious nor distrustful, so no one else present should be either.

• **Speak slowly.** This will calm you, increasing the odds that you will convey a sense of calm to others.

• **Take a deep breath,** then exhale even slower than you inhaled. This, too, will calm you and encourage those around you to be calm.

• **Keep your hands in view.** Those around you are likely to become more anxious during any confrontation if your hands are not where they can be viewed. The human brain worries that a hidden hand could be holding a weapon during a disagreement even if, rationally, this is extremely unlikely.

• **Use slow, calm hand movements when you make pacifying statements.** People are more likely to trust and believe you when your hand motions match your words.

"LET'S BE FRIENDS"

Our nonverbal signals can encourage people to feel a connection with us—or these signals can accidentally push them away...

• **Flash your eyebrows.** Immediately upon making eye contact with someone you want to know better, very dramatically arch your eyebrows at them for just an instant. Doing this sends a strong nonverbal signal that he/she matters to you.

• **Match up handshakes and hand movements.** People tend to form positive first impressions about those who have handshakes like their own. Begin your handshake with a moderate pressure, then tighten or lighten up your grip to mirror the handshake that you receive. Mirror the nature and intensity of this person's hand movements during the ensuing conversation, too.

• **Avoid face-to-face conversations.** People are most likely to feel a close, personal connection with you if you are positioned at right angles or side by side. If you cross your legs while seated, cross toward, not away from, the person you are speaking with. Crossing away sends the message that you are closed off.

Little-Known Sign Of a Liar

Habitual liars make *more* eye contact than honest people. Liars recognize that most people associate eye contact with honesty—so they deliver the expected behavior.

Psychology Today, 115 E. 23 St., New York City 10010, *www.psychologytoday.com.*

How to Tell If Someone Is Lying

Signs someone is lying… He or she leans forward and changes posture or position often. He licks his lips, folds or crosses his arms and blinks less often than usual. He may fidget…take frequent sips of water…smile more than usual…and laugh at inappropriate times during a conversation. He is likely to close his hands into fists or interlock his fingers…frequently touch his face…scratch or rub his nose …look away…and/or sigh deeply.

Alan Hirsch, MD, neurologist and psychiatrist, Smell & Taste Treatment and Research Foundation in Chicago, *www.smellandtaste.org,* and author of *How to Tell If Your Teenager Is Lying and What to Do About It* (Hilton).

Am I Boring You?

Signs that you may be boring your conversation partner…

The person fidgets or turns slightly away from you instead of being still, sitting upright and looking at you…he/she changes the subject abruptly…stays silent and does not interrupt you to pose any questions or to remark on something you said…asks simple questions just to appear polite, such as "Where did you go?"…gives clipped responses, such as "really" and "wow"…and doesn't ask you to elaborate or explain anything.

Gretchen Rubin, New York City–located founder and author of *The Happiness Project* (Harper). Her Web site is *www.happiness-project.com.*

How to Handle a Tough Conversation: Skip the Sugarcoating and Try These No-Fail Strategies

Holly Weeks, who is a speech consultant to the Urban Superintendents Doctoral Program at Harvard's School of Education, Boston. As the principal of Holly Weeks Communications, she consults and coaches on communication issues. Weeks is author of *Failure to Communicate: How Conversations Go Wrong and What You Can Do to Right Them* (Harvard Business). Her online site is *www.holly weeks.com.*

It's never easy to deliver bad news…own up to a mistake…or interact with people who become belligerent or defensive. *But it is important to have these difficult conversations because when we do, problems get re-* solved and we can move ahead confidently with our lives…

DON'T FALL FOR DIVERSIONS

People often use diversionary tactics when they feel threatened during conversations— sometimes without realizing that they are doing so. These tactics could include threats, lies, counteraccusations, anger and/or crying.

Example: When a neighbor asks a man to clear a large amount of debris from his yard, the man inexplicably flies into a rage. Assuming that the neighbor's request was polite and reasonable—and there was no established bad blood between the neighbors—it's likely that this outburst is not true anger, but just a diversion intended to make the neighbor back down.

What to do: Suppress your natural inclination to respond with shocked silence…a retreat…or inappropriate emotions and language of your own. Remind yourself that these responses are what this person wants to provoke.

Instead, take a moment to collect yourself… nod slowly in silent acknowledgment of what has been said…and make an accusation-free statement that refers to the diversionary ploy. Then redirect the conversation back to its intended destination. Keep your tone as neutral and emotion-free as possible.

Examples: "I know this is difficult, but the current situation is not working. What are we going to do to fix it?"…"We've been getting along well and this is a necessary conversation, although it has gone off track here, but I need to stay on the debris issue." If the diversionary strategy pointed fingers at you or others, or it raised other unrelated problems, try, "We can talk about the issues you raised next. Right now, we're talking about getting rid of the debris in your yard."

SKIP THE SUGARCOATING

It's normal to try to sugarcoat bad news, either by mixing good news in with the bad…or by trying to downplay the severity of the situation. We imagine that this sugarcoating cushions the blow. In fact, it mostly just makes it difficult for the person we're speaking with to figure out what we are trying to say and how important it is to us.

Example: A boss offers extended praise to an employee before mentioning in passing a performance problem that he/she would like to see addressed. The boss subsequently becomes angry when the employee fails to immediately address the problem, but the sugarcoating really is to blame. The employee did not understand that this problem was the true message and that the praise was sugarcoating.

What to do…

• **Deliver bad news in a straightforward manner,** and the odds increase greatly that your message will be understood. In many instances, it is best to come right out and say what needs to be said at the very beginning of the conversation.

Example: "Henry, the promotion has gone to someone else."

• **Use neutral tones.** Aim for the controlled voice from NASA communications—"Houston, we have a problem." Attempts at sympathetic body language or tone of voice might feel like kindness, but they can distract listeners from the content of your message.

• **Select nonprovocative words.** Straightforward doesn't necessarily mean harsh or blunt. If your news itself is tough, loaded language will make it even harder for the person to take it in.

Example: "Employees have complained that you act cocky and superior" is more likely to make a manager defensive than "Your recommendations would go down better if they were delivered in the style of one colleague helping another."

SEEK THE MIDDLE GROUND

We often notice only the extreme options available to us when we're embroiled in contentious conversations.

Examples: Many might imagine that the only possible response to aggression is to either become aggressive or back off…that the only response to an accusation is to apologize, deny it or make counteraccusations…that the only response to a raised voice is to become silent or to raise your own voice.

We fall into this polarized response trap because difficult conversations often feel like warfare, and battles usually have outcomes in which there is one winner and one loser or a stalemate. But difficult conversations are not wars, and we don't need to follow someone onto the battlefield. There is a way to speak reasonably regardless of how the other side is handling the conversation. Unfortunately, this solution is unlikely to be reached when both parties see only the extreme options open to them.

What to do: Before each statement during a contentious conversation, pause to consider whether what you are about to say is passive, aggressive or moderate. Passive responses include backing down, playing along or saying nothing even though you don't agree. Aggressive responses might include threats, accusations and attempts to mete out punishment.

Offering passive and aggressive responses can seem justified or even satisfying in that moment, but overlooked moderate responses are much more likely to steer difficult conversations toward productive outcomes.

Best: Familiarize yourself with a few widely applicable moderate responses before you engage in a potentially contentious conversation. That way you increase the odds that those responses will come to mind during the conversation, when emotions are running very high. Moderate responses are best said in a neutral, emotion-free tone. *Five possibilities…*

• **"It might be that we have an honest disagreement,"** or "It might be that we have a misunderstanding. Let's sort all this out before we get angry with each other."

• **Wait one beat after the other person's emotional outburst,** then say, "Let's go back to the facts."

• **"I do have a lot of respect for you,** and in the grand scheme of things, this is a small matter—but it is something we need to get past. What do you think we should do?"

• **"Although your opinion is very different from mine,** perhaps we could reconcile our points of view."

• **If you wish to be more forceful,** consider responding to aggressive behavior with, "That behavior isn't going to work."

ACKNOWLEDGE YOUR MISTAKES

When you are embroiled in a contentious conversation, admitting a mistake can feel like an admission of weakness or even a concession of defeat. We seem to dig our heels in even deeper when we realize that we might be wrong. Unfortunately, this only makes difficult conversations even harder to resolve.

Admitting a mistake and conceding a point actually can make you seem reasonable and fair-minded—if it is handled properly. It also can help keep the conversation moving forward, which is to everyone's benefit.

What to do: Remind yourself that admitting to an error is not what diminishes you in the eyes of others. Making an error might diminish you—but you have already done that. Responding immaturely or unproductively to an error also can diminish you—and by denying an obvious error, you are doing exactly that. If you can see that you have made a mistake, others probably can, too.

Make a simple statement that concedes the point, then redirect the conversation back to the larger topic. Do this both when you have made a factual error and when you make the error of being overly aggressive during a difficult conversation. If you act as though conceding the point does not diminish you, then others are unlikely to see you as diminished, either.

Examples: "I had my facts wrong—you're correct. Let's see how that affects the plan." "You know what? I shouldn't have said that. I'm sorry."

What to Say to a Jerk— The One Word That Will Stop Him in His Tracks

Mark Goulston, MD, a psychiatrist, business consultant, executive coach, and FBI and police hostage negotiation trainer, Santa Monica, California. Also a best-selling author, he writes a column on leadership for *Fast Company* and contributes to *Harvard Business Review*. His books include *Just Listen: Discover the Secret to Getting Through to Absolutely Anyone* (Amacom). His Web site is *www.markgoulston.com*.

Communication is challenging enough with the "normal" people in your life— the ones who desire to cooperate and make life better for everyone. When you are forced to deal with jerks—people who don't care about social give-and-take—communication can seem next to impossible, leaving you drained and upset.

Jerks tend to trigger powerful negative emotional reactions that take a long time to recover from and that interfere with clear thinking.

As a psychiatrist, I refer to jerks as "toxic people."

If being around a toxic person is having a destructive effect on your physical or emotional health, you may need to get that person out of your life completely. But in many cases, you can "neutralize" the negative effect that a toxic person has on you. *Here, simple ways to do it...*

•**Recognize when a person is toxic.** Everyone can be uncooperative and selfish some of the time—and the techniques in this article can work during those times. But a toxic person is different from a person who is just having a bad day.

Toxic people have a distinctive view of life. They view the world as having cheated them out of something or as owing them something. Nothing good that happens to them changes that perception for long.

In contrast to healthy people, who feel entitled to what they deserve...and neurotics, who do not feel entitled to what they deserve...toxic people feel entitled to what they don't deserve. They do not play by the usual rules of getting along with others. They feel justified in taking, with no compulsion to give.

This belief system reveals itself in different ways for different types of toxic people. A toxic bully may aggressively push others around to get his/her way, whereas a toxically needy person may feel entitled to have his hand held constantly or insist that other people fight his battles. Bullies scream and demand. Toxically needy people whine and complain.

•**Adjust your expectations.** We expect people to behave reasonably, and the shock that we feel when toxic people do not do so can be quite painful.

Toxic people sometimes may appear to be caring and cooperative. This behavior will last only until they get what they want. Don't be fooled into thinking that they have changed.

In addition, the strategies that usually work with nontoxic people—such as empathizing or appealing to fairness—do not work with toxic people.

Once you have identified a person as toxic, your smartest move is to protect yourself from being blindsided. Expect the person to act solely in his own interests even when he appears to be kind and caring.

• **Hold part of yourself back.** Toxic people get what they want by pushing others off balance. They do so by acting in ways that trigger rage, fear, guilt and other strong emotions in others. Remind yourself not to get emotionally engaged. This is their issue, not yours.

Helpful: Pause before responding. No matter what the toxic person says or does, make a practice of waiting several seconds or more before you reply. Stay calm.

The longer you wait before responding, the more the toxic individual may escalate his behavior. For example, he may get even angrier or whine even more. But the behavior is less likely to upset you, because you are keeping your emotional distance.

WHAT TO SAY TO A JERK

Three good responses to nearly every type of toxic person…

• **"Huh?"** This one word can stop a jerk in his tracks. Use a mild, neutral tone of voice. Do this whenever a toxic person says something utterly ridiculous but acts as though he is being perfectly reasonable. This response indicates that what the toxic person is spouting does not make sense. It works because it signals that you are not engaging with the content of what he said.

• **"Do you actually believe what you just said?"** Use a calm, straightforward tone, not a confrontational one. This question works because toxic people often resort to hyperbole to throw others off balance. They are prone to using the words "always" and "never" to drive home their points. However, don't expect the toxic person to admit that he is wrong. He is more likely to walk away in a huff—which

is fine because then you won't have to waste more energy dealing with him.

• **"I can see how this is good for you.** Tell me how it's good for me." This response is a useful way to deal with a toxic person's demands. If he stalls or changes the subject, you can say, "Since it's not clear how this is good for me, I'm going to have to say no."

Here are other responses to specific types of toxic people…

BYE TO BULLIES

A bully gets what he wants by scaring other people. Even when a bully behaves himself, his presence triggers fear because you never know when he will explode.

What to do…

Disengage: Most bullies use words and/or tone of voice as their weapons. Say silently to yourself, *This person is not going to physically harm me.* Picture his words as rubber bullets that, instead of hitting you between the eyes, zoom over your shoulder.

Caution: If there is any possibility that the person might get physically violent, then leave at once.

Respond: Take a deep breath, and say out loud, "Ah, geez, this is going to be one long conversation" or "You gotta be kidding" (said mockingly to show that the bully hasn't scared or offended you).

Whatever the bully's reaction—whether he demands an explanation or he continues to attack—you can calmly say, "You are upset, I'm starting to shut down, and before we get to anything constructive, the sun is going to set, and then we're going to have to start all over again tomorrow because I don't see us reaching any conclusion."

If he keeps pushing and says, "I am not upset—you're just not listening," you say, "Nah, forget it, it's gone, gone…the opportunity even to get into a conversation is gone, finito, flew the coop." The bully eventually will give up.

You can repeat this approach the next time. If the bully says, "Don't try that with me again," you just say, "Sorry, I find this exhausting, and I need to preserve my energy. If you can figure out a way to talk with me instead of at me, I am willing. Until then, count me out." Then walk away—which will be easy once you let go of the expectation that you will ever reach a win-win solution with this person.

NEUTRALIZE NEEDY PEOPLE

Unlike people who have a healthy need for others, toxically needy people expect constant help and attention and often use guilt to get it. No matter how much you do for them, it is never enough. They act like victims, suck you dry and leave you feeling depressed and incompetent because nothing ever gets better for them.

What to do…

Disengage: Imagine that the needy person has a hook that he is trying to snag you with, but the hook has missed you.

Respond: A needy person might say in a nails-on-a-chalkboard voice, "It's just not fair." Pause and calmly but firmly say, "It is completely fair to everyone that it affects."

GIVE IT TO TAKERS

The taker will constantly ask you for favors but never seems to have the time or energy to pitch in when you need help. Whereas needy people make you feel as if they are sucking you dry, takers make you feel as if they are grabbing at you.

What to do…

Disengage: Visualize the taker as a child grabbing at you to get your attention. Imagine yourself calmly tapping him on the wrist and saying, "Now, now, wait your turn."

Respond: Make a mental list of ways the taker could help you. The next time he asks for a favor say, "Sure! And you can help me out by…" If he balks, say, "I assume you don't mind doing a favor for me in return, right?"

Insist on a quid pro quo each time, and the taker will soon move on to an easier target.

More from Dr. Mark Goulston…

Eight Signs of a Jerk

A toxic person…

1. Interrupts.

2. Doesn't take turns.

3. Takes advantage of individuals who are down.

4. Gloats in victory.

5. Is sullen in defeat.

6. Is not fair.

7. Lacks integrity.

8. Is the kind of person you'll avoid if you possibly can.

Caught in the Middle Of a Feud?

Marjory Abrams, president of Boardroom Inc., 281 Tresser Blvd., Stamford, Connecticut 06901.

In my experience, being with people who don't get along is much harder than being one of the people in the feud.

"Forewarned is forearmed," advises relationship expert Dale Atkins, PhD, a psychologist in private practice in New York City and co-author of *I'm OK, You're My Parents: How to Overcome Guilt, Let Go of Anger, and Create a Relationship That Works.*

Here are Dr. Atkins's strategies to get you through uncomfortable times…

• **Practice visualization to put yourself in a peaceful, tension-relieving frame of mind.** Visualize yourself feeling happy during and after the event. Conjure up good sights, sounds and smells that give you pleasure.

• **Limit your exposure.** Instead of accepting a ride with one of the feuders, drive your own car. Instead of being a houseguest, consider a hotel stay. You may meet resistance the first time you stay elsewhere, but as time passes, it likely will be accepted.

• **Role-play how you'll handle tensions.** Think about which old arguments are likely to arise—and how you can avoid being drawn in. Set up signals with friends or family members to use when you need help changing the subject. Think of topics that get people talking about things that they love instead of things that make them angry.

• **Take a break.** Excuse yourself to go for a walk, call a friend, or simply use the bathroom as a refuge to compose yourself and regain perspective.

•**Be forgiving of weaknesses and annoying habits.**

My friend employs a technique that she learned from self-help guru Louise L. Hay: Any time a family member hurts her feelings, she says to herself, "I forgive you," which enables her to move on in peace.

Focus on the good, and be understanding of the not-so-good.

Help for the Grieving

When 18 people received weekly, 25-minute foot and/or hand massages for eight weeks following the death of a loved one, researchers found that the massages helped to diminish feelings of loneliness and provided physical comfort.

Journal of Clinical Nursing.

Time Makeover: Free Up Hours You Didn't Think You Had

Laura Vanderkam, a journalist based in New York City who writes frequently about how people spend their time. Her work has appeared in *The Wall Street Journal* and *USA Today*. She is author of *168 Hours: You Have More Time Than You Think* (Portfolio). Her Web site is *www.my168hours.com.*

Most of us have more free time than we realize. Even those who work 60 hours a week and sleep eight hours a night still have 52 additional hours each week. The problem is that we tend to burn many of those hours thoughtlessly on things that aren't vital or particularly enjoyable, such as watching TV or browsing the Internet.

Our lives would be more productive and fun if we consciously chose what to do with our time. *Here is an eight-step time-management makeover to do just that...*

Step 1: **Log how you spend your time for a week.** Record your activities in a notebook or on a free downloadable spreadsheet that's available on my Web site (*www.my168hours. com*, click "Your Time"). Make sure to include any breaks that you permit yourself in the middle of other tasks. If you think the week isn't representative of a typical week, record another week.

Step 2: **Create your "List of 100 Dreams."** There's a reason most of us don't spend much time pursuing the things we really want—we don't know what we really want.

Create a list of 100 things that you would like to accomplish—not just large, ambitious goals, but also smaller things that you suspect would make you excited or joyful...or that you might remember with fondness or pride when you look back on your life.

Examples: Your list might include vacation destinations that you would like to visit... projects that you want to complete related to your career or a hobby...skills that you would like to acquire...even books that you would like to read.

At least a few of the 100 dreams should be things that can be achieved in one day. These are likely to be checked off your list quickly, boosting your confidence in your ability to accomplish your more difficult dreams.

Examples: Reading a children's book you never got around to when you were a kid... attending a performance of a favorite opera... making an apple pie from scratch.

Helpful: If you cannot come up with 100 dreams, try just 25 and proceed with the following steps anyway. Return to your list periodically until you get to 100.

Step 3: **Identify your core competencies.** What do you do better than anyone else...and what are you better positioned to do than anyone else?

Examples: Perhaps no one is as good as you are at dreaming up new sales channels for your company's products...or at teaching young children.

We seem to feel most useful and happy when we devote time to tasks for which we see ourselves as irreplaceable. Examine your one-week time log. How much of your time are you devoting to your core competencies? You want to devote as much time to them as possible.

Step 4: **Clear the slate.** Rethink your time commitments. There are 168 hours in every week, and how we spend those hours is for us alone to decide. Yes, we all need to eat and sleep, and most of us need to do something to earn money—but it's empowering to start from scratch and rethink every time commitment, even those that seem inflexible.

Examples: If you are willing to earn less, you could quit your job and find a less time-consuming career. If you are willing to have simpler meals, you could save the time you spend cooking.

Step 5: **Print out a new, blank weekly log from my Web site**…or take out a fresh piece of paper. Fill in your new schedule with your priorities and options in mind. Start by thinking in broad terms about when you would like to work…sleep…spend time with family and friends…and engage in specific, structured leisure activities.

Example: If your goal is to spend more time with your young children or grandkids, you could leave the office at 4:00 twice a week, then make up that lost time by spending an hour or two responding to nonurgent work e-mails from home after the kids are in bed.

Also, put your morning hours to better use. The morning is when we are most alert and energetic—yet most of us waste this time puttering around, checking our e-mails or sitting in rush-hour traffic. Make the morning your time to pursue your most important dream… or to get some exercise. If you currently have no free time on weekday mornings, go to bed an hour earlier and get up an hour earlier.

Next, schedule your core-competency time. Block out specific time for work and personal time to pursue whatever it is that you do better than everyone else.

Finally, choose one or two entries from your "List of 100 Dreams," and write them into this week's schedule wherever you find openings. Larger dreams should be broken into specific

"actionable steps," which can be included on the schedule.

Example: If the dream is "to launch my own business," the first actionable step might be "speak with experienced business owners I know about how to get started."

Step 6: **Ignore, minimize or outsource things that you don't enjoy,** that aren't very important or that others could do as well as you. What household tasks do you like least? Which chores absorb the most time? Answers might include mowing the lawn, doing your laundry or picking up clutter. Pay someone to do all these things, or lower your standards— who says that you have to clean every week?

Step 7: **Fill up free moments with small sources of joy.** There are brief open blocks of time during even the busiest days. We tend not to take full advantage of this time because we are not properly prepared for it.

Compile a list of things that bring you joy that take 30 minutes or less…and another list of things that give you joy that take 10 minutes or less.

Examples: Reading a few pages from a novel…doing yoga stretches…or working on a crossword puzzle.

Step 8: **Tune up your schedule each year.** Does your life feel in balance? Are your major priorities being met? Are you making inroads on your 100 Dreams list? If not, again log your time for a week and search for time that could be put to better use.

Eventually, creating a life in which you have it all will no longer seem so hard.

Keep on Smiling

People who are in a good mood think creatively, finds new research. Volunteers who were uplifted (from watching videos of laughing babies, for example) performed better at creative problem-solving than those saddened (by listening to gloomy music, for example).

University of Western Ontario, *www.uwo.ca.*

Can't Seem to Get Organized? Here's What's Holding You Back...It's NOT That You Don't Have Time

Linda Samuels, founder of Oh, So Organized!, a professional organizing service based in Croton-on-Hudson, New York. She was given a CPO-CD designation (Certified Professional Organizer in Chronic Disorganization) from the nonprofit National Study Group on Chronic Disorganization, located in St. Louis. Samuels is author of *The Other Side of Organized: Finding Balance Between Chaos and Perfection* (Oh, So Publishing). Her Web site is *www.ohsoorganized.com*.

For the chronically cluttered, the most important part of getting more organized is not *doing* the cleaning and sorting—it's *finding the motivation* to do the cleaning and sorting. Without having motivation, organizing seems like a pointless and unpleasant chore and is continuously shunted to the bottom of the to-do list.

You can, however, transform organizing into something that you *want* to do, making the chore less painful and more likely to be seen through to completion...

HOW WILL IT HELP?

Before you begin organizing, think about how it will help you achieve something that matters deeply to you.

Would living in an organized home or working in an organized office...

• **Make you feel more calm and happier?**

• **Make you more efficient by eliminating time wasted looking for things?**

• **Improve your relationship with your spouse, who considers organization an important skill?**

• **Make it much easier to move around your home?**

• **Allow you to easily entertain?**

• **Make you appear more professional to a boss, improving your odds of promotion?**

If you're not sure how getting organized would help you reach your goals, take out a piece of paper and write words that convey how you would like your life to feel. If words such as "calm," "controlled," "peaceful," "efficient" or "simple" appear on your list, organizing can help.

Or clip pictures from magazines that convey what you want your life to look like. Pin these pictures to a bulletin board, and compare them to your actual surroundings. If your life is significantly more cluttered than the pictures, organization is the path to the life you want.

MINOR ANNOYANCES

If you cannot find a major motivation to get organized, search for minor annoyances that organizing could help you overcome. Carry a pocket-sized pad for three days, and jot down inconveniences caused by disorganization in your home or office.

These minor inconveniences might not be troubling enough to inspire you to fundamentally change your life and become organized—but they might be sufficiently annoying that spending a few minutes solving key problems will seem like time well-spent.

Rank the annoyances on your list, then do just enough organizing to solve the most exasperating of them. A few minutes' effort could improve your life measurably—and that might inspire you to tackle additional disorganization annoyances, too.

Examples: If your number-one disorganization annoyance is time wasted searching for your keys each morning, install a key hook by the door. If it is a cluttered kitchen counter that makes it difficult to prepare meals, spend a half-hour or so clearing the counter. Then think of a better way to control the things that tend to wind up on your counter, such as a basket to consolidate all the mail, newspapers and daily paperwork.

MEANINGFUL CLUTTER

It's perfectly normal to feel emotional bonds to certain possessions. In our minds, an object might represent a person who was once an important part of our life, such as a deceased spouse or parent...or a long-ago time in our life, such as the year that we spent pursuing a dream profession.

It can be extremely difficult to let go of all these emotion-laden objects, but we often get overwhelmed by our many possessions when we keep too much.

Better: Find a way to honor the memory of the person or time that the object represents without holding on to the object itself...

•**Take a picture of the item,** write a note about its meaning, then paste these in a scrapbook rather than keep the object itself.

•**Find the item a new home with someone who will get more use out of it** than you would now—perhaps give it to another family member or donate it to a charity.

•**Select one or two items from a large collection** to represent the group.

Examples: Select a favorite book to keep from an extensive library, then sell or donate the rest. Or select one favorite garment from a departed spouse's wardrobe to keep in his/her memory, then donate the rest to charity.

Do not attempt to let go of your meaningful clutter all at once, as such wholesale purging often causes people to dig in their heels and refuse to get rid of anything. It is better to give up just a few of these items initially. Dispose of more only after a few weeks have passed, when you discover that the initial culling was not as emotionally wrenching as you had feared.

THE DAILY 15

It's hard to find time for marathon organizing sessions and harder still to find the motivation. Instead, commit to organizing for just 15 minutes every day. Not only does a 15-minute-a-day commitment feel less daunting than a do-it-all-at-once approach, it turns organizing into a daily habit, improving the odds that you will stay organized.

For each 15-minute organizing session, do the following...

•**Target a specific task,** such as sorting a pile of mail or organizing your junk drawer.

•**Set a timer.** The rush of adrenaline that comes with working against a clock will help you accomplish more.

•**Put on music.** Choose music you enjoy, but lean toward calming songs if organizing conjures up feelings of anxiety in you...or upbeat songs if organizing makes you unhappy,

bored or lethargic. Singing along can provide an additional energy boost.

•**Monitor your self-talk.** If you mutter to yourself, *I hate doing this* or *This is a waste of time* before or during organizing sessions, the chore will seem unpleasant and be unsuccessful. Respond to such self-talk using positive thoughts, such as, *This will help me live the life I want.* Picture yourself living an organized life in a clutter-free home. Note how calm and secure this feels.

•**Consider enlisting an organizing buddy.** If you have trouble sticking to your daily organizing schedule, ask a friend who lives nearby to come over to help you. Offer to help this person with one of his/her household chores in exchange. Adding a social element makes organizing more pleasant.

Be sure to choose an organizing buddy who has a strong ability to focus and who is not judgmental.

Chewing Gum Makes You Smarter...and Other Surprising Brain Boosters

David Grotto, RD, LDN, registered dietitian and founder and president of Nutrition Housecall, LLC. He is also author of *101 Optimal Life Foods* (Bantam).

We all know to eat a healthy diet, but some brain-boosting foods may surprise you...

•**Chewing gum.** OK, it's not exactly a food, but it's more than just something to keep your mouth occupied. Researchers at Northwestern University found that people who chew gum have increased blood flow to the brain—and a corresponding increase in cognitive performance. People who chew gum also report a reduction in stress, which protects brain cells from stress-related hormones.

Recommended: Chew gum when you are stressed or have challenging mental work to do. Opt for sugarless.

•**Frozen berries.** Raspberries, blueberries and strawberries are among the best sources of brain-protecting antioxidants. Researchers from the Jean Mayer USDA Human Nutrition Research Center on Aging at Tufts University found that animals given blueberries showed virtually no evidence in the brain of the cell-damaging effects of free radicals—and they did better on cognitive tests.

Frozen berries typically contain more antioxidants than fresh berries because they're picked and processed at the peak of ripeness.

Recommended: One-and-a-half cups of frozen or fresh berries at least two to three times a week. Darker berries will contain the most antioxidants.

•**Turmeric.** It's one of the most potent anti-inflammatory spices. People who eat turmeric several times per week could have significant drops in *C-reactive protein*, a substance that indicates inflammation in the brain and other tissues.

A study that looked at more than 1,000 participants (average age 68.9) found that those who either often or occasionally ate turmeric performed better on mental-status evaluations than those who rarely or never ate it.

Recommended: Add at least one-quarter teaspoon of turmeric to recipes several times a week. (Turmeric is one of the spices in curry.)

•**Hazelnuts.** These contain the highest concentration of folate of all the tree nuts (including walnuts, almonds and pecans). Low levels of folate have been associated with poor cognition and depression. Other foods rich in folate include spinach, beans, oranges, avocados and wheat germ.

Recommended: One handful of hazelnuts several times a week.

•**Cilantro.** This herb, also known as coriander and Chinese parsley, has long been used in Iranian folk medicine for stress relief. Stress has been linked to a speeding up of the aging process of the brain. Modern research also has revealed the benefits of cilantro—an animal study demonstrated that cilantro eased stress.

Recommended: One tablespoon of fresh cilantro several times every week. It's often used in salsa and guacamole and to top tacos, chili, stews and soups.

THREE "GOOD" VICES

Perhaps you have heard that certain "bad foods," such as coffee, red wine and chocolate, are good for the heart. *They also are good for the brain...*

•**Coffee.** A Finnish study of more than 1,400 participants found that regular coffee drinkers were less likely to experience dementia than people who did not drink coffee. People who drank moderate amounts of coffee in midlife (three to five cups daily) had the lowest risk, probably because the antioxidants in coffee inhibit age-related brain damage.

The caffeine in coffee—a five-ounce serving of coffee typically contains 30 milligrams (mg) to 150 mg, depending on how it is prepared—also improves mental abilities. Studies of university students have shown that when students drink coffee before a test, they score higher than when they abstain.

Recommended: One to three cups per day. If coffee gives you the jitters, try green tea, which also is good for the brain but has slightly less caffeine.

•**Red wine.** Red wine contains *resveratrol*, a *polyphenol*, that helps prevent inflammation and oxidation of brain tissue. People who drink moderate amounts of red wine have lower risks for stroke and dementia. Laboratory studies indicate that red wine can decrease the accumulation of *beta-amyloid*, the substance found in the brains of Alzheimer's patients. (In a healthy brain, beta-amyloid is broken down and eliminated.) White wine also contains polyphenols but in lower concentrations than reds.

Recommended: Up to two glasses of wine daily for men and one glass daily for women. Moderation is important because too much alcohol has been linked to increased risk for dementia.

Alcohol-free option: Concord grape juice. Some research suggests that it could be just as healthy as red wine when it comes to improvement in cognitive skills. Aim for one cup a day.

•**Chocolate.** The cocoa *flavonols* in chocolate inhibit free radicals. Flavonols also relax the linings of blood vessels. This helps reduce high blood pressure, one of the leading causes of dementia.

One study, conducted at Brigham and Women's Hospital in Boston, found that participants who drank one cup of high-flavonol cocoa daily had, after two weeks, an average increase in brain circulation of about one-third.

Chocolates with a high percentage of cocoa don't necessarily have a high concentration of flavonols—processing techniques can destroy the protective compounds.

Recommended: Look for products that advertise a high flavonol content on the label (60% to 85%). One ounce is enough to get the benefits without unnecessary sugar and calories.

DON'T FORGET FISH

You probably have heard that fish is "brain food," but we couldn't do a brain-boosting article without mentioning it. One study of 3,660 adults age 65 and older found that those who ate omega-3–rich fish three times every week or more were 25% less likely to have silent infarcts, ministrokes that can happen repeatedly, leading to a condition known as multi-infarct dementia.

Memory Superfoods

Surprising foods, and a beverage, that can improve your memory…

•**Apples**—eating two or three a day increases levels of *acetylcholine*, a *neurotransmitter* that helps maintain memory, which decreases with age.

•**Chicken breast**—all foods high in *niacin*, such as chicken breast, fish and dairy products, appear to lower the risk for mental decline and Alzheimer's disease.

•**Coffee**—drinking three to five cups of coffee a day seems to reduce the risk for dementia and Alzheimer's.

Studies at University of Massachusetts, Rush Institute for Healthy Aging, Centers for Disease Control and Prevention, and University of Kuopio, Finland, reported in *Prevention*.

Common Spice Improves Focus

Cinnamon can help you stay very focused. It speeds the rate at which the brain processes visual cues. Try chewing cinnamon-flavored gum before doing something that will require quick responses, such as playing tennis. To make cinnamon a regular part of your diet, sprinkle one teaspoon of it on oatmeal or cereal at breakfast.

Daniel G. Amen, MD, Amen Clinics, Newport Beach, California, writing in *AARP The Magazine*, 601 E St. NW, Washington, DC 20049.

Mineral for a Better Mind

When 26 participants with mild memory loss had either a 1,000-microgram (mcg) *chromium picolinate* supplement or a placebo daily for 12 weeks, the supplement group performed better on memory tests while the placebo group showed no change.

Theory: This trace mineral reduces insulin resistance, a condition in which the body's cells don't use insulin properly. Too little insulin in the brain may contribute to poor memory.

If you're concerned about your memory: Ask your doctor about taking 400 mcg of chromium picolinate daily.

Caution: This supplement may affect dosage requirements for diabetes medications.

Robert Krikorian, PhD, associate professor of clinical psychiatry, University of Cincinnati, Ohio.

Speak Out for a Better Memory

Speak out loud to improve memory when studying. Reading words out loud makes them easier to remember. Identify which information is most important for you to remember, and read only that material out loud.

Colin MacLeod, PhD, professor in the department of psychology at University of Waterloo, Waterloo, Ontario, Canada, and leader of a study of more than 200 people, published in *Journal of Experimental Psychology: Learning, Memory, and Cognition.*

Is the Internet Making Us Stupid? What It's Doing to Our Brains

Nicholas Carr, a journalist located in Boulder, Colorado, whose writings regarding the social, economic and business implications of technology have appeared in *The New York Times, Wired, The Atlantic* and other publications. Carr previously served as executive editor of *Harvard Business Review* and was a principal at Mercer Management Consulting. He is the author of *The Shallows: What the Internet Is Doing to Our Brains* (Norton). His Web site is *www.nicholasgcarr.com.*

The Internet is changing our brains. Neurologists and psychologists have discovered that human brains process Internet pages differently than they do printed pages. That can affect how much we learn when we read—and even alter our brains themselves.

The human brain "rewires" itself depending on how it is used, an ability neurologists refer to as "plasticity." An experiment by UCLA psychology professor Gary Small, MD, showed that spending one hour per day on the Internet for just one week alters our neural pathways. That neural rewiring could have unfortunate consequences.

Example: During the past five centuries, reading books has helped train human brains to concentrate intently over extended periods of time, an ability that has helped our species produce ideas and inventions. If we abandon books in favor of the Internet, our ability to maintain focus and think up new ideas might diminish.

Other consequences of using the Internet and what we can do about them...

INTERRUPTION SYSTEM

When we read online, words are not the only information coming at us. There usually are eye-catching advertisements alongside the text and hyperlinks in the text in case we wish to jump to different Web pages on related topics. We might have our e-mail program open and a Facebook feed, too, alerting us each time a new message arrives. Even when a printed book is transferred to an electronic device connected to the Internet, it turns into something very much like a Web site, with links and other digital enhancements.

These distractions don't just slow our reading, they also make it less likely that we will understand and retain new knowledge.

Example: Canadian researchers asked 70 people to read a short article on a computer screen. Some read traditional text, while others read a version containing hyperlinks. Only 10% of people who read the traditional text reported any difficulty following this article—versus 75% of people who read the hyperlink version. Those who read traditional text did so faster, too.

Simply ignoring online distractions doesn't really work. We can choose not to click a hyperlink or open an e-mail message—but ironically, the fact that our brains must make this split-second decision to not be distracted is in itself enough of a distraction to interrupt our concentration.

Reading books often is portrayed as a passive activity when compared with surfing the Web, but the truth is, we think more deeply when we read printed pages than when we read Internet pages. The "quiet space" afforded by the printed page lets us mull over what we read. That quiet space usually doesn't exist online, so we are less likely to form reasoned conclusions about the validity of what we read or to develop unique ideas by combining the new information we read with things we already know.

What to do: When you wish to give your full attention to online or eReader text, close your e-mail program, your Facebook page and any other competing information feeds on the screen. Also, use software/settings that help to minimize interruptions. The free, easy-to-use programs Instapaper Text (at *www.instapaper. com/text*) and Readability (at *www.readability. com/addons*) strip away most, though not all, of the distractions from online sites, leaving mainly straightforward text. Or use the Safari 5 Web browser, which has a "Reader" button in the address field that works similarly (*www. apple.com/safari*).

LESS IS READ

The Internet places more information than ever at our fingertips—yet evidence suggests that it actually leads us to read and rely upon a smaller set of information resources, encouraging uncreative group thinking.

The trouble is that the Internet does not just provide information. It also subtly evaluates it for us. Search engines typically sort their results in order of popularity, and few of us scan past the first page of results.

Example: A study by James Evans, PhD, a sociologist from the University of Chicago, indicated that the increased availability of academic research on the Web has led academics to read and reference a narrower set of articles when they write journal articles. The Internet enables them to identify which prior journal articles are most popular with their peers and most related to their own research, and they often ignore the rest.

True, the most popular Web pages and articles are likely to be the most practical—but reading obscure authors, ideas and opinions has value, too. When we read things that most other people have not read, we increase the odds that we'll have original ideas.

The ease and speed with which we can find specific facts online carry a hidden cost, too. Prior to the Internet, we often had to dig deep into newspapers, magazines and books to locate the facts we needed. These days, search engines such as Google will take us to the desired snippet of data in seconds. Once we have found the fact that we are after, we typically stop reading. That is very unfortunate, because the time we previously had "wasted" searching through lots of resources gave us a chance to stumble across other important facts or ideas.

What to do: Scan beyond the first page of results when you use a search engine to explore a topic of interest. This will give you a chance to learn more than what almost everyone else interested in the topic already knows.

When an Internet search for a piece of information leads you to a compelling article, book or Web site, jot down its name, then explore it more fully when you have some free time.

LESS SOCIAL INTELLIGENCE

The Internet is no longer confined to simply our desktops. eReaders, smartphones and even vehicle dashboards increasingly permit us to bring the online universe wherever we go—a trend that will accelerate in the years ahead.

The danger of digital distractions while you drive already is very well-publicized. Less discussed is the potential danger that such portable distractions pose while we're just sitting around with friends and loved ones. Preliminary research by the Brain and Creativity Institute at the University of Southern California suggests that the distractions created by the use of mobile Internet devices make it less likely that we will fully grasp the psychological states of those around us. The weaker our grasp of other people's moods, the less able we are to show appropriate empathy, weakening the bonds that hold humans together.

What to do: Turn off digital devices when you spend time with people, or at the very least, silence the chime that notifies you when phone calls or new messages come in. Even if you don't stop in the middle of a conversation to check incoming messages, that chime alone could be just enough of a distraction to inhibit your ability to focus on your friends.

Win the Inner Game of Stress

John Horton, MD, a physician specializing in preventive medicine and stress, Westlake Village, California. He is coauthor of *The Inner Game of Stress: Outsmart Life's Challenges and Fulfill Your Potential* (Random House).

Stress creates unproductive panic, inhibits creative thought, contributes to chronic illness and is just plain exhausting. But no matter what is going on in our lives, we can tap into our inner resources to keep stress from doing damage. Different strategies work for different people.

We all are playing an inner game whether we recognize it or not. That means that while we are all involved in outer games (overcoming obstacles in the outside world to achieve our goals), we are at the same time faced with inner obstacles, such as fear, self-doubt, frustration, pain and distractions. Inner obstacles prevent us from expressing our full range of capabilities and enjoying time to the utmost.

The secret lies in knowing that you have choices about how you look at external events, how you delineate events, how you attribute meaning to them and how you react to them mentally and emotionally. The key is to recognize that every person has the internal wisdom to bypass the frustrations and fears that pull them into the negative cycle of stress.

BECOME YOUR OWN CEO

Feeling powerless and victimized is among the most common sources of stress. You are likely to feel more in control if you consider yourself the CEO of your life. *To do so…*

•**Write a mission statement.** What is the primary mission of your life?

Examples: To create prosperity for myself and my family…to pay attention to my inner life as well as my achievements…etc.

•**Identify your main product or service.** What do you provide to others? These could be specific to a particular business.

Example: As a doctor, my services would include being up-to-date in my knowledge… knowing the best specialists to refer a patient to…seeing patients quickly.

•**List your company's resources.** Include both your internal resources—positive personal traits, such as your compassion, intelligence and humor—and external resources—your financial assets, friends and possessions. Ask yourself whether you're getting as much from each of these resources as you could.

LOST CONTROL?

•**Consider whether you've given up too much control of your own corporation.** How much would it cost to buy back some shares?

Example: Did you sell too many shares of yourself for your home? If massive mortgage payments fill you with stress—or force you to remain in a job that fills you with stress—perhaps you should move into a smaller home and take back those shares.

This CEO thought process can serve as a reminder that we are not helpless. Your life is yours, and you get to decide everything. It is always your choice, even if you decide to comply with the wishes of someone else. Once you become aware of this, your freedom will evolve and your stress will ease.

REGAINING CONTROL

Trying to control things that are outside our control is enormously stressful, yet many of us do this. *When you feel stressed, consider…*

•**What don't I control here?**

•**What am I trying to control here?**

•**What could I control here that I'm not currently controlling?**

Confronting these questions can help us to focus on things that we can accomplish and reduce our stress over things that we cannot.

Example: When a man who is stressed over his wife's poor health asks himself these questions, he realizes her health is not something he can control, so he should stop trying to. What he can control is his attitude. If he's upbeat, he can help his wife be upbeat.

THE MAGIC PEN

Select a stress-causing situation in your life, then write down your usual inner dialog on this subject. Once you have written everything that comes to your mind, take out a new piece of paper and imagine that your pen has been magically endowed with just one of your positive inner resources. This resource might be your clarity, compassion, openness, serenity or patience—any quality that you consider a personal strength. Try to empty your mind of all thought, then let your magic pen write a message to you about this stressful subject. Don't censor the pen—let it write everything.

Example: A man feels guilty about his grown son, who can't find direction in life. If he endowed his pen with his compassion, the pen might write that he did his best to raise his son and that his son is doing his best to live his life.

19

Career Consultant

You're Hired! Inside Secrets to Landing a Job Over the Phone

mployers are increasingly using phone interviews to thin the herd of job applicants who apply for every opening in this uncertain economy. For these applicants, phone interviews present a different set of challenges—and a different group of opportunities—than traditional in-person interviews.

Examples: There's no way to make eye contact during a phone interview, which makes it more difficult to establish rapport and pick up nonverbal signals. However, applicants can consult notes during phone interviews, effectively turning them into open-book tests.

How well applicants handle the unfamiliar nuances of phone interviews often determines whether they have any shot at landing the job.

BEFORE THE PHONE INTERVIEW

Do not treat phone interviews casually just because they take place in the comfort of your home. *Prepare just as diligently as you would for an in-person interview, plus...*

●**Talk to a picture.** Search for a photo of your interviewer on LinkedIn.com or the employer's Web site.

Expand this photo to a reasonable size on your computer, print it and pin it up in front of you at your desk. We tend to sound more comfortable and natural when we're talking to a human face than a faceless voice.

Helpful: If you cannot find a picture of the interviewer or don't know who the interviewer will be, select a photo of someone you respect but do not fear—perhaps Abraham Lincoln or a business leader you hold in high regard.

Paul Bailo, CEO and founder of Phone Interview Pro, a career coaching company based in Trumbull, Connecticut, that specializes in phone communication for job seekers, *www.phoneinterviewpro.com.* He is author of *The Official Phone Interview Handbook* (Mirasmart).

●**Eliminate all distractions.** Select or create a clean, spartan room in your home for your call. Remove all projects and messes from this room. Lock the door before the interview, and ask family members to remain quiet and keep their distance. Postpone any landscaper visits scheduled for that day. If deliveries are expected, post a note on the door asking that packages be left without ringing the bell. If you have a dog prone to barking or whining, ask a friend to take the dog elsewhere during the interview, or at least put it in a part of your home far from where you will be taking the call.

●**If you're given a choice between placing the interview phone call or receiving it, opt to receive.** Having the interviewer place the call can foster a subtle sense in the interviewer that he or she is pursuing you, not the other way around.

●**Take the call on a landline.** A poor-quality connection is more likely on a cell or cordless connection and can be distracting. Turn off the call-waiting function before the interview to eliminate any other potential telecom distraction. If your landline has multiple extensions and there will be someone else in the home, tape notes to the extensions asking that they not be used.

If you cannot avoid taking this call on a cordless phone or cell phone, at least make sure it is fully charged.

●**Dress professionally.** Some job applicants conduct telephone interviews in jeans or bathrobes. Dress as if it is a face-to-face interview. The interviewer can't see you, but you can see yourself, and you are more likely to feel and sound professional if you look the part.

●**Hang up notes about the company and your qualifications on vertical surfaces near the phone.** Documents to post include a copy of your résumé…a list of questions to ask the interviewer…key facts and statistics about the company and its industry…and a list of the position's requirements and how you meet them.

These notes can provide useful reminders of what you wish to say and allow you to supply a level of detail that you likely could not if you were working from memory.

Posting these notes on walls and other vertical surfaces is better than laying them on a desk because it decreases the chance that an important paper will get covered and lost…it prevents the interviewer from hearing pages ruffle…and it allows you to sit upright—good posture encourages a strong speaking voice.

●**Take a lozenge or a teaspoon of honey one hour before the interview even if your throat feels fine.** Phone interviewers cannot see us, so they tend to form a mental image of us based in no small part on our voice. Using lozenges or honey increases the odds that the mental image your voice projects will be one of strength and vibrancy.

Also: Read a newspaper story out loud or sing a song prior to early morning phone interviews to stretch your vocal cords. Place a cup of water beside the phone before the call in case your throat begins to feel dry.

●**Call to confirm the interview 24 hours before the scheduled time.** This shows professionalism and responsibility. It also plants your name on the interviewer's mind for an additional day, making it more likely that you will be remembered at the end of the interview. And it lets you hear your interviewer's voice—or at least his or her assistant's voice—prior to the interview, humanizing this person and reducing your tension.

DURING THE PHONE INTERVIEW

When an interviewer calls you, answer the phone on the second or third ring. Answering on the very first ring can convey a subtle sense of desperation, and answering after the third ring makes you seem unprepared. *When you pick up…*

●**Say "Hello," not "Hi."** "Hi" does not sound professional.

●**Pursue small talk for up to 90 seconds.** This can develop rapport. Possible small-talk topics could include the difference in weather between the interviewer's location and your own (check that city's forecast online before the call)…or a positive recent mention of the company in the press.

Examples: "I wish I were down there today. I see it's 75 degrees" or "I saw that article regarding XYZ Co. in *The Wall Street Journal* yesterday."

• **Skip the "ums," "ahs" and "you knows," as they make job applicants sound nervous.** If you are prone to them, gently bite on your tongue as you mentally prepare responses to phone interviewers' questions. There's nothing wrong with pauses of as long as two to three seconds.

• **Speak in sound bites.** Nervous job applicants sometimes ramble on the phone, but concise answers sound more professional.

Helpful: Watch the evening news on TV, and listen to the people interviewed—their responses usually are no more than a sentence or two. Strive to make your responses just as concise. It is OK to follow up some of these concise answers with longer examples that illustrate your points, however.

• **As the interview draws to a close,** ask, "Is it OK if I contact you later if I have additional questions?" Receiving permission to do this decreases the odds that the interviewer will be annoyed later when you make contact with him to keep your name on his mind.

A day or two after the interview: Send the interviewer a three- or four-paragraph e-mail summarizing what you spoke about during the phone interview. Focus on how you can help the company make money or save money.

Three to four days after the interview: Send a handwritten thank-you note. This note should thank the interviewer for his/her time, not discuss the job. Use top-quality paper and a professional-looking stamp—no flowers or animals…flags are best.

Think Before You Act

Plan carefully before quitting your job no matter how unhappy you are at work.

What to do: Assume that you will be unemployed for a long time—so save much more than the usual three to six months of cash that you always should have on hand. Shop around for health insurance—employer coverage usu-

ally stops at the end of the month in which you resign, though you may be eligible for a health insurance extension through COBRA. Use up the money in your flexible spending account or you will probably lose it when you quit. Plan what to do with your 401(k)—you can roll it into an IRA or your next employer's 401(k) plan.

Kiplinger.com.

Severance Savvy

Severance packages are negotiable. Do not simply sign whatever severance agreement you are offered. Talk to your boss, the head of your division or the company CEO, not someone in the human resources department. Ask that health benefits be extended while you are being paid severance, or longer. If your stock options will soon vest or bonuses will be paid, ask for your share immediately.

Alan L. Sklover, JD, employment attorney, Sklover & Donath, LLC, New York City.

Are You Eligible for *Underemployment* Benefits?

Underemployment benefits are available in some states to individuals working part-time at lower wages than they used to receive. States offering underemployment benefits have different ways of calculating them—and they usually are available only to people working one or two days a week, not to workers with lower-paying jobs who go to them every day. But benefits also may be offered to full-time workers whose employers require them to reduce their hours.

What to do: Contact your state unemployment office to find out if these benefits are available and what the state's rules are.

Bankrate.com.

Job Hunting for the "Overqualified"

Marjory Abrams, president of Boardroom Inc., 281 Tresser Blvd., Stamford, Connecticut 06901.

My friend lost her job a year-and-a-half ago. She is in her 40s and has two decades of experience in her industry. But when she applies for a job—any job—she keeps hearing that she is "overqualified" and gets turned down. How is she supposed to respond to that?

Dr. Paul Powers, one of the country's preeminent management psychologists and author of *Winning Job Interviews* (at *www.drpaulpowers. com*), shared several pointers for job seekers who are facing the "overqualified" label...

• **Reframe your résumé.** If the first thing a potential employer reads about your job history is "vice president," he/she might assume that your salary requirements are too high. Instead, highlight all of the experience you have with the relevant, and even rudimentary, skills necessary to do the job. "Do not dumb down your résumé," advises Dr. Powers. "Just reduce the emphasis on high-level achievements."

• **Inject some humor.** Dr. Powers suggests approaching the situation with a little humor, for example, by saying, "Actually, I don't really have that much experience. I'm still only in my 20s. I just wrinkled prematurely." Then proceed to explain how your "overqualifications" actually are a positive quality—and that your experience, work ethic and maturity will be invaluable to the company.

• **Avoid lying.** Potential employers do worry that you will leave for a better position. Even if that's in the back of your mind, you still can be honest without derailing your chances.

Your response: "I know that our economy is looking at slower growth and that there will be fewer job opportunities in the future. So I'm here. I can make an immediate impact on this company from day one."

Job Hunting on the Internet

For more efficient online job hunting, go to company Web sites—they lead to more new hires than any other method except personal referrals. Try *www.linkup.com*, which pulls together postings just from company sites. Consider using niche boards to focus on a specific industry. Go to *www.internetinc.com* for a list of job boards by career field.

Caution: Pay-for-use job boards may claim more listings than they actually have and are not a good source of jobs.

SmartMoney, 1211 Avenue of the Americas, New York City 10036, *www.smartmoney.com*.

Résumés for Seasoned Job Seekers: Tricks and Traps

Do provide your cell-phone number and an e-mail address on a résumé, but don't list a fax number—it makes you seem dated. Devote at least half of a page to your most recent experience—résumés now can be longer than one page. Don't start with an objective—open with a summary explaining what you can do for the company. Also, do not use clichés such as *motivated, innovative, results-oriented* and similar words. Don't provide experience from more than 15 years ago unless it is truly outstanding. And, don't reveal when you got your academic degrees.

What else to do: If you have had a period of self-employment, make it a selling point by mentioning specific projects you handled and by naming clients.

Wendy Enelow, résumé writer and career coach in Coleman Falls, Virginia, and coauthor of *Cover Letter Magic* (JIST Works).

How to Shine in the Interview

To ace a job interview, take time the night before and the day of the meeting to relax and visualize exactly the outcome you desire. Arrive early, and use the extra minutes to talk with the receptionist and check out the decor and publications in the reception area to assess the atmosphere and come up with topics for conversation.

Throughout a meeting: Demonstrate your knowledge of an organization by saying something flattering about the organization, such as, "I am particularly happy to be talking with you because your company has a wonderful reputation for service to clients." Show that you are a good fit for the position by making a connection between your skills and the company's goals, which you can get from the company's annual report, Web site or by asking questions.

Nella Barkley, president and cofounder, Crystal-Barkley Corporation, Charleston, South Carolina, and coauthor of *The Crystal-Barkley Guide to Taking Charge of Your Career* (Workman). Her Web site is *www.careerlife.com*.

Earn High Pay Right Out of College

The highest starting pay after college goes to engineering majors. The starting median salary for a petroleum engineer is $93,000*... chemical engineer, $64,800...nuclear engineer, $63,900...electrical engineer, $60,800 and aerospace engineer, $59,400.

Lynn O'Shaughnessy, financial journalist, author of *The College Solution* (FT Press) and creator of TheCollegeSolutionBlog.com.

*Rates subject to change.

Dangerous Professions

Fishing is far more dangerous than police work. The fatal-accident rate for fishermen and related fishing workers is 200 per 100,000 full-time workers...compared to a rate of just 13.1 for police and sheriff's patrol officers and 4.4 for firefighters. Farming also is dangerous. The rate of fatal occupational injuries for farmers and ranchers is 38.5 per 100,000 full-time workers.

US Department of Labor data for 2009—the latest information available—reported on the Web at *www.marketwatch.com*.

Can't Find a Job? Start Your Own Business Says *Bottom Line/Personal* Founder Marty Edelston

Martin Edelston, founder and chairman of Boardroom Inc., which publishes *Bottom Line/Personal, Bottom Line/Health, Bottom Line/Natural Healing...Daily Health News* and *Healthy Woman from Bottom Line* e-letters...and numerous books, including *The World's Greatest Treasury of Health Secrets*. Edelston is author of *I-Power: The Secrets of Great Business in Bad Times*—it's available from *www.bottomlinepublications.com*.

With the unemployment rate hovering around 9%,* many people are having trouble securing work. Starting your own business may be the solution.

When I started Boardroom Inc. in my basement in 1972, I knew that I had a good idea. I saw the need for a publication that distilled practical how-to advice from America's leading business experts. Our writing would be clear and straightforward and would not bog the reader down in abstract philosophizing, jargon or wordy language. I titled the new publication *Boardroom Reports*.

Of course, it takes much more than a good idea to make a venture successful. In launching my business, I used lessons and principles that I had learned from the best business books and my decades of experience in a variety of jobs—from delivering milk as a 10-year-old to starting a mail-order book club and working

*Rate as of mid-August 2011.

as a business manager selling ads for a small magazine.

The strategies I used can help anyone start and grow a business…

●**Invest in the best expertise.** With my background in advertising sales, I knew that I could do a good job of marketing my idea. I also knew that while I could write sufficient promotional copy myself, I would need a professional to write truly great copy. I hired one of the country's leading copywriters, and he came up with what I considered an excellent headline.

I showed that copy to a group of luncheon buddies in the mail-order industry, and they thought I could do better. They all pushed me to retain the well-known copywriting genius Gene Schwartz, who wrote a brilliant headline and very powerful copy. The extra investment paid off when customers responded better to Gene's promotion. Brilliant copy is just as important today, whether you are marketing on the Internet or by mail.

●**Test your ideas.** Even though I believed passionately in my idea, I tested it before producing a single issue. I wanted to be sure that there was an audience that would be as excited about the publication as I was.

I did what's called a dry test. With a dry test, you measure interest through the response to a promotion without taking money for orders. I ran a series of small direct-mail campaigns and compared the response rates among different versions of the promotional copy. I then compared responses among the mailing lists rented from magazines and book programs.

Once I knew that there was a market for my idea, I retained a small staff—an editor and a secretary—to work with me on developing the product itself. I used the patterns revealed by testing to expand my mailing campaign and to get paying customers.

●**Look for low-risk ways to finance your new business.** I started Boardroom Inc. with just $30,000, which is the equivalent of about $155,000 in today's dollars. To protect my cash flow, I introduced projects in steps rather than all at once.

Example: Rather than launching one big, splashy direct-mail campaign, I did it a little at a time. Each week, I sent mailings to a new group of names on the lists I had rented. As payments came in, I was able to fund the next wave of promotion.

Revenue sharing is another financing method that always has worked well for me.

Example: Instead of paying up front for an ad for our product to appear in another publication, we offered that publication a 50-50 share of revenue resulting from the ad.

●**Involve your family.** The company that was handling all our fulfillment—the industry term for receiving and processing subscription orders and billing—couldn't seem to get the details right. I sat down with my wife and said, "I have an idea. Let's do the fulfillment ourselves. I'll buy used equipment, and you'll head the operation." She agreed, and we then put together a small team for her to manage, including a colleague of mine who had fulfillment experience, a former neighbor and my wife's sister-in-law.

Everyone worked in our basement on top of the Ping-Pong table—this was in the days before computers, when work was done mechanically or by hand. (The newsletter printing and mailing have always been handled by an outside company.) Within the first year, our three children also joined in. They were ages 9, 12 and 14 at the time, and they did an excellent job doing tasks, such as stuffing envelopes and arranging subscription orders in zip code sequence—surrounded by family and friends.

After two years, we relocated the operation out of our house to an office that was within walking distance of the junior and senior high schools, which made it safe and easy for our children to come to the office after school. Today my three children run the business.

●**Don't micromanage.** One reason my wife and I were able to work together successfully is that I did not tell her how to run her part of the operation. We set up regular meetings to make sure that we promptly addressed any questions and problems. It was important to treat the business portion of our relationship as business so feelings weren't hurt. During the workweek, while my wife supervised the fulfillment duties, I continued commuting to my magazine job in Manhattan. But I devoted evenings and weekends to developing our new business.

• **Tend to your relationships.** I have made a point of staying in touch with a wide circle of colleagues/friends throughout many years. These relationships have provided emotional support as well as valuable ideas, insights and resources.

Example: My network has helped us obtain office space more than once. In the early days, the inexpensive, temporary office I had arranged for my freelance editor was too cold. I realized how bad the situation was when I visited him one evening and saw him sitting at his typewriter wearing gloves with the fingers cut out. One of my neighbors had a satellite office in a good location. I offered to pay my neighbor to rent us a desk in his office for my editor, but he insisted on accommodating us at no charge.

Years later, I was looking for office space close to the New York Public Library, where we did a lot of our research. A longtime friend and colleague was partner at one of New York City's top advertising agencies, and its headquarters was across the street from the library. My friend promised me a good deal and sent me to talk to his office manager. Boardroom Inc. wound up subletting a marvelous office in that building near the library, and the agency even threw in some used furniture.

My network of contacts also has alerted me to important trends.

Example: After we had been in business for a few years, I heard through the grapevine that several other companies were planning to come out with publications that would compete with *Boardroom Reports.* I realized that we needed a complementary publication to set us apart. After many discussions with friends, I launched *Bottom Line/Personal.*

• **Give away a taste.** After *Bottom Line/Personal* was well-established, I was having lunch with my favorite list broker. We started brainstorming about possible directions for Boardroom Inc. When we first began talking about *Bottom Line/Personal*, the broker suggested that

we give away copies to new subscribers rather than requiring payment up front—this was a relatively new concept at the time. He told me that everyone who saw a copy wanted one—he joked that he and his wife fought over who would get to read each issue first because the information was so useful.

Based on his suggestion, we began offering free trial subscriptions, a strategy that appealed to customers and still works today.

Great Franchises Now

Reasonably priced home-based franchises are available from well-known brands. A Jazzercise franchise could be purchased for as little as $3,000,* and a business for planning cruises can be started for under $2,000. Other options for home-based business franchises include Stanley Steemer and Lawn Doctor.

The Kiplinger Letter, 1729 H St. NW, Washington, DC 20006, *www.kiplinger.com.*

*Prices subject to change.

A Second Chance...

Small-business borrowers are getting a second chance. Some banks that initially denied applications for small-business loans are agreeing to conduct a second review. Some are joining joint-review groups of banks to give potential borrowers access to more sources of capital.

What to do: If you are turned down for a small-business loan, request a review by the bank or its joint-review partners if it has any.

The Kiplinger Letter, 1729 H St. NW, Washington, DC 20006, *www.kiplinger.com.*

Free Software That Helps Your Business Run Smoothly

Free small-business tech tools can make it less expensive to start up or manage your company. OpenOffice (*www.openoffice.org*) is a variety of programs similar to Microsoft Office—and NeoOffice (*www.neooffice.org*) is a version of OpenOffice optimized for Macs. For sales tracking, invoicing and client-interaction monitoring, use phpBMS (*www.phpbms.org*). A small retailer could try out Lemón POS (*www.lemonpos.org*) for its point-of-sale software. And there are *almost-free* programs also worth considering. Dropbox (*www.dropbox.com*) will let you store and share files online—it is free for two gigabytes (GB) of space or $10/month* for 50GB and $20/month for 100GB. Google Apps (*www.google.com/apps*) gives businesses real-time collaboration and communication tools, supported by Google, for $50/year per user.

Entrepreneur.com.

*Prices subject to change.

How I Got on the *Today* Show—and Other Clever Ways to Get Free Publicity

Jane Pollak, whose egg-decoration business was featured on NBC's *Today* show and in publications ranging from *The New York Times* to *Country Living* magazine. Based in Westport, Connecticut, she is now a small-business coach and a speaker and, in 2002, was named the Home-Based Business Advocate for New England by the Small Business Administration. Pollak's also the author of *Soul Proprietor: 101 Lessons from a Lifestyle Entrepreneur* (Roberts). Her Web site is *www.janepollak.com*.

Celebrities are not the only ones who get on television talk shows and news programs. Unknowns who have distinctive passions, projects or talents are interviewed on these shows, too.

And, I should know. I was interviewed about egg decorating on NBC's *Today* show. Even though that was 10 years ago, I'm still asked how I, an unknown, got on the show. It is a good question and an important one. If you own any business, work on commission, have written a book or have a cause that is important to you, appearing on TV can provide unbeatable free publicity and legitimize you in the eyes of potential clients and allies.

Here's how to greatly increase your odds of getting on the air...

SET YOURSELF APART

The first step is to find a unique application for your passion or talent or a way to describe yourself that can make you seem distinctive. There are lots of talented artists in the world. I attracted a *Today* show producer's attention because I was one of the few artists painting eggs rather than canvases.

If what you do or make isn't very unique, search for a way to make your personal story sound distinctive. Are you the oldest person to be doing what you're doing? The one who has been doing it the longest? The only one to overcome a particular obstacle? Anything that makes your story seem special improves your odds of getting on TV.

Example: The Sticks and Stones Farm in Newtown, Connecticut, has received extensive media attention because it grows moss, an uncommon crop.

Alternate strategy: Attach a big-name celebrity or a well-known institution to your effort. If you read that someone famous has an interest in products or causes such as yours, send this celebrity a free sample of your work. If you receive a letter of thanks, quote this on your Web site and in other sales and public relations materials. Or you can donate examples of your work to respected institutions, such as local museums or the governor's mansion. If this institution uses your work or puts it on display, mention this prominently in your sales and PR materials.

GET A GREAT LOGO

A skilled graphic designer can develop an eye-catching logo for your business cards and stationery for about $500. That's money well-spent. If you want to be taken seriously and remembered, you must have something confidence-inspiring to hand to those who express an interest in your project. One of those people might be in television or might share your card with someone who is.

Helpful: When you see a logo that catches your eye, ask the business owner for the name of the person who designed the logo, then ask this designer to create a logo for you.

These days, businesses, and causes as well, need Web sites to attract attention and inspire confidence. A Web designer can create a site for you for a few thousand dollars or less. Or at least, use a free service such as WordPress.com, which guides you through the process of creating a Web site.

If what you produce is visual, you also will need professional-quality photos of your work for your printed marketing materials and Web site.

TALK TO EVERYONE

You never know which conversation could lead to television. My path to the *Today* show began with a conversation at a baby shower—the woman I was speaking with turned out to be a producer for the show (but that still was not quite enough—check out "Persist" below). Networking doesn't mean being a pushy self-promoter. Instead, get people you meet to talk about their challenges. When you help someone overcome a challenge, you create a lasting and grateful ally.

GET YOUR NAME OUT THERE

In addition to the above...

• **Send out press releases.** These could provide your take on current news stories related to your field. Make sure to send them to local newspapers and TV stations. National media outlets such as the *Today* show often find interview subjects by watching local media programming and reading regional newspapers.

Also, you might want to sign up for "Help a Reporter Out" (*www.helpareporter.com*), a free repository of sources for the media. Reporters send out specific queries, and you answer any that you're qualified to comment on.

• **Launch an online newsletter.** You can do this quickly and easily by logging on to *www.constantcontact.com*. This company provides templates with suggestions on what to put in your newsletter and sends out your newsletter for you. You can sign up for a free 60-day trial. After that, prices are based on the number of e-mail addresses, starting at $15 per month* for up to 500 addresses.

PERSIST

You should continue sending press releases and e-mailing contacts in the media until a recipient asks you to stop. My initial encounter with a *Today* show producer did not get me onto the program. I got on because I sent that producer updates about myself and my egg-decoration business for the next two years.

To be persistent without becoming a pest, make sure that some of your e-mails, letters or calls provide something of value without asking anything in return.

Example: Include a newspaper clipping with a quick note, reading, "I saw this story and thought it might interest you."

*Price subject to change.

Build Your Business With Social Networks

Draw in customers to your business using local social networks. Networks, including Foursquare (*www.foursquare.com*), Brightkite (*www.brightkite.com*), Gowalla (*www.gowalla.com*) and Loopt (*www.loopt.com*), allow friends to tell friends where they are physically located using smartphones. Small businesses can use these networks to entice customers who are in their neighborhoods by offering, maybe, a free cup of coffee. Also, consider offering customers something free after they visit your store five or 10 times so that they will keep mentioning your business on their smartphones.

Consensus of small-business owners who use location-based social networks, reported in *The Wall Street Journal, www.wsj.com.*

The Facebook Payoff: How to Use Social Media To Make Your Small Business Much More Successful

Sherrie A. Madia, PhD, director of communications, external affairs, at The Wharton School of the University of Pennsylvania, Philadelphia. She teaches social media and communications strategies to students and corporate clients and is coauthor of *The Social Media Survival Guide* (Full Court, *www.socialmediasurvivalguide.com*).

Facebook has more than 500 million active users—that's right, half a billion. So it is a great way for businesses and organizations to find new customers/members, strengthen connections with existing ones and conduct market research. *Here's how...*

FIRST THINGS FIRST

To launch a Facebook page for your business, you first need to set up a personal profile for yourself if you don't already have one. Follow the directions on *www.facebook.com* to set up that profile. Next, click on "Advertising" at the very bottom of the page. On the Facebook Advertising page, click on the Facebook Pages link, then on the green "Create a Page" button, and follow the directions to start an official page—also called a fan page—for your business. You will be asked to choose the category, select the name for your page and complete the detailed information. The main thing to remember with profiles and pages is that profiles are for people and pages are for businesses.

Establishing a page for a business on Facebook—or on a similar site, such as MySpace or LinkedIn—is just the first step, however. Your business's page will require ongoing attention and a well-thought-out strategy to truly benefit your business.

PROVIDE VALUE AND PROVIDE IT OFTEN

Post new content on your business's Facebook page at least once a week. Failing to do this could create the impression that you are not attentive to your customers. If you go on a vacation or are too swamped with work to provide new content for a while, explain this on the page and say when new content will resume.

No more than 20% of the content you put on your business's Facebook page should be obvious attempts at marketing. When Facebook pages read like extended advertisements, potential customers leave and never come back. Most of your content should be attempts to provide the page's visitors with something of value.

Three ways to provide value...

• **Give insider advice in your area of expertise.** Post articles or videos explaining how to use your company's products or supplying other do-it-yourself guidance.

• **Offer to answer questions or respond to complaints.** This shows potential customers that you are service-oriented, knowledgeable and willing to stand behind your products and services. But do this only if you can monitor your Facebook page regularly and respond to questions and complaints within a few days. Delayed response times to questions and complaints will only anger existing customers and scare off potential new ones.

• **Supply discounts or coupons.** Providing special savings is the single best way to lure traffic to your business's Facebook page. Many companies offer a discount or a coupon code when you sign up to become a fan of the page. This is a great way to produce traffic, increase fans and provide immediate value.

HUMANIZE YOUR COMPANY

Your company's Facebook page should not read like it is written by a businessperson—it should read like it is written by a person who happens to own a business. Let customers into your life a little. People who feel they know you personally are more likely to feel a bond with your company and consider it trustworthy.

Examples: Offer up a few details about your family or how you spend your time away from work. Mention your participation in local community organizations. Offer your personal opinion on issues related to your profession.

KNOW YOUR READERS

Market research firms charge thousands of dollars to figure out who customers are and what they want, but Facebook can supply this information to you for free.

When other Facebook users join your company's Facebook page, click on their images and learn what you can about them from their Facebook pages. The more you know about your customers, the easier it will be to sell to them. You might even notice patterns in the things that your customers tend to enjoy or the places they tend to live that could help you target marketing campaigns.

Example: You note that a handful of customers who have signed up for your business's Facebook page also have joined the Facebook page of a seemingly unrelated business across town. That business might provide additional customers who would be interested in what you do, and vice versa. Perhaps the owner of that business would let you put a flyer in his/ her window or a stack of your business cards by his register if you let him do the same.

If your competitors have Facebook pages, read up on those who have joined their pages, too. You might learn something about the potential customers you're failing to reach.

From time to time, ask for the opinions of visitors to your Facebook page. What do they think of all the products and services that you currently provide? What do they desire from your business that they are not getting? This can create loyalty-building interaction with customers and provide valuable feedback.

Example: Clothing retailer The Gap recently unveiled a new logo on Facebook—but it received such an overwhelmingly negative response that the company squelched the redesign. Without this Facebook feedback, The Gap would have wasted millions promoting a new logo that its customers didn't like.

PROMOTE YOUR PAGE

Include "Visit Our Facebook Page" and the page's user name on your receipts and invoices. Print your page's user name on your business card and your other marketing materials.

Make use of your other networks in conjunction with Facebook. Twitter can be particularly powerful in getting a message out quickly to your target group's cell phones when you have a last-minute deal, an exclusive special or a limited-time offer. Twitter will allow your Facebook fans to get the message first.

CREATE A FACEBOOK AD

Allocate a portion of your marketing budget to Facebook ads. (To develop a Facebook ad, just click the "Advertising" link at the bottom of the Facebook page, then click on the green "Create an Ad" button.) Facebook ads can be a great way to target niche groups at a relatively low cost. Facebook ads can be targeted based on user interests, age and location.

One of the beauties of the Facebook ad is that creating the content can be done in moments, and Facebook even will provide suggestions for ad content—such as how to use photos and keywords—based on the Web site address that you provide.

Set your Facebook ad spending caps (the total amount you're willing to spend per day on Facebook advertisements) low until you're certain that your ads are effective.

Also, choose the "Pay for clicks" billing option. With this, you pay only when Facebook users click the ad to visit your Facebook page or online site. This costs more than the "Pay for Impressions" options (where you pay each time your ad appears on any computer screen whether it's clicked or not) but often is more cost effective.

Unlike traditional ad campaigns, which may lock you in for six months or more, elements in Facebook ads (such as content and targeting) can be modified at any time and can be turned off entirely at any point.

Go Ahead and Doodle

When you're in a boring meeting, doodle. Doodling helps you stay awake and can increase your ability to remember information by nearly 30%.

Best: Draw something upside down. That wakes up the right side of the brain, which is responsible for energy and creativity.

Thom Lobe, MD, founder and medical director of the Beneveda Medical Group, Beverly Hills, California, www. beneveda.com.

Reputation Defenders

If negative comments about your business appear online, there are several things you can do to minimize the potential damage. For blogs, contact the person who wrote the post and ask him/her to remove it. Individual bloggers often are willing to remove posts to avoid the possibility of negative publicity. You may want to hire a firm that specializes in repairing a company's image online.

Examples: Reputation Defender (877-720-6488, *www.reputationdefender.com*) and Reputation Hawk (*www.reputationhawk.com*).

They will use techniques that make it more likely people will notice positive information regarding your company first when they go online. These techniques might include buying domain names that are similar to yours and promoting positive things about your business on social-networking sites, such as LinkedIn.com and Facebook.com.

SmartMoney, 1211 Avenue of the Americas, New York City 10036, *www.smartmoney.com*.

As a Small Business Grows...Different Federal Laws Apply

Barbara Weltman, Esq., an attorney in Millwood, New York, and author of *J.K. Lasser's Small Business Taxes* (Wiley). She's publisher of *Big Ideas for Small Business*, a free monthly e-newsletter at *www.barbaraweltman.com*.

As small businesses grow and staff up, they may cross some important thresholds that can affect their legal responsibilities. Below are various federal laws that business owners and their employees should be aware of as the business grows (to get state laws, go to *www.dol.gov/dol/location.htm*)...

TWO OR MORE EMPLOYEES

The *Fair Labor Standards Act* imposes minimum wage and overtime pay requirements on businesses that have at least two employees. And the *Equal Pay Act* says that equal wages must be paid to men and women performing substantially equal services.

MORE THAN 10 EMPLOYEES

The Occupational Safety and Health Administration (OSHA) requires businesses of every size to comply with all established safety and health standards. However, only the businesses with more than 10 employees must meet the reporting requirements covering workplace accidents and illnesses. Penalties can be imposed for violations of these rules.

15 OR MORE EMPLOYEES

These businesses can be subject to penalties under Title VII of the *Civil Rights Act* of 1964 if they discriminate on the basis of race, color, religion, sex or national origin. Also, all disabled employees are protected under the *Americans with Disabilities Act*, which forbids employers from discriminating on the basis of a disability. Employers must make reasonable accommodations for the disability.

20 OR MORE EMPLOYEES

Under the *Age Discrimination in Employment Act*, these businesses are barred from discriminating against an employee or a job applicant who is at least 40 years old on the basis of age.

Also, under the *Consolidated Omnibus Budget Reconciliation Act* (COBRA), an employee who leaves a business can continue to obtain health coverage for a fee for a specified period (usually up to 18 months) if the business had a health plan and at least 20 employees in the prior year.

FEWER THAN 25 EMPLOYEES

As part of the federal overhaul of health-care insurance, an employer with the equivalent of fewer than 25 full-time employees could qualify under the *Patient Protection and Affordable Care Act* (PPACA) for a tax credit of up to 35% of premium costs for providing health coverage to employees. Find details at *www.irs.gov*.

50 OR MORE EMPLOYEES

Under the recent health-care law described above, beginning in 2014, employers with at least 50 employees will be required to provide health coverage for employees by paying at least 60% of "minimum essential coverage" or pay a penalty of up to $2,000 per employee. However, if the business has no more than 100 employees, it will be able to obtain health coverage through government-supervised insurance exchanges set to be operational no later than 2014.

Also, workers at businesses with 50 or more employees are entitled under the *Family and Medical Leave Act* (FMLA) to 12 weeks of unpaid leave for the birth and care of a newborn, an adoption, the care of a family member with a serious illness or for the employee's own serious medical condition.

Note: California, New Jersey and Washington State now mandate some paid leave funded by employee payroll contributions.

How to Protect Your Small Business From Fraud

Stephen Pedneault, CPA/CFF, founder of Forensic Accounting Services, LLC, an accounting firm based in Glastonbury, Connecticut, that specializes in employee fraud. He is author of *Fraud 101: Techniques and Strategies for Understanding Fraud* and *Anatomy of a Fraud Investigation* and most recently wrote *Preventing and Detecting Employee Theft and Embezzlement: A Practical Guide* (all from Wiley). His Internet site is *www.forensicaccounting services.com.*

Workplace fraud siphons 7% of revenues from US organizations every year, and small- and mid-sized businesses are the most vulnerable. According to the Association of Certified Fraud Examiners, companies that have fewer than 100 employees lost a median $155,000 from employee theft in 2010. Unfortunately, the culture of trust that knits a small and/or family-held business together can make their owners easy targets.

In the so-called "fraud triangle" that makes fraud possible, the perpetrator typically has a financial need (which is even more prevalent during these uncertain economic times)...the ability to rationalize his or her deception...and an opportunity to commit fraud. *Although you can't do much to eliminate the person's finan-cial need or ability to rationalize, you can cut back on the opportunities...*

●**Split accounting functions.** To help prevent employees from diverting payments that the business receives, make sure that the person who receives incoming payments isn't the same person who posts them to your accounting system.

●**Reconcile incoming payments daily** with the amounts that get posted to your books and deposited in your bank—called three-way reconciliation. You or someone you designate should spot-check this procedure. If your bank gives you a desktop electronic check scanner, make sure that the device will credit funds only to your company's account. Otherwise, it's easy for an employee to scan in a check, direct it to a personal bank account, then shred the physical evidence and delete the check's image from your hard drive.

●**Protect your organization's own checks.** Locking up your checks and placing strict limits on who may sign them can help to discourage embezzlement, but these are just the first steps. Avoid signing blank checks ahead of a transaction, and never make a check payable to "Cash." Don't stock your business with erasable-ink pens, which employees can use to change the amount or the payee's name after you've signed. As for electronic transfers, though you can allow the employees to set them up, you should review them in advance and only you should be authorized to send them out.

●**Monthly bank statements need to be mailed either directly to your home or directly to you at work, not opened,** and you should review them right away. They should include images of all paid checks.

●**Pay specific attention to merchant statements from your credit card issuer for unusual deductions.** Employees could use your card terminal to improperly transfer funds to their personal credit card accounts.

●**Outsource your payroll.** This is an inexpensive, hassle-free way to dissuade employees from tampering with your payroll. An outside service will perform the administrative chores and assume all the compliance risks associated with the task—all you do is call in your employees' hours.

The major services, such as ADP and Paychex, are reliable. In contrast, a smaller service needs to be monitored to make sure that it doesn't neglect to pay your federal and state payroll taxes on time.

Small Businesses Shut Out

Small-business credit cards get no benefits from recent consumer-protection laws. On consumer cards, banks are limited in charging penalty fees and changing interest rates. These protections are not required for small businesses. If you run a small business, ask your card issuer if it is increasing protections voluntarily and, if so, what those protections are.

John Ulzheimer, president of consumer education, SmartCredit.com, Costa Mesa, California.

Slash Business Costs Now—Easy Dos and Don'ts

Some practical cost-cutting dos and don'ts for small businesses...

Do negotiate with all your data services and telecom providers for lower prices...eliminate any nice-to-use but unnecessary gadgets such as BlackBerrys...replace out-of-date computers with smaller, less expensive ones...create performance-based incentives...track expenses to find line items that can be eliminated. *Do not* stop all advertising and marketing...eliminate training...cut safety-related expenses...reduce product quality—those are short-term savings that can cause long-term problems.

Dennis J. Ceru, PhD, adjunct professor of entrepreneurship, Babson College, and the owner of Strategic Management Associates, consultants, both in Wellesley, Massachusetts.

Employee Wellness Programs Are Worth The Cost

Laurel Pickering, MPH, executive director, Northeast Business Group on Health, New York City, *www.nebgh.org.*

Employee wellness programs can more than offset their costs. One major study showed that businesses can save from $1.49 to $4.91 for every $1.00 spent on workplace medical screenings, gym memberships and other health-oriented programs, such as weight-management, health-coaching and on-site health education programs. These wellness programs result in less absenteeism...decreased health plan and workers' compensation/disability costs...and improved productivity while on the job.

Biggest payoff for your buck: Smoking-cessation programs.

Resources for employers: American Cancer Society at *www.acsworkplacesolutions.com/quit tobacco.asp* (for smoking)...Centers for Disease Control and Prevention, go to *www.cdc.gov/lean works* (obesity)...The Wellness Council of America at *www.welcoa.org* (corporate training and free information)...Wellness Proposals at *www.wellnessproposals.com* (free workplace proposals, newsletters and more).

How to Handle a Difficult Boss

Barbara Moses, PhD, president of BBM Human Resource Consultants Inc., in Toronto, *www.bbmcareerdev.com.* Her books include *What Next? The Complete Guide to Taking Control of Your Working Life* (Dorling Kindersley). Dr. Moses writes a column for Canada's *The Globe and Mail.*

Satisfying a difficult boss is always a challenge, but doing this becomes critically important in a tough economy with an elevated rate of unemployment. The last thing you want to do is provide your hard-to-satisfy manager an excuse to replace you.

If your boss exhibits one of the following behavior patterns, use these proven strategies for keeping your job and your sanity…

●**The Micromanager.** "Control freaks" worry that if they don't supervise every last detail of a project, chaos will ensue. Since their perfectionism results from insecurity, you need to reassure them.

Frequent progress reports go a long way toward calming down an intrusive perfectionist. You also might tell the boss that you are driven to do even better work when given some autonomy because you are a self-starter—but always explain how you plan to deliver the expected results. Finally, if you have made mistakes or missed deadlines in the past, tell the boss what you're doing to ensure that it won't happen again.

●**The Undecider.** Some managers give little in the way of direction and can't seem to decide what they desire—until something goes wrong. The trick here is figuring out why you are not getting enough guidance.

One possibility is that the boss is very busy. If that's the case, ask for input only when you require it. Get straight to the point, and present the issue simply—too many details make choosing a course of action more difficult.

Another explanation for chronic indecisiveness is, again, insecurity. Afraid of making the wrong decision, the boss won't make any decision. In this case, make a recommendation and explain why it's the best choice.

●**The Machiavelli.** Relentless career builders want only to impress their superiors and get ahead. Such managers take credit for everything their subordinates accomplish. They don't spend energy developing staff, but they frequently have "pets"—the people who make them look good.

This variety of boss has a fragile ego and needs a lot of attention. Preface your sentences with compliments, and be careful not to say anything that may be taken as a challenge. If the boss claims credit publicly for your work, do speak up—but share the limelight by using "we" and "our," rather than "I" and "my."

●**The Compulsive Critic.** Managers who do not ever seem satisfied with their employees' performance (even though the employees are doing good work) often are deeply angry. Sometimes they believe that recognizing good work in employees would diminish their own accomplishments.

For that reason, you shouldn't try to defend yourself if your boss disparages what you feel is fine work. Develop a thick skin. Often, you won't have to redo or change anything.

●**The Moody Personality.** Extreme mood swings, unpredictable reactions and irrational rages characterize borderline personality disorder, a condition that's hard to diagnose and treat.

Borderlines do not respond to reason because they have no insight into their behavior. And they don't respond to emotional appeals either because they're too absorbed in their own feelings to care about others.

The only way to cope with the borderline manager is to keep a low profile. Avoid getting dragged into dramas and confrontations. Do the best work you can, and rely on your colleagues for inspiration.

Ace Your Performance Review: Turn This Dreaded Event into a Career Booster

Sharon Armstrong, founder, Sharon Armstrong and Associates, a human resources consulting organization located in Washington, DC, *www.sharonarmstrongand associates.com*. She has 20 years of experience as a human resources consultant, trainer and career counselor and is author of *The Essential Performance Review Handbook* (Career).

At many companies, the end of the year is performance appraisal season. Employees generally consider these annual reviews unpleasant, but if you handle your performance review properly, it can improve your chance of surviving workforce reductions and earning raises or promotions.

In decades past, the typical procedure was for the boss to hand out completed evaluation forms to all employees and say "read this and sign it." These days, the final draft of a performance review typically is not written until after a one-on-one appraisal meeting, greatly enhancing the employee's ability to influence the outcome. Unfortunately, most employees fail to take advantage of this.

Here's what you can do to lay the groundwork for a successful performance appraisal, not only during the appraisal meeting itself, but also during the weeks and months leading up to it.

WHAT TO DO THROUGHOUT THE YEAR

Working hard throughout the year is not the only way to ensure a positive performance review at year's end…

•**Solicit performance updates from your boss throughout the year.** Employees sometimes fall short of their boss's expectations because they don't know what those expectations are. If your boss does not often initiate conversations about your performance goals, it's up to you to ask what objective, measurable targets you must reach to earn a positive appraisal.

Write down exactly what you are told. Then during the weeks or months that follow, write down how well you have met those specific expectations. Save these notes so that you can refer to them prior to your appraisal meeting.

Helpful: If you realize that you just won't reach one of your boss's expectations at any time during the year, meet with him/her about it immediately. Explain the unforeseen hurdles you might face…the additional resources you require…and your recommendation for how to proceed. Putting off this conversation only increases the odds that your failure to reach a goal will be the focus of your performance appraisal, rather than your prompt and professional response to the challenge.

•**Obtain a copy of your employer's performance appraisal form long before the appraisal.** Most likely this will be available on the company's Web site or through the human resources department. The form lays out the specific criteria on which employees are evaluated.

Periodically ask your boss how you are doing on these fronts. Your boss might not consider some of these categories of performance important, but if they appear on the appraisal form, they probably will play a role in your appraisal.

Example: Many appraisal forms ask that bosses rate an employee's personal and behavioral characteristics in addition to job performance. These ratings can be very subjective, so ask your boss to be as specific as possible about how you will be judged in these areas and how you could do better.

•**Keep a "positive feedback" file.** When a client tells you "great job," tell your boss and then write down the compliment as accurately as possible, along with the date, the speaker and the context. Store all of these notes in a file, along with copies of any e-mails or notes of praise you receive.

Bosses seldom give much weight to statements such as, "I think I did a good job" and "Everyone told me that I did a good job" from employees during performance appraisals, but they do tend to listen when employees quote specific examples of glowing praise received from the boss himself—or the boss's boss or an important client.

What to do in the days and weeks before your appraisal. You would not walk into a job interview without first doing some homework. Do not walk into your performance appraisal unprepared, either. *Find time to…*

•**Identify your most important accomplishments and most powerful praise from the past year.** If you attempt to talk about everything you achieved in the past year, you'll bore your boss or even anger him or her by dragging out the appraisal meeting.

Instead, attempt to talk about just your top three or four accomplishments and a similar number of kudos. Emphasize the most important, the most impressive and those from early in the year—your boss likely remembers your recent successes. Practice summarizing each in just a few sentences.

Example: "On March 3, you said to me, 'Amazing job with the Johnson presentation. I was afraid we might lose that account.' The Johnson account was worth $800,000 to our company this year."

● **Complete a self-evaluation.** Put yourself in your boss's position, and fill out a copy of your company's evaluation form for yourself. This should help you spot any errors or omissions when you read your boss's appraisal of you. It also could help you identify any areas where your boss might believe you came up short.

Work out reasoned responses to any shortfalls in case your boss mentions them during your appraisal meeting. Avoid making excuses. Instead, try to frame these shortfalls in a way that minimizes negativity. Quickly transition to how you will overcome or avoid similar problems in the future.

Example: "The result was not what any of us on the project wanted. We are about to implement a new sales forecasting model that should prevent future problems."

● **Seek feedback about your performance from your coworkers.** You can get feedback by asking coworkers directly for some assessment of your work at review time or get in the habit of doing so after major projects. You will report this positive feedback to your boss during your performance appraisal meeting.

● **Prepare an emergency plan.** Unexpected criticism during the performance review can upset you and trigger unproductive responses, such as arguing or freezing up. The secret to responding calmly to criticism is to compose a response in advance.

Example: Before your appraisal, picture your boss informing you that your efforts this year were not up to par, and imagine yourself calmly replying, "I am surprised to hear that my work was not sufficient. I thought I was working very well, but obviously, it was not perceived that way. I will work even harder this coming year and promise that you never again will have reason to feel this way."

DURING YOUR APPRAISAL

Cite your key accomplishments, most glowing praise and positive feedback, as discussed above. *Also...*

● **Discuss what you can contribute next year.** Performance appraisals typically focus in on the previous year. Employees who shift the conversation to what they can contribute in the future tend to seem more valuable and less self-centered to bosses.

Identify an element of your employer's current plans that plays into your strengths or an important project that no one else in the company could handle as well as you.

Example: "You've spoken about the importance of the Canadian market in 2011. No one in this department has better contacts in Canada than I do."

● **Connect yourself with your boss's performance goals.** Do not focus exclusively on how you met your performance targets. Also discuss how you helped your boss meet the expectations of his boss. If you do not know your boss's performance goals, you could ask, "Is there anything I can do to help you achieve your goals?"

● **If you feel your temper rising, think about your rebuttal option.** It is not in your best interest to become argumentative if you believe that your boss is unfairly critical during your appraisal. If you notice your temper rising, silently remind yourself that you have the option of filing a written rebuttal to your boss's written performance appraisal—almost all companies allow this. It is much easier to remain calm when you know that you'll have a chance to explain your position later.

Warning: File a rebuttal only if the final written appraisal is very negative and you can objectively show it to be incorrect. Otherwise, a rebuttal is likely to do more harm than good to your reputation and relationships within the company.

Example: Your boss claims you failed to achieve an important performance goal. File a rebuttal if you can show that you actually achieved this goal...or you can show that the missed goal is significantly different from the goal your boss presented to you during the year.

Win Support for Your Good Ideas! Overcome Naysayers, Nitpickers And Handwringers

John P. Kotter, who is Konosuke Matsushita Professor of Leadership, emeritus, at Harvard Business School, Boston, and the founder of Kotter International, a leadership advisory practice with offices in Boston, Chicago and Seattle, *www.kotterinternational.com*. He is also author of *Buy In: Saving Your Good Idea from Getting Shot Down* (Harvard Business Press).

Many of our best ideas really never go anywhere. They can come under attack by naysayers who misunderstand what we're proposing…fear change…disagree with every idea that they did not personally think up…or are motivated by private agendas or personal grudges.

If you ignore all these attacks or mishandle your responses to them, enthusiasm for your idea will wane. But if you learn how to defend yourself against attacks, you can get others to buy into your ideas.

A key way to defend yourself is to prepare for the inevitable attacks. The bigger the stakes, the greater the preparation that is necessary. *One way to prepare is to brainstorm some ways to defend your ideas against four of the most common and dangerous types of attacks…*

FEAR MONGERING

A critic compares your idea to a somewhat similar idea that failed in the past or spins a tale that ends with disaster of how your plan could play out. This critic likely will sprinkle his/her comments with lots of fear-generating words and phrases, such as "lawsuit"…"out of business"…"IRS audit"…or the name of some project or company that went down in flames. The logic of the attacker's argument might be weak, but logic often takes a backseat when seeds of fear are planted in listeners' minds.

Strategy: Respectfully discredit the comparison, then very quickly turn the discussion to words and subjects that trigger positive emotions. Do not attempt to employ logic to overcome fear mongering, as people's fears often overwhelm their ability to follow logical arguments. Avoid repeating scare words even to refute their relevance. Repeating these words only stokes listeners' fears.

Example: A coworker says of your business plan, "That sounds like what Enron did, and we all know what happened to Enron." Reply, "Thanks for raising this point. Naturally it is important to consider the experiences of other companies, but this plan is completely different from the plan that you just mentioned. Far from taking us in that direction, it should help us create jobs, capture market share and drive our profits and stock price higher. Are there any other questions?"

CONFUSION

A member of the audience raises highly technical, hard-to-understand objections when you present your idea. This critic might be someone with specialized education, such as an attorney or an engineer, who knows more about certain technical aspects of the idea than the other listeners, and he/she might have more credibility on the subject than you. That makes it very difficult for you to refute all the objections and for others to realize that you're right.

Strategy: Admit that this is not your main sphere of expertise, but explain that you have discussed these types of issues with experts and have been assured that they can be overcome. Offer to have your experts contact the critic after the meeting. This will make the critic appear very unreasonable if he continues to badger you during the meeting. Do not engage in lengthy debates about highly technical objections, even if you believe that you can refute them—the eyes and minds of everyone else listening will glaze over and their enthusiasm for your idea will be diminished.

Example: During your condo association meeting, you propose that any resident be allowed to post notices about upcoming events on the association's Web site. A computer expert on the condo board counters that this is not possible due to computer security reasons that no one else understands. Say, "Thanks for bringing that up. I'm not a computer security expert, but I have consulted with Web design pros about my idea. I'd be happy to put you in contact with them after the meeting if you'd like to discuss it further. Are there any other questions?"

DELAY

After you pitch your idea to decision makers, one of the listeners expresses a degree of support but suggests that it might be wise to wait until more information is available before proceeding...or that a task force should be created to study the idea fully...or that the idea should be put on the back burner until there is more money in the budget or more time in everyone's schedule. These delays usually are adopted when they're proposed because they sound prudent and reasonable and they allow people to put off making difficult decisions.

Trouble is, these delays often are not just delays. When an idea is put on hold, its momentum is lost and its window of opportunity could close. The person who proposed the delay might even understand this and be using delay tactics as a way to squelch your project while appearing to support it.

Strategy: Agree with the critic that there are a lot of issues that really need to be thought through—agreeing here will make you sound reasonable to other listeners. Then point out that you and your group already have thought through these issues and that any further delay reduces the odds for success.

Example: A coworker proposes a task force to study the potential market for the new product you proposed. Respond, "Absolutely, this needs to be thought through. That's why my group has been thinking this through and commissioning surveys to gauge the audience for the past two months. The results have been extremely encouraging. Now we are gathered here to make a decision. If we don't make this decision now, we greatly reduce the odds that we can get the product out in time for the holidays. Are there any other questions?"

CHARACTER ASSASSINATION

Your challenger doesn't attack your idea— he attacks you. He brings your qualifications into question or cites an old mistake you made as a reason not to listen to you. He even may insult you outright.

Strategy: Keep your cool. It's natural to feel angry when you are being personally attacked, but showing that anger will make you—and by extension, your idea—seem less rational. If you notice your emotions rising, search for friendly faces in the crowd and make eye contact with them. Such eye contact reassures us that we have allies, reducing our fight-or-flight reaction when we feel challenged.

Now objectively consider this personal attack. Was it something a rational person might consider a legitimate concern about you? Your best defense against these attacks is alliances, which means planning is required. Before you present an idea, consider whether there's anything about you personally that could give people reason to doubt this idea. Do you lack training in a field related to the idea? Have you presented similar ideas in the past that have failed? Do people in the group consider you overly conservative or brash? If so, make sure that you have already enlisted the support of others who are above reproach in this area.

Example: You intend to make a proposal to your town council, even though you have lived in the town for just one year. That makes you vulnerable to being painted as a know-nothing newcomer. Therefore, try to gain the support of well-respected, long-term residents before the meeting. If your limited knowledge of the town is cited during the meeting as a reason to ignore your idea, say, "You're absolutely right. That's why I discussed my idea with Jim Smith and Jane Jones, who each have lived here for more than 30 years. They are both very enthusiastic. Are there any additional questions?"

Be a Role Model

Employees work harder when they see that you are working harder yourself—setting a good example boosts commitment. Keep establishing new goals with specific deadlines. Give recognition to employees whether or not you can afford bonuses or any other material rewards. Be fair to everyone, including people you may not like—unfair treatment leads to resentment and harms productivity.

Tyler Cowen, PhD, professor of economics, George Mason University, Fairfax, Virginia.

Never Open with a Joke...and Other Secrets To Making a Great Speech

Bill Lane, manager, executive communications, for General Electric from 1983 to 2002 and speechwriter for longtime chairman and CEO, Jack Welch. Based in Easton, Connecticut, he is author of Jacked Up: The Inside Story of How Jack Welch Talked GE into Becoming the World's Greatest Company (McGraw-Hill).

Whether you're giving a pitch to your manager or a presentation before the town council, how you communicate all your ideas can be just as important as the concepts themselves. Unfortunately, mistakes by presenters are common and make it less likely that the audience will pay attention to or accept the message. *Here's what helps presentations succeed...*

• **Open by telling audience members why they must listen and reassuring them that you will be brief.** If you can't come up with an attention-grabbing opening, try a version of the following...

"Listen folks, I've got only five minutes of your time, but there is something you really need to know because it could become a major problem (or opportunity) for everyone in this room."

• **Never open with a joke, which can make you look like a lightweight.** Opening with a powerful anecdote relevant to the topic can be very effective.

• **Organize your presentation based on the person or people you are speaking to,** not just what you want to say. What topics interest your listeners? What are their greatest challenges? What is the personality of the key audience member (someone who can influence your career)? What statements or topics make this key audience member upset?

What follow-up questions does he/she tend to ask speakers? Find out as much as you can before you even begin to write your speech. The greatest sin in public speaking is giving a presentation without first developing a clear picture of your audience.

• **Ask for advice from people who have made presentations to these individuals in the past.** Also, call the key audience member and ask what he most wants your presentation to provide.

• **Make it shorter.** Shorter presentations are better—always. Assume that your first draft is too long, and cut it...then do the same with drafts two through four.

Example: At General Electric, Jack Welch shortened the length of most presentations at general manager meetings from about 20 minutes to 10 (although the CEO's "closing remarks" could be longer). The presentations were as informative as ever.

To keep presentations brief...

• **Reread every paragraph,** asking yourself, What will listeners take away from the speech? Remove anything that is not a take-away idea—which is something the audience can easily remember and use.

• **Eliminate most/all background information** and explanations of methodology. Few audience members care about these things.

• **Avoid phrases that signal a long presentation,** such as, "Later I'll cover..." or "Today I'm going to discuss the 10 things..."

• **Consider PowerPoint your enemy.** This computer program has become the standard tool for presenters—and it always hurts them. Complicated and bullet-point–filled PowerPoint slides distract from what you are saying and block the connection that you are striving to build with the audience—particularly if you turn your back to read the bullet points. Use PowerPoint only to depict occasional and dramatic points. Once your audience has had a moment to absorb a slide, clear the screen to return the focus to you.

•**Temper success stories.** When you give a speech about a big success, audience members' BS detectors start running on high. Add a paragraph about what you could have done better, and you will enhance your credibility.

Nodding Off at Your Desk?

To keep away afternoon sleepiness, drink some water—fatigue often is the result of dehydration. If that doesn't work, have a high-energy snack—some celery with a bit of peanut butter...or several bites of dark chocolate. Also, try going for a walk—low-intensity walking can raise your energy level by as much as 20%. Or, get some sunlight—exposure to sunshine for as little as 30 minutes (the amount of time it requires to shift your *circadian rhythm*) can boost your energy and mood.

Health Magazine, 1271 Avenue of the Americas, New York City 10020, *www.health.com/health*.

E-Mail Etiquette

Keep business e-mails quick, and put the most important matter at the top of the message. This is especially helpful for people who get most e-mails on their smartphones. Also, use bullet points to organize and simplify lengthy e-mails. Never send an e-mail in anger—and do not say anything that you would not say to the person directly. Always respond within 48 hours or at least acknowledge the e-mail and indicate a response date. Remember

to use the blind carbon copy (BCC) function if you're sending out a mass e-mail to people who don't know one another.

Judith Kallos, founder, BusinessEMailEtiquette.com, a Web site devoted to business e-mail etiquette, Senatobia, Mississippi.

More E-Mail Know-How

When e-mailing or texting to business associates, choose your words carefully so that you don't sound harsher than intended. Avoid changing meeting times and places via text or e-mail, as not everyone checks his/her phone or e-mails often. Do not give negative feedback via text or e-mail—do this in person. Never text or e-mail an apology—apologize in person or via phone if you can't meet the person face to face. Never resign from a position via text or e-mail. It is seen as unprofessional, and you may need a reference in the future, so don't burn bridges.

Barbara Pachter, business etiquette specialist, Cherry Hill, New Jersey, *www.pachter.com*, and the author of *Greet! Eat! Tweet! 52 Business Etiquette Postings to Avoid Pitfalls & Boost Your Career* (CreateSpace).

Starting a New Job? What *Not* to Do...

Marjory Abrams, president of Boardroom Inc., 281 Tresser Blvd., Stamford, Connecticut 06901.

Earlier in 2011, two high-profile executives crashed and burned in their new jobs. Jack Griffin survived for less than six months as Time Inc.'s CEO. Cathleen Black lasted only three months as head of New York City's public schools. Don't let this happen to you. *Here are steps for people in new leadership positions—whether a CEO or a team leader within a department—to improve the odds of making it...*

•**Do not move too fast.** Top management psychologist and executive coach Paul Powers, PhD, notes that new leaders generally have a three-month honeymoon before they need to make major moves. During the honeymoon, observe and collect information. Steer clear of preconceptions. Let people prove themselves. After the honeymoon, you typically have another three months to make some headway, such as implementing some personnel changes or initiating a new strategy.

•**Understand objections to your being hired.** People may feel that you don't know the business (as with Black) or the company (as with Griffin).

Remedy: Communicate what you bring—new markets, for example—but do not make any promises until you are ready to roll out a plan.

•**Learn from past mistakes.** Ask colleagues from previous firms what you did wrong and might have done differently.

•**Assemble a "personal advisory board"** of people from outside your new company to offer you guidance. Choose five or six people who know you well, have a variety of skills and will be brutally honest.

Finally, know who will be assessing your performance and how a good performance is defined. Both of you need to be on the same path.

Job Stress = Weight Gain

Stress on the job is associated with weight gain.

A recent finding: Obese or overweight men having the least authority at work gained more weight than those with more authority. Not having the authority to make decisions in the workplace has been linked to stress. Eating can help to decrease stress, because it releases mood-improving *endorphins.*

Jason Block, MD, instructor in medicine, Harvard University, Boston, and leader of a study of 1,355 people, published in *American Journal of Epidemiology.*

Plants That Boost Your Health While You Work

The most healthful plants for your office or home…

•**Areca palms are good air filters**—they need bright light (not necessarily direct) and moderate soil maintenance.

•**Peppermint can increase alertness**—it needs full or partial light and little care.

•**Gardenia's fragrance can improve emotional outlook**—it requires direct light and moderate attention.

•**English ivy can absorb volatile organic compounds**—it requires indirect light and is easy to care for.

James Dillard, MD, integrative-medicine physician in private practice, who served as assistant clinical professor at Columbia University Medical Center in New York City.

20

Safe and Sound

Don't Believe These Common Myths About Crime

Some of the things that people do to avoid crime actually *increase* their odds of becoming victims. *Here, the truth about common misconceptions about crime—plus important safety strategies…*

Myth: If you're mugged, throw your wallet or purse at the assailant and run. The mugger will stop to pick up your valuables rather than pursue you.

Reality: Many street criminals value respect above all else. Throwing your valuables could be taken as a form of disrespect. The mugger might use violence against you for this.

Better: Politely hand over all your valuables without making eye contact. Follow the mugger's directions, and do not say anything beyond, "Take my money…it's all yours."

Exception: If you hand over your valuables and the mugger continues giving you instructions, such as "get down on your knees" or "walk into that alley," it is time to run away. Muggers who do not leave quickly after obtaining a victim's possessions often intend to commit murder or sexual assault.

Myth: The best way to fight back against a male assailant is with a kick to the groin.

Reality: Attempts to disable assailants with kicks or punches to the groin almost always fail. Men typically experience an adrenaline influx when they commit assaults or muggings. One consequence of this big adrenaline rush is that their testicles retreat up close to their bodies, making their testicles a very difficult target to hit. Most men also are quite skilled at

Dale Yeager, expert criminal analyst who is CEO of SERAPH Corporation, a security consulting and training company located in Phoenixville, Pennsylvania. He is a federal law-enforcement trainer and instructor for the Neumann University Criminal Justice Program. Yeager received advanced training in forensic crime analysis at the Federal Law Enforcement Training Center. Go to *www. seraph.net* for more.

protecting their groin area when they realize that an attack might be coming. Even if an assailant's testicles are struck, the feeling of pain is not instantaneous. Your assailant might have enough time to seriously injure or kill you before feeling the full effects.

Better: If you do attempt a physical attack on your assailant, aim for a kidney. The kidneys are located on our sides, just above the waist—roughly where the thumbs rest when we stand with our hands on our hips. Kidneys are extremely sensitive. If an attacker comes at you, hit or slap the kidney or stab a pen in the area.

Myth: If you act confident, you are less likely to be targeted by criminals.

Reality: Criminals could mistake your show of confidence for arrogance and target you to take you down a peg. When a man acts very confidently, a male criminal might target him for assault to prove that the criminal is the top dog. When Americans abroad act confidently, they sometimes are targeted by criminals who consider the US their enemy. Rape-prevention groups often recommend that women walk/act with an exaggerated confidence whenever they feel threatened, but this can increase the risk for sexual assault.

Better: It is fine to feel confident, but don't act cocky. Arrogance can make you a target. Also, feigned confidence often seems unnatural and makes us stand out from crowds. Acting the way we actually feel helps us blend in, a far better way to avoid unwanted criminal attention.

Myth: The least safe areas are "bad neighborhoods" at night.

Reality: In my experience, the highest-risk areas for physical attacks by strangers are not bad neighborhoods but near nightclubs. The perpetrators usually are nightclub patrons who have had too much to drink.

Better: Stay out of nightclubs, and advise your adult children to do the same. If you do go to nightclubs in any kind of neighborhood, leave before midnight—most attacks happen later, when customers have been drinking for many hours. If you feel at all threatened when leaving a nightclub, ask a doorman or bounc-

er to keep an eye on you as you walk to your car. Avoid parking near nightclubs if you will be returning to your car after midnight.

Myth: Burglars won't come in if they know you're home.

Reality: Most break-ins happen between 2 pm and 9 pm, partly because this is when people are likely to have their doors unlocked. Burglars target those homes that appear easy to break into and move on to other homes if the first one selected proves challenging.

Better: Determine what your neighbors do for home security, then do that and a little bit more in your own home. Dogs, motion-detecting lights, deadbolts and alarm systems all can be effective deterrents. And be sure to lock all doors.

Myth: College campuses are safe.

Reality: Unfortunately, our colleges and universities are very unsafe. Security is extremely casual on most campuses, and burglary, assault and rape are distressingly common. Even prestigious colleges have crime problems.

Better: Impress upon your children that a college campus is not a safe haven and that attention must be paid to personal and property security.

Bye-Bye Burglars: Do-It-Yourself Home Security That Costs Less and Works Great!

Ralph Winn, a 40-year veteran of the security industry and cofounder of the Home Security Store, which sells all major brands of home security products. Prior to founding the Home Security Store, Winn founded and ran an alarm-installation company. Prior to that, he worked for Honeywell Security's Government Division and served as a security consultant to foreign governments, including Russia. Winn's online site is *www.homesecuritystore.com.*

J ust how much home security protection is enough—and how much do you need to pay for it?

Many security organizations advertise alarm systems for less than $100,* including installation. But that requires that you sign a multiyear alarm-monitoring contract costing perhaps $25 to $35 every month, which promises that the monitors will alert local police if the alarm is triggered.

You can avoid that monthly bill by installing your own unmonitored alarm system. Systems just like the setups supplied by security companies can be purchased for less than $300. Today's wireless technology makes them easy to install without having to drill holes and run wires through your walls.

IMPROVED SECURITY

While traditional security systems typically alert the security company when they detect a problem, self-installed alarm systems generally just call the home owner's mobile phone (or some other phone number), then the home owner notifies the police. This not only saves the monthly monitoring fee, it often improves home security. The false-alarm rate with professionally monitored alarm systems is so high that busy police departments often make responding to alarm company calls a low priority. The police generally arrive faster when the home owner calls.

Professional alarm monitoring might make sense if you cannot always answer your cell phone quickly...if you feel more secure knowing a professional is monitoring your alarm, including smoke and carbon monoxide detectors...or if your homeowners insurance provider offers a substantial discount—typically 10% to 20%—for maintaining a professionally monitored security system.

There's no need to pay high security-company monthly rates, even if you want professional monitoring, however. There are companies that will monitor your alarm system for much less if you buy and install it yourself.

Example: AlarmRelay charges $8.95 per month for monitoring services with a one-year contract. There's a onetime $35 start-up charge (800-624-6866, *www.alarmrelay.com*).

*Prices subject to change.

WIRELESS SYSTEMS

A home alarm system should include alarms for both the front and back doors and a motion detector inside the home. Having two motion detectors is even better—most home owners put one in the family room and the other in the master bedroom, the rooms most often targeted by burglars. *Top choices...*

•DSC PowerSeries 9047 wireless alarm kit (888-888-7838, *www.dsc.com*).

•The Honeywell Lynx Plus wireless security system (800-675-3364, *www.security.honeywell.com*).

•Visonic PowerMax+ wireless home security system (*www.visonic.com*).

These all are reliable and sell for around $200 to $300 when packaged with two compatible door alarms and one motion detector. Smoke detectors, carbon monoxide detectors and freeze detectors that detect dangerously low temperatures can be sensible add-ons and typically cost less than $100 apiece.

Alarms that sense when a window is opened may be worthwhile, but most homes have so many windows that adding these at $30 to $40 apiece can be expensive. Other types of window alarms identify the sound of glass breaking, but they are effective only if a window is shattered, not jimmied. Unless your home is in a particularly dangerous area or you have high-end valuables that make it a likely target, it is reasonable to do without the window alarms.

VIDEO MONITORING

A home alarm system is much more likely to scare away an intruder than to lead to his/her capture. If your goal is to identify trespassers and burglars so that they can be brought to justice or made to pay for damages, you'll also need a system for video-monitoring. This captures and stores images of those who venture onto your property so that you can prove to the police or in court which neighborhood teen has been vandalizing cars in your driveway (or which dog has been digging up your garden).

The range and clarity of reasonably priced digital security cameras have improved dramatically in just the past year. A system featuring two high-quality cameras with infrared capabilities to see in the dark, a digital recording device and a view screen can be purchased for around $400. The digital recorders packaged with these systems typically can be set to record constantly, only when motion is detected or on a specific schedule. Some video systems can send images to your computer or even your cell phone. *Top choices...*

•Lorex (888-425-6739, *www.lorextechnology. com*).

•SVAT (866-946-7828, *www.svat.com*).

These companies produce excellent, affordable security camera systems. For the price of $400, you can purchase a kit from either company featuring two cameras capable of crisp night-vision images at up to 40 feet, a digital recording device and an LCD monitor.

EVEN LESS EXPENSIVE ITEMS

For less than $100, it is possible to reduce the odds that a burglar will target your home. *Among these low-cost security products...*

•**Motion-activated floodlights.** Burglars in general steer clear of any homes that light up as they approach. Motion-activated floodlights are widely available for less than $30, but it is worth paying $70 to $80 to get solar-powered LED floodlights that don't need to be wired into the electrical system. *Top choice...*

•Maxsa 80 LED solar floodlight sells for about $75 (703-495-0661, *www.maxsainnovations.com*).

Avoid a bargain-basement solar-powered floodlight, which may be dim.

•**Fake TVs.** These produce a flickering colored LED light that effectively replicates the light emitted by a television. One of these TVs should convince anyone lurking outside during the night that someone is at home, awake and watching TV. It costs just $35, has a built-in timer and consumes far less electricity than leaving on an actual TV (877-532-5388, *www.faketv.com*).

•**Security company yard signs and window decals.** The security industry doesn't like to publicize this, but you can reduce the odds of a break-in by perhaps 50% just by posting signs warning that you have an alarm system, even if you don't really have one. *Example...*

•An alarm company yard sign with a solar light and eight window decals are available for $29.95 on my Web site (*www.homesecuritystore. com*) or by calling 888-501-7870.

SECURITY WHEN YOU'RE AT HOME

Most alarm systems primarily protect property when the home owner is away. *Two products that offer effective security when you are at home...*

•**Driveway alarms.** These sound a chime inside of the home when someone walks or drives up the driveway, giving the home owner a chance to see who's approaching before the person arrives. *Examples of ones that work well and sell for around $130...*

•Dakota Alert Wireless Motion Alert 3000 (605-356-2772, *www.dakotaalert.com*).

•The Optex Wireless 2000 Annunciator System (909-993-5770, *www.optexamerica.com*).

•**Front-door video/intercom systems.** The intercom allows an easy two-way conversation, while the video camera and monitor provide a better view than a peephole could.

Example: The Optex iVision wireless two-way video intercom offers a portable, hand-held monitor so you can see and speak with someone who rings the doorbell without even walking to the door. It has infrared capabilities so that you can see nighttime guests, and it records pictures of visitors, which you can show to the police later if you become suspicious. It sells for around $300.

UNNECESSARY ADD-ONS

If you have a contract with a security organization, it may try to convince you to add services that you may not need. Unless you have tremendously valuable possessions that make you likely to be targeted by professional criminals, a basic system should be sufficient. *Two unnecessary add-ons that you might be offered...*

•**Cellular service.** This lets your alarm system contact your security monitoring company even if a burglar cuts your phone lines. It typically adds $10 per month or so to the bill. Most home owners do not require cellular service, because the vast majority of burglars do not cut phone lines.

•**Video surveillance.** If this is something you want, buy and install a wireless system yourself, as discussed previously. This will be cheaper than paying your security company an extra $20 or more each month for video monitoring, and it offers no less security.

Why Big Trees Reduce Crime

Neighborhoods that have large trees tend to have less crime than areas with smaller trees.

Theory: Large trees indicate to criminals that an area is well cared for.

Geoffrey H. Donovan, PhD, research forester, Portland Forestry Sciences Laboratory, Oregon, *www.fs.fed. us/pnw/pfsl,* and coauthor of a study of 431 crimes, published in *Environment and Behavior.*

Convicts on the Loose

Convicts are being released early due to budget cuts. Oregon, Colorado, California and other states can save millions of dollars by releasing convicts before they have served their full prison sentences.

Example: A program in Illinois paroled 1,700 inmates within weeks of their convictions—50 were soon accused of new crimes.

The New York Times, www.nytimes.com.

What to Do If You Lose Your Wallet...

Lost your wallet? Whether you misplaced it or it was stolen from you, immediately call your credit card companies and request account number changes—do not cancel the accounts, or your credit score may drop. Also, file a report with the police in your hometown and the location where your wallet went missing, and

keep copies—you may need them as proof in later dealings. And have fraud alerts put on your credit card accounts by the three major credit bureaus—Equifax, Experian and Trans-Union. Have the department of motor vehicles flag your file so that a thief cannot pretend to be you and apply for a copy of your driver's license in your name with his/her photo. Finally, contact your bank to get a new ATM or debit card and, if your checkbook is missing, a new checking account number.

Sid Kirchheimer, consumer scam expert and author of *Scam-Proof Your Life* (AARP Books/Sterling), writing in *AARP Bulletin, www.aarp.org/bulletin.*

A New Use for Chili Powder

India's newest antiterrorism weapon is made with the world's hottest chili pepper. The hand grenade works the way tear gas does, choking suspects and flushing them out.

Time, Time-Life Bldg., Rockefeller Center, New York City 10020, *www.time.com.*

How to Survive a Nuclear Bomb: Simple Tactic Could Save Your Life

Irwin Redlener, MD, founder and director of the National Center for Disaster Preparedness, cofounder and president of the Children's Health Fund and a professor of population and family health at the Mailman School of Public Health at Columbia University, New York City. He is author of *Americans at Risk: Why We Are Not Prepared for Megadisasters and What We Can Do* (Knopf).

What if terrorists detonated a nuclear bomb in the US? Such an attack would be devastating, but it would be much more survivable than most people think. Hundreds of thousands of lives would be saved if people simply stayed where they were instead of fleeing.

WHAT TO EXPECT

A terrorist attack would probably occur with no warning. The main threat is that Al-Qaeda or another terrorist group could obtain bomb-grade material and make a crude but powerful nuclear device. Survival would depend on what you do in the first seconds, minutes and hours after a nuclear blast. *What to expect...*

• **A blinding flash is the first sign that there has been a nuclear explosion.** The intensity of the flash is the equivalent of 1,000 suns. Anyone who happens to be looking directly at the flash could be blinded—temporarily or permanently.

If you're ever suddenly surrounded by a brilliant flash of light, avoid the temptation to look for the source. If you are inside a building, do not look out a window.

• **Flying glass and debris.** Once you see the flash of light, you should protect yourself from flying glass and debris, which may come several seconds to a minute later, depending on how far from the detonation point you are. Flying glass and other debris are among the most lethal threats from a nuclear blast. Much of the damage is triggered by the explosion shock wave—a wall of pressure that expands outward from the explosion. The pressure is strong enough to rip buildings apart. It also will be accompanied by high winds that may reach 500 miles per hour. Look for cover away from flying glass and debris immediately.

• **Fallout.** The next biggest hazard is fallout. The mushroom cloud that's created from a nuclear explosion will consist of dust, pulverized concrete and other debris, all made highly radioactive from the explosion. Much of this material, known as fallout, will settle back down to Earth shortly following the big blast. It can start falling 10 minutes or more after the detonation.

Fallout can cause serious illness or death. Those who avoid it by staying indoors are far more likely to survive than those who go outside too quickly.

WHAT TO DO

• **Take shelter.** Any shelter is better than none. If you're in an office building when a blast occurs, run to an interior room, preferably one without windows. If you're in a multistory building, the safest floors will be the middle floors or underground areas. Fallout settles on the ground and on the roof. Ideally, you want as much distance as possible from both of those levels, so the middle floors are best.

If you are on the street and are completely exposed, get inside of the nearest building. If there is not a building close by, a parking garage is good—especially one that is well below ground. Modern cars offer little protection from fallout and should be abandoned for the better protection of multistory buildings or underground shelter areas.

If you happen to be in a one- or two-story home, the best options would be a basement, an interior hallway or a room without windows in the middle of the house.

Remain in the best shelter you can quickly find. This is the most important thing you can do to survive the radioactive aftermath of a nuclear explosion. Though the basic instinct might be to flee...reunite with family members...or get in your car and leave. Do not do it. Once you've found shelter, stay there for at least four to eight hours. Longer is probably better. It is best to wait for officials to inform you about the safest way to leave the region—otherwise, you could accidentally evacuate into areas of higher contamination.

Important: If your children are at school when there's a nuclear explosion, leave them there. This does go against every parent's instincts, but children will be much safer inside a school building than outside or in a car.

• **The nuclear fallout decays (it loses its radioactivity) rapidly.** It will lose half of its radioactivity in the first hour. The outdoor radiation levels will depend on the type of explosion and distance from the primary blast, but the levels will decrease with time. Levels at seven hours after bomb detonation will be one-tenth those at one hour.

• **Decontaminate immediately.** Individuals who receive large amounts of radiation from the initial blast or who are coated with nuclear fallout are far more likely to die from massive radiation sickness than those who limit their exposure.

If you're contaminated with fallout, take off your outer garments and wipe off fallout particles as you enter the shelter.

•**Cover your nose and mouth with a piece of cloth or a dust mask.** You don't want to inhale radioactive fallout in the hours or days after an explosion. Don't eat or drink anything that has been contaminated with fallout.

•**Wait for an all-clear.** Stay in your place of shelter until authorities advise leaving the area. A ground explosion is unlikely to disrupt all electronic communications. You might be able to use a radio, especially if it is battery or hand-crank powered. Even if cell-phone service gets disrupted, you still might be able to send and receive text messages.

More from Dr. Irwin Redlener…

Be Prepared

To protect yourself and your family in the event of a nuclear attack, have the following on hand…

•**Battery-powered radio.**
•**Flashlights.**
•**Extra batteries.**
•**Extra medications** (if you have a health condition).
•**Enough packaged food and bottled water to last three days.**
•**Surgical masks** (these are available at most pharmacies).
•**A whistle** to notify rescuers if you are trapped in rubble.

You might want to keep these items in your workplace as well.

Plan how you'll contact your family should you be separated. This might include meeting at a certain location in a certain number of days…or giving everyone in your family the phone number of someone outside your region whom you'll all contact.

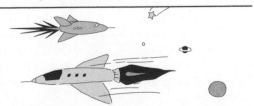

Scareware Ads On the Rise

These ads are online promotions for worthless antivirus software and other bogus varieties of computer protection. Clicking on them starts a fake scan indicating that the computer is infected with viruses—followed up by a sales pitch for a product that does not work. Scammers also design Internet pages that show up in Google search results, and when a user clicks the link, the scareware ad is launched…or the scammers steal people's Facebook and Twitter log-ons and then send tainted Web links to the victims' contacts.

What to do: Buy virus-protection software only from companies you know and trust… and go to their Internet sites directly, not via links.

Roel Schouwenberg, senior antivirus researcher at Kaspersky Lab, Woburn, Massachusetts, *www.kaspersky.com.*

Wi-Fi Warning

Some free Wi-Fi connections are big traps. Crooks steal information from people who sign onto these illegitimate networks, called *honey pots*, which are found at airports, restaurants and other public places. Account information, passwords and anything else typed to gain access to Web sites can be stolen by a honey pot operator, as well as anything stored on the computer's hard drive.

When using free Wi-Fi service: Limit your activities to ones that do not involve your personal or financial information, such as reading the news and watching videos.

Craig Crossman, technology columnist, McClatchy-Tribune newspapers in Asheville, North Carolina, and host of the nationally syndicated radio talk show *Computer America, www.computeramerica.com.*

How to Search the Web *Anonymously*

There are ways to surf the Web anonymously, although there is no guarantee that what you do won't be seen. *Here are two options...*

• **An anonymizer hides information that is coming from the user's computer.** It often is used by government agencies and corporations—it can make communication seem to come from an entirely different place. A company called Anonymizer (*www.anonymizer. com*) is a major provider of this type of service for $80 a year.*

• **Onion routing is another method of disguising the origin of most Internet activity.** It can be complicated, making it more appropriate for advanced users. You can use onion routing for free through *www.torproject.org*.

Randolph Hock, PhD, a previous reference librarian and currently a seminar and workshop provider and operator of Online Strategies, Vienna, Virginia, *www.onstrat. com*.

*Price subject to change.

Six Things *Never* to Say To a Police Officer If You Get Pulled Over

Steve Pomper, who has been with the Seattle Police Department for 19 years, *www.stevepomper.com*. He is author of *Is There a Problem, Officer? A Cop's Inside Scoop on Avoiding Traffic Tickets* (Lyons Press).

Motorists can rarely talk their way out of traffic tickets—but they do sometimes talk their way *into* them. They say things that annoy or anger police officers who might otherwise have let them off with a warning.

Six things never to say to a police officer when you're pulled over...

• **"Whatever."** The police feel disrespected when drivers dismiss them with the casual "whatever." That disrespect virtually ensures that they will receive tickets.

• **"I was not speeding."** Police officers are lied to so frequently that they tend to assume claims such as "I wasn't speeding" or "I didn't run that light" are dishonest. They even might interpret such denials as accusations that they are lying or incompetent. Drivers are more likely to be let off with warnings when they admit that they did something wrong. Do not admit to an infraction if you truly believe you are innocent, however.

• **"I know the mayor."** Never say to a police officer, "I know the mayor," "I know your captain" or "I know my rights." Police officers are not afraid of your powerful friends, and attempting such a power play increases the odds that the officer will write a ticket.

• **"I'm calling my lawyer."** Saying that you intend to call your lawyer will not scare a police officer—it will just annoy him/her. Police officers deal with lawyers all the time and are not frightened by them. It's even worse to tell a police officer that you are a lawyer or are married to one—some police officers may relish the opportunity to write you a ticket.

• **"I'm headed to the DMV."** You would be amazed at how often police officers hear, "I'm headed to the inspection station now" or "the DMV" when they pull over a vehicle that has an expired inspection sticker or registration. They hear it so often, in fact, that they assume it's a lie. The one "I'm headed to" that might get you out of a ticket is "I'm headed to the hospital"—but only if someone in the car truly looks injured, ill or about to give birth and only when you actually intend to drive to the hospital.

• **"Others were driving faster."** The fact that many drivers break the rules does not mean that there aren't any rules. A police officer would not let a burglar off just because other criminals have gotten away with their crimes. Making this argument shows a lack of contrition, increasing the odds that the officer will write a ticket.

Safety Features Really Do Saves Lives

S eat belts saved more than 13,000 lives in the US in 2008. Also in that year—the most recent for which statistics are available—front air bags saved 2,546 lives. More than 18,500 lives were saved from these and other vehicle safety features.

Report by National Highway Traffic Safety Administration, available at *www.nhtsa.gov* (click on "Seat Belts").

Fertilizer Fires and Other Home Hazards

Marjory Abrams, president of Boardroom Inc., 281 Tresser Blvd., Stamford, Connecticut 06901.

W alking through her neighborhood recently, my friend noticed fire trucks by a detached garage. Curious, she asked a firefighter what happened. "Fertilizer," he said. A bag had ignited in the garage.

The fact that fertilizer can combust shouldn't have surprised me much, since I know that terrorists have used it for making bombs. But I didn't know it could ignite on its own. Martha Curtis, senior chemical specialist of the National Fire Protection Association (NFPA), told me that fertilizer in an open package can absorb moisture, which destabilizes the product, triggering a heat-producing chemical reaction that can cause the package to ignite.

Moral of the story: Keep all bags of fertilizer tightly closed up, or store them in a metal container with a secure lid. (There is no heat buildup when fertilizer is spread on a lawn.)

Other little-known home hazards from the NFPA and Nick Gromicko, founder of InterNACHI (International Association of Certified Home Inspectors)…

●**Glass shower doors.** These sometimes shatter without warning. Check shower-door hardware regularly to make sure that fasteners are tight to prevent doors from falling off the track or wall. Replace the glass if you detect any cracks.

●**Electric blankets.** These may overheat if bedding is placed on top or if pets sleep on them when in use. Folding electric blankets can damage the coils and cause overheating. Roll them instead.

Best: Discard all electric blankets that have cracks in the wiring, plugs or connectors.

●**Exercise equipment.** If you have young children, store equipment in a locked room. Even nonelectrical and unplugged equipment can injure or kill. In 2009, the four-year-old daughter of boxer Mike Tyson was strangled by a cord connected to a treadmill.

●**Pet doors.** Install locks so that burglars can't use them to break in when you're away on vacation.

Also: Don't put them into the wall between the house and the garage. Any opening makes it easier for garage fires to spread into the home.

●**Home fire sprinkler systems.** Some systems in the northern US contain antifreeze, which actually may feed kitchen grease fires or other fires. If antifreeze is present in your system (have it checked out by your sprinkler contractor), it should be drained and the antifreeze replaced with water. Insulate the pipes to prevent freezing.

●**Trees.** Beware of any trees that lean more than 15 degrees from the vertical—especially if they were originally straight.

Clue: Uplifted soil on the side opposite the lean.

Other tree hazards include partially broken-off tops or limbs (also known as "hangers" or "widow makers")…cracks that extend through most of the trunk…and cankers—areas on the trunk or a limb in which the bark is sunken or missing.

My apologies if I have just made you afraid to relax in and around your home. There is no need for wild paranoia…just some prudent caution.

Handy Home Lockboxes

Home lockboxes for emergency use are helpful for people with medical conditions. These boxes are about 2½ inches wide by 4 inches long and are mounted over the top of the front door so that they are visible to emergency responders. The lockboxes can contain medical information about the person inside the home, emergency notification numbers and keys to the home. Combinations to unlock the boxes are kept in 911 dispatch computers and released to emergency personnel en route. These boxes can be purchased through your local fire department, typically for $100 to $250.*

Jack Parow, Fire Chief (ret.), Chelmsford (Massachusetts) Fire Department, and president and chairman of the board, International Association of Fire Chiefs, Fairfax, Virginia, *www.iafc.org*.

*Prices subject to change.

The Best Fire Alarm

Photoelectric fire alarms react quicker than ionization alarms for detecting smoldering fires, such as those ignited by cigarettes in upholstered furniture and bedding materials.

But: In controlled experiments, some research has shown that ionization alarms react earlier than photoelectric alarms when detecting the fast-flaming fires, such as those involving paper. The International Association of Fire Chiefs (IAFC) recommends that a home have both of these sensing technologies installed in their proper locations.

Alan Perdue, director, emergency services, Guilford County, North Carolina, and former chair, IAFC Fire and Life Safety Detection, Greensboro, North Carolina, *www.iafc.org*.

Smoke Alarm Smarts

Do not put smoke alarms in laundry rooms, kitchens and garages. Fumes and steam can cause the alarms to go off unnecessarily.

To get maximum safety: A smoke alarm needs to be on every level of your home. Install smoke alarms inside each bedroom and outside each sleeping area...in the basement (on the ceiling at the bottom of the stairs)... and in the attic if it is used as living space. Smoke alarms should be mounted on ceilings (at least four inches away from the walls) or high on walls (no more than 12 inches below the ceiling).

Lorraine Carli, vice president of communications, National Fire Protection Association, Quincy, Massachusetts, *www.nfpa.org*.

Thunderstorm Safety

If you hear thunder, seek shelter immediately—preferably in a large, enclosed building or in a metal, hard-top car, with the windows and doors closed.

If shelter is not available: Stay away from groups of people...steer clear of open fields, water, flag poles, metal bleachers, picnic shelters that have only a roof and things made of metal that are not enclosed, such as bicycles, golf carts and fences. Avoid being the tallest object in the area—but do not lie prone. Instead, minimize contact with the ground by squatting on the balls of your feet to protect yourself against ground flashes (lightning that travels on the ground).

Family Safety & Health, 1121 Spring Lake Dr., Itasca, Illinois 60143, *www.nsc.org*.

Index

Stents, assessing need for, 51
Steroids, 4. *See also* Corticosteroids
St. John's Wort, 89
Stock investments, 169–81
Stress
  biofeedback in controlling, 40
  coffee and tea easing, 69, 70
  exercise injury link to, 75–76
  heart attack link to, 4
  laughter reducing, 87
  managing, 301–2
  natural treatment for, 55
  weight gain link to, 324
Stroke. *See also* Brain health
  aspirin in preventing, 2–3
  diagnosing, 10
  diet soda link to, 9
  rehabilitation after, 10–12
  risk of, 9, 43–44
  surgery in preventing, 51–52
Success
  conversation style for, 289–91
  inner chicken theory in, 283–85
  nonverbal messages for, 286–88
  time makeover for, 294–95
Sugar, arthritis link to, 104
Suicide, 29, 270
Sun protection, 62, 65–66, 103–4
Supplements. *See also* Herbal treatments;
    Natural treatments; Vitamins;
    specific supplements
  in Alzheimer's prevention, 107
  aspirin taken with, 3
  drugs interacting with, 41
  for migraine prevention, 62
  NSAIDs and, 46–47
  storing, 207
Surgery. *See also* Doctors; Hospitals;
    Medical issues; *specific conditions*
  and advocates, 40, 54, 166
  anesthesia during, 53, 108
  assessing need for, 51–53
  errors during, 48–49
  delirium after, 50
  ICU after, 50–51
  LASIK, 22–24
  sleepy doctors performing, 33
  to stop snoring, 68
  sutures vs. staples used in, 53
Sushi, mercury in, 30
Sweat, bad-smelling, 91
Sweet potatoes, as cancer fighter, 94

T

Taxes
  audit tips, 165–67
  debt forgiveness affecting, 164
  in e-mail scams, 167
  on estates, 223–30 (*see also* Estate
    planning)
  free preparation of, 164
  law changes, 160–62
  liens filed for unpaid, 164
  and profit and loss reporting, 163
  property, 163–64
  questions about, 159–60
  refunds on, 125, 165
  Retirement Savings Contribution Credit,
    219
  return form errors, 157–59
  and unmarried couples, 141
  and vehicle credits, 164
Tea
  black, 88, 97, 110
  chai, 60
  diabetes risk and, 103
  for flatulence, 70
  green, 88, 92, 97, 110, 298
  as stress reliever, 69

for weight loss in men, 82
Teenagers. *See* Children/teenagers
Teeth. *See* Oral health
Telephones
  computers instead of, 247–48
  driving while using, 260
  home security systems using, 327, 328
  job interviews on, 303–5
  recorded phone sales on, 204–5
  refurbished and prepaid, 204
  tinnitus from using, 24
  travel tips and, 237
  and waiting on hold, 205
Television
  cable costs, 204
  on computers, 248–49
  fake, for home security, 328
  financial news on, 185
  heart health link to, 6, 71–72
  3-D, 9
Temperature, heart attack link to, 5
Tendons, healing technique for, 77–79
Tennis, paddle or platform, 250
Terrorism, 329–31
Testicular cancer, 120
Therapy, types of, 27–29, 40, 61, 82
Thiamine, sources of, 92
Thyroid gland, 24–26
TIAs (transient ischemic attacks), 52
Time makeovers, 294–95
Tinnitus, 3, 24, 44
Toe-touch test, for heart health, 6
Toilet seats, rashes from, 65
Toothbrushes, 57, 64
Tourette's syndrome, 62
Towels, bacteria on, 57
Trans fats, and depression risk, 29
Travel. *See also* Air travel; Hotels
  bargains for, 235–37
  car rental and, 243
  credit card tips for, 237–38
  on cruises, 245
  for health and longevity, 86
  hotel savings, 243–44
  hotel safety, 244, 246
  multigenerational, 246
  off-season, 235–36
  passports for, 237
  pets and, 245
  road accidents during, 245
  safety tips for, 237, 245, 246
  into space, 246
  tips for successful, 233–34, 246
Triphala, for constipation, 70
Turmeric, 41, 298

U

Urinary tract health
  catheter use in, 44
  hydration link to, 109
  infections (UTIs), 92, 109, 117
  medication side effects and, 7, 43
  urine, strange-smelling, 92

V

Vacations. *See* Air travel; Hotels; Travel
Vaccines, 116, 269, 277
Variable annuities, 211–12
Vegetable juice, for weight loss, 82
Vegetables, grilling, 94. *See also specific*
Video calls, 247–48
Vinegar, reducing blood sugar, 102–3
Vision, 12, 21, 62. *See also* Eye health
Visualization therapy, 40, 82
Vitamin B, 47, 62. *See also* Folates
Vitamin C, 46, 97
Vitamin D, 83, 108
Vitamin E, 46–47, 97, 103, 107
Vitamin K, 5, 8

Vitamins, daily multi, 8, 110, 116, 207. *See
  also* Herbal treatments; Natural
  treatments; Supplements; *specific
  vitamins*
VNS (vagus nerve stimulation), for
  depression, 28–29
Volunteering, at animal shelter, 221–22

W

Waist circumference, 73, 83
Walnuts, for high blood pressure, 101
Water
  cleaning with hot, 57
  coconut, 79–80
  cold shower benefits, 58
  consumption recommendation, 92, 109
  filtered, 107
  mineral, 101–2
Weed removal, nontoxic, 251–52
Weight. *See also* Diet; Exercise
  danger of too little, 80–81
  excess, around waist, 73, 83
  longevity link to, 81
  nighttime light link to, 84
  older women gaining, 73
  stress link to gaining, 324
Weight lifting, 117
Wellness programs, 316
Whey, for lowering blood pressure, 101
Whistle-blowers, in fraud cases, 188
Whole grains, for lowering blood
  pressure, 101
Widows/widowers, Social Security
  benefits for, 216
Wills. *See* Estate planning
Wine, health benefits of, 103, 113, 298
Women. *See also* Breast health
  aspirin therapy for, 2
  exercise needs of older, 73
  fracture risk for, 12
  heart health and height of, 5–6
  hot flash treatment for, 115
  insurance benefits for, 145
  money guide for unmarried, 142
Work. *See also* Businesses; Interviews;
    Résumés
  clashing styles at, 168
  dangerous, 307
  defending your ideas at, 320–21
  difficult boss at, 316–17
  e-mail etiquette at, 323
  healthful plants for, 324
  heart health link to, 7
  highest-paying, 307
  looking for, 158, 303–5, 306–7
  and Millennial generation, 274–75
  NEAT lifestyle at, 73
  new job tips, 323–24
  performance review tips, 317–20
  preparing to quit, 305
  public speaking for, 322–23
  role models at, 322
  self-esteem at, 168, 286–88
  sleepiness at, 323
  underemployment benefits and, 305
  words of wisdom on, 167–68

Y

Yards, 250–52, 279–80. *See also* Gardens;
  Homes; Insects
Yield, higher, from money, 181–83
Yoga, for better sex, 113
Yohimbe bark extract, for erectile dys-
  function, 112–13

Z

Zinc, sources of, 92